Fuel Cells: Their Electrochemistry

Fuel Cells:
Their Electrochemistry

J. O'M. Bockris
Electrochemistry Laboratory
University of Pennsylvania

S. Srinivasan
State University of New York
Downstate Medical Center

McGraw-Hill Book Company
New York
St. Louis
San Francisco
London
Sydney
Toronto
Mexico
Panama

Fuel Cells: Their Electrochemistry

This book was set in Times New Roman by The Universities Press and printed on permanent paper and bound by The Maple Press Company. The drawings were done by Searles. The editors were B. J. Clark and Dorothy Graham. Stuart Levine supervised the production.

Preface

The first fuel cell was made by Grove in 1839. At the Bunsen Gesellschaft in 1894 Ostwald pointed out that if chemical reactions were carried out electro-chemically, it would in principle become possible that the entire free energy change of a reaction could be converted directly into electricity. By contrast, if chemical reactions were carried out thermally, the maximum amount of the energy difference between reactants and products that could be converted to mechanical work would be the enthalpy change in the reaction multiplied by the Carnot efficiency fraction. Ostwald therefore suggested a change in the direction of development of technology—from a thermally oriented to an electrochemically oriented one. He pointed out not only the prospective gains in the efficiency of conversion of the energy in the fuel but also the dangers of air pollution in cities were the use of thermal chemical reactions to give energy to continue.

Lack of understanding of electron transfer reactions across interfaces, in particular of the concept of overpotential, prevented realization of Ostwald's suggestions. Until the 1950s, the essential role of overpotential in electrochemical energy conversion was understood by few workers in the field of the electro-chemistry of interfaces. Correspondingly, even at the present time, few chemists outside this field understand the central concept of overpotential in electro-chemical reactions.

The first fuel cell to appear in a practical device was Bacon's in 1959. The auxiliary power of American space vehicles was provided by hydrogen-oxygen fuel cells from 1966.

Three books on fuel cells have appeared heretofore, one of which is in English. The theoretical material of these books is largely descriptive. A book on the basic electrochemical theory, that is of fuel cells is hence much needed. Knowledge of other basic disciplines, in particular hydrodynamics and materials science, is also necessary for the worker concerned with fuel cells.

The fact that the study of electrode reactions in modern terms was delayed until the 1950s is remarkable. Although such studies are now done extensively in many laboratories, particularly in the U.S.S.R., the concepts developed have not been incorporated into textbooks of physical chemistry, nor has there yet been widespread realization of the breadth of the areas in science in which electron transfer processes across interfaces involving ionic solutions play a decisive part may thus be made. For example, it is not widely realized that chemical reactions with no net charge transfer may occur spontaneously by the opposite function of cathodic and anodic reactions, exchanging charges with a common electron-conducting phase. The implications of such electrochemical mechanisms for chemical reactions may be extensive, particularly for molecular biochemistry.

Moreover, few high school or university students know that there is a new field concerned with the interactions between interfacial electric currents and matter, which underlies many aspects (electricity storage, stability of metals, operation of the nervous system) of existence. It is difficult for those who enter the area of electrochemical energy conversion to become acquainted with the basic theory of the subject. If they attempt to learn it solely from reading—the area is too new to be in the standard university curriculums—they find only advanced monographs in fundamental electrochemistry or have had to fall back upon texts published before 1952, that is, before the development of electrode kinetics.

There seems little doubt that electrochemical energy conversion and storage will soon play an important part in the technological picture. Thus, the use of electrochemical methods is the principal path by which we may meet the long-term problems of air pollution. The delay in the introduction of the study of the new electrochemistry in universities has become the rate-determining step in the radical revisions in technology made essential by pollution and the need for the application of more rational uses of fossil fuels than that of obtaining energy from their combustion with air.

The writing of this book has thus been influenced by the absence of education in electrochemistry in high schools and in universities. We start with a chapter describing the electrochemical method of energy conversion in the context of the main methods for direct-energy conversion to electricity. We then give a fairly detailed summary of the kinetics of interfacial electrochemical reactions, at a level that will be understood by those who have had a course in chemical kinetics. In the following chapters, we cover most of the energy-conversion-oriented electrochemical theory, in particular porous electrode theory, electrocatalysis, and the kinetics and mechanisms of oxygen electrodes. We end with a descriptive chapter on fuel cells as they appear in the later 1960s to whet, as it were, the research workers' appetites.

The authors wish to thank the National Aeronautics and Space Administration for financially supporting the work on the book (Contract No. NsG 325) and Ernst Cohn, head of the Electrochemical Division, for very stimulating discussions on fuel cells and other direct-energy-conversion methods. During the period of writing the book, we had valuable discussions and/or help from many present and past members of the Electrochemistry Laboratory, particularly from Drs. Argade, Cahan, Damjanovic, Genshaw, Gileadi, Hurwitz, Mannan, Matthews, Muller, Reddy, Stoner, Swinkels, and Wroblowa and

Messrs. Brusic, Razumney, and Subramanyam.   The authors acknowledge constructive discussions on direct-energy-conversion methods with Professors Altman, Nanis, and Schrenck of the Direct Energy Conversion Institute, University of Pennsylvania.   Visits to the Fuel Cell Laboratories of Allis-Chalmers Manufacturing Company, Esso Research and Engineering Company, General Electric Company, General Motors Corporation, Leesona Moos Corporation, Puerto Rico Nuclear Research Center, and United Aircraft Corporation were profitable in respect to the writing of the last chapter of the book.

Several of the authors' colleagues have read chapters and offered advice. The principal ones are Dr. R. G. Watson (British Admiralty), Dr. H. Oswin (Leesona-Moos), Dr. C. Heath (Esso), Dr. G. Schrenck (University of Pennsylvania), Dr. H. Horowitz (Esso), and Mr. K. R. Williams (Shell).

One of us (S. S.) wishes to thank Professor. P. N. Sawyer of the State University of New York, Downstate Medical Center, Brooklyn, for his patience and understanding, during the writing of part of the book.

On the nonscientific side, splendid jobs were done by Mrs. J. J. Laws (typing practically all drafts of the manuscripts) and by Mr. Charles Searles (artwork).   One of us (S. S.) wishes to express his gratitude to his wife and members of his family for the opportunities provided, encouragement given, and sacrifices made during the writing of the book.

J. O'M. Bockris
S. Srinivasan

Contents

CHAPTER 2
BASIC ELECTRODE KINETICS

CHAPTER 3
THERMODYNAMIC ASPECTS OF ELECTROCHEMICAL ENERGY CONVERSION

CHAPTER 4
SOME ELECTRODE KINETIC ASPECTS OF
ELECTROCHEMICAL ENERGY CONVERSION

CHAPTER 6
ELECTROCATALYSIS

CHAPTER 8
ELECTRODIC REACTIONS OF OXYGEN

CHAPTER 9
AN OUTLINE OF FUEL-CELL RESEARCH TECHNIQUES

CHAPTER 10
TYPES OF FUEL CELLS

Fuel Cells: Their Electrochemistry

CHAPTER ONE

Direct Energy Conversion: Methods and Advantages of the Electrochemical Method

1 SOURCES AND FORMS OF ENERGY

The primary sources of energy can be classified under (1) solar, (2) gravitational, (3) nuclear, and (4) geothermal energy.   Solar energy originates from the energy of proton-proton and carbon-nitrogen nuclear-fusion reactions. Geothermal energy is a result of radioactive decay and temperature at the earth's core, which arises probably from heat produced in stellar reactions.   Hence, of the four sources of energy mentioned—and five if chemical energy (see below) is considered as a source distinct from solar energy—only nuclear and gravitational energy are fundamental sources of energy.   Of course, other sources of energy exist, e.g., energy of the earth's magnetic field.   However, no attempt has as yet been made to use these sources in energy-conversion devices.

The main forms in which energy is manifested are heat, light, electricity, magnetism, gravitational fields, and the kinetic energy of macro-size bodies (known as mechanical energy).

Solar energy may be considered as the primary source of the energy of all forms of life on earth.   Vegetation, hence coal and oil, is created by photosynthesis.   During this process, carbon dioxide and water are converted to oxygen, fats, proteins, sugars, starches, and other carbohydrates by chlorophyll, a pigment which absorbs solar energy.

Solar energy is the source of the energy in foods, and other fuels, and is part of the heat which reaches the earth's surface.   The chemical energy of fossil fuels, which is the most widely used source of energy at the present time, is generally regarded as a primary source of energy.   However, it must be considered as one source of energy derived from solar energy.   Chemical energy is a result of the energy liberated during a chemical reaction, e.g., the burning of fossil fuels to carbon dioxide and water.   One of the commonest ways in which this chemical energy is manifested is in the form of heat liberated during the course of the reaction.   This heat energy is converted into mechanical energy by using the work of expansion of the heated gases to push pistons into cylinders and do mechanical work.   This mechanical work is then used to drive a generator and thus produce electricity.   Because of the two stages involved, this method of creating electrical energy is called "indirect energy conversion."   In recent times, efforts have been made to carry out the combination of fossil fuels with oxygen in an electrochemical cell, in which case there is a direct transformation of chemical to electrical energy, thus bypassing the intermediate state of heat and mechanical energy.   The extent of conversion of heat energy liberated† in chemical reactions to mechanical energy is limited by Carnot's theorem.   The direct conversion of chemical to electrical energy which takes place electrochemically does not suffer from this limitation (Chap 3).   Hence, the efficiency of conversion of chemical energy to electricity is reduced from a maximum hypothetical value near 100 percent only by extrinsic factors subject to research and engineering.

Gravitational energy is converted into electrical energy mainly by hydroelectric power generators.   Of the methods used today for large-scale power generation, this method is by far the best, being highly efficient, reliable, inexhaustible, and economical.   However, the method depends on the existence of large waterfalls, which are rare.   Further, there is a limit in the length of transmission lines at which point the loss of power in the lines makes the electricity thus produced uneconomical.   There are some very big units for hydroelectric power generation in the United States, U.S.S.R., and many other countries.   This method yields about 5 percent of the world's requirements of electrical energy.   The efficiency of conversion of gravitational energy in the form of hydroenergy to electrical energy is about 75 to 95 percent.[1]

Nuclear energy is liberated during nuclear fission, nuclear fusion, or radioactive decay.   The binding energy of atoms in molecules is of the order of a few electron volts, whereas that of nucleons (protons and neutrons) in the atomic nucleus is on the order of a few million electron volts.   Consequently, the energy changes during nuclear reactions exceed those during chemical reactions by a factor of about 1 million.   As examples, one may consider the following reactions:

---

† It may be wondered whether the heat absorbed in an endothermic reaction may be used as the source of mechanical energy, whereby the working fluid cools, the gas contracts, and the piston is sucked into the cylinder and thus does mechanical work (the reverse of the former case where the gas expands by the heat liberated in an exothermic reaction).   In practice, however, the use of endothermic reactions to provide mechanical energy is not viable because the free energy of the chemical reaction must be negative if it is to occur spontaneously; and in an endothermic reaction (ΔH positive), a negative free-energy change can only be obtained by the effect of the $T\,\Delta S$ term on ΔG.   Thus, if ΔG is a negative value, $T\,\Delta S$ has to be large and negative with $|T\,\Delta S| > |\Delta H|$—and thus it would be a poor source of mechanical energy at best.

Chemical: $\qquad$ $2H_2 + O_2 \rightarrow 2H_2O + 5.92$ ev $\hfill$ (1.1)

Nuclear fission: $\qquad$ $_{92}U^{235} + {}_0n^1 \rightarrow {}_{38}Sr^{94} + {}_{54}Xe^{140} + {}_0n^1 + {}_0n^1$

$$+ 2 \times 10^8 \text{ ev} \qquad (1.2)$$

Nuclear fusion: $\qquad$ $_1H^2 + {}_1H^2 \rightarrow {}_2He^3 + {}_0n^1 + 3.2 \times 10^6$ ev $\hfill$ (1.3)

Radioactive decay: $\qquad$ $_1H^3 \rightarrow {}_2He^3 + \beta + 1.5 \times 10^4$ ev $\hfill$ (1.4)

There are several paths for the conversion of nuclear energy to electrical energy. The most widely used path today is the controlled-fission nuclear reactor. The energy liberated in nuclear fission is in the form of the kinetic energy of the fission fragments (about 80 percent) and of neutrons and electromagnetic energy (e.g., γ radiation). This energy finally degrades into heat energy by means of collision with surrounding gas molecules. Thus, an atomic power plant differs from a conventional power plant in that the boiler of the latter is heated by coal or oil and that of the former is heated by heat led to it by means of an exchanger fed by a reactor. There are some direct methods of converting nuclear energy to electricity. One of these is by using the ionizing properties of solids and gases. For example, an electrode may be coated with a substance which emits α particles radioactively. The electrode is surrounded by a spherical cavity which acts as a collector for the emitted (charged) particles. Hence, a potential difference develops between the two electrodes and from this difference a current can be tapped and energy produced.[2] This type of converter is at present impractical because the high resistance between cathode and anode makes the power output per unit weight of this device poor. An indirect way of utilizing nuclear power is in radiochemically regenerative fuel cells (Chap. 3, Sec. 6.6; Chap. 10, Sec. 3.4). Here, the product of the fuel-cell reaction is converted into its reactants by means of heat or ionizing radiations generated during the course of a chemical reaction.

Geothermal energy arises as a result of the heat energy in the interior of the earth which, in turn, arises from the heat of the molten core and the energy of nuclear reactions undergone by the slight radioactivity of some constituents of the planet. So far hardly any effort has been made to convert geothermal energy into electrical energy, although this appears feasible. For example, it may be possible to insert thermoelectric devices into the earth's crust or lead tubes of water (or some other liquid) deep into the earth and then vaporize it and convert the heat of the working fluid to mechanical and then electrical energy. Here as in the case of hydroelectric power generation, geographical location plays an important role.

2 NECESSITY OF CONVERSION TO ELECTRICAL ENERGY AND OF DEVELOPING DIRECT-ENERGY-CONVERSION METHODS

With the passage of time, the energy requirements of man increase (Fig. 1). A major aspect of our present civilization is that mechanical energy under man's

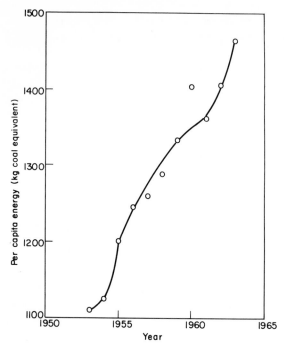

Figure 1   Per capita energy consumption (data for 173 countries in the world with a combined population of 3,218 million people in 1963) for the years 1953 through 1963. [Plot constructed from data in World Energy Supplies 1960–1963, *Stat. Papers Ser. J.*, 8 (1965).]

control is replacing the mechanical human energy produced by the human body. Electrical energy is the one and only form of energy which can be easily made, is convenient to transport, and can be used in a controlled manner.   It is not always necessary to obtain the appropriate form of energy from the primary energy source via electrical energy.   However, use of electricity as the power source, which may in turn be obtained from the primary energy sources by conventional or other methods, is usually the most convenient form; and transformation of electrical to other forms of energy takes place at practically 100 percent efficiency.

Since the form of energy most frequently required by man is electricity, it is obvious that one would look for direct methods of conversion of energy from its primary forms, e.g., chemical, solar, nuclear, and gravitational.   The conventional methods, apart from hydroelectric power generation, pass through the intermediate stage of conversion of heat energy into mechanical energy. Thus, inherent in them is the Carnot limitation.   In addition, moving parts subject to mechanical failure are used in conventional systems.   The advent of space research gave tremendous impetus to the consideration of direct methods of energy conversion because of the simplicity, reliability, and lessened weight and volume required in these methods. If conversion of energy from a primary source to electricity can be made in one step, the efficiency should be higher than were the conversion to occur in many more steps apart from considerations of the Carnot cycle, which intrinsically limits the efficiency of conventional indirect and of some direct methods. Various direct-energy-conversion methods will be briefly dealt with in the following section.

3 METHODS FOR DIRECT ENERGY CONVERSION

3.1 General

The purpose of the present chapter is to review the methods of direct energy conversion and deal with the advantages of the method of electrochemical energy conversion. The other methods of direct energy conversion, which are being widely investigated, are thermoelectric, thermionic, photovoltaic, and magnetohydrodynamic methods. There are some recent excellent books[3-5] on direct energy conversion, which consist of individual chapters for each of these methods. Thus, in the present section, all these methods except the electrochemical one, which is the subject matter of the present book, are presented only briefly and along the following lines: (1) principles of method, (2) criteria determining performance, (3) present state of development, and (4) advantages, disadvantages, and possible applications. The electrochemical method is also presented in a similar manner but in more detail, and in Sec. 4 a classification is made of the various types of electrochemical energy converters in addition to a historical survey. A detailed comparison of the different methods of energy conversion depending on the type of application is made in Sec. 5.

3.2 Thermoelectric Energy Converters

3.2.1 Principles of Method

This method[3-5] is based on the Seebeck effect. According to this effect, a potential gradient is set up when the junctions of two dissimilar conducting or semiconducting materials are maintained at different temperatures. Thus, when the ends (*B*) are connected through a load (*L*), as in Fig. 2, a current flow will be observed.

Two other thermoelectric effects are relevant. The Peltier effect is the opposite of the Seebeck effect. Instead of maintaining the junctions at different temperatures, if a current is passed from an external power supply through the two junctions, there will be a heating effect at one junction and a cooling one at the other. The Peltier effect is important because it gives a method of heating and cooling, i.e., a method for transferring heat energy. The Thompson effect refers to the fact that when an electric current flows through a conducting

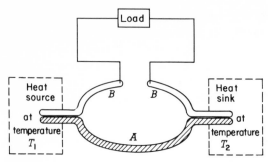

Figure 2 The basic unit of a thermoelectric energy converter. *A* and *B* are two different thermoelectric materials.

medium in which a temperature gradient exists, the heat absorbed or rejected by it is proportional to both the current flowing through it and the temperature gradient.

3.2.2 *Important Criteria Determining Performance*

A parameter that combines all the thermoelectric effects and determines the effectiveness of the materials in a thermoelectric generator is the figure of merit (Z) and is given by

$$Z = \frac{S}{\kappa\rho} \tag{3.1}$$

where S is the thermoelectric voltage per degree due to the Seebeck effect, κ is the thermal conductivity of the material, and ρ is its electrical resistivity. The efficiency of a thermoelectric generator is given by[3]

$$\epsilon = \frac{T_1 - T_2}{T_1}\frac{1}{F(M)} \tag{3.2}$$

where

$$F(M) = 1 + \frac{2}{T_1 Z} + \frac{M}{T_1 Z} + \frac{1}{M}\left(\frac{1}{2}\frac{T_1 + T_2}{T_1} + \frac{1}{T_1 Z}\right) \tag{3.3}$$

M is given by

$$M = \frac{(T_1 - T_2)S - IR_i}{IR_i} \tag{3.4}$$

In Eqs. (3.2) to (3.4), T_1 and T_2 are the temperatures at the hot and cold junctions, respectively, I is the current flowing through the generator, and R_i is its internal resistance. The limiting efficiency (the Carnot efficiency) occurs when $F(M)$ in Eq. (3.2) is unity.

The efficiency of the conversion of heat to mechanical energy was shown by Carnot to be

$$\epsilon = \frac{T_1 - T_2}{T_1} \tag{3.5}$$

and the model considered in the deduction of Eq. (3.5) is that of a gas expanding due to the increase of temperature caused by the insertion of a heat source and the transformation of work done as expansion to mechanical energy. In the limit, the same expression for the efficiency would apply to that of thermoelectric converters. The reason is the same as that which applies to the conversion of heat to mechanical energy in a heat engine. The energy of the gas molecules is kinetic and proportional to the temperature. At the beginning of the expansion, the temperature is T_1 and finally it is T_2. Thus, the gas molecules transfer a part of the kinetic or thermal energy into work and this part is proportional to $T_1 - T_2$, the balance being rejected to the heat sink. Thus, the electrons in a thermoelectric converter similarly pass through a temperature difference ($T_1 - T_2$), and since their energy arises from the thermal energy applied at the hot end of the circuit, the amount expressed as a potential driving a current is proportional to the difference in temperature, because the energy retained by the electrons at the cold end is proportional to the lower temperature. From Eq. (3.3) it follows that $F(M)$ reaches unity when Z is very large. High values of Z are obtained by using materials which have a large value of S and low values of κ and ρ.

The terminal voltage is the Seebeck voltage less the ohmic drop (IR_i). Thus

$$E = S(T_1 - T_2) - IR_i \tag{3.6}$$

The power output is given by

$$P = I[S(T_1 - T_2) - IR_i] \tag{3.7}$$

3.2.3 Present State of Development

Just as in the case of batteries and fuel cells, it is necessary to connect thermoelectric devices in series for higher power outputs. One such arrangement is shown in Fig. 3.[4] The output voltage of the thermoelectric generator is a product of the number of single units and the terminal voltage across a single unit. Many materials have been tested for applications in thermoelectric devices. Extrinsic semiconductors are the best.[3-5] The compounds that are widely used in the intermediate-temperature range are the tellurides and selenides of lead, bismuth, and antimony to which some p- or n-type doping agent is added. At high temperatures the silicides and sulfides are used. At very high temperatures, the oxides may be used. Most of the present-day work is being carried out at temperatures below 1000°C. Lead telluride is the most common material in thermoelectric devices at the present time.[6]

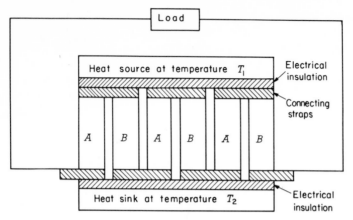

Figure 3   A series connection of thermoelectric energy converters.[4]
A and *B* are two different thermoelectric materials.

Solar, fossil fuel, radioisotope, and reactor heat sources are being used for the operation of thermoelectric generators.   Only small units (100 watts or less) have been built.   The highest efficiency and power/weight ratio reported to date are 10 percent and 25 watts lb^{-1} (weight of generator only), respectively.[6]

3.2.4   *Advantages, Disadvantages, and Possible Applications*

Thermoelectric converters have the following characteristics.   Their energy/ unit weight ratios are small, mainly because the required ratios of electrical to thermal conductivity for high figures of merit are found only with the heavy materials.   All thermoelectric materials presently known are unstable.   They sublime readily and hence there is an upper limit to the temperature at which these materials may be used.   The mechanical properties are also very poor. Most of these materials are very brittle and difficult to fabricate.   Prospects of future applications of thermoelectric devices are not too optimistic because large temperature differences are necessary for high efficiencies, which lead to material instability or diffusion of doping agents across the junction of the two metals. Large-scale applications of thermoelectric devices are limited unless molecular engineering can eventually lead to a brand-new material.   The overall efficiency of thermoelectric generators is of the order of only a few percent.   Isotope thermoelectrics are currently being designed for space applications[4] such as in SNAP 27, but it is expected that this application will be replaced in a few years by other power systems such as isotope thermionic systems.

3.3   Thermionic Energy Converters

3.3.1   *Principles of Method*

Thermionic energy conversion is the direct conversion of heat to electricity by the heating of an emitter (cathode) to a high temperature and a consequent emission of electrons from it.[3-5]   The electrons reach the collector (anode), which is at a considerably lower temperature just as in a diode, and then pass through an external circuit before finally returning to the cathode (Fig. 4). Solar, nuclear, or chemical energy may be used as the heat source.   The use of nuclear fission as a heat source appears attractive since the fuel element may itself be used as the electron emitter (cathode).   This would help greatly in reducing the weight of the system.

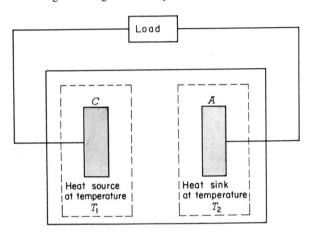

Figure 4   The basic unit of a thermionic energy converter. *C* is the emitter (cathode); *A* is the collector (anode).

3.3.2   *Important Criteria Determining Performance*

The emission of electrons from a heated metal was first observed by Edison in 1880.   The rate of emission of electrons from the cathode is given by the Richardson equation:[3-5]

$$i_c = A T_1^2 \exp \left(-\Phi_c \frac{e}{kT_1} \right) \tag{3.8}$$

where i_c represents the current density at which emission occurs from the emitter at a temperature T_1; Φ_c is its work function; and A is the thermionic constant and is equal to 120 amp $^\circ K^{-2}$ cm^{-2}.

   The potentials of the collector V_a and the emitter V_c in a thermionic energy converter would depend partly on the space charge in the region between anode and cathode which is in turn dependent on the current being drawn from it.   The potential distribution between the anode and the cathode is as shown in Fig. 5. Thus, the net current density generated by the thermionic energy converter is given by

$$i = i_c - i_a$$
$$= A \left[T_1^2 \exp \left(-\frac{V_c F}{RT_1} \right) - T_2^2 \exp \left(-\frac{V_a F}{RT_2} \right) \right] \tag{3.9}$$

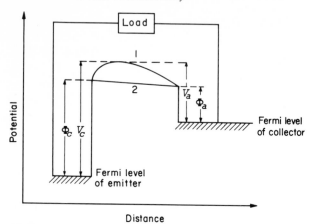

Figure 5   Potential distribution between anode and cathode in a thermionic energy converter.   Curve 1, without Cs vapor; curve 2, with Cs vapor.

In the above equation, the current density due to the reverse process of emission of electrons from the collector to the emitter is also taken into account.   The suffix *a* denotes the anode.   The anode has a lower work function than the cathode and is at a considerably lower temperature.   Thus, the reverse current is generally small.

It is sometimes thought that the work function of the emitter should be smaller than that of the collector so that the rate of escape of electrons from the emitter according to Eq. (3.8) would be higher than that from the collector. However, the situation is radically different, as can be seen from the following considerations.   Figure 5 represents a basic thermionic converter together with the external load through which the net current generated from the thermionic converter passes.   In order that the current may flow spontaneously through the load, the thermionic work function of the emitter must be larger than that of the collector, for only then will there be a net potential difference $(\Phi_c - \Phi_a)$ across the two electrodes that will drive the electrons from the collector to the emitter through the load.   Within the converter, there is net electron emission from the cathode because the emitter is at a considerably higher temperature than the collector.   The ideal converter is one with a fairly low emitter work function but with a still lower (at least by 1 volt) collector work function.

The open-circuit voltage V_R is found by setting $i_c = i_a$ in Eq. (3.9).   The efficiency ϵ of the thermionic energy converter is defined as the ratio of its power output per unit area of the cathode divided by the heat input into the cathode for the same area.   The latter can be calculated if it is assumed that the only energy losses from the electrodes are the electrical energies leaving them, together with the thermal energy of these electrons, that is, $2kT$ per electron.   At a current density of i_c, the number of electrons sec^{-1} cm^{-2} is i/e, and hence the loss of energy due to the thermal energy of the escaping electrons is $i2kT/e$.   Thus, the total energy loss at an electrode per unit time is $iV + i2kT/e$. Hence, the efficiency is

$$\epsilon = \frac{(i_c - i_a)(V_c - V_a)}{i_c(V_c + 2kT_1/e) - i_a(V_a + 2kT_2/e)} \tag{3.10}$$

Generally the reverse current is small. Hence, when $i_c \gg i_a$ the expression for ϵ reduces to

$$\epsilon = \frac{V_c - V_a}{V_c + 2kT_1/e} \tag{3.11}$$

An upper limit to the efficiency of the thermionic energy converter may be obtained by assuming that the term $2kT/e$ is small compared with V_c. Further, it may be shown that maximum efficiency is given when the relation between V_a, V_c, T_2, T_1 is[3-5]

$$V_a = \frac{V_c T_2}{T_1} \tag{3.12}$$

Using Eq. (3.12) in (3.11) it is seen that

$$\epsilon = \frac{T_1 - T_2}{T_1} \tag{3.13}$$

Thus, the maximum efficiency of a thermionic energy converter is the Carnot efficiency, as may be expected since in this method there is also a conversion of heat to electrical energy. The power density of a thermionic energy converter is given by

$$P = (i_c - i_a)(V_c - V_a) \tag{3.14}$$

The main reason why V_c and V_a differ from Φ_c and Φ_a, respectively, is because of the creation of a space charge by the electrons between the anode and the cathode. The closer these values are to the respective work functions, the better is the performance of the thermionic energy converter.

3.3.3 Present State of Development

The essential requirements for the satisfactory performance of a thermionic energy converter are (1) optimum work function of the emitter, (2) low collector work function, and (3) minimum spacing between the electrodes. An optimum value of the work function for a cathode operating between 1500 and 1600°C is between 2.3 and 2.4 ev. The lower the collector work function, the higher is the output voltage. A satisfactory value is 1 ev.

A close spacing of the electrode reduces the space-charge effect. At present the closest spacing obtained[3-5] is of the order of 10^{-3} cm. However, this figure is not attained easily in practical devices. Another method of reducing the space charge is by introduction of cesium vapor into the energy converter. Cesium is chosen because it has the lowest ionization potential and thus the positive ions thus easily formed neutralize the space charge. The potential distribution for a case in which the space charge is completely eliminated by cesium vapor is shown in Fig. 5. The barrier for electron transfer is thus reduced by reduction in space charge.

The metals most commonly used as emitters are tantalum and tungsten. Oxides, borides, and carbides have also been used. It is necessary to choose collector materials with low work functions. Because of the low operating temperature of the anode, the rate of electron emission from the anode is low. Nickel, stainless steel, molybdenum, and the oxides of barium and strontium have been widely used as collector materials.

Another important effect that arises by the introduction of Cs into the interelectrode spacing is a lowering of the emitter and collector work functions. This occurs by adsorption of Cs on the electrodes. A lowering of the emitter work function results in a marked increase in the current generated by the converter. From the practical point of view as well, the low-pressure cesium converter has another advantage in that it is not necessary to have as low interelectrode spacing as in the vacuum thermionic energy converter. It is necessary to have electrode spacings of about 25 μ in the latter, whereas with the cesium converter electrode spacings of about 1 mm can be used.

Work is being carried out to develop flame-heated[7] and solar[8] thermionic energy converters. A 1.5-kw solar thermionic energy converter is being studied for space applications.[8] The best value of its efficiency reported is 11 percent. The power/weight ratio obtained in this system at the present time is of the order of 2 watts lb^{-1}.

3.3.4   *Advantages, Disadvantages, and Possible Applications*

During the past 10 years, considerable improvements have been made in thermionic energy conversion. Devices with a lifetime of over 10,000 hr have been built.[8] Power densities of the order of 40 watts cm^{-2} have been attained for some systems using cathodes operating at a temperature of 2000°K.[5] Progress in materials preparation and in an understanding of additives can be expected to lead to long life converters with overall systems efficiencies of about 15 percent. A disadvantage of the method is that high temperatures are required, which leads to problems of material stability. The area of nuclear-reactor thermionics is receiving a great deal of attention. A combination of a nuclear thermionic and a liquid-metal turbine cycle could lead to systems which might have an overall efficiency above 40 percent and may be considered for large-scale power generation. Though somewhat heavy, solar thermionic generators are particularly suited for long-space applications.[8]

3.4   Photovoltaic Energy Converters

3.4.1   *Principles of Method*

This method is different from the preceding methods in that light energy, not heat energy, is converted into electricity.[3-5] It is the only direct-energy-conversion method, apart from the electrochemical one, which is free of the Carnot limitation.   The photovoltaic effect was first discovered by Becquerel (1839), who observed a voltage change on exposing an electrode in solution to light. A photoelectric energy converter is made by exposing light to a *pn* junction. A photon with sufficient energy collides with an electron and transfers its energy to the latter.   The electron may then have sufficient energy to become free and hence create a hole.   This process can occur across the *pn* junction (Fig. 6).   It will act in such a way that the *p*-type region becomes positive and the *n*-type region negative.   When the *p* and *n* regions are not connected externally, this current is balanced by the forward bias.   However, when the two regions are connected through an external load, a part of the current I_g flows through this load.   Figure 6 represents a schematic arrangement of a photovoltaic energy converter.   A typical device is prepared by diffusing a *p* material (e.g., boron) into a heavily doped *n*-type (e.g., silicon) wafer to form a *p*-type film a few microns thick.   Electrical contacts to the top and bottom are made by electroplating some metal on a small portion of each of these regions.

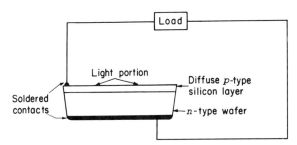

Figure 6   The basic unit of a typical photovoltaic energy converter.

3.4.2   Important Criteria Determining Performance

The current-density–voltage relation at a *pn* junction across which a potential drop *V* exists is[3-5]

$$i_j = i_L\left(1 - \exp\frac{VF}{RT}\right) \tag{3.15}$$

where i_j is the total current due to both hole and electron flow across the junction and i_L is the dark or saturation current density.   The current density that flows through an external load is given by

$$i = i_p + i_j \tag{3.16}$$

where i_p is the current density arising out of electron transfer across the *pn* junction by exposure of the *p* side of the cell to light.
    Combining Eqs. (3.15) and (3.16),

$$i = i_p - i_L\left[\exp\left(\frac{VF}{RT}\right) - 1\right] \tag{3.17}$$

The open-circuit voltage $V_{i=0}$ is when $i = 0$ and is given by

$$V_{i=0} = \frac{RT}{F} \ln \left(\frac{i_p}{i_L} + 1 \right) \tag{3.18}$$

The power density is expressed by

$$P = iV = V \left\{ i_p - i_L \left[\exp \left(\frac{VF}{RT} \right) - 1 \right] \right\} \tag{3.19}$$

The efficiency of conversion is the ratio of the electrical power output to the photon energy input in unit time. Thus

$$\epsilon = \frac{iV}{N_p e E_p} \tag{3.20}$$

where N_p is the number of incident photons per square centimeter of surface in unit time, e is the electronic charge, and E_p is the average photon energy in electron volts. The maximum efficiency predicted according to this equation for solar cells is of the order of 20 percent.

3.4.3 Present State of Development

Silicon solar cells have been used the most. Though silicon occurs in the form of SiO_2 most abundantly, the cost of the silicon itself is high because of the need for zone refining, an operation mostly still carried out by hand. A series connection of the cells is possible. Cadmium sulfide solar cells are at present being widely investigated. The efficiencies with these cells are only about 3 to 4 percent[9] as compared with 15 percent for silicon solar cells.[10] Theoretically it is possible to obtain power outputs of the order of 25 mw cm⁻². However, since the thickness of the cell is small, the power/volume ratio may be relatively large. Power/weight ratios of over 100 watts lb⁻¹ have been achieved.[10]

3.4.4 Advantages, Disadvantages, and Possible Applications

One of the biggest advantages of this type of energy converter is that it converts solar energy directly into electrical energy. The fuel cost is thus zero, and the efficiency of its utilization is not too important from this point of view. This advantage is to a great extent offset by the fact that large areas of solar cells are required for any desired power levels. At the present time, the estimate is that the cost per watt is about $400 for silicon solar cells[5] and $50 per watt for CdS solar cells.[5] An increasing amount of attention is being given to "thin-film" photovoltaic cells. It is likely that in the next few years there will be break-throughs in the fabrication of such thin-film devices which might lower their cost sufficiently so that terrestrial applications will become feasible. (Thus automation would lower the cost of the manufacture of zone-refined silicon.)

   A significant advantage of solar cells is that they are relatively light (100 watts lb⁻¹) compared with some other direct-energy-conversion devices such as thermoelectric ones. Solar cells ranging in power levels from a few hundred milliwatts to a kilowatt have been developed for space applications.[4,5] They have long life, which is another advantage for long-duration space missions. They do not require high operating temperatures.

Just as is the case with all energy-conversion devices using solar energy as the energy source, it is necessary to couple solar cells with some storage device when a continuous power supply is required. Thus, one can combine the storage device with a hydrogen-oxygen fuel cell which also has a high power/weight ratio compared with that of thermionic or thermoelectric devices. During the daytime, the solar cell is used as the power supply for the necessary applications and also regeneration of hydrogen and oxygen from water, which is the fuel-cell product formed during the dark periods when the fuel cell is used as the power source. Of course, other electrochemical energy storage devices can also be used.

Some of the problems with solar cells are radiation damage and temperature degradation.[4,5] There is a considerable amount of work in progress to reduce these effects in solar cells.

3.5 Magnetohydrodynamic (MHD) Energy Converters

3.5.1 Principles of Method

In this method, a high-temperature plasma, consisting of a mixture of positive and negative ions, moves through a magnetic field and in a direction perpendicular to it.[3–5] Under these conditions, an electric field is induced in a direction mutually perpendicular to the direction of the magnetic field and the direction of motion of the particles, and the positive ions and electrons will be directed toward opposite electrodes, as shown in Fig. 7. If the two electrodes are connected externally through a load, then a current will flow through this circuit. Thus, in a magnetohydrodynamic generator, the translational energy of the ionized particles is converted to electrical energy.

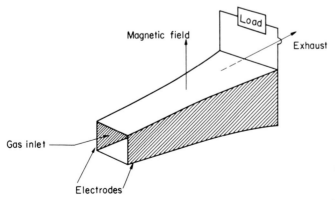

Figure 7   The basic unit of a magnetohydrodynamic energy converter.[5]

The idea of magnetohydrodynamic power generation evolved from the early work[3–5] of (1) Faraday, who researched on mercury flowing in a glass tube in the presence of a magnetic field, (2) Crookes, who studied the nature of species in discharge tubes, and (3) Langmuir, who drew a similarity between the electrical properties of ionized gases. (The name "plasma" for hot ionized gases was first used by Langmuir.)

3.5.2 Important Criteria Determining Performance

The electric potential developed across the electrodes (Fig. 7) under open-circuit conditions E_o is given by

$$E_o = Bvd \tag{3.21}$$

where B is the strength of the magnetic field, v is the velocity of the hot ionized gas, and d is the distance between the electrodes. The internal resistance R_i of the generator per square centimeter is given by

$$R_i = \frac{d}{\sigma} \tag{3.22}$$

where σ is the specific conductivity of the ionized gas between the electrodes.

The current density obtained in the external circuit when the external resistance is R_e is expressed by

$$i = \frac{E_o}{R_i + R_e} \tag{3.23}$$

The power density of the MHD generator is given by

$$P = Ei \tag{3.24}$$

where E is the potential difference across the terminals of the electrodes. The efficiency of conversion is the ratio of the power output to the enthalpy flux ΔH into the generator. Thus

$$\epsilon = \frac{Ei}{\Delta H} \tag{3.25}$$

where ΔH is the heat input into the generator in unit time. Some power is required to supply the magnetic field. However, for large installations the amount of power required is small in comparison with the power output of the generator.[3–5] Since there is a conversion of heat to electricity, the Carnot limitation applies. However, since very high temperatures are used, the maximum efficiencies are high,[11] being from 50 to 60 percent.

3.5.3 Present State of Development

It is necessary to heat the source of working fluid to ionize it. Temperatures of around 3000 to 4000°K are required. Ionization is induced by the natural process of thermal agitation. The process is accelerated, however, by seeding into the chamber a small amount of easily ionizable material (for example, Cs vapor). The ionized gas passes through the energy-conversion chamber where the electric power is generated. The gas then enters a condenser and is recirculated back to the boiler (Fig. 8). Efficiencies of about 160 percent have been reported.[11] The heat source may be fossil or nuclear fuels. The successful development of MHD generators depends largely on the material problems

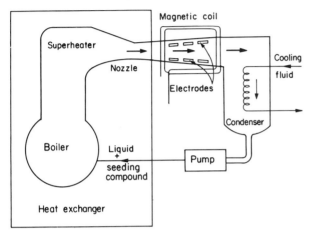

Figure 8   The mode of operation of a MHD generator.[3]

associated with temperatures of 3000 to 4000°K. The exhaust gas leaves the generation chamber at a high temperature. It may then be used as the heat source for a steam generator to produce steam for a conventional power plant.

Work is in progress to develop magnetohydrodynamic generators to deliver power in the megawatt range; there is little prospect of developing practical MHD generators for low-power outputs.

3.5.4 *Advantages, Disadvantages, and Possible Applications*

Magnetohydrodynamic energy conversion is being mainly considered for large-scale power generation.[3-5] There are no moving parts and thus mechanical problems are eliminated. The higher temperature of the working fluids used here as opposed to those used in conventional power plants makes it possible to attain higher efficiencies. The problem of finding materials which are stable at the temperatures concerned has not shown signs of tractability hitherto. The use of MHD generators is attractive because of the relatively high efficiencies.[3-5] The hot ionized gases can be recirculated. It should be possible to attain efficiencies of over 60 percent. The present estimates are that the initial cost would be under $100 per kilowatt.[11] Under these conditions, MHD generators should prove to be competitive with conventional engine generators. There is a greater enthusiasm about the development of MHD generators in Europe than in the United States.[12]

3.6   Electrochemical Energy Converters

3.6.1   *Principles of Method*

Electrochemical energy conversion is the conversion of the free-energy change of a chemical reaction directly into electrical energy.   As will be seen in Chap. 3, the relation between the free-energy change of a chemical reaction, ΔG, and the thermodynamic reversible potential of the cell, E_r, in which this overall reaction occurs is given by

$$\Delta G = -nFE_r \tag{3.26}$$

where n is the number of electrons transferred from the anode to the cathode during one act of the overall reaction and F is the Faraday constant.

In an electrochemical electricity producer (ecep) (Fig. 9), by making use of gaseous reactants (e.g., hydrogen and oxygen), the anodic and cathodic reactants are fed into their respective chambers.   The electrolyte layer is between

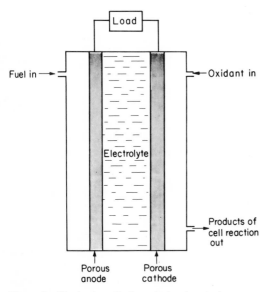

Figure 9   The basic unit of an electrochemical energy converter.

the two electrodes.   The half-cell reaction at the anode yields electrons, which are transported through the external circuit and reach the cathode.   These electrons are then transferred to the cathodic reactant.   The circuit is completed by the transport of ions from one electrode to the other through the electrolyte. As an example, one may consider the hydrogen-oxygen fuel cell in acid electrolyte in which the reactions at the two electrodes and the overall reaction are

Anode: $H_2 \rightarrow 2H^+ + 2e_0^-$ (3.27)

Cathode: $O_2 + 4H^+ + 4e_0^- \rightarrow 2H_2O$ (3.28)

Overall: $2H_2 + O_2 \rightarrow 2H_2O$ (3.29)

The current carriers through the solution in this case are largely hydrogen ions. The standard free-energy change for reaction (3.29) is -113.38 kcal at $25°C$ and correspondingly the thermodynamic reversible potential of the cell is 1.229 volts.

3.6.2   Distinction between Electrochemical Electricity Producers and Storers

The distinction between fuel cells and batteries is a very clear one, though often misunderstood. Basically fuel cells and batteries are devices for essentially different objectives. In the case of the former, the objective is the *conversion of* the energy of chemical reactions directly into electricity. In the case of the latter, called illogically a battery, the objective is to *store* electrical energy. The energy is obtained from electricity, e.g., hydroelectricity, and is temporarily *stored* in the battery, the logical name of which would be electrochemical electricity storer (eces).

The only basic similarity between an electrochemical electricity producer (ecep) and an electrochemical electricity storer is in the act of producing electricity—a charge transfer across electrode-electrolyte interfaces. There are several secondary differences between ecep and eces. For example, the ecep usually uses gaseous fuels, whereas the reactants in eces are usually crystalline solids—but this is secondary and a historical factor in the development of eces which essentially was at a standstill for many years but has recently been revived.

Finally, a source of confusion must be clarified. In conventional terminology, one speaks of primary and secondary batteries. The impression is given that these devices are similar. However, a primary battery is in essence a fuel cell in the sense that its reactants are converted into products and electricity without the prospect of being regenerated, whereas the main point of the secondary battery is the reversible nature of the charge and discharge processes, so that chemical materials in it are never destroyed (or only so after many years) and serve as intermediate storers of electrons.

A more detailed discussion of this subject is dealt with in Chap. 4.

3.6.3   Important Criteria Determining Performance

In the case of a fuel cell which acts ideally, the terminal-cell potential is constant and is equal to the thermodynamic reversible potential of the cell at any value of the current density drawn from the cell. In order that the efficiency of electrochemical energy converters may be compared with those of other energy-conversion devices, it is necessary to have a common base. Most of the other systems discussed previously convert heat energy into electricity. The heat energy in many cases is provided by the heat of a chemical reaction. The efficiency for these cases is defined as the work output divided by the heat input. Thus, in an analogous manner, the heat input for the electrochemical energy converter should be taken as the enthalpy change of the reaction (ΔH). The work output in an electrochemical energy converter which operates at the thermodynamic reversible potential of the cell is the free-energy change of the reaction (Chap. 3). Thus, the ideal efficiency of an electrochemical energy converter is defined by the equation

$$\epsilon = \frac{\Delta G}{\Delta H} = -\frac{nFE_r}{\Delta H} \tag{3.30}$$

Generally, ΔG is quite close to ΔH and hence the efficiency of fuel cells which perform ideally would be close to unity. In some rare cases (for example, the electrooxidation of carbon to carbon monoxide) the numerical value of ΔG exceeds that of ΔH, which means that in these cases the ideal efficiencies exceed unity.

In the case of practically all fuel cells, the terminal-cell potential decreases with increasing current density drawn from the cell. The main reasons for this decrease can be shown to be (Chap. 4): (1) the slowness of one or more of the intermediate steps of the reactions occurring at either or both of the electrodes, (2) the slowness of mass-transport processes (e.g., reactants to and/or products from the electrode), and (3) ohmic losses through the electrolyte (in some rare cases, there are ohmic losses at the electrodes themselves). Under the conditions where all these forms of losses exist, the terminal-cell potential is given by

$$E = E_r - \eta_{act,a} - \eta_{act,c} - \eta_{conc,a} - \eta_{conc,c} - \eta_{ohm} \tag{3.31}$$

where the η's with the appropriate suffixes represent the magnitudes of the losses of the first two types at the anode a and the cathode c and of the third type generally in the electrolyte. The potentials expressing these losses are termed "overpotentials." The three types of overpotentials are given the names activation, concentration, and ohmic, respectively. When the terminal-cell potential is E, the energy output during the formation of 1 mole of products in the cell becomes nFE. Under these conditions, the efficiency is expressed by

$$\epsilon = -\frac{nFE}{\Delta H} \tag{3.32}$$

The magnitude of each type of overpotential increases with current density drawn from the cell. Hence [cf. Eq. (3.31)], the terminal-cell potential and the efficiency of the cell decrease with increasing current density.

There is—more rarely—another reason for the loss in efficiency of an electrochemical energy converter. This loss is owing to the fact that either there is an incomplete conversion of the reactants at each electrode to their corresponding products or sometimes the reactant from one electrode diffuses through the electrolyte and reaches the other electrode, where it reacts with the reactant at this electrode. The overall efficiency, taking into account this loss, is obtained by multiplying the efficiency expressed by Eq. (3.32) by ϵ_f which is the faradaic efficiency. The ratio ϵ_f represents the amount of product formed to that expected theoretically on the basis of complete conversion and is often equal to unity.

The various η's may be expressed in terms of the current drawn from the cell, as will be seen in Chap. 4. The terminal-cell potential–current-density relation for a cell is the most fundamental one for a cell. From it, the expression for the efficiency of a cell is obtained using Eq. (3.32). Also, one can obtain the power-density P–current-density i relation for the cell. This relation is given by

$$P = iE \qquad\qquad (3.33)$$

E is expressed as a function of current density using Eq. (3.31) and the various equations found in Chap. 4. Qualitatively, one can predict that the Pi relation must pass through a maximum. P tends to zero when i tends to very small or very large values (in the latter case because polarization reduces E toward zero) but has appreciable values at intermediate values of i.

3.6.4 Present State of Development

A brief description of the various types of fuel cells is given in Sec. 4, whereas details of all these types are presented in Chap. 10. The most successful systems at the present time are the various types of hydrogen-oxygen fuel cells. The use of hydrogen-oxygen fuel cells in Gemini space flights[13] and in Apollo space flights[14] indicates a measure of the success achieved in the past 10 years of research. The power output of these units is of the order 1 to 2 kw. The efficiencies of these systems are in the region of 50 to 70 percent. Power/weight ratios of 15 to 20 watts lb^{-1} have been obtained. The projected figures are over 20 watts lb^{-1}. An effort is being made to develop electrochemical energy converters using organic fuels (Chap. 10). A sufficiently high degree of success has been achieved with hydrocarbon-air fuel cells operating in the intermediate-temperature range considering the fact that hydrocarbons were thought of being electrochemically inert up to about 7 or 8 years ago. Even at the present time, efficiencies of hydrocarbon-air fuel cells exceed those of conventional engines using these fuels. However, the relatively good efficiencies in the case of hydrocarbon fuel cells are being obtained using the expensive platinum as the electrocatalyst. Work is in progress to develop other electro-catalysts as well as to lower the platinum content of the electrodes by altering their structure. Simultaneously, work is in progress to develop indirect hydrocarbon-air fuel cells. Here, hydrogen is obtained from the hydrocarbon by the steam-reforming reaction and it is the anode reactant. The advantage of using hydrogen is that its electrode reaction is relatively reversible (i.e., there is little departure of the potential at the hydrogen electrode with increasing current drain from the cell). Another advantage is that electrocatalysts considerably cheaper than platinum may be used as hydrogen electrodes.

There is work going on using many other types of fuels. Hydrazine-air fuel cells are well-developed. Unfortunately, the cost of hydrazine is at present too high to consider these fuel cells for various applications. The performance of methanol-air fuel cells is promising. An electrically regenerative cell of considerable promise in the transportation field is the lithium-chlorine fuel cell.[15]

A high-temperature system which has been developed is the one using solid electrolytes.[16] Very compact cells have been fabricated. The fuels used are hydrogen or carbon monoxide both of which are obtained from the water-gas or steam-reforming reaction. Power densities of 0.6 watt cm^{-2} have been obtained. High power/weight ratios (100 watts lb^{-1}), excluding auxiliaries, have been reported.

3.6.5 Advantages, Disadvantages, and Possible Applications

The attractive feature of electrochemical energy conversion is the prospect of achieving very high efficiencies. To a large extent, this promise has already been fulfilled, e.g., with practically realized hydrogen-oxygen, hydrazine-oxygen, lithium-chlorine, and hydrogen-bromine fuel cells. Another advantage is that high energy/weight or energy/volume ratios can be obtained. They are higher than the corresponding ratios of any other mode of converting energy for systems in which energy must be supplied without refueling for the range 10 to 1,000 hr (cf. Fig. 10). This advantage is elaborated in Sec. 5. It is this advantage which has made the fuel cell the forerunner for space power systems.

The fuel cell is generally simple. There are no moving parts apart from pumps in the auxiliary system. At least one type of fuel cell has been developed which, in different versions, operates from 50 to 1200°C. They are noiseless and fumeless. They can be constructed at any required power level.

Besides space applications, many others have been considered, particularly with respect to mobile power. Thus, extensive work is at present in progress for the application of fuel cells as power sources to drive the much-needed electric cars. Also, they are being actively developed in small units as a source of electric power for homes, industries, etc. Fuel cells, like the other direct-energy-conversion devices, produce direct current. There are many applications for direct current, as, for example, in the case of many manufacturing processes and for some considered forms of future transportation in which trains run in tubes under the influence of linear accelerators. For applications needing

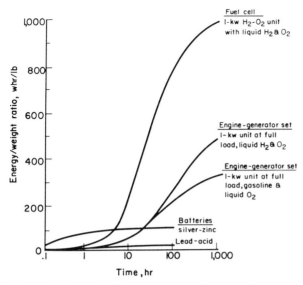

Figure 10 Energy/weight ratio as a function of space-mission duration for some energy converters.[31]

alternating current, conversion from direct current can be made without significant loss of efficiency.

4 TYPES OF ELECTROCHEMICAL ENERGY CONVERTERS

4.1 General

The present book deals with the fundamental aspects of electrochemical energy conversion. Thus, in this introductory chapter, it will be useful to describe briefly the various types of fuel cells. A more detailed description is found in Chap. 10. Also in this section, it will be worthwhile to record some historical facts, since the concept of fuel cells, just like the other direct-energy-conversion devices, is not a new one.

4.2 Classification

There are several types of fuel cells and nearly as many types of classifications have appeared in the literature. In the present book, some attempt has been made to give a fairly general type of classification, as shown in Table 1. Herein, they all come under direct, indirect, or regenerative fuel cells. In a direct fuel cell the products of the cell reaction are discarded, whereas in a regenerative fuel cell the fuel-cell reactants are regenerated from the products by one of several methods as indicated in the table. The two types—direct and regenerative fuel cells—are akin to primary and secondary batteries, respectively. A

TABLE 1 Classification of Fuel Cells

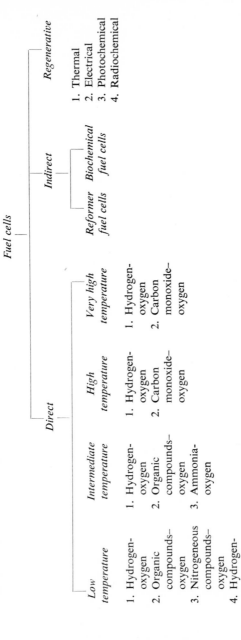

Fuel cells

Direct			Indirect		Regenerative
Low temperature	Intermediate temperature	High temperature	Very high temperature	Reformer fuel cells	Biochemical fuel cells	Thermal, Electrical, Photochemical, Radiochemical

Direct:

Low temperature
1. Hydrogen-oxygen
2. Organic compounds-oxygen
3. Nitrogeneous compounds-oxygen
4. Hydrogen-halogen
5. Metal-oxygen

Intermediate temperature
1. Hydrogen-oxygen
2. Organic compounds-oxygen
3. Ammonia-oxygen

High temperature
1. Hydrogen-oxygen
2. Carbon monoxide-oxygen

Very high temperature
1. Hydrogen-oxygen
2. Carbon monoxide-oxygen

Indirect:

Reformer fuel cells

Biochemical fuel cells

Regenerative
1. Thermal
2. Electrical
3. Photochemical
4. Radiochemical

third type in the case of fuel cells is the indirect fuel cell. Examples of these types are the reformer fuel cells using organic fuels and biochemical fuel cells, in which one of the fuels is a biochemically important substance, decomposed by means of an enzyme in solution (sometimes supplied by adding bacteria or other living materials which contain enzymes) to a simple fuel, e.g., hydrogen. The bulk of fuel-cell research is concerned with the development of primary fuel cells. A further subdivision according to the temperature range in which the fuel cell operates appears satisfactory, and for this purpose the following scheme is adopted: the low-, intermediate-, high-, and very-high-temperature fuel cells operate in the ranges 25 to 100°C, 100 to 500°C, 500 to 1000°C, and over 1000°C, respectively.

In each of these temperature ranges, one may divide the different types of fuel cells further, depending on the type of fuel or oxidant used. These are also shown in Table 1. Some of these fuels may exist naturally or may be easily produced from the naturally occurring ones. Under organic compounds, one may think of a variety of potential fuels, e.g., hydrocarbons, alcohols. One may also consider the electronically conducting form of carbon (graphite) as a fuel. The nitrogenous fuels which have been used are ammonia, hydrazine, and the methyl-substituted hydrazines. Oxygen, either pure or as in air, is being used in practically all fuel cells as the oxidant. In a few cases, as seen from Table 1, the halogens are being used.

A final subdivision is possible from the point of view of the nature of the electrolyte used. This is not presented in the table, although some system is followed in Chap. 10 where the various types of fuel cells are discussed. From the temperature ranges, one may infer that aqueous electrolytes are used invariably in the low-temperature range and mostly so at intermediate temperatures; molten electrolytes are used sometimes at intermediate temperatures and always at high temperatures; solid electrolytes (e.g., mixed oxides where the oxide ion is the current carrier in the electrolyte) are used at very high temperatures.

The various types of regenerative fuel cells are mentioned in Table 1. Much of current research with the regenerative cells is with electrical regeneration. In this special case, the electrochemical energy converter passes over into an electrochemical energy storer.

4.3 Historical

The idea of fuel cells is not a new one. Sir William Grove, in 1839, was the first to observe that when hydrogen and oxygen are supplied separately to two platinum electrodes immersed in sulfuric acid, a current is produced in the external circuit connecting the two platinum electrodes through a load.[17] The term fuel cells was only coined 50 years later by Mond and Langer, who somewhat improved Grove's hydrogen-oxygen fuel cells.[18] William Ostwald realized the great potentialities of fuel cells—for example, the possibility of obtaining high thermal efficiencies.[19]   Ostwald also conceived the idea of using carbon as the fuel with oxygen or air as the oxidizing agent.   This idea was taken up by Jacques† who built a 1.5-kw fuel-cell battery using a carbon rod as the anode material.[20]   The electrolyte used was fused sodium hydroxide.   Haber and Brünner interpreted that Jacques' cell was actually a hydrogen-oxygen cell in the sense that hydrogen was produced by the chemical reaction of carbon with sodium hydroxide.[21]   Baur and others worked on coal-based fuel cells.[22]   The pioneer of the modern phase in fuel-cell research is F. T. Bacon.[23]   He started work in the thirties to develop a hydrogen-oxygen fuel cell using cheap catalysts (nickel anode and lithiated nickel oxide cathode) which operates at moderate temperatures (200 to 240°C) and pressures (30 to 40 atm) using an alkaline electrolyte.   It was fully developed into a multikilowatt generator by 1952. Davytan researched on molten carbonate electrolyte fuel cells which operate at temperatures of over 500°C using hydrogen or carbon monoxide as fuels.[24] Similar work was commenced in the early fifties by Ketelaar and Broers.[25] Since about 1958, a wide variety of fuel-cell research programs has been under way, and at the present time several thousand people are engaged in fuel-cell research and development in many countries.

5   A COMPARISON OF THE VARIOUS DIRECT-ENERGY-CONVERSION DEVICES AND THEIR POSSIBLE APPLICATIONS

5.1   Criteria for Comparison

A comparative study of the various energy-conversion systems is a very difficult task.   Several factors have to be considered before such a comparison can be made.   For example, it is necessary to know whether the energy-conversion device is required for space or terrestrial applications.   The choice of the energy-conversion system would then depend on the required power level and the duration and type of the mission.   Terrestrial applications can be broadly divided into two types—military and civilian.   Here, too, the power level required must be known first.   A further subdivision takes into account whether the energy-conversion device is required as a stationary or mobile power source.   In the case of civilian use, cost is an important factor.

On a fairly general basis, the following criteria have to be considered in a comparative study of the various energy-conversion devices: (1) efficiency, (2) power/weight ratio, (3) power/volume ratio, (4) life expectancy, and (5) cost of the energy conversion device per kilowatt.   It must be pointed out that in the case of a particular application, it does not necessarily follow that all these

† Jacques' article was first published in *Harper's Magazine* in 1897 and included a detailed design for powering a ship by an electrochemical energy converter!   The essential advantage of much more energy for much less weight was stressed by Jacques on the basis of a tabulated comparison of the weights needed for the electrochemical and thermal methods.

factors have to be taken into account. The necessary criteria would depend on the type of application. Table 2 shows a comparison of the various energy-conversion devices taking into consideration all these factors. Two types of figures are quoted: the best available up to 1969 and the apparent limits of what seem feasible.† In the columns entitled "Intangible factors" and "Comments" are presented the advantages and disadvantages of each system and some possible applications. In some ways, the preparation of a table of this type is premature. Most of the work on direct-energy-conversion devices has taken place in the past few years, and in many of these cases considerable improvement is being achieved with the passage of time. Furthermore, these figures would strongly depend on the magnitude of the power output of the energy-conversion device. In the preparation of this table, this point has not been taken into consideration. For comparative purposes the performance figures of some indirect-energy-conversion devices—gas turbines, internal-combustion engines, and diesel engines—are also presented. The table reflects the considerable progress achieved with the various direct-energy-conversion devices, most of which have been subject to considerable research effort for less than a decade.

In the following sections, the conclusions which may be drawn from Table 2 regarding the suitability of application of the various energy-conversion devices are dealt with. Space applications are first considered, followed by terrestrial applications for civilian and military use.

5.2 Space Applications

The need for lightweight energy production in space led to the awakening of interest particularly in fuel cells. The electrical power needed for space applications varies from a few watts to 100 kw—e.g., communication and weather satellites require only a few watts, whereas manned space laboratories require 100 kw. It is necessary that the power-production devices for these applications have a long life.

Because of the cost of putting a pound of substance into space (around $5,000 per pound), the weight/energy ratio of the energy-conversion system is an important factor. The weight of an energy-conversion device includes that of the necessary auxiliaries. A distinct advantage of electrochemical electricity producers is their high efficiency, which leads to favorable energy/weight ratios. In Fig. 10, the energy/weight ratio is plotted as a function of mission duration for some of the energy-conversion devices assuming that the device operates at a power level of 1 kw. Similar figures may be constructed for different power levels.[31] From such plots, a plot can be made showing the regions of applicability of the various energy-conversion devices for space missions of varying duration and requiring different power outputs. This is shown in Fig. 11 and is colloquially referred to as the "map of the Balkans." It may be seen that fuel

---

† For calculations of power/weight and power/volume ratios, the weights and volumes of only the energy converter were taken into account.

TABLE 2 Comparison of Available Data and Maximum Feasible Performance Data of Energy Converters

Method of energy conversion	Efficiency, %		Power/wt hp lb⁻¹		Power/vol. hp ft⁻³		Life expectation		Cost/power $ hp⁻¹		Intangible factors	Comments
	Best available till 1969	Maximum feasible	Best available till 1969	Maximum feasible	Best available till 1969	Maximum feasible	Best available till 1969	Maximum feasible	Best available till 1969	Minimum feasible		
Thermoelectric[6]	10	12	0.03	0.1	1.1	2	3 years	Greater than 10 years	400	200	No moving parts, virtually maintenance-free. Noise-free, will operate over wide temperature range. Efficiency independent of size	Cost relatively high. Covers wide range in power levels
Thermionic[26]	22	32	0.03	0.1	1	3	1½ years	Greater than 10 years	400	100	Same as thermoelectric materials problems owing to high temperature and Cs vapor	High temperature necessary—2000°K. Covers wide range of power levels
Photovoltaic[10]	15	25	0.6	1.0	80	130	5 years	Greater than 10 years	70,000	40,000	Simplest device. Long life. High temperature not required	Wide range of power levels. Cost too high. Necessary to develop types other than silicon solar cells. Needs energy storage (fuel cells)

Magento-hydrodynamic[11,27]	60	70	1.6	2	1,200	20,000	Tests carried out for 1 week	Greater than 10 years	70	45	Same as thermionics but higher temperatures cause more problems	Only for high power levels ($>$1 Mw). Field in infancy
Low-temperature fuel cells[28]	70	90	0.04	1	3	30	Greater than 2 years	Greater than 10 years	400	100	High efficiency at low temperatures. Easy to operate. No problem of corrosion	H_2-O_2 cells best-developed. Cost of H_2 and its storage are main problems
High-temperature fuel cells[16,29]	60	90	0.2	2	10	50	1 year	Greater than 10 years	100	30	Polarization is low at both electrodes. Carbonaceous fuels may be used in molten carbonate or solid electrolytes	Problems of corrosion. Wide range of power levels
Gas turbine[30]	28		1		70		1 year		25		Many moving parts	Low initial costs, cheap fuel. No cooling or ignition
Internal-combustion engine[30]	27		0.3		7		5 years		3		Many moving parts	Low initial costs. Operates well over wide range of temperatures and pressures
Diesel engine[30]	42		0.2	0.2	8		10 years		3		Many moving parts	Low fuel costs. Hard starting in cold weather (below 5°C)

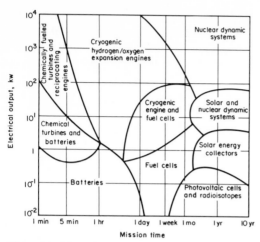

Figure 11 Plots showing regions of applicability of the various energy converters depending on mission duration and power output required.[4]

cells are best for space missions ranging from a few hours to a month and for power levels of up to 100 kw. Their state of development is a good deal ahead of any other direct-energy-conversion device and is indeed expected to be so, particularly because of the need for electrochemical electricity producers in space vehicles and lunar explorations.

Photovoltaic energy converters are useful for very long missions, but only up to power levels of about 1-kw output. In the medium power range of 0.1 to 10 kw and for long missions, thermionic or thermoelectric energy converters, solar and nuclear sources, respectively, are suitable. If the power level is sufficiently high (of the order of 10 kw) and for missions longer than a month, nuclear systems become enormously advantageous. Some caution must be taken in using plots of the type shown in Fig. 11. Most of the energy-conversion systems are in an early stage of development and other factors may limit their range of applicability. A very important criterion for considering energy-conversion devices for space application is their reliability. From this point of view hydrogen-oxygen fuel cells and photovoltaic cells are at present outstanding, but this situation may be modified, particularly by means of the results of increased research on the properties of materials.

5.3 Civilian Terrestrial Applications

For civilian terrestrial applications, two of the most important factors determining the choice of an energy-conversion system are its initial and running costs. Taking into account an amortization factor for the initial cost, one may calculate the total cost per kilowatthour. In Chap. 7, these calculations are presented for the various types of fuel cells. An important factor determining the total cost per kilowatthour for any energy-conversion device is the efficiency of the system. From this point of view, as may be seen from Table 2, fuel cells have a significant advantage over all other energy-conversion systems.   It has been reported that the annual cost for petroleum products in the United States is nearly equal to the national defense budget (nearly $50 billion).[32]   Thus, if the efficiency of utilization of these fuels could be doubled, as seems likely if fuel cells were used to drive vehicles, one would see a national cost savings of the order of one-third the cost of defense.

There are several types of terrestrial applications.   For large-scale power generation (>1 Mw), magnetohydrodynamic generators appear most promising.   They will have to compete with nuclear reactors.   An advantage of magnetohydrodynamic generators is that there are no moving mechanical parts and operation is silent.   Fuel cells should also come in useful in this direction. In these cases, the high-temperature molten-carbonate electrolytes making use of natural gas are likely to be used since they use cheap electrocatalysts and are the most economical.   Hydrogen-oxygen fuel cells combined with a nuclear reactor may also be used.   During off-peak periods, hydrogen and oxygen may be produced electrolyzing an aqueous solution.   During peak periods these gases may then be used in a fuel cell.   The present estimate of the initial cost of high-temperature hydrocarbon-air fuel cells using molten electrolytes is around $100 per kilowatt, which is practically the initial cost of engine generator sets.   An advantage of fuel cells is that they can be built for any desired power level.   Thus, instead of having large central power stations, individual home units could be built for heating and lighting, with natural gas as the fuel.   For large-scale power generators, power/volume ratios should also be high.   MHD generators and fuel cells satisfy this requirement.

A classical analysis of the possible use of electrochemical energy converters as a source of mechanical power for (1) delivery and industrial trucks, (2) automobiles, (3) construction equipment, (4) light aircraft, (5) locomotives, (6) outboard motors, and (7) marine application was carried out by Adams et al.[33] They concluded that it would be necessary to develop fuel cells using low-cost fuels, e.g., hydrocarbons, for fuel cells to be competitive with present power sources.

For a mobile power source, high power/weight and power/volume ratios are required.   At the present time the best fuel cells have power/weight ratios of only one-fifth that of internal-combustion engines (Table 2).   But with further research, it should be possible to increase power/weight ratios of some fuel-cell systems to values of the same order as internal-combustion engines. It is unlikely, however, that fuel cells will be made as light (in respect to power per unit weight†) as jet engines.   The figures of power/volume ratios presently available are competitive with those of internal-combustion engines.

An advantage of fuel cells over internal-combustion engines as a mobile power source is that fuel cells have higher torque characteristics at lower speeds, whereas the reverse is the case with internal-combustion engines.[32]   Higher

---

† Confusion must be avoided here.   Thus, it is *power* per unit weight which at present is not as good for fuel cells as, for example, internal combustions.   In *energy* per unit weight, fuel cells are *much better* than any other type of converter.

torque at lower speeds is required for acceleration.   Furthermore, the efficiencies of fuel cells are higher at lower speeds, whereas the converse is true for internal-combustion engines.   Air pollution is becoming a serious problem in many cities with the increasing number of automobiles.   With fuel-cell-driven cars, this problem could be eliminated.

The advent of thin-film photovoltaics may result in a competition with fuel cells for some terrestrial applications.   However, solar photovoltaic power makes electrical energy storage mandatory.   Clearly this need would necessitate the development of regenerative fuel cells.   It is a little noted fact that electrochemical devices provide the only practical way of storing electricity if it is to be available on demand.

Thermoelectric devices have been built as small power sources.   For example, 50-watt units that use the heat energy of the sun are used to drive water pumps.   Small units are also being used to power radios.   A 150-watt unit making use of the energy derived by burning any solid fuel (coal, charcoal, etc.) is being developed for communication purposes.   Silicon solar cells are also being developed for the same purposes.

There are many medical applications (e.g., pacemakers) that make use of small batteries at the present time.   It is necessary, however, to replace these batteries periodically.   The prospect of electrochemical power sources for permanent implantation in the body is undergoing intensive research.   Its realization would immediately enable more permanent heart pacemakers; but the larger aim particularly is to make a completely artificial heart driven by an electrochemical power source.   It may thus be possible to feed a permanent implanted fuel cell—a semipermeable membrance around its cathode that allows an ingress of oxygen in blood while another semipermeable membrane allows ingress of sugars.   The future of such devices for providing electrical energy within the body may lead to considerable development of artificial organs, for example, potentiostatically controlled vascular prostheses.

Long life of energy-conversion devices is vital in considering them for terrestrial applications.   At the present time, data on life expectancy are too small to make meaningful statements.   Hypothetically, all direct-energy-conversion methods with no moving parts should have a longer life than indirect-energy converters (e.g., diesel engines, internal-combustion engines) with plenty of moving parts.   For large-scale terrestrial applications, systems which are considered most suitable are high-temperature fuel cells using electroorganic fuels and magnetohydrodynamic generators.   The stability of materials under these conditions is an essential requirement and awaits exploration.   This factor seems to favor the development of fuel cells (1000°C) over magneto-hydrodynamic generators (3000 to 4000°C).

5.4 Military Terrestrial Applications

An advantage of the direct-energy-conversion methods over the conventional ones is that they operate silently.   In addition, due to transportation costs, loss by evaporation, pilfering, spilling, enemy action, etc., the cost of fuel in a combat vehicle is about several dollars per gallon.[32]   (Estimates as high as $10 per gallon have been made.)   It is thus necessary to use fuels more economically. In this respect, fuel cells should have an advantage over the other energy converters.   Another considerable advantage of fuel cells for military purposes is that they decrease chances of infrared detection.

Thermoelectric and thermionic energy converters are also being built as small power sources for military applications.

6   SUMMARY OF ADVANTAGES OF ELECTRO-CHEMICAL ENERGY CONVERTERS

Fuel cells already play a dominant role in the field of direct energy conversion in space.   The essential advantage of fuel cells is that chemical energy is converted directly to electrical energy, by which method the fundamental limitation of the Carnot cycle, which applies to most other direct methods as well as to all indirect methods, is avoided.   Thus, theoretically it should be possible to attain high efficiencies.   To a great extent this expectation has been fulfilled.   A variety of fuels may be used.   Fuel cells can be adapted for any desired temperature range.   The operation of the cells is simple compared with that of indirect devices. Cells can be made in any required shape and size.   The exhaust gases are not noxious and are nonpollutant.   The devices operate silently.   In some cases (e.g., hydrogen-oxygen fuel cells) potable water is produced.   In the case of space applications, and for certain practical mission times and power levels, electrochemical electricity producers seem to have no rivals (Fig. 11).

7   A FEW WORDS ON THE CONTENTS OF THIS BOOK

The fuel cell is an electrochemical device.   Its performance is mainly determined by the kinetics of the reactions occurring at the electrode and by the transport processes through the solution and in the electrode.   Hitherto, no book concerned with energy conversion has presented the substantial theoretical background which is the basis of electrochemical electricity producers.   The next eight chapters, therefore, will deal with the fundamental aspects of the theory of electrochemical energy conversion and neglect the engineering side.   The last chapter will summarize the present status of development of various types of fuel cells.

REFERENCES

1. Thirring, H.: "Energy for Man," Harper & Row, Publishers, Incorporated, New York, 1957.

2. Plummer, A. M., and J. N. Anno: Conference on Direct Energy Conversion, Nov. 4–5, 1963, Office of Technical Services, Department of Commerce, Washington, D.C., 1964, pp. 170–180.

3. Chang, S. L.: "Energy Conversion," Prentice-Hall, Inc., Englewood Cliffs, N.J., 1963.

4. Angrist, S. W.: "Direct Energy Conversion," Allyn and Bacon, Inc., Englewood Cliffs, N.J., 1964.

5. Sutton, G. W. (ed.): "Direct Energy Conversion," McGraw-Hill Book Company, New York, 1966.

6. Westinghouse Electric Corporation (via R. Novak), private communication, 1969.

7. Martini, W. R.: Flameheated Thermionic Converter Research, final report, July 1, 1961–June 30, 1963, Atomics International, contract no. DA-36-039SC88982, AD 428094.

8. TRW, Inc.: Advanced Solar Thermionic Power Systems, *Office Tech. Serv., Dept. Comm., Tech. Doc. Rept.* ASD-7DR-62-877 (AD295917), 1962.

9. Schaeffer, J. C.: "Thin Film CdS Front Wall Solar Cells," Secs. A-1 and A-2, AF 33(615)-1049 DDC No. 451543.

10. Loferski, J. J.: *Proc. IEEE*, **51**, 667 (1963); in "Summer Course on Space Power Systems," August, 1968, European Space Research Organization, Paris, France, in press; Brown University, private communication, 1969.

11. Avco Everett Research Laboratory (via J. Klepeis), private communication, 1969.

12. Altman, M.: Private communication, University of Pennsylvania, 1969.

13. Maget, H. J. R.: Chap. 4, in C. Berger (ed.), "Handbook of Fuel Cell Technology," Prentice-Hall, Inc., Englewood Cliffs, N.J., 1968.

14. Morril, C. C.: *Proc. Ann. Power Sources Conf.*, **19**, 38 (1965).

15. Swinkels, D. A. J.: *J. Electrochem. Soc.*, **113**, 6 (1966).

16. Archer, D. H., R. L. Zahradnik, E. F. Sverdrup, W. A. English, L. Elikan, and J. J. Alles: *Proc. Ann. Power Sources Conf.*, **18**, 36 (1964); D. H. Archer: *Mechanical Engrg.*, **42** (1968).

17. Grove, W. R.: *Phil. Mag.*, **14**, 127 (1839).

18. Mond, L., and C. Langer: *Proc. Roy. Soc. (London)*, **46**, 296 (1889).

19. Ostwald, W.: *Z. Elektrochem.*, **1**, 122 (1894).

20. Jacques, W. W.: *Z. Elektrochem.*, **4**, 129 (1897).

21. Haber, F., and R. Brünner: *Z. Elektrochem.*, **10**, 697 (1904); **12**, 78 (1906).

22. Baur, E., and H. Preis: *Z. Elektrochem.*, **43**, 727 (1937).

23. Bacon, F. T.: Chap. 5, in G. J. Young (ed.), "Fuel Cells," vol. 1, Reinhold Publishing Corporation, New York, 1960.

24. Davytan, O. K.: *Bull. Acad. Sci. USSR, Classe Sci. Tech.*, **107**, 125 (1946).

25. Broers, G. H. J., and J. A. Ketelaar: Chap. 6, in G. J. Young (ed.), "Fuel Cells," vol. 1, Reinhold Publishing Corporation, New York, 1960.

26. Thermo Electron Engineering Corporation (via F. Rufeh), private communication, 1969.

27. Yaffe, S. A.: *Aviation Week*, Jan. 20, 1969.

28. Kordesch, K. V.: *Proc. Ann. Power Sources Conf.*, **19**, 17 (1965); K. V. Kordesch: Chap. 3, in C. Berger (ed.), "Handbook of Fuel Cell Technology," Prentice-Hall, Inc., Englewood Cliffs, N.J., 1968.

29. Archer, D. H., E. F. Sverdrup, and R. L. Zahradnik: *Chem. Eng. Progr.*, **60**, 64 (1964); D. H. Archer and R. L. Zahradnik: *ibid.*, **63**, 55 (1967).

30. Allison Division, General Motors Corporation (via J. P. Kern), private communication, 1969.

31. Mitchell, W.: Chap. 1, in W. Mitchell (ed.), "Fuel Cells," Academic Press Inc., New York, 1963.

32. Szego, G.: Economics, Logistics and Optimisation of Fuel Cells, Institute for Defense Analysis Res. Paper P. 208, 1965.

33. Adams, D. K., et al.: "Fuel Cells—Power for the Future," Harvard Business School, Harvard University, Cambridge, Mass., 1960.

CHAPTER 2

Basic Electrode Kinetics

1 BACKGROUND TO THE PRESENT CHAPTER

In the previous chapter, it was emphasized that the ideal or maximum efficiency of an electrochemical energy converter depends upon electrochemical thermodynamics whereas the real efficiency depends on electrode kinetics. One reason why interest in electrochemical energy conversion did not arise for such a long time is because the field of electrode kinetics was not developed in the West until the 1950s. The fact that the real efficiencies were so much less than the ideal efficiencies was regarded until recently as a mysterious one. As interest arose in power systems for space and ground mobile (e.g., electric car) applications, the fundamental theory underlying the direct electrochemical conversion of chemical energy to electricity—electrode kinetics—became important. For mobile applications, the power per unit weight, as well as the efficiency, are important factors to be considered. Since power is the rate of producing energy, the kinetics of the electricity producing interfacial charge-transfer reactions, i.e., electrode kinetics, became important.

As mentioned in the previous paragraph, delay in the development of electrode kinetics has been a primary drawback to the realization of electrochemical energy conversion. At the time of writing, this difficulty still exists to some extent because modern electrode kinetics has been developed in the past 15 years only—and predominantly by a very small group of about a dozen teams of research workers. The number of scientists in the world who at present have a comprehensive knowledge of this new field is in the low hundreds. Moreover, at the present time, only one comprehensive presentation of the field is available—and most of the material in this is ten years old.[1]

For these reasons, and because a knowledge of electrode kinetics is so important for those carrying out research in electrochemical energy conversion, the basic theory of electrode kinetics is presented in this chapter. All deductions in this basic chapter on the rates of charge-transfer reactions assume that the reaction surfaces are smooth and planar in a macro sense—i.e., the electrodes are wires or foils. In fuel cells, however, because of improved mass-transport conditions (Chap. 5) and probably greater effective area per apparent geometric area of the surface, electrodes are always porous.   It would be confusing to present the basic theory of charge transfer with the extra complications, which are involved with porous media.   This will be added to the present considerations in Chap. 5.

2   STRUCTURE OF ELECTRIC DOUBLE LAYERS

2.1   General

A knowledge of the structure of the electric double layer is of fundamental importance in the study of electrode kinetics.[2,3]   An electric double layer exists whenever two phases are in contact except in the case of a gas-gas, nonpolar-nonpolar-liquid, or gas-nonpolar-liquid interfaces.   Of interest in electrochemical energy conversion are the interfaces between a metal, or semiconductor, and an electrolytic solution.

2.2   Metal-solution Interfaces

2.2.1   *Types of Interfaces: Ideally Polarizable and Nonpolarizable Interfaces*

A *polarizable* interface is characterized by the absence of any component, charged or uncharged, which is common to both phases, from which it follows that equilibrium cannot exist across the interface.[4]   The system Hg/K^+Cl^- is an example of an almost ideally polarizable interface.   Such an interface can be compared with an ideal electrical capacitor which can be charged up to any desired potential without leakage of charges from one plate of the capacitor to the other.   An electrode kinetic, or electrodic, way of looking at an ideally polarizable interface is one in which the rate constant of the charge-transfer reaction occurring at the interface tends to zero.

Conversely, at a *nonpolarizable* interface, there is always thermodynamic equilibrium of a common charged component across the interface.   The interface $Ag/AgNO_3$ is a good example of an almost ideally nonpolarizable interface.   The electrical analog of a nonpolarizable interface is a leaky capacitor.   Such a capacitor resists changes in potential by allowing the passage of charge across the interface.   In electrode kinetic terminology, an ideally nonpolarizable interface is one in which the rate constant of the charge-transfer reaction occurring at the interface tends to infinity.

The two types of double layers described here are in fact idealizations; in real cases, some charge passes across a polarizable interface upon change in potential and some change of potential occurs at a nonpolarizable interface upon passage of charges across the interface.

The bulk of double-layer research has been carried out at the mercury-solution interface.   The main reason is that this interface is a particularly polarizable one.[5-7]   Thus, the current that flows in an outer circuit during charging of the interface largely depends upon properties of the capacitor, of which such surfaces are analogs. There is a limitingly low leak, or passage, of current across this double layer. A study of charging-up and charge-transfer processes which occur at nonpolarizable interfaces is more difficult, both experimentally and theoretically, for the currents flowing in the outer circuits are sometimes hard to separate into those due to capacitor-like properties of the interface and the electrode kinetic or capacitor-leak-like properties.

2.2.2 Double-layer Theories

2.2.2.1 The Compact-layer Model. In the theories of Quincke[8] and of Helmholtz,[9] the double layer was regarded simply as equivalent to a parallel-plate condenser consisting of two layers of charge of opposite sign and separated by a fixed distance (Fig. 1)—for example, electrons in the metal and positive

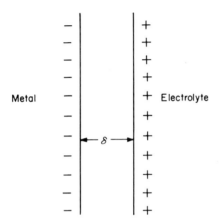

Figure 1 Compact-layer model of an electric double layer.

ions in solution. From elementary electrostatics, it follows that in a parallel-plate condenser

$$C_{M-2} = \frac{\epsilon}{4\pi\delta} \tag{2.1}$$

where C_{M-2} is the capacity of the double layer, ϵ is the dielectric constant of the intervening medium, and δ is the distance between the plates. Using $\delta = 3$ Å and $\epsilon = 6$, C_{M-2} is 17.7 μf cm^{-2}.

The differential capacity at any potential is the first derivative of the charge with respect to potential at this potential (that is, dq/dV). The integral capacity at any potential is simply the charge divided by the potential at this potential. In the case of the compact-layer model, the differential and integral capacities are equal. This is not so for other models of the double layer, which are discussed in the following sections. Since experimental determination of the capacities yield differential capacities, only the expressions for differential capacities are given for the other models. Though this value is in fair agreement with the relatively lengthy portion *DE* of the differential capacity vs. potential curve (Fig. 2), there are two main drawbacks to this simple parallel-plate-condenser model.   (The value of the capacity in the section *DE* is quoted quite frequently as the double-layer capacity.   However, the double-layer capacity

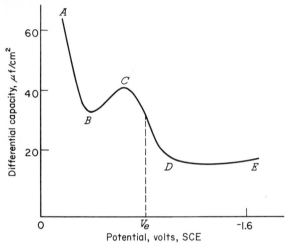

Figure 2   A typical plot of differential capacity vs. potential of mercury electrode.

varies significantly with potential, as seen from Fig. 2.)   First, it cannot account for the observed variation of differential capacity with potential[5,6] (Fig. 2). Second, it cannot explain the insensitivity of the capacity to the radius of the ion[10] in the region *DE*, where the capacity is reasonably constant with changes in the nature of ions present in solution (for the values of δ would be expected to follow those of the ionic radii).

2.2.2.2 Diffuse-layer Model.   Gouy[11] and Chapman,[12] working independently, pointed out that the ions in the electric double layer would not be firmly attached to the plates but that there would be an equilibrium of the ions due to the thermal and electrical fields in the double layer and that Maxwell-Boltzmann statistics is applicable for the charge distribution of these ions as a function of potential in the solution (Fig. 3).   An idealized form of the potential-distance relation for this theory is as given in Fig. 4.   This theory has been treated explicitly elsewhere.[6,13]   The diffuse charge q_D in the case of a 1-1 electrolyte is given by

$$q_D = \sqrt{\frac{2kTn_0\epsilon}{\pi}} \sinh \frac{e_0 V}{2kT} \tag{2.2}$$

where ϵ is the dielectric constant of the electrolyte, n is the number of ions of positive or negative sign per unit volume in the bulk of the electrolyte, and V is the potential drop from the metal to the bulk of the solution.

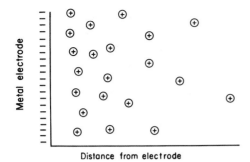

Figure 3 A typical charge distribution in the electrolyte according to diffuse-layer model of an electric double layer.

The differential capacity of the double layer is thus

$$C_{2-b} = \frac{dq}{dV}$$

$$= \sqrt{\frac{n_0 \epsilon e_0^2}{2\pi k T}} \cosh \frac{e_0 V}{2kT} \tag{2.3}$$

The capacity is a minimum at $V = 0$ and rises to very large values symmetrically on either side of $V = 0$.

For 1 N solution and with $\epsilon = 80$, C_{2-b} is 230 μf cm^{-2} and for a 10^{-3} N solution, C_{2-b} is 7.25 μf cm^{-2} (Ref. 3). The value quoted for a 1 N solution is far from the value of the observed capacity, 16 to 17 μf cm^{-2}, which was predicted from the earlier compact-layer model. Another reason why the diffuse-layer

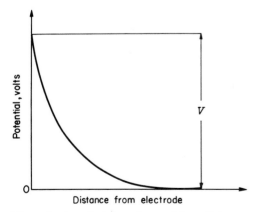

Figure 4 A typical plot of potential vs. distance according to the diffuse-layer model of an electric double layer. The potential in bulk of the electrolyte is taken as zero.

model is unsatisfactory is because it does not predict the observed capacity-potential relation.   It does, however, predict some potential variation of the capacity, unlike the previous theory.   It is worthwhile mentioning here that the agreement between calculated and experimental values is very good in sufficiently dilute solution.   The difficulties of the Gouy-Chapman theory are that the observed capacity-potential relations are not parabolic for higher concentrations where the observed capacity is of an order of magnitude lower than expected and the predicted shape is not observed at potentials far from the potential of zero charge.

2.2.2.3   Compact-diffuse-layer Model.   The first theory of the double layer which reproduces many of the essential features of the experimental capacity-potential curves is that due to Stern[14] who introduced in 1924 a model for the double layer which essentially united both previous theories.   According to this theory, the total charge on the solution side is divided between the compact and diffuse layers.   The total potential difference V between the metal and the bulk of the solution drops at first linearly from V_M in the metal to V_2 in the compact layer and thereafter decays exponentially to V_b in the bulk of the solution (Fig. 5).   The combined model can be considered as two capacitors in series.   Under these conditions,

$$V = (V_M - V_2) + (V_2 - V_b) \tag{2.4}$$

Differentiation with respect to charge on the metal gives

$$\frac{\partial V}{\partial q_M} = \frac{\partial}{\partial q_M} (V_M - V_2) + \frac{\partial}{\partial q_M} (V_2 - V_b) \tag{2.5}$$

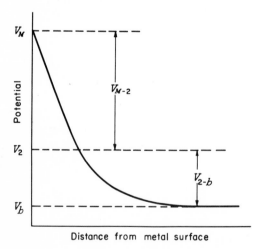

Distance from metal surface

Figure 5 A typical potential-distance relation according to the compact-diffuse-layer model of an electric double layer.

But $q_M = q_D$ (where q_D is the total diffuse charge). Thus

$$\frac{1}{C_T} = \frac{1}{C_{M-2}} + \frac{1}{C_{2-b}} \tag{2.6}$$

where C_{M-2} and C_{2-b} are the capacities of the compact and diffuse parts of the double layer and C_T is the overall capacity. The relation (2.6) is the expected one for two capacitors in series.

In the previous sections (2.2.2.1 and 2.2.2.2), it was shown that C_{M-2} is of the order of 18 μf and C_{2-b} is over 200 μf for concentrations of above 1 N. Hence, from Eq. (2.6) it follows that the contribution to the overall capacity by the diffuse double layer is insignificant at these concentrations. The implication of this theory is that if the concentration of ions in solution is small enough to make C_{2-b} the predominant term in the expression for C_T according to Eq. (2.6), the charges are spread out in the solution under the simultaneous effect of electrical and thermal forces. Conversely, if C_T depends mainly on C_{M-2}, which is the case in solutions of high concentrations (>1 N), then the charges are all concentrated on the solution side of the compact layer. Thus, except in very dilute solutions, this model is essentially similar to the compact-layer model and suffers from the same drawbacks as the latter—viz., it cannot explain the constancy of the capacity on mercury (16 to 17 μf cm^{-2}) in the presence of various ions at the more cathodic potentials, since one would expect a dependence of the capacity on the radius of the ion, and one cannot interpret the change in capacity with potential at potentials anodic to the region of constant capacity (Fig. 2).

2.2.2.4 Triple-layer Model.[15-17] Though the presence of specific adsorption of ions on the electrode was realized by Stern,[14] a distinction between the potential of the adsorbed and diffuse charge was not taken into consideration. This was first considered by Essin and Markov,[15] who defined a potential drop across the compact layer (V_{M-1}) and across the diffuse layer (V_{2-b}). This same idea was put forward later by Grahame[16] who considered the locus of centers of unhydrated ions in contact with the metal as the inner Helmholtz plane (IHP), and the corresponding locus of centers of the solvated anions and cations closest to the metal as the outer Helmholtz plane (OHP). Thus, the potentials at the inner and outer Helmholtz planes are V_1 and V_2, respectively; the reference potential in the bulk of the solution taken is V_b.

On the basis of this model (Fig. 6) Devanathan[17] derived the following expression for the differential capacity of the double layer (C):

$$\frac{1}{C} = \frac{1}{K_{M-1}} + \left(\frac{1}{K_{1-2}} + \frac{1}{C_{2-b}}\right)\left(1 - \frac{dq_1}{dq_M}\right) \tag{2.7}$$

K_{M-1} and K_{1-2} are the integral capacities of the space between the metal and the IHP and between the IHP and OHP, respectively; C_{2-b} is the differential

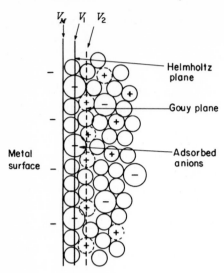

Figure 6 Triple-layer model of an electric double layer.[17]

capacity of the diffuse double layer; and dq_1/dq_M represents the rate of change of the specifically adsorbed charge with the charge on the metal. The following interesting points arise from Eq. (2.7):

(*i*) If dq_1/dq_M were zero, the resulting equation would be analogous to the one for the electrostatic capacity of three capacitors in series with individual capacities K_{M-1}, K_{1-2}, and C_{2-b}—hence the name "triple-layer model." Further, if C_{2-b} is large, since K_{M-1} and K_{1-2} are constants, the capacity would be a minimum when dq_1/dq_M is zero because dq_1/dq_M can only be either zero or positive—on the anodic side owing to contact (i.e., specific) adsorption of anions and on the cathodic side owing to possible contact adsorption of cations. Then:

$$\frac{1}{K_{M-2}} = \frac{1}{K_{M-1}} + \frac{1}{K_{1-2}} \tag{2.8}$$

where K_{M-2} represents the integral capacity of the region between the metal and the OHP.

(*ii*) When dq_1/dq_M exceeds unity, as it would on strong polarization, the differential capacity attains large values. If C tends to infinity, the electrode is being converted from a polarizable to a nonpolarizable one.

(*iii*) The capacity minimum, observed in the vicinity of the electrocapillary maximum in dilute solutions, is due to C_{2-b} being quite small under these conditions, and hence becoming the predominant capacity-determining term. This can also be seen from Eq. (2.6).

2.2.2.5 Water-dipole Model.[18-20] In the above models, the potential drop across the metal-solution interface is interpreted only on the basis of a charge distribution across the interface and analogies are drawn between electrostatic capacitors and the double layer. However, there is yet another contribution to the potential drop across the metal-solution interface. This arises because of the dipole moment of neutral molecules which are adsorbed on the electrode. The contribution of the adsorbed neutral molecules to the potential has been taken into account in recent times although it was first pointed out by Lange and Mischenko.[18]

Bockris and Potter[19] were the first to introduce the effect of the field-dependent contribution of oriented water dipoles into the field of electrode kinetics.

Recently a model of the double layer was proposed by Bockris, Devanathan, and Müller,[20] taking into consideration the presence of specifically adsorbed ions and in particular adsorbed water molecules. According to this model, the electrode is covered with strongly oriented adsorbed water molecules and some partially solvated ions, depending on the charge q_M on the metal. The locus of the specifically adsorbed ions is the inner Helmholtz plane. Adjacent to this layer is a layer of solvated ions. The locus of centers of these hydrated ions is the outer Helmholtz plane (Fig. 7).

An important quantity in the calculation of the capacity of the double

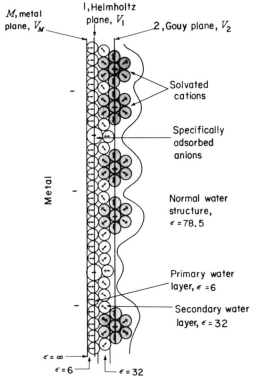

M, metal plane, V_M

1, Helmholtz plane, V_1

2, Gouy plane, V_2

Metal

Solvated cations

Specifically adsorbed anions

Normal water structure, $\epsilon = 78.5$

Primary water layer, $\epsilon = 6$

Secondary water layer, $\epsilon = 32$

$\epsilon = \infty$

$\epsilon = 6$

$\epsilon = 32$

Figure 7 Water-dipole model of an electric double layer.[20]

layer is the dielectric constant of the medium between the metal and the inner Helmholtz plane and between the inner and outer Helmholtz planes. It was pointed out earlier that the water molecules adsorbed on the electrode are strongly oriented, being either parallel or antiparallel to the field. Completely oriented water corresponds to a saturated dielectric and thus should have a dielectric constant of about 6 to 7.

Adjacent to this water layer, there is a second layer of water molecules on the solution side which is partly oriented by the field and disoriented by thermal fluctuations. This layer is similar to the secondary hydration sheath of an ion. Some of these water molecules also form a part of the primary hydration sheath of the ions located in the outer Helmholtz layer. A calculation of the dielectric constant of this second layer is rather difficult, but there is evidence[21] which suggests that it is in the region of 30 to 40.

Using this model of the double layer, the constancy of the capacity in the negative side of the capacity-potential relation (Fig. 2) can be rationalized. Thus, as already indicated, the dielectric constant ϵ varies as one departs from the metal-solution interface towards the solution. The relation between potential difference and charge in a condenser shows that the potential difference is inversely proportional to the dielectric constant. Hence the potential difference at the metal-solution interface would largely depend on the structure of the layer very close to the electrode where the dielectric constant is in the region of 6. When the ion size varies, the further contribution to the capacitance caused by the increasing size of the ion is muted by the fact that this occurs in the high-dielectric-constant region. In this way, with ions of varying size, the capacitance can be seen to be relatively constant. Numerous calculations on the basis of this model agree well with experiment.

The interpretation of the other region of the capacity-potential plot, which is dependent on the types of ions present, can also be made using the model described in this section, although the considerations are more complex and will not be treated in detail here. There is a quantitative agreement between the calculated and experimental values of the capacity-potential relation in these sections for the various ions.

The water-dipole model of the electric double layer at the metal-solution interface is also important in considerations of adsorption of organic molecules on electrodes. It is a subject that has direct bearing on electrochemical energy conversion, because a rationalization of the region of potential in which adsorption of organic fuel occurs is of vital importance in the kinetics of electrochemical-charge-transfer reactions involving these species. It has been known[22] since the 1920s that the relation between degree of coverage of an adsorbent on an electrode and potential is parabolic and relatively symmetrical with potential (Fig. 8). This behavior may be rationalized using the water-dipole model of the double layer. Water molecules are adsorbed on the surface and discourage access of organic molecules to adsorption sites over most ranges of potential. Water molecules are bound to the electrode at least partly by electrostatic forces that are directly

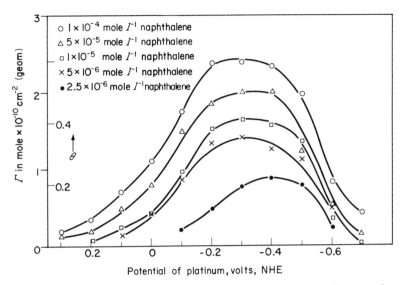

Figure 8 A typical coverage-potential relation for electrosorption of an organic compound. Case illustrated is adsorption of naphthalene on platinum from 0.9 N NaClO₄, 0.1 N NaOH for varying bulk concentrations of naphthalene.[24]

proportional to the charge on the electrode. When this charge approaches zero, the water molecules are held relatively poorly to the surface and organic molecules (fuels) can replace them to adsorb on the electrode. As the charge on the electrode changes sign and increases in magnitude, the water molecules are reattracted (or readsorbed) on the surfaces with their dipoles oriented oppositely to that obtaining when the electrode had its former sign of charge. The result is that organic molecules are repelled and decrease in coverage at extremes of charges. Thus, in an electrochemical energy converter (fuel cell), oxidation of the organic fuel may occur on the electrode only over a narrow range of potential (0.2 to 0.4 volt) across the metal-solution interface, where the coverage of the electrode with the organic fuel is quite high.

The mathematical theory of organic adsorption[20,23a] is well-supported by the experimental work of organic adsorption on mercury[23] and on some solid metals.[24,25] In addition to the electrostatic interaction of water and organic molecules with the electrode, it has been shown that it is also necessary to take into consideration chemibonding between these species and the electrode. In some cases, the organic molecule may undergo direct discharge from solution, i.e., become a radical in the act of discharge; and in such systems the coverage-potential relation should not be parabolic.

2.2.2.6 Summarizing Remarks on Models for the Double Layer. The first model for the structure of the double layer is analogous to a parallel-plate condenser with a plane of charges on the metal and a second plane of opposite charges in the solution.   According to this model, the capacity of the double layer should be independent of the potential across the metal-solution interface, which contradicts the experimentally observed behavior.

The next model considered that the charges in the solution side are not located in one plane but diffuse into the bulk of the solution.   This model yields a parabolic dependence of capacity on charge.   Though this model is satisfactory for very dilute solutions (concentration $< 10^{-3}$ mole l^{-1}), the predicted values of the capacity are far too high in concentrated solutions.

A combination of the compact-diffuse-layer models proved to be more satisfactory but, except in very dilute solutions, became in practice identical with the first model.   Furthermore one would expect, on this model, a dependence of the capacity on the radius of ions present in solution, but the observed capacity in the region of constant magnitude is practically independent of the ion present.   It cannot explain an increase in the capacity which occurs in the anodic region.

The next model defined three layers—the metal surface, an inner Helmholtz layer that is the locus of centers of specifically adsorbed ions, and an outer Helmholtz plane that is the locus of centers of the first layer of hydrated ions. This model has several satisfactory features, but could not give rise to an interpretation of the constant capacity on the negative branch or the hump on the anodic side.

In all the above models, the role of water was ignored, even though it is the predominant species in solution.   The presently accepted model[20,23b] is that the electrode is covered with a layer of completely oriented water molecules. Specific adsorption of ions occurs in certain regions of potential by a replacement of some of these water molecules by the partially desolvated ions.   The second layer of water molecules is not so oriented because these water molecules are under the influence of both the electric field and thermal fluctuations.   They are like the secondary hydration sheath around an ion.   Some of these water molecules belong to the hydration sheaths of a layer of ions that are situated in the outer Helmholtz plane.   The dielectric constant of the first layer of oriented water molecules is 6 to 7 and of the second partly oriented layer is about 30 to 40. Considering the double layer as two capacitors in series, one with a low value of $\epsilon = 6$ and the other a high value of $\epsilon \sim 40$, the region of constant capacity in the *C-V* relation is understood.

2.3   Semiconductor-solution Interfaces

The semiconductor-solution interface differs from the metal-solution interface mainly in that the electron density in the semiconductor is relatively low.   Thus, an appreciable potential drop exists within the semiconductor, whereas there is no potential drop within a metal.   There are three characteristic regions at a semiconductor-solution interface (Fig. 9), assuming that specific adsorption is absent.   Two of the regions, namely, *BC* and *CD*, are identical with that existing at a metal-solution interface.   The third is the space-charge region *AB*

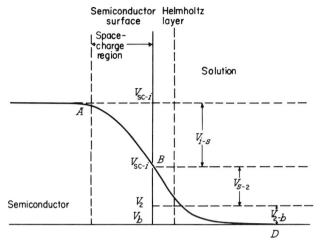

Figure 9 Potential distribution at semiconductor (*p*-type) electrolyte interface.[65]

which may extend to a considerable distance within the semiconductor (this distance depends on the carrier concentration; for a carrier concentration of 10^{14} electrons cm^{-3} the length of this region is some 10^{-4} cm). The potential distribution in the space-charge region is analogous to that in the diffuse-layer region in the electrolyte.   The charged species, which contribute to the potential distribution in the space-charge region, are mobile electrons, holes, or immobile impurity ions.   The immobility of one of the charged species (ions) distinguishes it from the diffuse layer in solution.   Brattain and Garret[26] were the first to study the problem of the double layer at the semiconductor-electrolyte interface. They used a method similar to that in the Gouy-Chapman theory.   A major part of the potential drop occurs in this region (i.e., *inside* the semiconductor).   This is in contrast to the metal-solution interface where most of the potential drop occurs in the compact layer *BC*.   The total potential drop from the interior of the semiconductor to the bulk of the electrolyte is given by (cf. Fig. 9)

$$\Delta V = (V_{sc-i} - V_{sc-s}) + (V_{sc-s} - V_2) + (V_2 - V_b) \tag{2.9}$$

Differentiating Eq. (2.9) with respect to the total charge, it follows that

$$\frac{1}{C} = \frac{1}{C_{i-s}} + \frac{1}{C_{s-2}} + \frac{1}{C_{2-b}} \tag{2.10}$$

where C represents the overall capacity and the C's with the appropriate suffixes on the right-hand side are the capacities of the respective regions in Fig. 9.

The regions from the surface to the outer Helmholtz plane and from the outer Helmholtz plane to the bulk of the electrolyte are similar to those at the metal-solution interface.   The expression for C_{i-s} is similar to that for C_{2-b} but somewhat more complex.

In the above treatment, it has been assumed that surface states[†] are absent. If surface states are present, the treatment of the potential distribution within the semiconductor is very similar to that of the structure of the double layer at a metal-solution interface in the presence of contact adsorption. At a high density of surface states, most of the potential drop in the space-charge region is reduced and the semiconductor then behaves like a metal.

3   KINETICS AT METAL-SOLUTION INTERFACES

3.1   Types of Half-cells

A number of chemical reactions can be carried out at electrodes, which when suitably combined in cells yield electrical energy. The majority of these reactions occur at metal-solution interfaces. The reactions can broadly be considered to be of the following types.

3.1.1   Metal Dipping in Solution of Its Salt

In this case, an electrode reaction may be represented by

$$M^+ + e_0^- \to M \tag{3.1}$$

where M is the metal. As an example, M may be lithium, as used in the lithium-chlorine electrochemical engine (see Chap. 10).

3.1.2   Gas Electrodes

A second type of electrochemical reaction which is common is where the reactant is a gas and the electrode functions only as a donor or acceptor of electrons. This type of electrode reaction is frequently encountered in electrochemical energy conversion, where the gases concerned are hydrogen, oxygen, chlorine, and hydrocarbons. With hydrogen the overall electrode reaction is

$$\tfrac{1}{2}H_2 \to H^+ + e_0^- \tag{3.2}$$

which is one of the most common half-cell reactions in a fuel cell.

3.1.3   Redox Systems

As in the case of gas electrodes, the electrode is an inert conductor and serves the purpose of a donor or acceptor of electrons to one of the oxidation states of some ion in solution, e.g.:

$$Fe^{3+} + e_0^- \to Fe^{2+} \tag{3.3}$$

Redox systems are of importance in one type of regenerative electrochemical energy conversion system (Chaps. 6 and 10).

---

† Surface states are caused by electron traps in the surface whereby the quantum states for electrons on the surface differ from that in the bulk. There are many causes for the existence of surface states, for example, the presence of adsorbed hydrogen atoms.

3.1.4 Electrodes of the Second Kind

The above electrode systems are referred to as "electrodes of the first kind." An "electrode of the second kind" consists of a metal in contact with an insoluble salt of the metal immersed in a solution containing another electrolyte which possesses the same anion as has the relatively insoluble salt. The calomel electrode is an example of this type. The overall electrode reaction is

$$Hg_2Cl_2(s) + 2e_0^- \rightarrow 2Hg(s) + 2Cl^-(l) \tag{3.4}$$

3.2 Types of Reactions

Just as in ordinary chemical reactions, electrochemical reactions may also be broadly divided into three types—single-step, consecutive, and parallel reactions. Examples of these types are as follows.

3.2.1 Single-step Reactions

The dissolution of lithium in the lithium-chlorine cell (Chap. 10) takes place in a single step:

$$Li \rightarrow Li^+ + e_0^- \tag{3.5}$$

The kinetics of this type of reaction is relatively simple.

3.2.2 Consecutive Reactions

A good example of a consecutive electrodic reaction is the anodic oxidation of oxalic acid. One of the suggested reaction paths[27] is

$$H_2C_2O_4 \rightarrow HC_2O_4(ads) + H^+ + e_0^- \tag{3.6}$$

$$HC_2O_4(ads) \rightarrow HCO_2(ads) + CO_2 \tag{3.7}$$

$$HCO_2(ads) \rightarrow CO_2 + H^+ + e_0^- \tag{3.8}$$

The kinetics of reactions of these types is generally complicated, particularly in the case of electroorganic reactions, where there may be many steps. However, there are some consecutive electrochemical reactions which take place in a few steps, e.g., the hydrogen-evolution reaction.

3.2.3 Parallel Reactions

This type of reaction is not common. It is encountered in the anodic oxidation of certain organic compounds, some of which may be used as fuels in electrochemical electricity producers. Such a reaction may be represented by

$$A \rightarrow B \begin{array}{c} \nearrow C_1 \\ \searrow C_2 \end{array} \tag{3.9}$$

where each of the steps may involve a number of intermediate consecutive steps.

The electrooxidation of methanol in acid or alkaline media[27a] is a good example. In acid solutions, carbon dioxide is the principal product with traces of formaldehyde and formic acid. In alkaline solution, the formate ion which is an intermediate is somewhat difficult to be oxidized further to the carbonate ion.[28]

3.3   Concept of Rate-determining Step (rds)

3.3.1   *General*

A term frequently used in chemical kinetics is the "rate-determining step" of an overall reaction. In general terms, it may be defined as the step which determines the velocity of the overall reaction. This concept holds both in the case of consecutive and of parallel reactions, as will be seen in the following sections. Further, since many electrochemical reactions proceed by a consecutive mechanism (and few by a parallel-path mechanism), one should expect this concept to apply equally well in these cases. In the subsequent sections, the meaning of the term rate-determining step as applied with respect to both consecutive and parallel reactions is elucidated by considering some analogies. In addition, it is shown mathematically that under certain conditions the velocity of the overall reaction is approximately equal to that of the rate-determining step and that the rate-determining step has the highest energy barrier with respect to the initial state of the reaction (Fig. 10).

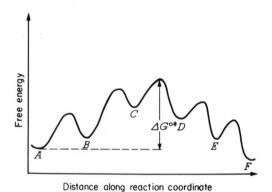

Figure 10   A typical free-energy–distance relation for a consecutive reaction.

3.3.2   *Rate-determining Step in a Consecutive Reaction*

3.3.2.1   Electrical Circuit Analog. A method of bringing out the concept of rate-determining step is by considering an electrical circuit (Fig. 11) with a number of resistances in series. The current through this circuit is given by

$$I = \frac{E}{R_1 + R_2 + R_3 + R_i} \qquad (3.10)$$

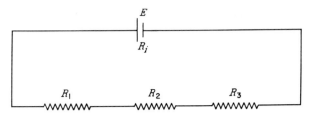

Figure 11 Electrical analog of rate-determining step in a consecutive reaction. If R_2 is much greater than $R_i + R_1 + R_3$, it determines the current through the circuit.

where E is the electromotive force of the cell, R_i is its internal resistance, and R_1, R_2, and R_3 are the resistances in series. The internal resistance of the cell can be assumed to be small. If, in addition, R_1 and R_3 are each much smaller than R_2, then

$$I \approx \frac{E}{R_2} \tag{3.11}$$

Thus, the resistance R_2 alone is overwhelmingly effective in determining the current, i.e., the reaction rate through the circuit.

3.3.2.2 Roadblock Analog. A further analogy to explain the concept of rate-determining step is to consider two cities connected by a road of varying widths. If the width of one of the sections of the road is much narrower than the rest, a bottleneck or roadblock is created here, and the flow of traffic between the two cities is determined by the flow rate over this narrow section (Fig. 12).

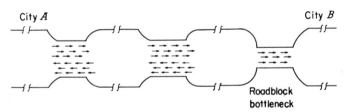

Figure 12 Roadblock analog for rate-determining step in a consecutive reaction.

From the diagram, it can be seen that on reaching the roadblock, many cars have to turn back, which in a sense is like saying that all steps prior to the rate-determining step are virtually in equilibrium (see Sec. 3.3.2.3).

3.3.2.3 Proof That the Velocity of the Overall Reaction Is That of the Rate-determining Step and That all Steps other than Rate-determining Steps Are Virtually in Equilibrium. The concept of the rate-determining step is clearly brought out in the following treatment of consecutive reactions.[29]   Christiansen[30] has developed an expression for the velocity of a general reaction of the type

$$A_0 + A_1 + \cdots + A_n \to B_1 + B_2 + \cdots + B_n + B_{n+1} \tag{3.12}$$

which proceeds through the intermediate steps

$$A_0 + A_1 \underset{v_{-1}}{\overset{v_1}{\rightleftharpoons}} X_1 + B_1 \tag{3.13}$$

$$X_1 + A_2 \underset{v_{-2}}{\overset{v_2}{\rightleftharpoons}} X_2 + B_2 \tag{3.14}$$

The series of intermediate steps continues, a typical step being

$$X_{i-1} + A_i \underset{v_{-i}}{\overset{v_i}{\rightleftharpoons}} X_i + B_i \tag{3.15}$$

and the last step is

$$X_{n-1} + A_n \underset{v_{-n}}{\overset{v_n}{\rightleftharpoons}} B_n + B_{n+1} \tag{3.16}$$

$X_1, X_2, \ldots, X_{n-1}$ represent reactive intermediates in the consecutive reaction. The overall net forward rate is given by

$$v = v_n - v_{-n} \tag{3.17}$$

Using the stationary state hypothesis for each of the intermediates $X_1, X_2, \ldots, X_{n-1}$, it follows that

$$\frac{d[X_i]}{dt} = v_i - v_{-i} - v_{i+1} + v_{-(i+1)} = 0 \tag{3.18}$$

that is,

$$v_i - v_{-i} = v_{i+1} - v_{-(i+1)} \tag{3.19}$$

for $i = 1, 2, \ldots, n - 1$.   It follows, therefore, that

$$v_1 - v_{-1} = v_2 - v_{-2} = \cdots = v_n - v_{-n} \tag{3.20}$$

The overall net forward rate may also be expressed by

$$v = \overrightarrow{v} - \overleftarrow{v} \tag{3.21}$$

where $\overrightarrow{v}$ and $\overleftarrow{v}$ are the overall forward and reverse velocities, respectively. Christiansen showed that:

$$\frac{1}{\overrightarrow{v}} = \frac{1}{w_1} + \frac{w_{-1}}{w_1} \frac{1}{w_2} + \cdots + \frac{w_{-1}w_{-2} \cdots w_{-(i-1)}}{w_1 w_2 \cdots w_{i-1}} \frac{1}{w_i} + \cdots$$

$$+ \frac{w_{-1}w_{-2} \cdots w_{-(n-1)}}{w_1 w_2 \cdots w_{n-1}} \frac{1}{w_n} \tag{3.22}$$

and

$$\frac{1}{\overleftarrow{v}} = \frac{1}{w_{-n}} + \frac{w_n}{w_{-n}} \frac{1}{w_{-(n-1)}} + \cdots + \frac{w_n w_{n-1} \cdots w_{i+1}}{w_{-n} w_{-(n-1)} \cdots w_{-(i+1)}} \frac{1}{w_i}$$

$$+ \frac{w_n w_{n-1} \cdots w_2}{w_{-n} w_{-(n-1)} \cdots w_{-2}} \frac{1}{w_{-1}} \quad (3.23)$$

where

$$w_1 = v_1 \qquad w_{-1} = \frac{v_{-1}}{[X_1]} \quad (3.24)$$

$$w_2 = \frac{v_2}{[X_1]} \qquad w_{-2} = \frac{v_{-2}}{[X_2]} \qquad \text{etc.} \quad (3.25)$$

The last relation is

$$w_n = \frac{v_n}{[X_{n-1}]} \qquad w_{-n} = v_{-n} \quad (3.26)$$

$[X_1], [X_2], \ldots, [X_{n-1}]$ are the steady-state concentrations of the intermediates $X_1, X_2, \ldots, X_{n-1}$, respectively. Thus, if the rate constants for all the forward and reverse steps and the steady-state concentrations of all reactants and products are known, the overall velocities (forward and reverse) of the reaction may be obtained.

By using Eqs. (3.22) to (3.26), it follows that

$$\frac{1}{\overrightarrow{v}} = \frac{1}{v_1} + \frac{v_{-1}}{v_1} \frac{1}{v_2} + \cdots + \frac{v_{-1} \cdots v_{-(i-1)}}{v_1 \cdots v_{i-1}} \frac{1}{v_i} + \cdots$$

$$+ \frac{v_{-1} v_{-2} \cdots v_{-(n-1)}}{v_1 v_2 \cdots v_{n-1}} \frac{1}{v_n} \quad (3.27)$$

$$\frac{1}{\overleftarrow{v}} = \frac{1}{v_{-n}} + \frac{1}{v_{-(n-1)}} + \cdots + \frac{v_n v_{n-1} \cdots v_{i+1}}{v_{-n} v_{-(n-1)} \cdots v_{-(i+1)}} \frac{1}{v_{-i}} + \cdots$$

$$+ \frac{v_n v_{n-1} \cdots v_2}{v_{-n} v_{-(n-1)} \cdots v_{-2}} \frac{1}{v_{-1}} \quad (3.28)$$

Consider a specific step g such that

$$v_g \ll v_i \quad (3.29)$$

for $i = 1, 2, \ldots, n$ except $i = g$. Using Eqs. (3.20) and (3.21), it follows that

$$v_g = v + v_{-g} \quad (3.30)$$

and

$$v_i = v + v_{-i} \quad (3.31)$$

It follows from Eqs. (3.29) to (3.31) that

$$v_{-g} \ll v_{-i} \quad (3.32)$$

for $i = 1, 2, \ldots, n$ except $i = g$.

It follows from Eq. (3.20) that

$$v_i - v_g = v_{-i} - v_{-g} \qquad (3.33)$$

for all i except $i = g$.   On introducing the condition (3.29) and the consequent inequality (3.32), Eq. (3.33) reduces to

$$v_i \approx v_{-i} \qquad (3.34)$$

for all i except $i = g$.

Thus, all steps other than the gth step are virtually in equilibrium.   If this condition together with inequalities (3.29) and (3.32) is introduced into Eqs. (3.27) and (3.28), it may be seen that

$$\frac{1}{\overrightarrow{v}} \approx \frac{1}{v_g} \qquad (3.35)$$

$$\frac{1}{\overleftarrow{v}} \approx \frac{1}{v_{-g}} \qquad (3.36)$$

The forward and reverse velocities of the overall reaction are effectively equal to the corresponding velocities of the gth step, which is referred to as the rate-determining step of the overall reaction.

Though the velocity of the overall reaction is effectively that of the rate-determining step, there is some effect of the velocities of the other steps on the velocity of the overall reaction, as is seen from Eqs. (3.27) and (3.28) and also from the electrical analog [Eq. (3.10)].

In the case of electrochemical reactions, which proceed by a consecutive mechanism, the velocities of the reactions are expressed in terms of current densities.   The current densities i are obtained by multiplying the velocities, as given by Eqs. (3.35) and (3.36), by nF where n is the number of electrons transferred in the overall reaction and F is the Faraday.   Thus:

$$\overrightarrow{i} = nF\overrightarrow{v} \qquad (3.37)$$

$$\overleftarrow{i} = nF\overleftarrow{v} \qquad (3.38)$$

3.3.2.4   Activated-state Treatment of Rate-determining Step.   It is interesting to know how the energy of activation of the overall reaction is connected to the energy of the transition state.   Eyring et al.[31] considered this question with respect to consecutive reactions of the type

$$A \rightarrow B \rightarrow C \rightarrow D \rightarrow E \rightarrow F \qquad (3.39)$$

The energy path along the reaction coordinate for the above reaction sequence may be regarded, for example, as that in Fig. 10.   Eyring et al. showed that the rate-determining step is the step which has the highest standard free energy of the activated state with respect to the initial state. Thus, for the case illustrated, the rate-determining step is the step from C to D. The rate-determining step is not the step with the highest activation energy; that is, though step B → C has a higher activation energy than step C → D, the latter is still the rate-determining step. This is because the velocity of a reaction is a product of a rate constant and a concentration term. Since the step B → C has a high activation energy, the concentration of C is so small that it makes $k_{C \to D}[C]$ less than $k_{B \to C}[B]$. The overall forward velocity is hence $k_{C \to D}[C]$. In order that the concentration of the intermediate may be expressed in terms of the concentration of the reactant A, it is necessary to make the assumption that steps A → B and B → C are virtually in equilibrium. This assumption is valid so long as the transition state between C and D has an energy higher than that of the transition states of any of the other steps by about 1.4 kcal mole^{-1} for a reaction at room temperature. (This figure is arrived at by assuming that if the velocity of any step exceeds that of a particular step by at least ten times at room temperature, then the latter step is the rate-determining step.) Thus, the overall forward velocity is given by (see Fig. 10)

$$\vec{v} = k_{C \to D}[C]$$

$$= k_{C \to D}[B] \exp \left(\frac{-\Delta G^0_{B \to C}}{RT} \right)$$

$$= k_{C \to D}[A] \exp \left[-\frac{(\Delta G^0_{A \to B} + \Delta G^0_{B \to C})}{RT} \right]$$

$$= \frac{kT}{h} [A] \exp \left(-\frac{\Delta G^{0 \ddagger}}{RT} \right) \tag{3.40}$$

where $\Delta G^{0 \ddagger}$ represents the difference in standard free energies of the activated complex between C and D, and of the initial state A.

For a consecutive reaction of this type, these conclusions also follow from the treatment in Sec. 3.3.2.3, in which it was deduced that all steps other than the rate-determining step are in equilibrium, viz., the rate-determining step has the highest barrier with respect to the initial state or final state for the forward and reverse reactions, as seen from Eq. (3.40). This idea also follows from the fact that though a consecutive reaction is written as a sequence of intermediate steps according to classical mechanics, it is only particles which can surmount the barrier from A to D that are effective for the reaction. Thus, using Boltzmann statistics, Eq. (3.40) again follows.

3.3.3 Rate-determining Step in a Parallel Reaction

3.3.3.1 Electrical Circuit Analog. The electrical analog of parallel reactions is represented by the circuit in Fig. 13. The current flowing through

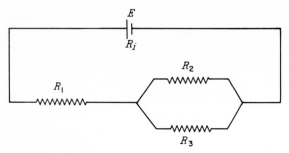

Figure 13   Electrical analog of rate-determining step in a parallel reaction. If resistances R_2 and R_3 are each considerably larger than $R_i + R_1$ but R_2 is much less than R_3, current through the circuit is determined by R_2.

the cell is given by

$$I = \frac{E}{R_i + R_1 + \left(\dfrac{R_2 R_3}{R_2 + R_3}\right)} \tag{3.41}$$

Suppose R_i and R_1 are much less than R_2 or R_3; also let $R_2 \ll R_3$, then

$$I \approx \frac{E}{R_2} \tag{3.42}$$

Thus, the branch of the parallel circuit with the smaller resistance (which is, however, larger than any resistance in series with it) determines the current. The electrical circuit analog enables one to understand why a reaction chooses a certain path.

3.3.3.2   Roadblock Analog.   In the case of the road between two cities, the case of alternate narrow bridges may be considered. The flow of traffic in the widest of the alternate narrow bridges although narrower than any other sections of the road leading to or from the bridge determines the overall rate of flow of traffic (Fig. 14).

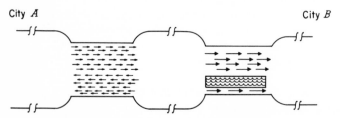

Figure 14   Roadblock analog for the rate-determining step in a parallel reaction.

3.3.3.3 Proof That the Velocity of the Overall Reaction is That of the Rate-determining Step. The concept of rate-determining steps is also useful in the case of parallel reactions. Suppose a reaction of the type

$$A \underset{v_{-1}}{\overset{v_1}{\rightleftharpoons}} B \overset{v_2}{\underset{v_3}{<}} \begin{array}{c} C_1 \\ \\ C_2 \end{array} \tag{3.43}$$

is considered. For simplicity, the velocities of the reverse steps of $B \to C_1$ and $B \to C_2$ may be assumed to be negligible. Under these conditions, using the stationary-state hypothesis for the intermediate B, it follows that

$$v_1 - v_{-1} = v_2 + v_3 \tag{3.44}$$

If

$$v_2 \gg v_3 \tag{3.45}$$

then

$$v_1 - v_{-1} \approx v_2 \tag{3.46}$$

Further, if

$$v_1 \gg v_2 \tag{3.47}$$

then

$$v_1 \approx v_{-1} \tag{3.48}$$

Thus, the first reaction is in equilibrium and the most rapid of the parallel paths determines the rate of the overall reaction.

3.3.4 Rate-determining Steps in Reactions with a Dual or Coupled Mechanism

In the above treatment, it has been assumed that the rate of the overall reaction is predominantly influenced, or determined, by one step, which has been found to be the case generally in consecutive reactions. However, if the standard free energies of the activated complexes in two steps of a consecutive reaction are nearly equal and higher than that of any other step with respect to the standard free energy of the initial and final states, the forward velocities of these steps will be nearly equal and the velocity of the overall reaction will be governed by the velocities of these *two* steps. Such a mechanism is called a "dual mechanism,"[32] i.e., *two* steps control the rate predominantly. A consecutive reaction in which the velocities of the reverse steps of each of the consecutive partial reactions is negligible in comparison with the corresponding forward velocities is referred to as a "coupled reaction," [32] because as the velocity of one step changes, the velocity of the other will change to the same degree.

3.4 Velocity of a Chemical Reaction

3.4.1 *Single-step Reaction*

According to the transition state theory,[31] the velocity v of a reaction of the type

$$A + B \rightleftarrows [AB]^{\ddagger} \rightarrow C + D \tag{3.49}$$

is given by

$$v = \frac{kT}{h} [A][B] \exp\left(\frac{-\Delta G^{0\ddagger}}{RT}\right) \tag{3.50}$$

where $\Delta G^{0\ddagger}$ is the standard free energy of activation of the reaction.   The path of the reaction may be depicted as in Fig. 15.

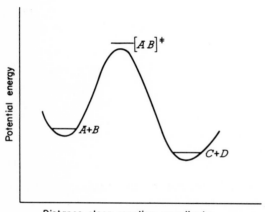

Figure 15   Potential-energy profile along the reaction path for a single-step reaction.

v may be also expressed in the form

$$v = \frac{kT}{h} [A][B] \exp\left(-\frac{\Delta H^{0\ddagger}}{RT}\right) \exp\frac{\Delta S^{0\ddagger}}{R} \tag{3.51}$$

where $\Delta H^{0\ddagger}$ and $\Delta S^{0\ddagger}$ are the enthalpies and entropies of activation, respectively.   Thus, using Eq. (3.51), the rate constant k_0 is given by

$$k_0 = \frac{kT}{h} \exp\frac{\Delta S^{0\ddagger}}{R} \exp\left(\frac{-\Delta H^{0\ddagger}}{RT}\right) \tag{3.52}$$

In Eq. (3.52), if the linear variation of k_0 with temperature is neglected in comparison with its exponential variation, the equation is then similar to the empirical Arrhenius equation

$$k_0 = A \exp\left(-\frac{E^{\ddagger}}{RT}\right) \tag{3.53}$$

where $E^{\ddagger}$ is the energy of activation for the process.

For a rigorous calculation of the velocity of the reaction, it is necessary to attempt a relatively accurate calculation of potential-distance relations such as those in Fig. 15. This type of figure can be obtained only for very simple reactions, and even then with severe approximations.[33]

The main difficulty in obtaining the potential energy versus distance along the reaction coordinate plot is that it should be possible to express the potential energy as a function of distances for each of the interactions involved. The complexities of such calculations according to the method of Eyring et al.[31] are considerable except in the case of reactions involving simple atoms or molecules.

Absolute calculations of rates of more complex reactions are not yet possible because of the absence of knowledge of the potential energy of the system as a function of the distances between the various atoms involved. If more than three atoms are involved in a reaction, there is an increase in the number of variable internuclear distances and the calculations become still more complex.

It is easier to calculate the ratio of the velocities of isotopic reactions than the absolute velocities themselves from potential-energy surfaces.[31] This is because isotope effects depend primarily on the *differences* in the vibrational frequencies of the activated states and initial states for the isotopic species. In calculations of actual velocities of reactions, *absolute* values of the energies of activation and of many other partition functions are involved, which is obviously a more difficult calculation than a calculation of partition-function ratios.

3.4.2 Consecutive Reaction

In Sec. (3.3.2), it was shown that the velocity of a consecutive reaction is represented essentially by the velocity of the rate-determining step. The forward and reverse velocities of the consecutive reaction (3.12) may be expressed by:

$$\overrightarrow{v} = k_g K_1 K_2 \cdots K_{g-1} \frac{[A_0][A_1] \cdots [A_g]}{[B_1][B_2] \cdots [B_{g-1}]}$$

$$= \frac{kT}{h} \frac{[A_0][A_1] \cdots [A_g]}{[B_1][B_2] \cdots [B_{g-1}]} \exp\left(-\frac{\Delta G_g^{0\ddagger}}{RT}\right) \tag{3.54}$$

$$\overleftarrow{v} = k_{-g} K_{-(g+1)} K_{-(g+2)} \cdots K_{-n} \frac{[B_g][B_{g+1}] \cdots [B_n][B_{n+1}]}{[A_{g+1}][A_{g+2}] \cdots [A_n]}$$

$$= \frac{kT}{h} \frac{[B_g][B_{g+1}] \cdots [B_{n+1}]}{[A_{g+1}][A_{g+2}] \cdots [A_n]} \exp\left(-\frac{\Delta G_{-g}^{0\ddagger}}{RT}\right) \tag{3.55}$$

where K_1, K_2, ..., K_n are the equilibrium constants of the intermediate steps and $K_{-(g+1)}$, $K_{-(g+2)}$, ..., K_{-n} denote the reciprocals of the respective equilibrium constants; $\Delta G_g^{0\ddagger}$ and $\Delta G_{-g}^{0\ddagger}$ are the standard free energies of activation of the forward and reverse directions of the overall reaction and are given by

$$\Delta G_g^{0\ddagger} = G^{0\ddagger} - G_1^0 \tag{3.56}$$

$$\Delta G_{-g}^{0\ddagger} = G^{0\ddagger} - G_n^0 \tag{3.57}$$

G_1^0 and G_n^0 are the standard free energies of the initial and final states, respectively, and $G^{0\ddagger}$ is the standard free energy of the activated complex of the overall reaction (i.e., the activated complex of the gth step in the series).

A knowledge of electrochemical kinetics is very useful in the theory of electrochemical energy conversion. For example, the efficiency of an electrochemical electricity producer and its power (Chap. 4) depend on values of rate constants for the interfacial charge-transfer reactions. These in turn depend on the velocity of the rate-determining step, although other factors such as adsorptive properties of reactants and intermolecular forces among the species adsorbed on the electrode also play an important role. *The velocity of the rate-determining step is the primary factor which determines the power and efficiency of electrochemical energy conversion.* It is for this reason that this topic is dealt with in some detail in this chapter.

3.4.3 Parallel Reaction

The velocity of the parallel reaction (3.43) is the sum of the parallel velocities from $B \rightarrow C_1$ and $B \rightarrow C_2$, respectively. If this reaction were to take place in a number of intermediate steps from $A \rightarrow B$, $B \rightarrow C_1$, and $B \rightarrow C_2$, they may in turn be considered as separate consecutive reactions and velocity expressions may be written as before.

3.5   Types of Rate-determining Steps in Electrochemical Reactions

3.5.1   Mass-transport Control

The rate-determining steps in this classification include mass transport under pure diffusion or diffusion-convection conditions. In addition, when the rate-determining step is the transport of an ion or electron through a solid phase, this type of control is also considered under mass transport.

3.5.2   Homogeneous-step Control

These refer to situations in which the rate-determining steps occur in solution before the particles reach the electrode.

3.5.3   Heterogeneous-step Control

Under this classification is included rate-determining charge-transfer control which is most commonly observed in electrode kinetics. However, it could embrace all other kinds of rate-determining surface reactions, e.g., combination of radicals, nucleation, crystal growth, surface diffusion. The present classification of types of rate control in electrochemical reactions is illustrated in Table 1.[34]

TABLE 1   Classification of Electrode Processes[34]

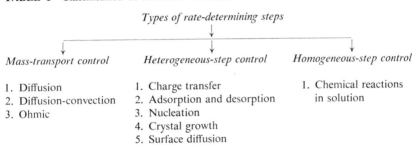

Mass-transport control	Heterogeneous-step control	Homogeneous-step control
1. Diffusion	1. Charge transfer	1. Chemical reactions in solution
2. Diffusion-convection	2. Adsorption and desorption	
3. Ohmic	3. Nucleation	
	4. Crystal growth	
	5. Surface diffusion	

3.6   Charge-transfer Processes

3.6.1   *Comparison of Chemical Reactions with Electrochemical Reactions*

The velocity of an ordinary chemical reaction can be increased by either an increase in concentrations of reactants or an increase of temperature. The dependence of velocity on concentrations of the reactants is small, since reaction rates depend on a simple power of the concentration. Further, this variation is limited to only a small range of concentration of a particular reactant over which it can be varied. The variation of reaction rates with temperature is significant. However, for the increase of a reaction rate by 10^3 times for a reaction with activation energy 10 kcal mole^{-1}, it is necessary to increase the temperature from 300 to about 500°K. The use of temperature for the substantial acceleration of a reaction rate may therefore not always be experimentally feasible. It may involve modification of equipment and other factors.

The essential feature of an electrochemical reaction is that it involves interfacial charge transfer. Thus, its reaction rate would be expected to depend on the electric potential difference at the interface. In Sec. 3.4 it was shown that the rate constant for a chemical reaction may be expressed by the Arrhenius equation (3.53). In many electrochemical reactions, the current is found to vary exponentially with potential across the metal-solution interface. Hence (but see Sec. 3.6.2), the rate constant for an electrochemical reaction may be empirically expressed by

$$k = k^0 \exp KV$$

$$= A \exp\left(-\frac{E^{\ddagger}}{RT}\right) \exp KV \tag{3.58}$$

where V is the metal-solution potential difference (neglecting diffuse-layer effects) and K is a constant.

Bowden and Rideal[35] were the first to point out that remarkable control is possible through this extra-potential-dependent term and that it is far in excess of any variation due to concentration or temperature. For example, it is possible in the case of some electrochemical reactions to increase the rate of a reaction by 10^{10} for a change in potential of a little over 1 volt (by trivial modification of experimental conditions, e.g., by varying the external electrical resistance in the circuit),[36] whereas this degree of variation of reaction rate is not possible in the case of chemical reactions.

In addition, two other characteristics make chemical and electrochemical reactions different. Electrodic reactions always are heterogeneous, whereas many chemical reactions are homogeneous. Finally, heterogeneous chemical reactions take place on surfaces principally occupied by the adsorbed reactants. Electrochemical reactions, in aqueous and nonaqueous solutions, occur on substrates which are always covered by solvent molecules and sometimes anions.[37] The concentrations of both these species are potential-dependent.

3.6.2 Effect of Potential Difference across Electrode-Electrolyte Interface on Electrochemical Rate Constants—a Simple Picture

The effect of potential on electrochemical rate constants may be visualized from potential-energy diagrams.[38] As an example, a reaction of the type

$$M + AB^+ + e_0^- \rightarrow MA + B \tag{3.59}$$

is considered, in which M is the metal and AB^+ is a diatomic ion. The potential-energy barrier for this reaction, which takes place at the metal-solution interface, will be considered. The potential-energy–distance (from the metal) relation for the reaction, assuming a linear transition state, when the metal-solution potential difference is zero ($V = 0$) is as shown in curve 1 of Fig. 16. In the presence of a metal-solution potential difference V, the additional energy of the ion due to its electrical energy in the region between the two minima is linear (because the potential variation between the metal and the outer Helmholtz plane is linear) and is given by curve 2 (diffuse-layer effects are ignored). Under these conditions, the potential-energy–distance relation (curve 3) for the reaction may be obtained by superposition of curves 1 and 2. If it is assumed that the electrical potential in the final state is zero, then the superposition of curves 1 and 2 results in a vertical shift of the right-hand minimum (initial state) by VF. At the same time, the maximum of the curve is only shifted by a fraction of VF (because of the linear variation in potential between the metal and the outer Helmholtz plane), i.e., $(1 - \beta)\,VF$, where $0 < \beta < 1$; β depends on the position of the maximum and is referred to as the "symmetry factor." A more detailed treatment of the symmetry factor is presented in Sec. 3.6.9. The symmetry factor represents the fraction of the contribution of electrical energy to the activation energy of an electron-transfer reaction. Thus, if k_0 and k are the rate constants in the absence ($V = 0$) and

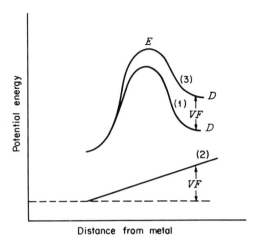

Figure 16 The relation of potential energy to distance along the reaction coordinate for a charge-transfer reaction in the absence (curve 1) and in the presence (curve 3) of metal-solution potential difference *V*—simple picture. Curve 2 represents the electrical energy of charged species as a function of its distance from metal.

in the presence of a metal-solution potential difference ($V = V$), the relation between the two rate constants is given by (cf. Fig. 16)

$$k = k_0 \exp\left(-\frac{\beta VF}{RT}\right) \tag{3.60}$$

According to Eq. (3.60), it is seen that the activation energy of an electrochemical reaction of the type (3.59) varies linearly with the potential drop across the metal-solution interface (i.e., with the electrode potential).

3.6.3 Potential-energy Calculations for Electro- chemical Reactions—a More Realistic Approach

A method of obtaining the potential energy as a function of the distance along the reaction coordinate in the case of the hydrogen-electrode reaction was first introduced by Horiuti and Polanyi (1935).[39]   According to this treatment, the activation energy is represented by the difference in height from the intersection point of the curves of potential energy vs. distance along the reaction coordinate for the stretching of the bond being broken (i.e., between A-B) and that being formed (i.e., between B-C) for a reaction of the type

$$AB + C \rightarrow A + BC \tag{3.61}$$

to the minimum of the potential-energy curve for the bond being broken (i.e., between A-B).   For the purpose of constructing this potential-energy profile, it is assumed that the extreme atoms are fixed and the transition state

$(A \cdots B \cdots C)$ is linear.   An analogous electrochemical reaction is represented by Eq. (3.59).   It is necessary in this case to substitute electrochemical energies rather than chemical energies to obtain the potential-energy diagram.   The change in height of the barrier with polarization of the electrode was represented by a vertical shift in the potential-energy curve of the initial state.   Thus, in Fig. 17 curve PQR represents the potential-energy-distance plots for the reactants for varying B-A$^+$ distance when $V = 0$; $P'Q'R'$ represents a similar plot when the metal-solution potential difference is V, the difference in height between the two minima being VF; and XYZ represents the potential energy curve for the stretching of the M-A bond.   The difference in heights from S to Q and S' to Q' gives the effect of potential on reaction rates.

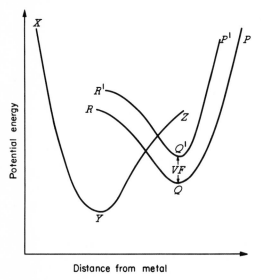

Figure 17   Potential-energy–distance relation for charge-transfer reaction in the absence and in the presence of metal-solution potential difference V—a more realistic picture.

This method was applied numerically by Butler,[40] who made an estimate of the activation energy for the discharge of protons on nickel according to the slow-discharge mechanism of the hydrogen-evolution reaction.   In a detailed treatment, Parsons and Bockris[41] calculated the symmetry factor for this reaction and showed how it could vary with change of the determining parameters.   Despic and Bockris[51] showed that the likely numerical value would be 0.5 ± 0.1.

3.6.4   A Simple Picture of the Symmetry Factor

It has been observed experimentally that the symmetry factor is constant over a wide range of potential.   This can at once be shown to follow if the potential-energy–distance relations for the initial and final state curves are linear in the

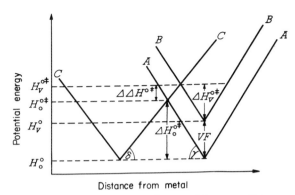

Figure 18 Linear analogs of potential-energy–distance relations in the absence and in the presence of metal-solution potential difference V.

region of their point of intersection. According to this treatment,[36] the potential-energy–distance relation is as shown in Fig. 18. The curves in this figure are the linear analogs of the curves in the previous figure.

As seen from Fig. 18,

$$\Delta H_v^{0\ddagger} + VF = \Delta H_0^{0\ddagger} + \Delta\Delta H^{0\ddagger} \tag{3.62}$$

It can easily be shown[13] that

$$\Delta\Delta H^{0\ddagger} = VF\frac{\tan\delta}{\tan\delta + \tan\gamma} \tag{3.63}$$

Thus

$$\Delta H_v^{0\ddagger} = \Delta H_0^{0\ddagger} - \beta VF \tag{3.64}$$

where

$$\beta = \frac{\tan\gamma}{\tan\delta + \tan\gamma} \tag{3.65}$$

If $\tan\delta = \tan\gamma$, then $\beta = \frac{1}{2}$. Linearity of potential-energy curves near the point of intersection is a good approximation; thus, by a change of potential, β would remain constant over a range of potential. However, if the applied potential is varied considerably, the approximation may no longer hold, causing changes in β with change of applied potential (see Sec. 3.6.9).

3.6.5 Stoichiometric Factors

Stoichiometric factors are analogous to orders of reactions in chemical kinetics. The concept of stoichiometric factors was introduced into electrode kinetics by Vetter[42] and by Parsons.[42a] Consider a reaction of the type

$$aA + bB + \cdots + ne_0^- \rightarrow xX + yY + \cdots \tag{3.66}$$

which proceeds by a consecutive mechanism.   If the rate-determining step for this reaction is

$$lL + mM + \cdots + n'e_0^- \rightarrow pP + qQ + \cdots \tag{3.67}$$

and its velocity is given by

$$v = ka_L{}^l a_M{}^m \cdots \exp \frac{\alpha VF}{RT} \tag{3.68}$$

the stoichiometric factors are l for species L, m for species M, and so forth, i.e., the stoichiometric factors are the powers to which the concentrations of each of the entities are raised in the expression for the velocity of the reaction

$$l = \left(\frac{\partial \ln v}{\partial \ln a_L} \right)_{a_m \cdots V, T} \tag{3.69}$$

where α is the transfer coefficient.   In the reaction scheme chosen, it has been assumed that the reactants in the rate-determining step do not enter into the reaction scheme in steps preceding it.   If this is not the case, however, the expressions for the reaction orders are more complex and in some cases even yield fractional values.

3.6.6   Current-potential Relations at a Single Electrode

3.6.6.1   Relation between Velocity and Current.   In heterogeneous catalysis, the reaction velocities are expressed in terms of velocity per unit area of the surface.   The analogous term in electrochemical kinetics is the current density i, which is the current per unit area of the surface.   The relation between velocity v and current density i depends on the number of electrons transferred in one act of the overall reaction n.   It is therefore possible to write

$$i = nFv \tag{3.70}$$

3.6.6.2   Expression for Net Current Density.   All rates of electrochemical reactions (as measured by a current measuring device placed external to the cell) are, in principle, a measure of the net reaction rate and are expressed in amperes per square centimeter (measured current per unit area of the electrode).   In most technological work current density is expressed in amperes per square foot (1 amp ft$^{-2} \approx 1$ ma cm^{-2}).   The measured current density is, however, the net current density i and is given by

$$i = \overrightarrow{i} - \overleftarrow{i} \tag{3.71}$$

where $\overrightarrow{i}$ is the forward current and $\overleftarrow{i}$ is the reverse current (Fig. 19).

The convention is that if a process involves the transfer of electrons from the metal to species in solution, the net current is cathodic, and if the reverse process occurs, the net current is anodic (Fig. 19).

If, for simplicity, the electrode reaction is

$$O + e_0^- \rightarrow R \tag{3.72}$$

where O and R represent the oxidized and reduced species, respectively, the net current density may then be expressed by

$$i = F \left\{ k_f^0 c_0 \exp\left(-\frac{\beta VF}{RT} \right) - k_r^0 c_R \exp\left[(1 - \beta)\frac{VF}{RT} \right] \right\} \tag{3.73}$$

where k_f^0 and k_r^0 are the rate constants of the forward and reverse reactions in the absence of a metal-solution potential difference, as seen from Sec. 3.6.2.

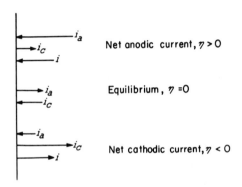

Net anodic current, $\eta > 0$

Equilibrium, $\eta = 0$

Net cathodic current, $\eta < 0$

Figure 19 Net anodic, zero, or net cathodic overall reactions at an electrode. Direction of arrow represents direction of electron flow.

3.6.6.3 Exchange Current Density of Reaction. The *exchange current density* is the velocity, in amp cm^{-2}, of the forward or backward reaction at equilibrium. An equal number of charged particles (ions or electrons) cross the interface just as in chemical equilibrium and an equal number of moles are formed and decomposed in unit time. Under these conditions, the net current density is zero and it follows from Eq. (3.73) that the exchange current density is given by

$$i_0 = Fk_f^0 c_0 \exp\left(-\frac{\beta VF_r}{RT} \right)$$

$$= Fk_r^0 c_R \exp\left[(1 - \beta)\frac{VF_r}{RT} \right] \tag{3.74}$$

where V_r is the metal-solution potential difference at equilibrium.

Exchange current densities are *analogous* to rate constants in chemical reactions. Unlike rate constants, exchange current densities are concentration-dependent, as seen from Eq. (3.74). However, concentration variations are not very significant when compared with the range of variations in the rate constants in this equation. Values of exchange current densities vary by about

20 decades, e.g., from 10^{-18} amp cm^{-2} for the oxygen-evolution reaction on gold[43] to 10^2 amp cm^{-2} for some metal-deposition reactions.[36]   This range of variation is far greater than that observed in chemical kinetics.

3.6.6.4   Equilibrium Potential of Electrode for Reaction.   The electric potential difference between metal and solution when the net current is zero is called the equilibrium potential of electrode for the reaction.   The expression for the equilibrium potential is obtained by both forms of V_r found in Eq. (3.74):

$$V_r = \frac{RT}{F} \ln \left(\frac{k_f^{\,0}}{k_r^{\,0}} \right) + \frac{RT}{F} \ln \frac{c_0}{c_R} \tag{3.75}$$

The same equation is obtained thermodynamically by considering the reaction (3.81) under equilibrium conditions (Nernst equation).   The first term on the right-hand side of Eq. (3.75) is the *standard equilibrium potential* of the electrode—viz., the equilibrium potential when the concentration of each of the reactants and products is 1 mole l^{-1}.

3.6.6.5   Overpotential.   The potential of the electrode when a net current flows through the electrode $(i \neq 0)$ diminished by the equilibrium potential (when $i = 0$) is called the overpotential.   The overpotential may be regarded as the extra potential necessary to reduce the energy barrier of the rate-determining step to a value such that the electrode reaction proceeds at a desired rate. Cathodic processes are associated with a negative overpotential and anodic processes with a positive overpotential.   In earlier times, it was generally stated that when the electrode potential departs from its equilibrium value, the electrode is "polarized."   The name overpotential is now restricted to the case when the departure of the electrode potential from the equilibrium potential is owing to the slowness of one of the steps of the electrode reaction.   The term polarization is used in more complicated cases, e.g., when more than one electrode reaction affects the potential as in a corrosion reaction; in this case the equilibrium potential has no clear concept.

Using Eq. (3.74), Eq. (3.73) reduces to

$$i = i_0 \left\{ \exp \left(-\frac{\beta \eta F}{RT} \right) - \exp \left[(1 - \beta) \frac{\eta F}{RT} \right] \right\} \tag{3.76}$$

where η is the overpotential and is equal to the difference $(V - V_r)$.   This equation is of central importance in electrode kinetics.   If $\beta = \frac{1}{2}$, Eq. (3.76) becomes

$$i = -2i_0 \sinh \frac{\eta F}{2RT} \tag{3.77}$$

Relations such as (3.76) and (3.77), the starting equations for the so-called Tafel equation (see Sec. 3.6.6.6), are central to the understanding of fuel cells.

They give the basis of the relation for the voltage sacrifice (overpotential) involved in supplying power at a certain level. Overpotential also affects efficiency of energy production (Chap. 4). As the current density increases, efficiency decreases. The treatment in this chapter involves individual electrodes. In an electrochemical electricity producer, two of these are coupled. Equations relating current density to cell potential are derived in Chap. 4.

3.6.6.6 Tafel Equation. At highly negative overpotentials, the second exponential term on the right-hand side of Eq. (3.76) is negligible compared with the first, and the equation reduces to

$$\eta = \frac{RT}{\beta F} \log i_0 - \frac{RT}{\beta F} \log i$$

$$= a + b \log i \tag{3.78}$$

This equation is identical with the empirical equation proposed by Tafel[44] (1905) and is commonly referred to as the Tafel equation. The Tafel parameters a and b are characteristic of the electrode reaction and are obtained experimentally from a plot of η versus $\log i$.

3.6.6.7 Linear Current-potential Relation. At low overpotentials $[|\eta| < (RT/F)]$, the exponentials in Eq. (3.76) may be expanded in a series, and the terms higher than the linear terms in η may be neglected. Under these conditions, the current-potential relation is

$$\eta = -\frac{RT}{F} \frac{i}{i_0} \tag{3.79}$$

Thus, a plot of i versus η in the low overpotential region is linear and passes through the origin.

3.6.7 Stoichiometric Numbers

The equations in the previous subsections hold for the case when a simple reaction or a consecutive reaction of the type (3.66) is considered. However, more general are consecutive reactions of the type where some intermediate steps, including the rate-determining step, take place several times when the overall reaction takes place once—for example, in the oxygen-evolution reaction, one of the suggested paths[36] is

$$4H_2O + 4M \rightarrow 4MOH + 4H^+ + 4e_0^- \tag{3.80}$$

$$4MOH \rightarrow 2MO + 2M + 2H_2O \tag{3.81}$$

$$2MO \rightarrow 2M + O_2 \tag{3.82}$$

Overall

$$2H_2O \rightarrow 4H^+ + O_2 + 4e_0^- \tag{3.83}$$

For such reactions, it is necessary to introduce another parameter, the stoichiometric number, to obtain current-potential relations.

The stoichiometric number v of a reaction is defined as the number of times the rate-determining step takes place for one act of overall reaction. This term was first defined by Horiuti and Ikusima,[45] and a term very simply related to it was introduced into electrode kinetics by Bockris and Potter.[19]

From the definition of stoichiometric numbers, it follows that

$$i = \frac{i_r}{v} \tag{3.84}$$

where i is the overall net current density (the one measured in the external circuit) and i_r is the net current density of the rate-determining step, which may have to take place several times to keep up with the rate of the overall reaction.

Equation (3.76) represents the current-density–overpotential relation for a simple one-electron transfer reaction. In the case of a multielectron transfer reaction [of the type (3.83)], the general form of the current-density–overpotential relation is

$$i = \frac{i_r}{v} = i_0 \{\exp\left(\alpha \eta F/RT\right) - \exp\left[-(1 - \alpha)\eta F/RT\right]\} \tag{3.85}$$

α is referred to as the *transfer coefficient* of the reaction and depends on the mechanism of the overall reaction. The relation between α and β has been investigated by several workers,[42a,45a] and it may be expressed by the equation

$$\alpha = \frac{s}{v} + r \tag{3.85a}$$

where s and r are the numbers of electrons transferred in steps preceding and in the rate-determining step, respectively. The application of the stoichiometric number for determining mechanisms of reactions will be outlined in Chap. 9.

3.6.8 Effect of the Double-layer Structure

3.6.8.1 Influence of Diffuse Layer. In the current-potential relations deduced so far, it has been assumed that the total potential drop is across the compact layer. In dilute solutions, this assumption is not correct and the total potential difference may be expressed as

$$V = V_{M-2} + V_{2-b} \tag{3.86}$$

as seen from Fig. 5. Frumkin introduced two corrections to the current-potential relations[46] [e.g., Eq. (3.73)] which are applicable in dilute solutions. Since the reaction site for the charge-transfer process is at the compact layer, only the potential V_{M-2} and not V should affect the potential-dependent part of the electrochemical rate constant. Further, the reactants in the charge-transfer step are only the ions at the compact layer. The concentration of the reactants $c_{0,e}$ in the Helmholtz layer is related to the concentration of the ions

$c_{0,b}$ in the bulk for the reaction (3.72), through the equation (z_i is the valency of the discharging ion in the compact layer)

$$c_{0,e} = c_{0,b} \exp \left(- \frac{V_{2-b} z_i F}{RT} \right) \tag{3.87}$$

Thus, under conditions in which the anodic current of reaction (3.72) is negligible compared with its cathodic current, Eq. (3.73) becomes

$$i = F k_f^0 c_{0,b} \exp \left(- \frac{V_{2-b}(z_i - \beta)F}{RT} \right) \exp \left(- \frac{\beta V F}{RT} \right) \tag{3.88}$$

3.6.8.2 Effect of the Double-layer Structure on the Tafel Slope. In the absence of double-layer corrections, it may be seen from Eq. (3.88) that the Tafel slope is $-RT/\beta F$. Inclusion of diffuse-layer effects results in Eq. (3.88). V_{2-b} changes with potential and this variation must be considered in arriving at the Tafel slope. Using Stern's theory for the double layer,[14] Bockris, Ammar, and Huq[47] showed that the Tafel slope decreases from $-RT/\beta F$ as the potential approaches the potential of zero charge. It is in this region that the variation of V_{2-b} with V is significant. Since the lowering of the Tafel slope should be observed only near the point of zero charge, one can understand the lack of variation of Tafel slope over nearly 1 volt in the case of the hydrogen-evolution reaction on mercury in dilute hydrochloric acid.[41]

More detailed aspects have been considered by Gierst.[3,48]   Currents depend upon V_{2-b} and its variation with potential and concentration.   Such variations affect ecep because of the central dependence of power and efficiency upon the *i-V* relation.

3.6.8.3 Effect of Adsorption of Organic Compounds on Tafel Slopes. The influence of organic adsorption on Tafel slopes was considered by Frumkin[49] and by Bockris and Srinivasan.[50]   Organic adsorption causes a change in the contribution of the dipole potential (χ potential) to the total potential drop across the metal-solution interface.[20]   The effect of change in χ potential with *V* is analogous to the change in V_{2-b}.   Tafel slopes are generally increased by organic adsorption as well as by changes in V_{2-b}.

3.6.9 A More Realistic Picture of the Symmetry Factor β

The relation between the cell potential and the current density in a fuel cell (Chap. 4) is a very basic one in electrochemical energy conversion.   A factor which is of considerable importance in the derivation of this relation is the symmetry factor β.   A simple treatment of the symmetry factor was outlined in Sec. 3.6.4.   A more detailed analysis of the symmetry factor is desirable.   This can be done in two ways—by classical and quantum mechanical approaches. The former is dealt with in this section and the latter in the following one.

In Sec. 3.6.4, an expression for the symmetry factor was derived by linearizing the potential-energy–distance curves for the initial and final states. The effect of potential was obtained by a vertical shift of the initial-state curve by an amount corresponding to the change in electrical energy. In this treatment, owing to the assumption of linear potential-energy–distance curves, it follows that the symmetry factor is independent of the applied potential.

The linearization of potential-energy–distance relations is a good approximation for reactions with low i_0 but not for reactions with medium or high i_0. Despic and Bockris[51] studied the influence of potential on the symmetry factor for the reaction

$$Ag^+ + e_0^- \rightarrow Ag \tag{3.89}$$

using the method of intersection of Morse curves (Fig. 20) to represent the relation of the potential energy to the distance along the reaction coordinate

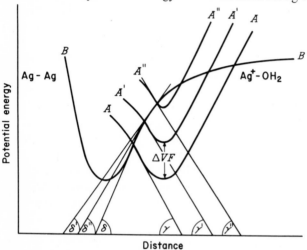

Figure 20 Potential-energy–distance relations for discharge of Ag^+ ions at various metal-solution potential differences.[51] As the potential of the electrode changes, the relative slopes of curves A and B change, and hence β varies with potential [cf. (Eq. 3.65)].

during the course of the reaction. This treatment may be summarized as follows: Let the symmetry factor at an overpotential η be β_η. It is possible to express the current density at the overpotential η by

$$i = k(c_{Ag^+}) \exp \left(- \frac{\Delta H_2^{0\ddagger}}{RT} \right) \tag{3.90}$$

where $\Delta H_2^{0\ddagger}$ is the activation energy at the overpotential η. On increasing the overpotential by $d\eta$, the current density increases by di and the current-potential relation is given by

$$i + di = k(c_{Ag^+}) \exp \left(- \frac{\Delta H_2^{0\ddagger} + \beta_\eta d\eta F}{RT} \right)$$

$$= i \exp \left(- \frac{\beta_\eta d\eta F}{RT} \right) \tag{3.91}$$

Since $d\eta$ is small, the exponential in Eq. (3.91) may be linearized and the equation itself becomes

$$di = -i\frac{\beta_\eta F\, d\eta}{RT} \tag{3.92}$$

Integrating Eq. (3.92) between i_0 and i when the overpotential increases from 0 to η,

$$\ln\frac{i}{i_0} = -\frac{F}{RT}\int_0^\eta \beta_\eta\, d\eta \tag{3.93}$$

The Tafel equation for a charge-transfer step is

$$\ln\frac{i}{i_0} = -\frac{F}{RT}\beta\eta \tag{3.94}$$

Using the last two equations, the equation

$$\beta = \frac{1}{\eta}\int_0^\eta \beta_\eta\, d\eta \tag{3.95}$$

results.

Equation (3.95) shows that the symmetry factor may vary with potential though it does not show the extent to which a variation of β with potential would occur. This has been worked out quantitatively by Despic and Bockris and a qualitative account of their theory is given here. β is expressed by Eq. (3.65), which shows that it depends on the relative slopes of the potential-energy curves for the initial and final states at the point of their intersection (Fig. 20). The effect of change of electric potential will be reflected in these potential-energy curves by a change in the relative position of the initial- and final-state curves (Sec. 2.6.3). Suppose the change in electrode potential is ΔV in the negative direction. Thus, curve A will be shifted up by ΔVF. It can be seen qualitatively that for this change in potential, the relative slopes of $A'A'$ and BB at the point of intersection are hardly changed and hence β, too, is unaffected. However, if the potential difference is made more cathodic, such that the curve AA is in position $A''A''$, under these conditions the relative slopes of $A'A'$ and BB and hence β are considerably altered from that at lower potentials. It means that the effect of potential on the current density (and hence power in an ecep) is reduced at very high overpotentials as compared with that at lower overpotentials.

3.6.10 Mechanism of Charge-transfer Reactions— a Quantum Mechanical Treatment

3.6.10.1 General. In Secs. 3.6.2 and 3.6.9, methods of making potential-energy calculations to obtain activation energies for reactions and the effect of potential on reaction rate were indicated. However, from such calculations, one does not see readily at what stage the electron transfer occurs, though it has generally been assumed that electron transfer occurs at the intersection point of the curves representing the stretching of the bonds being broken and formed. Though this assumption is correct, it is interesting to know why this is so. The answer is obtained from a quantum mechanical treatment of charge-transfer reactions.[40,41,52-55] For simplicity, this theory will be illustrated in the following sections where the slow discharge mechanism of the hydrogen-evolution reaction is discussed. The mechanism of other electrode reactions can be described in a basically similar manner.

3.6.10.2   Process of Electron Transfer from Metal to Solvated Proton. Just as there is a potential-energy barrier for the transfer of the proton from its solvation sheath to the metal (or in general for a chemical reaction to occur), there is an energy barrier for the transfer of an electron from the metal to the solvated proton in solution. The energy barrier for electron transfer is obtained in principle by considering (1) the image interaction (given by $e^2/4x$) between the metal and the electron and (2) the coulombic interaction (given by e^2/x) between the electron and the solvated proton. For a certain fixed distance of the proton from the metal, the potential-energy–distance relation for electron transfer from the metal to the proton in solution is represented by a curve of the form of Fig. 21. To construct such potential-energy diagrams, it is first necessary to determine the levels AB and CD represented in this figure. The level AB is simply determined by bringing an electron from infinity in vacuum to the Fermi level of the metal. Thus, level AB is below the zero level of energy by Φ, the work function of the metal. Determination of the level CD is somewhat more complex. It is the energy required to bring an electron from infinity to the solvated proton. This process involves (1) desolvation of the ion H_3O^+, (2) electron acceptance, (3) formation of the M-H bond, and (4) a repulsion

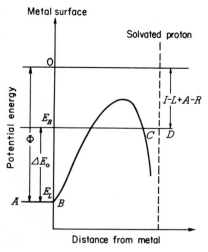

Figure 21 Potential-energy curve for transfer of an electron from metal to solvated proton.

between the adsorbed hydrogen atom and water molecules. Thus, the energy level CD is below that of the zero level by $I - L + A - R$ where I is the ionization energy of the hydrogen atom, L is the interaction energy between the proton and the solvent molecules when the proton is at the assumed distance from the metal, A is the adsorption energy between the hydrogen atom at this specified distance and the metal, and R is the repulsion energy between the hydrogen atom and the water molecule, to which the proton was attached as in the H_3O^+ ion prior to its neutralization. The energy at the levels $AB(E_L)$ and $CD(E_R)$ may be expressed by the equations

$$E_L = -\Phi \tag{3.96}$$

$$E_R = -(I - L + A - R) \tag{3.97}$$

Numerical calculations, carried out to determine the barrier for electron transfer, *show that the activation energy for the classical transfer of the electron from the metal to the proton in solution is too high, and the observed current densities for electrode reactions cannot be explained on the basis of classical electron transfer*. The only other possibility is the tunneling of electrons from the metal to ions in solution. This mode of transport of electrons occurs, for example, in the cold emission of electrons from a metal into vacuum.

One of the conditions for tunneling of electrons from the Fermi level of the metal AB to the proton in solution is that there must be vacant levels in the solvated proton with energy equal to that of the Fermi level of the metal. This condition may be expressed mathematically by

$$E_L \geqslant E_R \tag{3.98}$$

Using Eqs. (3.96) and (3.97), this condition becomes

$$\Phi \leqslant I - L + A - R \tag{3.99}$$

Figure 21 is constructed assuming that the bare proton is at the equilibrium distance from the water molecule to which it is bonded as an H_3O^+ ion. The stable hydrated proton is assumed to be situated at the outer Helmholtz plane. Thus, when the proton is in this stable position, Fig. 21 shows that the condition (3.99) is not satisfied, i.e., there are no empty states for the electron in the acceptor proton, and electron transfer cannot occur from the metal to the proton.

The condition (3.99) may be rewritten in the form

$$R - A \leqslant I - L - \Phi \tag{3.100}$$

The left-hand side of this equation represents the energy of the hydrogen atom after neutralization, whereas the right-hand side represents the energy of the hydrogen ion and of the electron in the metal before neutralization for any assumed distance of the hydrogen ion (or atom) from the metal. The quantities R, A, and L are not constants. They depend on the distances of the hydrogen atom and ion from the metal and from the water molecule. One can now

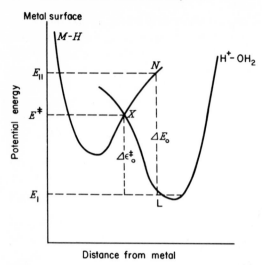

Figure 22   Potential-energy–distance relation for transfer of proton from H_3O^+ to metal.

construct the curve for the initial state of the system, $M(e) + H^+\text{-}OH_2$, as the proton is being stretched from its equilibrium position in the outer Helmholtz plane.   Likewise, it is possible to plot the energy of the final state, $M\text{-}H \cdots H_2O$, which represents the energy of the system after the electron transfer has occurred for varying distances of the hydrogen atom from the metal.   Such a potential-energy diagram consisting of both curves, which may be referred to as the "proton transfer curve," is illustrated in Fig. 22.   When the proton is in its initial state, the energy gap from AB to CD in the electron-transfer curve (Fig. 21) is the energy represented by the vertical distance LN in the proton-transfer curve (Fig. 22).   It is clear that the only way of reducing the energy gap between AB and CD and thus bringing about the condition of Eq. (3.100) so that tunneling of electrons to the proton in solution can begin is by activating the $H^+\text{-}OH_2$ bond, i.e., stretching the $H^+\text{-}OH_2$ bond.   From Fig. 22, it is seen that the energy gap is reduced to zero when the proton is stretched up to the intersection point of the potential-energy curves.   From this figure, it is also seen that only a fraction of the energy represented by the line LN [which is equal to the energy difference ΔE_0 of the gap between AB and CD of the electron-transfer curve (Fig. 21)] is necessary to bring the proton up to the intersection point.   Thus, to the left of the intersection point in Fig. 22, electron transfer can occur from the metal to the proton, whereas to the right of this curve, no such (tunnel) transfers can occur.   This discussion, in terms of tunneling of electrons, thus indicates that it is necessary to stretch the proton of the $H^+\text{-}OH_2$ bond up to the intersection point of the potential-energy–distance relation for the stretching of this bond with that for the stretching of the M-H bond, so that tunneling of electrons can occur, i.e., charge transfer takes place.

Once electron transfer occurs, the resulting H atom may then enter the ground state of the system $MH + H_2O$, that is, the final state, or reform a proton by electron tunneling back to the metal. The discharge step may be represented by the equation

$$H_3O^+ + M(e_0^-) \rightarrow [H_2O \cdots H^+ + M(e_0^-)]^{\ddagger}$$
$$\updownarrow$$
$$[H_2O + H \cdots M]^{\ddagger} \rightarrow H_2O + \text{H-M} \tag{3.101}$$

The curves in Figs. 21 and 22 are for the case when the metal-solution potential difference is zero. When a potential difference V is applied across the interface, the energy gap ΔE changes (cf. Sec. 3.6.3) according to

$$\Delta E_v = \Delta E_0 + VF \tag{3.102}$$

This equation arises from the assumption that the minimum of the initial-state curve is shifted vertically by VF from that of the curve when $V = 0$. Figure 22 shows that the extent of stretching required is up to the intersection point. One may write that

$$\Delta \epsilon_0^{\ddagger} = \beta \Delta E_0 \tag{3.103}$$

and

$$\Delta \epsilon_v^{\ddagger} = \beta \Delta E_v$$
$$= \beta(\Delta E_0 + VF) \tag{3.104}$$

Thus, the change in activation energy $(\Delta \epsilon_v^{\ddagger} - \Delta \epsilon_0^{\ddagger})$ caused by an application of a metal-solution potential difference V is βVF. By considering a linear analog of potential-energy curves, it can be shown that β, as expressed by Eq. (3.103), which represents the fraction of energy of the gap between AB and CD necessary to close this gap, is the same as the symmetry factor of the reaction. Thus β as given by Eq. (3.65) and also Eq. (3.104) relates it to the bond-stretching constants of the potential-energy curves (cf. Fig. 22) and thus to the spectroscopically determinable aspects of these bonds. These relations lie at the basis of the attempt to relate electrochemical theory of energy conversion to the relevant basic molecular and atomic quantities.

3.6.10.3 Derivation of Quantum Mechanical Expression for the Rate of Electron Transfer from Metal to Ion in Solution.

In Sec. 3.6.11 the expression for rate of the slow discharge step in the hydrogen-evolution reaction is derived on the basis of the transition-state theory from a consideration of the stretching of the H^+-OH_2 and M-H bonds. It is assumed that the electron transfer occurs rapidly at the intersection point of the initial- and final-state curves (Fig. 22).

In this section, the rate of the overall reaction of the evolution of $H_2 (2H_3O^+ + 2e_0^- \rightarrow H_2 + 2H_2O)$† is considered, on the assumption that the net

---

† The hydrogen-evolution reaction is chosen because it is closer to types of reactions occurring in fuel cells than are redox reactions which have also been treated extensively in the fundamental theory of charge transfer at electrode-electrolyte interfaces.[53,54]

rate of electron transfer at the intersection point of the potential-energy curves for H^+-OH_2 and M-H bond stretching determines the rate. When the metal-solution potential difference is zero, this rate may be expressed by the relation

$$(i)_{V=0} = ek_{E_f}W(E_f)[W(\Delta\epsilon^0\ddagger)]n_{H_3O^+} \tag{3.105}$$

where e is the electronic charge, k_{E_f} is the frequency factor (number of electrons with Fermi energy E_f colliding with unit area of surface at metal-solution interface in 1 sec), $W(E_f)$ is the probability of their being able to tunnel through the electron barrier (Fig. 21), $W(\Delta\epsilon_0\ddagger)$ is the probability that an H_3O^+ ion is in a suitably stretched position for electron transfer to occur, and $n_{H_3O^+}$ is the number of H_3O^+ ions populating unit area of the outer Helmholtz plane.

k_{E_f} is approximately given by[13,56]

$$k_{E_f} = 4\pi m \frac{(kT)^2}{h^3} \tag{3.106}$$

$W(E_f)$ is given by[57]

$$W(E_f) = \exp\left\{-\left(\frac{4\pi l}{h}\right)[2m(E_x - E_f)]^{1/2}\right\}^\dagger \tag{3.107}$$

where E_x is the energy at the top of the electron-transfer barrier and l is the distance between the metal and the hydrogen ion to which electron transfer occurs. $W(\Delta\epsilon_0)$ in Eq. (3.105) gives the fraction of the H_3O^+ ions that are suitably stretched so that condition (3.100) for quantum mechanical electron transfer is fulfilled. For this distribution a Boltzmann expression may be used. Thus

$$W(\Delta\epsilon_0\ddagger) = \exp\left(-\frac{\Delta\epsilon_0\ddagger}{kT}\right) \tag{3.108}$$

Using Eqs. (3.106) to (3.108) in Eq. (3.105),

$$(i)_{V=0} = e4\pi m \frac{(kT)^2}{h^3} \exp\left\{-\left(\frac{4\pi l}{h}\right)[2m(E_x - E_f)]^{1/2}\right\} \exp\left(-\frac{\Delta\epsilon_0\ddagger}{kT}\right) n_{H_3O^+} \tag{3.109}$$

In the presence of a metal-solution potential difference, the expression for the current density becomes

$$(i)_{V=V} = e4\pi m \frac{(kT)^2}{h^3} \exp\left\{-\left(\frac{4\pi l}{h}\right)[2m(E_x - E_f)]^{1/2}\right\} \exp\left(-\frac{\Delta\epsilon_v\ddagger}{kT}\right) n_{H_3O^+} \tag{3.110}$$

Dividing Eq. (3.110) by Eq. (3.109),

$$\frac{(i)_{V=V}}{(i)_{V=0}} = \exp\left(-\frac{\Delta\epsilon_v\ddagger - \Delta\epsilon_0\ddagger}{kT}\right) \tag{3.111}$$

† The expression shown here for $W(E_f)$ is an oversimple one. It corresponds to the assumption that the barrier in Fig. 21 is a square one. Corresponding equations are available for more realistic barriers, but they introduce considerable mathematical complexities.

From Eqs. (3.103) and (3.104),

$$\Delta\epsilon_v{}^{\ddagger} - \Delta\epsilon_0{}^{\ddagger} = \beta V F \tag{3.112}$$

Thus, Eq. (3.111) becomes

$$\frac{(i)_{V=V}}{(i)_{V=0}} = \exp\left(-\frac{\beta V F}{RT}\right) \tag{3.113}$$

By comparing the rates at $V = V_r + \eta$ and $V = V_r$, it follows that

$$i = i_0 \exp\left(-\frac{\beta\eta F}{RT}\right) \tag{3.114}$$

which is the familiar Tafel relation (3.78).

3.6.11 Potential-energy Calculations for Reactions at Metal-solution Interfaces

The first numerical potential-energy calculation for electrochemical reactions was made by Parsons and Bockris in the case of the proton-discharge mechanism on a metal.†,[41] Since this calculation may serve as a nucleus for eventual potential-energy calculations in the case of more complicated electrochemical reactions, it is summarized in this section.

In the proton-discharge reaction, a proton is transferred from the solution side of the electric double layer to an adsorption site on the metal M with simultaneous desolvation of the proton and its neutralization:

$$M + e_0{}^- + H^+\text{-}OH_2 \rightarrow M\text{-}H + H_2O \tag{3.115}$$

Using the transition-state theory, the rate constant for this reaction, k_D, is given by

$$\begin{aligned}
k_D &= \kappa \frac{kT}{h} K^{\ddagger} \\
&= \kappa \frac{kT}{h} e^{-\Delta G^{0\ddagger}/RT} \\
&= \kappa \frac{kT}{h} e^{-\Delta H_v{}^{0\ddagger}/RT} e^{\Delta S^{0\ddagger}/R}
\end{aligned} \tag{3.116}$$

κ is the transmission coefficient, $\Delta G^{0\ddagger}$ is the standard electrochemical free energy of activation, $\Delta H_v{}^{0\ddagger}$ is the standard heat of activation when the metal-solution potential difference is V, and $\Delta S^{0\ddagger}$ is the standard entropy of activation. In the calculation of k_D, four states in the course of the reaction were considered: (1) initial state—hydrogen ions at unity activity in the bulk of the

---

† The potential-energy calculation summarized in this section is relevant to the quantum mechanical calculation dealt with in the preceding section. It is the calculation behind Fig. 22 of that section. It also directly gives the rate of the proton-discharge reaction if the tunneling probability for electrons is near to unity. Physically, it gives the rate of attainment of the tunneling condition [$W(\Delta\epsilon_0{}^{\ddagger})$] in Eq. (3.105).

solution; (2) adsorbed state—the solvated proton in the compact double layer, at unit surface activity on the electrode; (3) activated state—the activated complex between the hydrogen ion and the electrode at unit surface activity; (4) final state—the hydrogen atoms at unit surface activity, adsorbed on the electrode. The heat contents of states (2) and (4) correspond to the potential energy of the initial and final states, respectively, for the slow-discharge step.

The variation of the potential energy with displacement of the proton from state 2 to 4 was calculated using Morse equations for the H^+-OH_2 (the H_2O molecule being treated as an atom), and M-H interaction energies. The repulsive energy between H and H_2O was also taken into account.

The energy corresponding to the intersection of the curves for states 2 and 4 with increasing distance of the proton from its equilibrium position in H^+-OH_2 to its equilibrium position in M-H, assuming reasonable values for the thickness (δ) of the compact layer,[9] is that of the activated state, H_c; and hence the heat of activation may be obtained. A typical curve in such a calculation is shown in Fig. 23. Parsons and Bockris varied δ between 1.5 and 2.0 Å to estimate the dependence of the heat of activation on the uncertainty in this parameter.

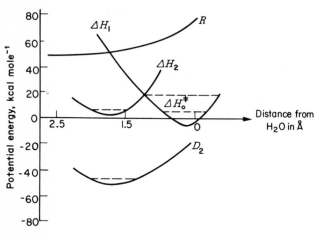

Figure 23 Potential-energy-profile diagrams for obtaining the heat of activation in the hydrogen-evolution reaction on mercury.[41]

In order that the free energy of activation may be obtained, the entropy of activation is required. Owing to the difficulty in evaluating partition functions in solution, it is not possible to evaluate the latter quantity accurately. However, Parsons and Bockris obtained an approximate value for the entropy of activation by assuming that two degrees of translational freedom of the hydrogen atom on the mercury surface are lost in passing over from the final to the activated state. The entropy of activation is then obtained from the entropies of the initial and activated states.

The symmetry factor was calculated from the energies of activation, at various metal-solution potential differences, obtained from potential-energy diagrams at these potentials similar to the one constructed at $V = 0$.

Parsons and Bockris showed that a potential-energy curve calculation was consistent with the observed value of the heat of activation at the potential of zero charge on the electrode, about 16 kcal mole^{-1}. It was also found that the calculated difference in heats of activation for the proton-discharge reaction on mercury and nickel at the reversible potential (which value may be determined more accurately than that of the individual heats of activation) is 11 kcal mole^{-1}, which value is consistent with the observed difference of 12 to 14 kcal mole^{-1}.

The most probable value of the calculated symmetry factor was found to be 0.51, whereas the experimental value of β on Hg in 0.1 N HCl is 0.45 to 0.51. Similar calculations have been made for electrodic reactions other than that of proton discharge on metals.[41a]

3.6.12 Contribution of Quantum Mechanical Tunneling of Protons to Rates of Electrode Reactions

In Sec. 3.6.10 it has been shown that quantum mechanical tunneling of electrons is an essential process in electrode reactions, all of which are subject to quantum mechanical, rather than classical, treatment. However, the distribution of particles to which electron tunneling occurs was assumed to be classical, and the question naturally arises as to whether there is not some quantum mechanical tunneling of ions through the energy barrier as well. It is well-known that quantum mechanical tunneling is a process, the rate of which depends exponentially on the mass of the particle tunneling, so that one sees immediately that ion tunneling is much less probable than is electron tunneling. The most likely ion or atom that can tunnel is the proton or hydrogen atom (or its isotopes). Results of the extent to which proton tunneling occurs through energy barriers[60,60a,60b] are of fundamental importance to fuel cells because many of the important and potentially important reactions in electrochemical energy conversion involve proton or hydrogen atom transfer (for example, in the electrooxidation of hydrogen or of hydrocarbons).

In this section, the subject of tunneling of the heavier reactant species (e.g., hydrogen ion or atom transfer) is briefly considered. According to the classical theory of reaction rates,[27] the transmission coefficient κ of reactant particles with energy less than the activation energy $E^{\ddagger}$ is zero and is unity (reflection of particles is not considered in the classical theory) for particles with energy greater than $E^{\ddagger}$. Quantum mechanically, it is possible for κ to have a finite value for particles with energy less than $E^{\ddagger}$ and also to have a value less than unity for particles with energy greater than $E^{\ddagger}$. The net contribution of this nonclassical penetration and nonclassical reflection to the classical rate is expressed by a tunneling factor κ.† The magnitude of κ depends on the dimensions

---

† The symbol κ has other definitions as well.[31]

of the energy barrier for the reaction and also on the mass of the particle being transferred. For hydrogen atom or ion (or its isotopes) transfer reactions, κ may have appreciable values depending on the height and width of the one-dimensional barrier along the reaction coordinate.[58] Further, in the case of transfer of hydrogen atoms (or isotopes) between heavy end atoms, it may be assumed in the calculation of κ that the end atoms are fixed during the transfer of the central H atom or its isotopes. For heavier atom transfers κ may be taken as unity. It is interesting to see how the tunnel effects introduce only a correction factor κ to the classical rate. Considering the slow-discharge mechanism of the hydrogen-evolution reaction, the quantum mechanical rate is given by

$$i_{q,1} = k_1 c_{H_3O^+} \int_{E_0}^{\infty} W(E) \exp\left(-\frac{E - E_0}{kT}\right) dE \tag{3.117}$$

where k_1 is a frequency factor, $W(E)$ is the probability of proton tunneling at energy level E, and E_0 is the zero-point energy of the initial state of the reaction. The integral is evaluated from E_0 to ∞, since quantum mechanically there is a probability (W) of leakage through the barrier for $E^0 \leqslant E \leqslant E^{\ddagger}$ (where $E^{\ddagger}$ is† the energy at the top of the barrier) and a probability of reflection when $E > E^{\ddagger}$. The classical rate (i.e., the rate without allowance for proton tunneling) is given by

$$i_{cl} = k_1 c_{H_3O^+} kT \exp\left(-\frac{E^{\ddagger} - E_0}{kT}\right) \tag{3.118}$$

From Eqs. (3.117) and (3.118), the tunneling correction factor is

$$\kappa = \frac{i_q}{i_{cl}} = \frac{1}{kT} \exp \frac{E^{\ddagger} - E_0}{kT} \int_{E_0}^{\infty} W(E) \exp\left(\frac{E - E_0}{kT}\right) dE \tag{3.119}$$

The rate of the reaction is then given by

$$i_q = \kappa i_{cl} \tag{3.120}$$

i_{cl} is calculated according to the equations developed in Sec. 3.6.11. κ is calculated according to Eq. (3.119) and hence the quantal rate of the electrode reaction is obtained.‡

In order that an expression for $W(E)$ may be obtained it is necessary to know the shape of the one-dimensional barrier along the reaction coordinate. The closest fit to the real barrier is the Eckart barrier.[59]

---

† The frequency factor k is also quantized, but it concerns electrons tunneling to protons (Sec. 3.6.10) which have tunneled through the barrier. Levich[60a] has made a unified treatment in which the tunneling of protons and electrons has been simultaneously taken into consideration.

‡ Calculation of the quantum mechanical rate according to Eq. (3.117) alone is invalid since the zero point energy of activated state is neglected here. Hence the quantum mechanical rate is obtained by multiplying the classical rate (which takes into consideration the zero point energy of the activated state) by a tunneling correction factor [Eq. (3.120)].[105]

Calculations of κ have been made by Bockris and Matthews[60] for various values of barrier parameters (length, width, height) and temperatures. Comparison of the computed values with the corresponding experimental data for the hydrogen-evolution reaction on mercury was then used to determine the most probable barrier parameters. The experimental data available for comparison are the Tafel slope and the hydrogen-tritium separation factor and its variation with potential.[61] From the experimental data of the H-T separation factor as a function of potential, it was then shown that tunneling of protons contributes significantly to the observed rate—e.g., about 85 percent at the reversible potential and 70 percent at an overpotential of 1 volt for hydrogen evolution on mercury in acid solutions.

As pointed out previously, since tunneling depends on the mass of the particle being transferred, its contribution is appreciable only in the case of hydrogen atom or ion transfers (or those of its isotopes), and is negligible for transfer of heavier atoms.

3.7 Mass-transfer Controlled Processes

3.7.1 Types of Mass-transfer Processes

3.7.1.1 Diffusion. The simplest of the mass-transport processes is diffusion, and it arises because of differences in the chemical potentials of the solute (ions or molecules) at various points in the solution. Diffusion-controlled processes are encountered at relatively high current densities, when either the reactants are consumed at the electrode at a rate faster than that at which they are supplied by diffusion or when the products are formed at an electrode at a rate faster than that at which they diffuse into the bulk of the solution. Thus, in the case of fast electrode reactions (high exchange current densities), diffusion effects are met with at low overpotentials, and vice versa.

Another type of diffusion process is involved when porous electrodes are used. In this case, it is caused by the transport of gas molecules through the pores of these electrodes (see Chap. 5).

3.7.1.2 Convection. There are two types of convection—forced and natural. Forced convection is a result of some externally caused stirring of the solution. Natural convection arises owing to differences in densities in different parts of the solution. Differences in densities may be a result of nonuniform temperature or concentrations. The latter are caused by the electrode reaction itself, which by the consumption or production of species lowers or increases the density in layers near the surface.

3.7.1.3 Migration. Migration is the motion of ions in solution caused by the force exerted on them by the electric field between cathode and anode during current flow.

3.7.2   Minimization of Transport by Convection and Migration

A study of mass transport in the presence of all three types is difficult.   Migration is eliminated by using an excess of supporting electrolyte, the ions of which carry current between the two electrodes but do not take part in the electrode processes.   Thus, the ions which take part in the later processes are only negligibly affected by electric migration.   Forced convection is diminished by working in still solutions.   This leaves only natural convection to be dealt with. This is minimized by making measurements at times so short such that density changes at electrodes are too small to cause significant natural convection.

Under these short time conditions (<1 μsec), diffusion alone governs mass transport.   The advantage of achieving this condition is that the mathematical theory of diffusion is considerably more developed than that of other forms of transport.   Diffusion in electrochemistry is analogous to heat transfer in solids.   Thus, the mathematical treatment in diffusion problems is very similar to that in heat transfer.

3.7.3   Steady-state Diffusion-controlled Deposition Processes

3.7.3.1   *Relation of Current Density to Diffusional Flux.*   Consider a reaction of the type

$$M_b{}^{n+} + ne_0{}^- \to M \tag{3.121}$$

which occurs at a planar electrode. M^{n+} and M are the oxidized and reduced forms of an anion (e.g., a metal-deposition reaction).   Diffusion of the reactant M^{n+} from the bulk to the interface is the rate-determining step.   This diffusion step is represented by

$$M_b{}^{n+} \to M_e{}^{n+} \tag{3.122}$$

The suffixes b and e denote the bulk and the electrode-electrolyte interface, respectively.   In order that the rate of this step may be ascertained, it is necessary to use Fick's first law of diffusion.   Thus, assuming that there is a concentration gradient of the reactant only in a direction x which is perpendicular to the plane of the electrode,

$$Q = -D\frac{dc}{dx} \tag{3.123}$$

where Q and dc/dx are the flux across a laminar of unit area and the concentration gradient, respectively, from the electrode. D is the diffusion coefficient, which is almost concentration-independent.   Suppose the current density at which the reaction takes place is i; then

$$\frac{i}{nF} = -D\left(\frac{dc}{dx}\right)_{x=0} \tag{3.124}$$

In other words, the rate at which M^{n+} diffuses to the electrode is equal to the rate at which it is consumed at the electrode.

3.7.3.2 Concept of Diffusion Layer. In order that $(dc/dx)_{x=0}$ may be evaluated, Nernst and Merriam introduced the concept of the diffusion layer[62]— a layer near the electrode where the concentration varies linearly from the bulk value c_b to the concentration at the electrode c_e. Beyond this diffusion layer, the concentration is taken as independent of distance (Fig. 24). The thickness of the diffusion layer is designated by δ. In unstirred solutions, at planar

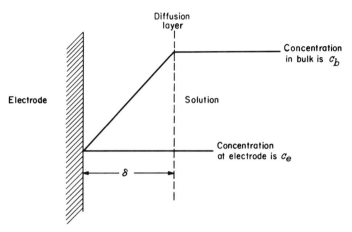

Figure 24 Concept of diffusion layer.

electrodes, the value of δ is about 5.10^{-2} cm after steady-state behavior has been set up. Using the Nernst-Merriam model, it follows that

$$\left(\frac{dc}{dx}\right)_{x=0} = \frac{c_b - c_e}{\delta} \tag{3.125}$$

3.7.3.3 Expressions for Current Density as a Function of Overpotential and for the Limiting Current Density. Using Eqs. (3.124) and (3.125), one may write

$$i = DnF\,\frac{c_b - c_e}{\delta} \tag{3.126}$$

As the current density is increased a stage is reached when the ions of M^{n+} at the electrode are being consumed so fast that the concentration gradient of *AB* increases to its limiting value, corresponding to $c_e = 0$. The limiting current density i_L is given by

$$i_L = \frac{DnFc_b}{\delta} \tag{3.127}$$

From Eqs. (3.126) and (3.127), it follows that

$$\frac{i}{i_L} = \frac{c_b - c_e}{c_b} = 1 - \frac{c_e}{c_b} \tag{3.128}$$

In order that the currents may be expressed as a function of potential, it is first necessary to relate the concentration ratio in Eq. (3.129) to the potential. For this purpose, it may be assumed that the electrode reaction is sufficiently fast (high i_o) so that it may be considered reversible with respect to the concentration of ions near the electrode (i.e., all steps preceding or succeeding the rate-determining step are considered to be virtually in equilibrium). Under these conditions, it follows that

$$(V)_{i=0} = V^0 + \frac{RT}{nF} \ln c_b \tag{3.129}$$

$$(V)_{i=i} = V^0 + \frac{RT}{nF} \ln c_e \tag{3.130}$$

where the suffixes $i = 0$ and $i = i$ denote net current densities of zero and i, respectively, at the electrode. Thus, the diffusion overpotential η_D is given by

$$\eta_D = (V)_{i=i} - (V)_{i=0} = \frac{RT}{nF} \ln \frac{c_e}{c_b} \tag{3.131}$$

Using Eq. (3.131) in (3.128), it follows that

$$i = i_L \left(1 - \exp \frac{n\eta_D F}{RT} \right) \tag{3.132}$$

When η_D is small, the exponential may be linearized in Eq. (3.132), which then reduces to

$$i = -i_L \left(\frac{n\eta_D F}{RT} \right) \tag{3.133}$$

i.e., the diffusion overpotential varies linearly with the current density. This equation is analogous to the current-density–overpotential relation at low overpotentials for activation-controlled processes. When η_D is high and negative in Eq. (3.132), the limiting current is reached.

An i-η_D curve is represented schematically in Fig. 25. AB is the linear portion which corresponds to low overpotentials. CD is the region of limiting current density. At D, another electrochemical reaction with a more negative standard reversible potential takes over as shown by section DE of the curve.

Limiting mass-transport-control phenomena are extremely important in fuel-cell electrodics. It is also the origin of the use of porous electrodes, for in these configurations may be found a layer of solution which exists between the (gaseous) fuel and the electrode substrate (or particles of catalyst) and which is much less thick than it would be in a planar electrode situation (Chap. 5). In the latter case, the solution is sufficiently present to let δ attain the stated limiting value of about 0.05 cm. Thus, δ in certain areas of the interior of a porous electrode is less than 0.05 cm by 10^1–10^2 times (indeed, its reduction in

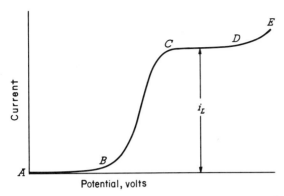

Figure 25 Current-density–potential relation for diffusion-controlled process.

magnitude corresponds to the thickness of menisci which cover the catalyst inside the pores). Correspondingly [cf. Eq. (3.127)], the limiting (or maximum) current density is greatly increased over that of the planar electrode situation, and thus the power producible from a fuel cell per unit external area of its electrodes is greatly increased (cf. Chap. 5).

3.7.4 Steady-state Diffusion-controlled Dissolution Processes

An example of this type is the dissolution of metals [i.e., the reverse of reaction (3.121)]. There is a buildup of concentration of metal ions near the electrode, and the slow step in such systems is the diffusion of metal ions from the electrode to the bulk of the solution. Thus, the concentration gradient is in the opposite direction to that in the former case. An equation analogous to (3.132) is obtained in this case as well:

$$i = i_L \left[\exp \left(\frac{n \eta_D F}{RT} \right) - 1 \right] \tag{3.134}$$

In this equation, i_L is the limiting current density for the corresponding cathodic reaction. Since η_D is positive in this case, no limiting current density is reached as follows from the physical picture (for the anode is an inexhaustible source). As in the former case, at small overpotentials, i varies linearly with η. At higher overpotentials, $\exp(n \eta_D F / RP) \gg 1$ and Eq. (3.134) reduces to

$$\eta_D = \frac{RT}{nF} \ln i - \frac{RT}{nF} \ln i_L \tag{3.135}$$

This relationship is similar to the Tafel equation (3.78).

3.7.5 Non-stationary-state Diffusion Control

Considerations of kinetics of charge-transfer reactions at interfaces have hitherto been for reactions in the steady state. No variation of rate with time has been accounted for. However, electrochemical energy converters have to be switched on, switched off, or varied in power output. Consequently, there is the necessity of considering the variations of current density or potential with time. Time variations in activation-controlled processes are very fast and are not of much interest in considering the performance of electrochemical electricity producers. Time variations in diffusion-controlled processes, which are slower, are considered in this section, in which reaction (3.121) under non-stationary-state diffusion control is analyzed. For this purpose it is assumed that M^{n+} is being reduced at a constant current density i. The starting equation for non-stationary-state diffusion control is Fick's second law:

$$\frac{dc}{dt} = D \frac{d^2c}{dx^2} \tag{3.136}$$

The boundary conditions for this problem are

$$c = c^0 \quad \text{for } 0 \leqslant x \leqslant \infty \quad \text{at } t = 0 \tag{3.137}$$

and

$$i = DnF \left(\frac{dc}{dx}\right)_{x=0} \quad \text{for all } t \tag{3.138}$$

The solution to this problem has been shown to be[63]

$$c = c^0 - \frac{2it^{1/2}}{\pi^{1/2}nFD^{1/2}} \exp\left(-\frac{x^2}{4Dt}\right) + \frac{i}{nFD} \operatorname{erfc} \frac{x}{2D^{1/2}t^{1/2}} \tag{3.139}$$

From Eq. (3.139), it follows that the concentration of M^{n+} at the electrode $(x = 0)$ is given by

$$(c)_{x=0} = c^0 - Pt^{1/2} \tag{3.140}$$

where

$$P = \frac{2i}{\pi^{1/2}nFD^{1/2}} \tag{3.141}$$

Since diffusion of M^{n+} to the electrode is considered as the slow step while the succeeding steps at the electrode are considered to be fast (i.e., virtually in equilibrium), the Nernst equation may be used to express the electrode potential as a function of time. Thus

$$E = E^0 + \frac{RT}{nF} \ln \frac{c^0 - Pt^{1/2}}{c^0} \tag{3.142}$$

where E^0 represents the potential at $t = 0$.

The transition time τ is defined as the time at which the concentration at the electrode reaches zero. From Eqs. (3.140) and (3.141) τ is given by[†]

$$\tau^{1/2} = \frac{\pi^{1/2}nFD^{1/2}c^0}{2i} \tag{3.143}$$

[†] The equation is valid for short times when natural convection is absent (cf. Sec. 3.7.2).

When t reaches the value τ, it follows from Eqs. (3.141) and (3.142) that, mathematically, the potential at the electrode tends to $-\infty$. A typical galvanostatic transient is shown in Fig. 26. In practice, when t reaches τ, the potential changes rapidly to a more negative potential or more positive value depending on whether the process is cathodic or anodic, at which some other electrode reaction takes over.

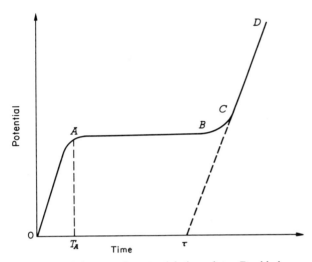

Figure 26 Galvanostatic potential–time plot. Double-layer charging time T_A and transition time τ are shown.

The dependence of transition time on c^0 and i is given by Eq. (3.143). These variations have been tested experimentally in a number of cases.[63] Also, a plot of $i\tau^{1/2}$ versus i should yield a straight line with zero slope, which result has also been verified experimentally. Different types of behavior are observed if a chemical step in solution precedes the electrode reaction.[63a]

The equations deduced in this section are important both academically and in practice: for example, it is possible to test whether a reaction is under diffusion control by plotting $i\tau^{1/2}$ versus i, which according to Eq. (3.143) has to be linear with a zero slope.

This equation also gives the basis of a calculation of the duration of the time during which an electrode reaction can be run at a current density above the limiting current density i_L. The latter quantity is the maximum rate at which the reaction can occur for an indefinite time in the steady state and is given by Eq. (3.127). According to Eq. (3.143), τ is the time during which a constant current density i ($i > i_L$) may flow before some other process takes over. The physical significance of τ is the time necessary for an electrode process to use up the charge carriers in the diffusion layer. Thus, τ values would be the basis of an approach to the theory of the action of a fuel cell under conditions in which a particularly high current drain was needed (e.g., in acceleration for a fuel-cell-powered car).

The real calculation of the transition time when using porous electrodes is more complicated than that given here.   However, τ may be approximately calculated for planar electrodes, and it may be assumed that τ is about a hundred to a thousand times longer using porous electrodes for the same electrode reaction.

3.7.6   Mass Transfer by Diffusion and Migration

In the preceding treatment, it was assumed that there is an excess of supporting electrolyte in the solution (i.e., excess indifferent electrolyte such that the transport of the reactant species M^{n+} to the electrode by migration is negligible). It is interesting to examine the case under which transport of M^{n+} occurs both by diffusion and migration (which occurs significantly in the absence of excess supporting electrolyte).

In the steady state, the total current density at which M^{n+} is reduced at the electrode according to Eq. (2.121) is given by

$$i = i_D + i_M \tag{3.144}$$

where i_D and i_M represent the current equivalent of the fluxes due to transport of M^{n+} to the electrode in a direction perpendicular to it by diffusion and migration, respectively.

The value of i_D is given by Eq. (3.126).   In the bulk of the solution, the current density i is equal to that transported by migration.   The migration current due to M^{n+} is expressed by

$$i_M = t^+ i \tag{3.145}$$

where t^+ is the transport number of the M^{n+} ion.   Introducing Eqs. (3.126) and (3.145) into (3.144),

$$i = \frac{DnF}{1 - t^+} \frac{c^0 - c_e}{\delta} \tag{3.146}$$

Since t^+ is between 0 and 1, the current density under condition of transport by diffusion and migration is always greater than under diffusion conditions only. Thus, to minimize overpotential caused by mass-transfer limitations, it is better to have transport of the reactant species to the electrode by both diffusion and migration.

3.7.7   Treatment of Convective Transport

In quite a number of electrochemical measurements, the electrolytes are stirred.   Thus, there is forced convection.   Electrolytes are stirred by means of a mechanical stirrer (e.g., movement of the electrode itself), by gas bubbling, by the influence of local heat development, or by ultrasonic methods.   Further, even in the absence of stirring, if the transition times are fairly long (greater than a few seconds for a planar electrode), natural convection sets in because of depletion of reactant ions near the electrode, and this thereby causes density variations.

A theoretical analysis of mass-transfer processes in the presence of convection is quite difficult. However, working under convective-transport conditions greatly helps in reducing mass-transport limitations.

Some simple cases of convection can be treated theoretically, using the principles of hydrodynamics. One of them is the derivation of the rate of mass transfer to a large rotating electrode (to eliminate edge effects) in the presence of an excess of supporting electrolyte. For this case, Levich[64] showed that the diffusion-layer thickness is given by

$$\delta = 1.62 D^{1/3} v^{1/6} \omega^{-1/2} \tag{3.147}$$

where D is the diffusion coefficient of the reactant in the electrolyte, v is the kinematic viscosity, and ω is the angular velocity. Thus, using Eq. (3.147) in (3.127), the expression for the limiting current density becomes

$$i_L = \frac{n F D^{2/3} \omega^{1/2} c^0}{1.62 v^{1/6}} \tag{3.148}$$

Equation (3.148) has been confirmed by experiment for the dependence of i_L on ω for a wide range of angular velocities.[64] This equation also gives the variation of i_L with D and v. With a rotating-disk electrode, i_L varies linearly with $D^{2/3}$, whereas in the absence of convection i_L varies directly with D.

Rotating electrodes have not hitherto been used in ecep's. Spinning-disk electrodes have, however, been used. They give a method of increasing the limiting current density and hence the power density of the fuel cells.

The use of rotating devices may, of course, lead to the possibility of mechanical breakdown, and one present advantage of fuel cells—the absence of moving parts—would be lost.

There have been several attempts[64,64a] to treat mass transport under tubulent-flow conditions. Although exact calculations have not been made so far, equations relating the diffusion-layer thickness to the Reynolds number and to the Prandtl number have been obtained.

4 KINETICS AT SEMICONDUCTOR-SOLUTION INTERFACES

4.1 General

The need to discuss electrode processes at semiconductor-electrolyte interfaces arises because there is an increasing prospect that semiconductors may be used in electrochemical energy converters as electrodes. They are already being used, in a formal sense as, for example, the use of the lithiated nickel oxide electrode for the oxygen electrode in one of the most highly developed hydrogen-oxygen fuel cells (Chap. 10). The prospect of future use of semiconductors is bright because in the region of potentials in which most fuel-cell electrodes operate, most of the nonnoble metals dissolve anodically and hence cannot serve as electrocatalysts in these electrochemical energy converters. Some semi-conductors, particularly organic ones, seem promising in this direction. A number of lesser known materials such as the tungsten bronzes are also quite acid resistant and are potential fuel-cell electrocatalysts.

4.2   Charge-transfer Processes

The treatment to be followed here[65-67] is analogous to that of charge-transfer processes at the metal-solution interface. The main differences are considerations of (1) the Helmholtz layer potential with respect to the overall potential drop and (2) the concentration of the electrons at the surface of the semi-conductor.

For simplicity, the diffuse-layer potential in the solution (V_{2-b} in Fig. 9) will be considered to be absent because practically all fuel cells use concentrated solutions of electrolytes. The forward and reverse currents, for a reaction of the type

$$O + e_0^- \rightarrow R \tag{4.1}$$

where O and R are the oxidized and reduced species of the redox couple, are

$$\overrightarrow{i} = Fk_1 a_O a_{e_0,s} \exp\left(\frac{-\beta V_{s-2}F}{RT}\right) \tag{4.2}$$

$$\overleftarrow{i} = Fk_{-1} a_R \exp\left[\frac{(1-\beta)V_{s-2}F}{RT}\right] \tag{4.3}$$

k_1 and k_{-1} are the rate constants of the forward and reverse reaction when the Helmholtz potential V_{s-2} is zero (see Fig. 9). If the electrons are assumed to behave ideally, then their activity may be replaced by their concentration. The concentration of electrons at the surface may be related to their concentration in the interior of the semiconductor by the equation (see Fig. 9)

$$c_{e_0,s} = c_{e,i} \exp\left(-\frac{V_{i-s}F}{RT}\right) \tag{4.4}$$

It is also possible to write (see Fig. 9)

$$V = V_R + \eta = V_{i-s} + V_{s-2} \tag{4.5}$$

where V_R is the reversible potential of the electrochemical reaction for the chosen conditions and η is the overpotential. At highly cathodic potentials, the reverse current is negligible compared with the forward one (that is, $\overleftarrow{i} \ll \overrightarrow{i}$). Using Eqs. (4.4) and (4.5) in Eq. (4.2),

$$i = \overrightarrow{i} = Fk_1 c_O c_{e_0,i} \exp\left[-\frac{(V_R + \eta - V_{s-2})F}{RT}\right] \exp\left(-\frac{\beta V_{s-2}F}{RT}\right)$$

$$= i_0 \exp\left[\frac{(1-\beta)V_{s-2}F}{RT} - \frac{\eta F}{RT}\right] \tag{4.6}$$

where

$$i_0 = Fk_1 c_0 c_{e_0,i} \exp\left(-\frac{V_R F}{RT}\right) \tag{4.7}$$

Suppose $\eta \gg V_{s-2}$ (i.e., the Helmholtz potential is a small fraction of the space-charge potential difference), then

$$\frac{\partial \eta}{\partial \ln i} = -\frac{RT}{F} \tag{4.8}$$

Equation (4.8) shows that when the Helmholtz potential difference is small (i.e., most of the potential difference is within the semiconductor), the Tafel slope is half that normally encountered with metals for simple charge-transfer reactions. As $\eta \to 0$, but yet with the conditions that $\eta \gg V_{s-2}$, it can easily be shown that

$$i = -\frac{i_0 \eta F}{RT} \tag{4.9}$$

which is the same relation obtained at the metal-solution interface at low overpotentials ($|\eta| \ll RT/F$).

The brief treatment, particularly the one leading to Eq. (4.8), depends on the assumption of small surface-state concentrations. (For a definition of surface states, see Sec. 2.3.) If the concentration of surface states is high (10^{14} cm^{-2} or more), then the situation is similar to that in the case of metals, and the potential drop is mainly at the electrode-electrolyte interface. If, however, the concentration of surface states is small, then most of the potential drop is (as in Fig. 9) in the space-charge region of the semiconductor.

4.3 Mass-transfer Controlled Processes

Just as in the case of diffusion-controlled processes at metal-solution interfaces, here too diffusion may be rate-controlling. However, in addition to the normal diffusion of ions through the solution, a slow diffusion process may be caused by the supply of current carriers (e.g., electrons) from the bulk of the semiconductor to the surface. The mathematical treatment of such a problem is, however, complex.

Schockley[68] has considered the case when the surface of a p-type semiconductor is made more negative. The regions of different electron concentration within the semiconductor during passage of current are depicted in Fig. 27. The diffusion region exists only when current flows. The diffusion current density i_e may be expressed as

$$i_e = FD_e \left(\frac{dc_{e,x}}{dx}\right)_{x=x} \tag{4.10}$$

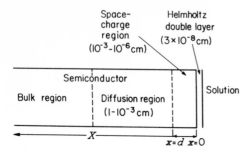

Figure 27 Regions of different electron concentration within semiconductor during passage of electric current.[65]

where D_e is the diffusion coefficient of the electrons through the semiconductor and c_e is the concentration of electrons at a distance x from the surface.

Under equilibrium conditions, the rate v at which hole-electron pairs are being generated by heat or by light is equal to the rate of recombination of holes and electrons. During the electrode reaction, this equilibrium does not exist and the net rate of generation of electrons u at a point x is given by

$$u = v - k_r(c_{e,b} - \delta c_{e,x})(c_{p,b} - \delta c_{p,x}) \tag{4.11}$$

where $\delta c_{e,x}$ and $\delta c_{p,x}$ are the decrease in electron and hole concentrations, respectively, from their corresponding equilibrium concentrations $c_{e,b}$ and $c_{p,b}$ in the bulk at the point x. Since $\delta c_{p,x} \approx 0$, and $v = k_r c_{e,b} c_{p,b}$, Eq. (4.11) reduces to

$$u = k_r c_{p,b} \delta c_{e,x}$$
$$= \frac{\delta c_{e,x}}{\tau_e} \tag{4.12}$$

where τ_e is the lifetime of the excess electrons in the p-type semiconductor. (The lifetime of a reactant for a bimolecular reaction is given by $1/kc$.)

Using Eq. (4.12) and Fick's second law,

$$\frac{c_{e,b} - c_{e,x}}{\tau_e} = D_e \frac{d^2 c_{e,x}}{dx^2} \tag{4.13}$$

Solving the above diffusion equation with the boundary conditions that

$$c_{e,x} = c_{e,b} \quad \text{at } x = \infty \tag{4.14}$$

and

$$c_{e,x} = c_{e,d} \quad \text{at } x = d \tag{4.15}$$

then

$$c_{e,x} = -\left[(c_{e,d} - c_{e,b}) \exp\left(-\frac{x}{\sqrt{\tau_e D_e}}\right)\right] + c_{e,b} \tag{4.16}$$

Differentiating Eq. (4.16), it follows that

$$\frac{dc_{e,x}}{dx} = \frac{1}{\sqrt{\tau_e D_e}} (c_{e,b} - c_{e,d}) \exp\left(-\frac{x}{\sqrt{\tau_e D_e}}\right) \tag{4.17}$$

At $x = 0$:

$$\left(\frac{dc_{e,x}}{dx}\right)_{x=0} = \frac{1}{\sqrt{\tau_e D_e}} (c_{e,b} - c_{e,d}) \tag{4.18}$$

The limiting current density is given from Eqs. (4.10) and (4.18) by

$$i_{e,L} = \frac{FD_e}{\sqrt{\tau_e D_e}} c_{e,b} \tag{4.19}$$

The maximum rate at which electrons can be supplied from the interior of the semiconductor to the electrode-electrolyte interface is $i_{e,L}$, as expressed by Eq. (4.19). There is no such limitation in the case of a metal. A knowledge of $i_{e,L}$ is of extreme importance in the choice of semiconductors as fuel-cell electrodes because even if they may be suitable electrocatalysts, a limitation due to a low rate of supply of electrons may exist. Hence, Eq. (4.19) is useful in obtaining this information. τ_e may be determined by photoelectric excitation of the process across the interface which gives the time taken for the current to decrease due to electron exhaustion.

4.4 Comparison of Electrode Kinetics at Metal-solution and Semiconductor-solution Interfaces

4.4.1 Electron Concentration

In a metal, there is an infinite supply of free electrons, whereas in a semiconductor there is a shortage of free electrons. There are two causes for attaining a limiting current in semiconductor electrode kinetics, one of which is, as in metal electrode kinetics, due to exhaustion of the reactant in solution. The other is due to electron exhaustion within the semiconductor.

4.4.2 Regions of Potential Distribution

At a metal-solution interface, in concentrated solutions, the total potential drop is across the Helmholtz layer. In the absence of surface states, the total potential drop is practically entirely within the semiconductor.

4.4.3 Origin of Electrons

In a semiconductor, there are two types of electrons, depending on whether they are from the conduction or valence band.[67] It is thus possible for ions in solution to have charge transfer from both types of electrons.

4.4.4 Exchange Current Densities

For reactions at a metal-solution interface, by definition the exchange current density is the same in both anodic and cathodic directions. In semiconductor electrode kinetics, since the diffusional limitation on charge carriers may be different for anodic and cathodic processes, the apparent exchange current densities obtained by extrapolation of anodic and cathodic Tafel plots may not necessarily be equal.

5 ADSORPTION ISOTHERMS AND THEIR INFLUENCE ON ELECTRODE KINETICS

5.1 General

Reactions at electrodes may be considered as one of the types of heterogeneous catalysis with one additional intensive variable—the potential drop at the interface. The nature of the surface plays an important role in two respects. First, the rate of an intermediate step may depend on the heat of adsorption of the reactant and products on the surface. Second, the rate of this step may also depend on the available or free surface on the electrode. The intermediate steps may be charge-transfer or chemical steps. The latter may precede or succeed the charge-transfer step or steps in the overall reaction. The adsorption characteristics of the metal may also change the path of a complex reaction. For example, a reaction intermediate may sometimes desorb from the surface without further reaction. Diffusion may also play an important part in adsorption. Adsorption kinetics strongly depends on the type of isotherm governing the adsorption of a particular species.

Until the late fifties, adsorption isotherms were little accounted for in electrodics, except by the Russian school. With the advent of interest in electrochemical energy conversion, particularly using organic fuels, considerable attention has been drawn towards determining the electrosorption behavior of organic compounds used as fuels. A knowledge of this electrosorption behavior is required at two levels—one at a simple level where it is necessary to know the extent to which the organic compound is adsorbed as a function of potential for a certain concentration of the species in solution. Generally this relation is parabolic (Fig. 8). If a fuel is poorly adsorbed, the rate of the overall charge-transfer reaction involving it will tend to be low. The second is at a more sophisticated level. It is difficult to gain information about the rds in the oxidation of the fuel unless adsorption properties are known in detail. A prerequisite to this knowledge is obtained from the type of isotherm governing the adsorption process. Interpretation of variation of current density with potential depends strongly on the type of these adsorption isotherms.

5.2 Types of Adsorption Isotherms

5.2.1 Langmuir Isotherm

The Langmuir isotherm[69] was first derived from a kinetic viewpoint. Suppose a reaction of the type

$$A^+ + e_0^- \rightarrow A_{ads} \tag{5.1}$$

is considered. (It is not necessary to consider only charge-transfer cases. The subsequent reasoning will also hold for a reaction of the type $A_{soln} \rightarrow A_{ads}$. The charge-transfer reaction may be considered as a more general case.) The rate of the forward reaction is given by

$$v_1 = k_1 c_{A+} (1 - \theta) \exp\left(-\frac{\beta VF}{RT}\right) \tag{5.2}$$

since the forward velocity depends on the free surface in addition to the concentration of the reactant. Similarly, the velocity of the reverse reaction is given by

$$v_{-1} = k_{-1} \theta \exp\left[(1 - \beta)\frac{VF}{RT}\right] \tag{5.3}$$

k_1 and k_{-1} are the rate constants of the forward and reverse reactions when the metal-solution potential difference is zero. θ is the degree of coverage of the adsorbed species A on the electrode. θ is related to the surface concentration c_A by the relation

$$c_A = k'\theta \tag{5.4}$$

where k' is the surface concentration when $\theta = 1$. At equilibrium,

$$\frac{\theta}{1 - \theta} = \frac{k_1 c_{A+}}{k_{-1}} \exp\left(-\frac{VF}{RT}\right) \tag{5.5}$$

Equation (5.5) reduces to a linear variation of θ with c_{A+} (Henry's isotherm[70]) when $\theta \ll 1$. This model ignores lateral interactions. It assumes that all sites on the surface are equivalent and the adsorbed species are immobile on the surface.

5.2.2 Isotherm of Frumkin and of Temkin

The Langmuir isotherm may be written in the more general form

$$Kc \exp\left(-\frac{VF}{RT}\right) = \frac{\theta}{1 - \theta} = c \exp\left(\frac{-\Delta G^0}{RT}\right) \exp\left(\frac{-VF}{RT}\right) \tag{5.6}$$

where $K = k_1/k_{-1}$. By considering lateral interactions and by analogy with van der Waals' equations for gases, Frumkin[71] modified the above equation to

$$Kc \exp\left(-\frac{VF}{RT}\right) = \frac{\theta}{1 - \theta} \exp\left(\frac{r\theta}{RT}\right) \tag{5.7}$$

The interaction energy parameter r is negative when lateral interaction is attractive, and it is positive when there is repulsion between the adsorbed species.

Temkin[72] considered the more general case of lateral interactions and non-uniformity of surface arising from knowledge of gas-adsorption studies. Using these conditions, Temkin derived an equation of the same form as that of Frumkin.

A simple way of obtaining Eq. (5.7) is as follows. In the case of most adsorbents, the heat of adsorption, and hence the free energy of adsorption, decreases linearly with coverage. The standard free energy of adsorption (with $V = 0$) when the coverage is θ may then be expressed as

$$\Delta G_\theta^0 = \Delta G_0^0 + r\theta \tag{5.8}$$

where ΔG_0^0 is the standard free energy of adsorption at zero coverage and r is an interaction energy parameter. On introducing Eq. (5.8) into Eq. (5.6), Eq. (5.7) results.

At intermediate values of coverage $(0.2 < \theta < 0.8)$, when $\theta/(1 - \theta)$ is unimportant relative to $\exp(r\theta/RT)$ in Eq. (5.7), one obtains an equation, sometimes called the Temkin isotherm:

$$r\theta = -VF + RT \ln K + RT \ln c \tag{5.9}$$

Further, when r is very small or at very small coverages, Eq. (5.7) reduces to the Langmuir equation. This is also the case when $\theta \to 1$, but in this case the equilibrium constant K_h is not the same as that (K_e) for the low-coverage region. The relation between these two equilibrium constants is given by

$$\frac{K_h}{K_e} \approx \exp\left(-\frac{r}{RT}\right) \tag{5.10}$$

If r is taken as 6 kcal mole^{-1}, the two Langmuir isotherms are obeyed in the two regions $0 < \theta < 0.2$ and $0.8 < \theta < 1.0$.

The variation of free energy of adsorption with coverage [Eq. (5.8)] may be due to intrinsic heterogeneity of the surface, lateral interaction effects, or induced heterogeneity effects.

5.3   Influence of Types of Isotherms on Electrode Kinetics

5.3.1   Langmuir Conditions

A reaction of the type

$$M + A^- \to MA + e_0^- \tag{5.11}$$

$$2MA \to 2M + A_2 \tag{5.12}$$

can be considered where the product A_2 is a gas.

The rates of the forward (v_1) and reverse reactions (v_{-1}) of step (5.11), assuming Langmuir conditions, are

$$v_1 = k_1 c_{A^-} (1 - \theta) \exp \left(\frac{\beta VF}{RT} \right) \tag{5.13}$$

$$v_{-1} = k_{-1} \theta \exp \left[-(1 - \beta) \frac{VF}{RT} \right] \tag{5.14}$$

and similarly for step (5.12),

$$v_2 = k_2 \theta^2 \tag{5.15}$$

$$v_{-2} = k_{-2}(1 - \theta)^2 P_{A_2} \tag{5.16}$$

where c_{A^-} is the concentration of the ion A^- in solution; θ is the degree of coverage of the surface with MA; P_{A_2} is the partial pressure of A_2; and the k's are the respective rate constants indicated by the appropriate suffixes. If the desorption step is rate-determining, the discharge step may be considered to be virtually in equilibrium (see Sec. 3.3.2.3). Thus, from Eqs. (5.13) and (5.14), it follows that

$$\theta = \frac{K_1 c_{A^-} \exp (VF/RT)}{1 + K_1 c_{A^-} \exp (VF/RT)} \tag{5.17}$$

When $K_1 \exp (VF/RT) \ll 1$, $\theta \to 0$ and is given by

$$\theta = K_1 c_{A^-} \exp \left(\frac{VF}{RT} \right) \tag{5.18}$$

Under these conditions,

$$1 - \theta \approx 1 \tag{5.19}$$

Thus Eqs. (5.15) and (5.16) reduce to

$$v_2 = k_2 K_1^2 c_{A^-}^2 \exp \left(\frac{2VF}{RT} \right) \tag{5.20}$$

$$v_{-2} = k_{-2} P_{A_2} \tag{5.21}$$

From Eqs. (5.20) and (5.21) the net current density i may be expressed in the form

$$i = i_0 \left[\exp \left(\frac{2\eta F}{RT} \right) - 1 \right] \tag{5.22}$$

where

$$i_0 = 2Fk_2 K_1^2 c_{A^-}^2 \exp \left(\frac{2V_R F}{RT} \right)$$

$$= 2Fk_{-2} P_{A_2} \tag{5.23}$$

and η is the overpotential. When $K_1 \exp (VF/RT) \gg 1$, $\theta \to 1$, and

$$1 - \theta = \frac{1}{K_1 c_{A^-} \exp (VF/RT)} \tag{5.24}$$

Under these conditions, it is possible to write [cf. Eqs. (5.15) and (5.16)]

$$i = i_0 \left[1 - \exp \left(-\frac{2\eta F}{RT} \right) \right] \tag{5.25}$$

where:

$$i_0 = 2Fk_2 \tag{5.26}$$

$$= 2F \frac{k_{-2}}{K_1^2 c_{A^-}^2} P_{A_2} \exp \left(-\frac{2V_R F}{RT} \right) \tag{5.27}$$

It is seen from these limiting conditions of $\theta \to 0$ or $\theta \to 1$ that either the forward or the reverse of step (5.12), respectively, proceeds at a limiting current density determined by some activation-controlled process at the electrode.

For the reaction considered, all steps are dependent on the coverage. The second step, a chemical reaction, is only indirectly dependent on potential: the dependence arises through the coverage of intermediate-potential relation.

Langmuir conditions are valid only when $\theta \to 0$ or $\theta \to 1$, an often observed condition. It may be necessary to invoke other adsorption conditions (e.g., Temkin) to find out what theoretical values of Tafel slopes would correspond to given mechanisms in the coverage range $0.2 \leqslant \theta \leqslant 0.8$, of the intermediate MA, where interactions between adsorbed species or surface heterogeneity may be important.

5.3.2 Temkin Conditions

The use of these conditions was first made by Temkin,[72] and in greater detail by Thomas[73] for the hydrogen-evolution reaction. Conway et al. have subsequently used it for the oxygen-evolution reaction[74] and for the anodic reaction of nickel oxide.[75]

Assuming now a Temkin isotherm for the adsorption of the species MA in the reaction sequence (5.11), (5.12) which was formerly treated according to the Langmuir adsorption—one may find out how the kinetic parameters are affected. Thus, taking into consideration the variation of free energy of adsorption of the intermediate MA with coverage [cf. Eq. (5.8)],

$$v_1 = k_1 (1 - \theta) c_{A^-} \exp \left(\frac{\beta VF}{RT} \right) \exp \left(-\frac{\gamma r\theta}{RT} \right) \tag{5.28}$$

$$v_{-1} = k_{-1} \theta \exp \left[-(1 - \beta) \frac{VF}{RT} \right] \exp \left[(1 - \gamma) \frac{r\theta}{RT} \right] \tag{5.29}$$

The exponential terms in θ in Eq. (5.28) and (5.29) may be visualized in the same way as the exponential term in V. The term γ is analogous to a symmetry factor.

In the intermediate-coverage range, the variation of linear terms in θ is considerably less than the exponential terms in θ. Hence, Eqs. (5.28) and (5.29) may be reduced to

$$v_1 = k_1 c_{A-} \exp\left(\frac{\beta VF}{RT}\right) \exp\left(-\frac{\gamma r\theta}{RT}\right) \tag{5.30}$$

$$v_{-1} = k_{-1} \exp\left[-(1-\beta)\frac{VF}{RT}\right] \exp\left[(1-\gamma)\frac{r\theta}{RT}\right] \tag{5.31}$$

The forward and reverse velocities of the second step, represented by Eq. (5.12), remembering again that the adsorption energy of the species MA depends on coverage, are given by

$$v_2 = k_2 \theta^2 \exp\left(\frac{2\gamma r\theta}{RT}\right)$$

$$\approx k_2 \exp\left(\frac{2\gamma r\theta}{RT}\right) \tag{5.32}$$

$$v_{-2} = k_{-2}(1-\theta)^2 \exp\left[-2(1-\gamma)\frac{r\theta}{RT}\right]$$

$$\approx k_{-2} \exp\left[-2(1-\gamma)\frac{r\theta}{RT}\right] \tag{5.33}$$

Under Temkin conditions, where $0.2 < \theta < 0.8$, in Eqs. (5.32) and (5.33) the variations of the preexponential terms in θ are small compared to those of the exponential ones and thus the approximate forms of the equations are found on the second line of each equation. Again assuming that the first step is virtually in equilibrium, when the second step is rate-determining, it follows from Eqs. (5.30) to (5.33) that

$$v_2 = k_2(K_1 c_{A-})^{2\gamma} \exp\left[\frac{2\gamma VF}{RT}\right] \tag{5.34}$$

$$v_{-2} = k_{-2}\left(\frac{1}{K_1 c_{A-}}\right)^{-2(1-\gamma)} \exp\left[-2(1-\gamma)\frac{VF}{RT}\right] \tag{5.35}$$

Since the currents are proportional to the velocities, it follows, from Eq. (5.34), that for the cathodic reaction

$$\frac{\partial V}{\partial \ln i_2} = \frac{RT}{2\gamma F} \tag{5.36}$$

and from Eq. (5.35), that for the anodic reaction

$$\frac{\partial V}{\partial \ln i_{-2}} = \frac{RT}{2(1-\gamma)F} \tag{5.37}$$

Thus, it is seen from Eqs. (5.22), (5.25), (5.36), and (5.37) that the rate of variation of overpotential with current density of a reaction depends on the type of isotherm which governs the adsorption of reactants (e.g., the fuel in an electrochemical electricity producer). In mechanism determinations, the slope $dV/d \ln i$ is one of the most useful mechanisms indicating criteria but only under the condition that prior knowledge about the type of adsorption isotherm is available.

5.4   Adsorption Pseudocapacitance and Its Variation with Potential

5.4.1   General

Another useful parameter about which one should have some knowledge in the electrode kinetics of fuel-cell reactions is pseudocapacitance. Adsorption pseudocapacitance is defined as the differential capacitance caused by a change in coverage with potential of an electroactive intermediate which is usually formed in a fast charge-transfer step preceding the rate-determining step. This is obtained from short-time studies of the potential variation at electrodes during switching on or off the current. Electrical capacity is defined as the rate of change of charge with potential. The charge q is related to the coverage by the relation

$$q = q_0 \theta \tag{5.38}$$

where q_0 is the charge when $\theta = 1$.

In the previous section, it was found that the coverage of an intermediate varies with potential for several reactions. The relationship of coverage to potential depends on the type of isotherm chosen. Under these conditions, it is necessary to define a differential capacitance[76] by the relation

$$C_{ps} = \left(\frac{\partial q}{\partial V} \right)_{c,T,P} = q_0 \left(\frac{\partial \theta}{\partial V} \right)_{c,T,P} \tag{5.39}$$

Grahame[77] called this capacitance "pseudocapacitance." It arises in quite a different manner from the normal ionic double-layer capacitance. The latter can be compared with that of an ideal condenser, where all the charge is used up in increasing or decreasing the metal-solution potential difference and there are no electrons crossing the interface. The order of magnitude of this capacitance is 15 to 20 μf cm^{-2} (cf. Sec. 2.2.2.1) on a smooth electrode (for example, Hg). It is only this capacity that arises at an ideally polarizable electrode, and it is constant with potential for about 0.5 volt on the negative side of the point of zero charge for a Hg electrode (Fig. 2).

5.4.2   Conditions under Which Pseudocapacitance Arises

Pseudocapacity is found in reactions in which a charge-transfer step precedes the rate-determining step. Under these conditions, the charge-transfer step may generally be considered to be fast and virtually in equilibrium.

Figure 28 represents the equivalent circuit for an electrode reaction [e.g., Eqs. (5.11) and (5.12)] in which pseudocapacity exists. In the circuit, R_1 and R_2 are the equivalent resistances of the steps represented by (5.11) and (5.12), respectively, C_{dl} is the double layer capacity, and C_{ps} is the pseudo-capacity. Since step (5.12) is assumed to be rate-determining, $R_2 \gg R_1$ (Fig. 28).

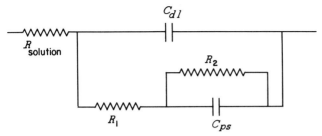

Figure 28   Equivalent circuit for reaction represented by Eqs. (5.11) and (5.12).

5.4.3   *Theoretical Treatment of Pseudocapacitance*

Dolin and Ershler[76] were the first to investigate pseudocapacity. They considered the variation of capacitance with potential on a platinum electrode during hydrogen evolution with superimposed alternating current. They found values of up to 2,000 μf cm^{-2} at a few hundred cycles per second, which decreased to 20 μf when the frequency was very large.

Any theory of pseudocapacitance would depend on the type of isotherm chosen for the adsorbed species. Bockris and Kita[78] developed a theory using Langmuir conditions. If the first step (5.11) is considered to be in equilibrium, it follows from Eqs. (5.6) and (5.39) that

$$\frac{q_0}{C_{ps}} = \frac{dV}{d\theta} = \frac{RT}{F} \frac{d \ln (\theta/1 - \theta)}{d\theta}$$

$$= \frac{RT}{F} \frac{1}{\theta(1 - \theta)} \tag{5.40}$$

Thus

$$C_{ps} = \frac{q_0 F}{RT} \theta(1 - \theta) \tag{5.41}$$

From Eqs. (5.41), it can be seen that C_{ps} has a maximum value when $\theta = \frac{1}{2}$, at which coverage it is given by

$$C_{ps} = \frac{q_0 F}{4RT} \tag{5.42}$$

and the variation of C_{ps} with θ is symmetrical around $\theta = \frac{1}{2}$.

For hydrogen adsorption, with 10^{15} sites cm^{-2}, $C_{ps} = 1.6 \times 10^3\ \mu f\ cm^{-2}$, which value agrees with the experimental value of Dolin and Ershler.[76]   By expressing θ as a function of potential using Eq. (5.17),

$$C_{ps} = \frac{q_0 F}{RT} \frac{c_A - K_1 \exp{(VF/RT)}}{[1 + c_A - K_1 \exp{(VF/RT)}]^2} \tag{5.43}$$

The relation of C_{ps} to V is graphically represented in Fig. 29.   The width of the bell-shaped curve at $C_{ps} = 100\ \mu f\ cm^{-2}$ (assuming a suitable roughness factor) is about 0.2 volt.   The position of the curve depends on the value of the coverage at the reversible potential θ_0.

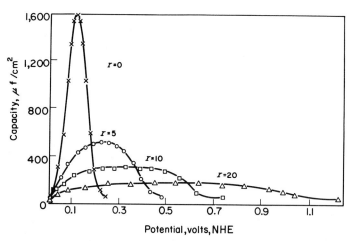

Figure 29   Pseudocapacitance-potential relations for Langmuir ($r = 0$) and Temkin ($r \neq 0$) conditions.   (r is interaction energy parameter.)[74]

Conway and Gileadi[74] have considered the case of Temkin adsorption of the intermediate.   Under Temkin conditions, it follows from Sec. 5.3.2 that

$$\frac{q_0}{C_{ps}} = \frac{dV}{d\theta} = \frac{RT}{F} \frac{d \ln{(\theta/1 - \theta)}}{d\theta} + \frac{r}{F} \tag{5.44}$$

Comparison of Eq. (5.40) with (5.44) shows that it is possible to write, after dividing throughout by q_0 [cf. Eq. (5.41)],

$$\frac{1}{C_{ps}} = \frac{1}{C_L} + \frac{1}{C_T} \tag{5.45}$$

Thus, the pseudocapacity is a series combination of two capacity terms— one just as in the Langmuir case C_L and the other C_T depending on the heterogeneity parameter r.   To obtain a plot of C_{ps} versus potential, one proceeds indirectly: from a plot of C_{ps} versus θ, using Eq. (5.44), and V versus θ, using Eq. (5.7), it is possible to obtain the C_{ps}-V relation graphically.   Such plots for various values of r are also shown in Fig. 29.   The case $r = 0$ represents

Langmuir adsorption conditions. It may seem that even with a relatively small value of r, the capacity maximum is lowered. For $r \neq 0$ the capacity maximum C_M is given analytically by the equation

$$C_M = \frac{q_0 F}{4RT + r} \tag{5.46}$$

Further, when $r \neq 0$, the dependence of C_{ps} on potential covers a wider range of potential than in the Langmuir case. At high values of r, C_{ps} is independent of V, as was shown for hydrogen adsorption on Pt^{79} and oxygen adsorption on $Ni.^{75}$

Gileadi and Conway[80] have extended their treatment to cases in which the first step is not in quasiequilibrium, even though the second step is rate-determining—as, for example, in reaction scheme (5.11) followed by (5.12). Expressions for the pseudocapacity where the rate-determining atom-ion desorption step follows the discharge step have also been worked out. The pseudocapacity is dependent on K_{NE} (*NE* equals nonequilibrium)—the ratio of rate constants for the rate-determining and prior radical-producing step. K_{NE} is a measure of the extent to which equilibrium in the radical-producing step is disturbed.

The usefulness of this work in electrochemical energy conversion may be seen in the following way. If in the case of a certain reaction, pseudocapacitance is exhibited and can be measured as a function of potential, the value of the Temkin coefficient r can be obtained and, therefore, it becomes easy to find out whether various mechanism-determining criteria (e.g., Tafel slope, reaction orders) must be interpreted as a Temkin scheme or not. This knowledge should help in the evaluation of mechanism, and hence in providing a rational basis for seeking catalyst materials.

6 KINETICS OF ADSORPTION OF NEUTRAL MOLECULES

6.1 General

Adsorption of neutral molecules is often encountered in the course of a number of reactions of interest to fuel cells. They may be typified by the electro-oxidation of hydrocarbons and alcohols. The first stage in such a reaction is the diffusion of the dissolved reactant towards the electrode, followed by its electro-sorption. Generally, one assumes that the diffusion process is fast compared with reactions at the electrode surface. But certain time effects observed in studies on potentiostatic electrooxidation of hydrocarbons indicate that the diffusion process is initially slow, whereas at longer times there is a period during which the adsorption process itself is hindered.[81]

The neutral molecule may or may not be a reactant in the reaction under consideration. The importance of the diffusion and adsorption process is apparent.   If it is not a reactant, the adsorption of a species alters the available sites for the electrochemical reaction.   It could also affect the surface potential and hence the electric field at the interface.

The kinetics of the adsorption process depends on the type of isotherm governing the adsorption and also on whether pure diffusion or diffusion-convection conditions exist.   Some of these cases[82–84] are considered in the following subsections where it is assumed that diffusion of species towards the electrode is the slow step.

6.2   Diffusion Followed by Adsorption under Conditions of Henry's Isotherm

This case was first treated by Delahay and Trachtenberg.[82]   The process of diffusion and of adsorption of a species A on to a planar electrode may be represented by

$$A_b \rightarrow A_e \tag{6.1}$$

$$A_e \rightarrow A_{ads} \tag{6.2}$$

The suffixes b, e, and ads stand for the species in the bulk of the electrolyte at the electrode-electrolyte interface and in the adsorbed state.

In the non-steady state, the diffusion of the species A towards the electrode is given by

$$\frac{dc}{dt} = D \frac{d^2c}{dx^2} \tag{6.3}$$

where D is the diffusion coefficient of the species A in the electrolyte and x is a direction perpendicular to the surface.   The rate of the adsorption step is expressed by

$$v_a = \frac{d\Gamma}{dt} = kc(o,t)$$

$$= -D\left(\frac{dc}{dx}\right)_{x=0} \tag{6.4}$$

where Γ is the surface concentration of the adsorbed species A on unit area and $c(o,t)$ is the concentration at the electrode.   Equation (6.4) is a boundary condition for the differential equation (6.3).   The other boundary conditions are

$$c(x,o) = c^0 \tag{6.5}$$

$$c(\infty,t) = c^0 \tag{6.6}$$

c^0 is the bulk concentration of A.

The solution to the differential equation (6.3) with boundary conditions (6.4) to (6.6) is given by

$$\frac{c(x,t)}{c^0} = \left[1 - \exp\left(\frac{x}{K} + \frac{Dt}{K^2}\right) \text{erfc}\left(\frac{x}{2\sqrt{Dt}} + \frac{\sqrt{Dt}}{K}\right)\right] \tag{6.7}$$

Thus

$$\frac{c(o,t)}{c^0} = \left(1 - \exp\frac{Dt}{K^2}\,\text{erfc}\,\frac{\sqrt{Dt}}{K}\right) \tag{6.8}$$

where K is related to k by the relation

$$K = \Gamma_m k \tag{6.9}$$

Γ_m is the maximum value of the surface concentration of the adsorbed species. If Dt/K^2 is large, Eq. (6.8) reduces to†

$$\frac{c(o,t)}{c^0} = 1 - \frac{K}{\sqrt{\pi Dt}} \tag{6.10}$$

But

$$\Gamma_t = Kc(o,t) \tag{6.11}$$

and

$$\Gamma_e = Kc^0 \tag{6.12}$$

$$\frac{\Gamma_t}{\Gamma_e} = 1 - \frac{K}{\sqrt{\pi Dt}} \tag{6.13}$$

Equation (6.13) may be rewritten in the form

$$t^{1/2} = \frac{K}{\sqrt{\pi D}}\left(1 - \frac{\Gamma_t}{\Gamma_e}\right)^{-1} \tag{6.14}$$

Defining the rise time τ as the time taken for the coverage on the surface to reach 97 per cent of its equilibrium value,

$$\tau = 1.1\frac{K^2}{\pi D} \times 10^3 \tag{6.15}$$

τ is the time necessary for the coverage on the electrode to reach a value corresponding to nearly the equilibrium value. An interesting feature of Eq. (6.15) is that this time is independent of the concentration of the species in

$$\dagger \exp x^2 \,\text{erfc}\, x = \frac{1}{x\sqrt{\pi}}\left[1 - \frac{1}{2x^2} + \frac{1.3}{(4x^4)} + \cdots\right]$$

$$= \frac{1}{x\sqrt{\pi}} \qquad \text{for } x \gg 1$$

Using $x = D^{1/2}t^{1/2}/K$, Eq. (6.10) is obtained from Eq. (6.8) for the stated conditions.

solution.   This may at first seem to be a difficult result to rationalize because intuitively one would expect that with higher concentrations in solutions, smaller τ values result.   But the rate of desorption from the surface is also faster for higher values of concentration (since equilibrium values of θ for higher concentrations are also higher).   The net result is an independence of τ on concentration of species in solution.   This independence is only observed in the case of Henry's isotherm.

The experimental rise time for the adsorption of dibutyl ketone on mercury is in fair agreement with the calculated value.[85]

6.3 Diffusion Followed by Adsorption under Langmuir Conditions at Short Times

This case corresponds to one where $c(o,t) \ll c^0$.   This condition may also be expressed by the inequality

$$c^0 \gg \frac{\theta_t}{k(1 - \theta_t)} \tag{6.16}$$

where θ_t is the coverage of the electrode at time t.   However, if the times are short such that θ_t is small, then condition (6.16) becomes $c^0 \gg \theta_t/k$.   For this case, the solution to Eq. (6.3) with boundary conditions (6.4) to (6.6) is

$$c(o,t) = \frac{2D^{\frac{1}{2}}\pi^{-\frac{1}{2}}c^0}{K} t^{\frac{1}{2}} \tag{6.17}$$

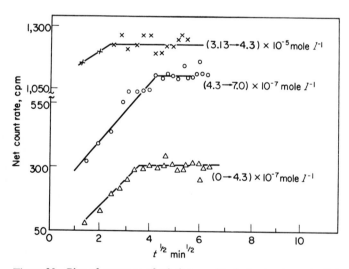

Figure 30   Plot of coverage of ethylene on Pt electrode at a potential of 0.4 volt (NHE) vs. square root of time for specified initial (c_1) and final (c_2) concentrations $(c_1, c_2$ in mole per liter) at 70°C.[86]

and the surface concentration is given as a function of time by

$$\Gamma_t = (2D^{1/2}\pi^{-1/2}c^0)t^{1/2} \tag{6.18}$$

for short times when the coverage of the adsorbent is low.

A plot of Γ_t versus $t^{1/2}$ is linear only for short times. The time variation of the adsorption of ethylene on Pt in 1 N H_2SO_4 follows Eq. (6.18) at short times (Fig. 30).[86]

6.4 Diffusion under Stirred Conditions Followed by Adsorption

The last two treatments are not applicable under the conditions when there is forced convection, e.g., stirring of solution. A crude treatment under these conditions and at low coverages is as follows and perhaps applies to real situations (at times of minutes or more) more frequently than do equations considered above, where pure diffusion is studied.

An approximate analysis can be made when convective transport is also present.[82] The diffusional flux of the species, to be adsorbed on the electrode, through the electrolyte is equal to the rate of change of its coverage on the electrode with time. Thus

$$\frac{d\Gamma_t}{dt} = D\frac{c^0 - c(o,t)}{\delta} \tag{6.19}$$

For the linear isotherm,

$$\Gamma_e = Kc^0 \tag{6.20}$$

and

$$\Gamma_t = Kc(o,t) \tag{6.21}$$

Using Eqs. (6.20) and (6.21) in Eq. (6.19),

$$\frac{d\Gamma_t}{dt} = \frac{D}{K\delta}(\Gamma_e - \Gamma_t) \tag{6.22}$$

Integration of the above equation with the boundary condition that at

$$t = 0 \qquad \Gamma_t = \Gamma_0 = 0 \tag{6.23}$$

then

$$\ln\frac{(\Gamma_e - \Gamma_t)}{\Gamma_e} = -\frac{Dt}{K\delta} \tag{6.24}$$

$$\Gamma_t = \Gamma_e\left[1 - \exp\left(-\frac{Dt}{K\delta}\right)\right] \tag{6.25}$$

The coverage is derived as a function of time assuming that δ, the diffusion-layer thickness, is constant.   Suppose the transition time τ is the time required for the coverage to attain 97 per cent of its equilibrium value,

$$\tau = 3.5 \frac{K\delta}{D} \tag{6.26}$$

The coverage-time relation derived in this section would apply to a long-time adsorption process (greater than 10 sec) where there is convective transport.   Such is the case for adsorption of hydrocarbons on electrodes where it takes about 1,000 sec to reach adsorption equilibrium (Chap. 7).   Since τ varies with δ, it is dependent on stirring conditions.   This case has been treated more thoroughly in Sec. 10, Chap. 4, under time effects of reaction rates.

7   PHOTOELECTRODE KINETICS

7.1   General

The effect of light on electrode reactions is akin to its effect on chemical reactions (photochemistry).[87a]   Very little work has been done in this field.

The number of electrons n_v emitted in a second by a metal in vacuum per unit of incident light energy is given by[87]

$$n_v = \frac{mc^2}{h^2 v^2} \left(1 - \frac{\phi_M}{hv} \right) \tag{7.1}$$

where m is the mass of the electron, c is the velocity of light, ϕ_M is the work function of the metal, and v is the frequency of light of standard intensity I_0.

If the metal is immersed in an electrolyte, the effective work function becomes $\phi_M + \chi$, where χ is the surface potential difference at the metal-solution interface.[36]   Under these conditions, the number of electrons emitted per second becomes

$$n_s = \frac{mc^2}{h^2 v^2} \left(1 - \frac{\phi_M + \chi}{hv} \right) \tag{7.2}$$

7.2   Charge-transfer Reactions under Illumination

For a reaction of the type

$$M^+ + e_0^- \rightarrow M \tag{7.3}$$

the net current density under illumination may be given by:

$$i = \overrightarrow{i} + i_p - \overleftarrow{i} \tag{7.4}$$

$\overrightarrow{i}$ and $\overleftarrow{i}$ are the forward and reverse current densities with no photoeffects and i_p is the photo-current density. Using Eq. (7.2), i_p may be expressed by the equation

$$i_p = \frac{Fmc^2}{h^2v^2} \frac{I_v}{I_0} \left(1 - \frac{\phi_M + \chi}{hv}\right) \tag{7.5}$$

where I_v is the intensity of illumination. At the potential V_L the net current density is given by

$$i = \overrightarrow{k} c_{M^+} \exp\left(-\frac{\beta V_L F}{RT}\right) + F \frac{I_v mc^2}{I_0 h^2 v^2}\left(1 - \frac{\phi_M + \chi}{hv}\right) - \overleftarrow{k} \exp\left[(1 - \beta)\frac{V_R F}{RT}\right] \tag{7.6}$$

Equation (7.6) may be rewritten as

$$i = i_0 \left\{\exp\left(-\frac{\beta V_P F}{RT}\right) - \exp\left[(1 - \beta)\frac{V_P F}{RT}\right]\right\} + F \frac{I_v mc^2}{I_0 h^2 v^2}\left(1 - \frac{\phi_M + \chi}{hv}\right) \tag{7.7}$$

where

$$i_0 = \overrightarrow{k} c_{M^+} \exp\left(-\frac{\beta V_{D,R} F}{RT}\right)$$

$$= \overleftarrow{k} \exp\left[(1 - \beta)\frac{V_{D,R} F}{RT}\right] \tag{7.8}$$

and

$$V_P = V_L - V_{D,R} \tag{7.9}$$

The subscripts L and D signify "light" and "dark." When the net current is zero, let V_P be equal to $V_{P,R}$. Then

$$i_0 \left\{\exp\left[(1 - \beta)\frac{V_{P,R} F}{RT}\right] - \exp\left(-\frac{\beta V_{P,R} F}{RT}\right)\right\} = F \frac{I_v mc^2}{I_0 h^2 v^2}\left(1 - \frac{\phi_M + \chi}{hv}\right) \tag{7.10}$$

As seen from Eq. (7.10), $V_{P,R}$ will be positive with respect to $V_{D,R}$. Two cases may now be distinguished:

(i) If

$$V_{P,R} \gg 2.303 \frac{RT}{F} \tag{7.11}$$

$$V_{P,R} = -\frac{RT}{(1 - \beta)F} \ln i_0 + \frac{RT}{(1 - \beta)F} \ln\left[F \frac{I_v mc^2}{I_0 h^2 v^2}\left(1 - \frac{\phi_M + \chi}{hv}\right)\right] \tag{7.12}$$

Thus, there is a linear relationship between the *equilibrium photopotential* and the logarithm of the intensity of light at constant frequency.

(*ii*) More appropriate, however, is the condition

$$V_{P,R} \ll 2.303 \frac{RT}{F} \tag{7.13}$$

Under these conditions,

$$V_{P,R} = \frac{RT}{i_0 F} F \frac{I_v}{I_0} \frac{mc^2}{h^2 v^2} \left(1 - \frac{\phi_M + \chi}{hv} \right) \tag{7.14}$$

and thus $V_{P,R}$ varies directly with I_v at constant frequency. The threshold frequency (the minimum frequency required to observe light effects) is given by

$$v_0 = \frac{\phi_M + \chi}{h} \tag{7.15}$$

The maximum value of $V_{P,R}$ is observed when

$$\frac{\partial V_{P,R}}{\partial v} = 0 \tag{7.16}$$

that is,

$$v_M = \frac{3}{2h} (\phi_M + \chi)$$

$$= \frac{3}{2} v_0 \tag{7.17}$$

It has been shown[88] that for a silver electrode in dilute halide solutions, a threshold frequency exists and the photo-potential passes through a maximum at $v_M = 1.3 v_0$. The predicted variation of $V_{P,R}$ with I_v at constant frequency has also been observed.

7.3   Role of Dyes in Photoelectrode Processes

It has been known for long that electrodes that are sensitive to light are affected even more when they are coated with dyes.[89] It was subsequently shown that similar effects are observed even when the dyes are present in solution.[90]

When dyes of a certain type (D) are illuminated, they may be promoted to a singlet state. From this state, the dye may undergo a radiationless transfer to a triplet state, which is metastable. It can then undergo reaction with some reducing agent in solution. Reduction of the dye D to DH changes its concentration and thereby alters the potential of an electrode in solution.[91] Suppose the potential determining reaction of the dye in solution is

$$DH \rightarrow D + H^+ + e_0^- \tag{7.18}$$

The photo-induced potential is expressed by

$$V = V^0 + \frac{RT}{F} \ln \frac{D}{DH} - \frac{RT}{2.303F} pH \tag{7.19}$$

Assuming that concentration overpotential arises only because of changes in concentration of the reduced form of the dye at the electrode,

$$\eta_{conc} = \frac{RT}{F} \ln \frac{c_{i,e}}{c_{i,b}} \tag{7.20}$$

where $c_{i,e}$ is the concentration of the reduced form of the dye at the electrode and $c_{i,b}$ is the corresponding bulk concentration. In the bulk of the solution, the reduced form is produced by illumination of the oxidized form (D). Thus, $c_{i,b}$ may be expressed by[92]

$$c_{i,b} = k' c_r \gamma I_v \tag{7.21}$$

where k' is a constant, c_r is the concentration of the reducing agent, γ is the quantum efficiency, and I_v is the light intensity. Thus,

$$\eta_{conc} = \frac{RT}{F} \ln \frac{c_{i,e}}{k' c_r \gamma I_v} \tag{7.22}$$

Thus, η_{conc} can be reduced by increasing the concentration of the reducing agent or the light intensity. Examples of the dye-reducing-agent systems are phenosafranine-EDTA and proflavine-ascorbic acid.[91]

Equations in this section are potentially important for fuel cells since this method instead of the highly expensive photovoltaic method (Chap. 1, Sec. 3.4) may be used to transduce light directly to electric power. Descriptions of such devices have already been made.[93]

8 CORROSION AND MIXED POTENTIALS

8.1 Importance of a Study of the Mechanism of Corrosion

Apart from the aspects considered in the preceding sections, there are two problems that are of central importance and mutually to some extent alternate paths of progress for fuel cells. The main goal in electrochemical energy conversion is to obtain systems in which the rate constants of the electrode reactions are high so that efficiency and the power are maximized. Thus, electrocatalysis is one of the long-term problems in the development of electrochemical energy converters. However, in the absence of sufficiently good electrocatalysts, the alternate route is to use higher temperatures. Thus, if, for instance, temperatures as high as those used in some other types of energy converters (thermoelectric, thermionic) were used, overpotential losses in fuel cells would be negligible. High-temperature fuel-cell systems often use molten electrolyte (e.g., molten LiCl in the Li-Cl_2 fuel cell or mixtures of molten carbonates in the hydrocarbon-air fuel cells). The problem that predominates when using high operating temperatures is the instability of materials. There are two main types of causes for the instability and decay of materials. The first is erosion, which arises as a consequence of physical impact of one phase with another—for example, the wearing away of rocks by rain. The second, by far the most common, cause for the instability of materials, is corrosion due to electrochemical reactions which cause the surface metal atoms to ionize.[94a] due to electrochemical reactions which cause the surface metal atoms to ionize. Such ionization is coupled with a cathodic reaction (e.g., hydrogen evolution or oxygen reduction) so that the net current due to the dissolution (i.e., corrosion) process is zero.

The research carried out hitherto on these problems often shows a lack of understanding of fundamental electrochemistry. For this reason, some aspects of the electrochemical theory of the stability of metals will be presented in this section.

8.2   Reactions Occurring during Corrosion

The understanding of corrosion mechanisms was delayed because it was only in the early fifties that it was generally agreed even among electrochemists (and much later among metallurgists) that the basic mechanisms of corrosion are electrochemical in origin, although Hoar and Evans[94] and Wagner and Traud[95] had presented much evidence of this 30 years earlier. Corrosion may be compared with a cell reaction in the following manner. Figure 31 represents a cell in which a metal is dissolving at electrode A according to the reaction

$$M \rightarrow M^+ + e_0^- \tag{8.1}$$

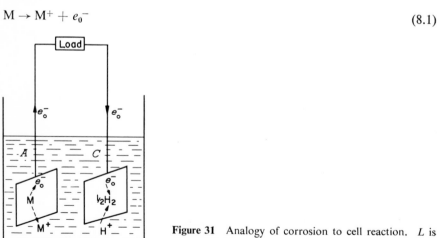

Figure 31 Analogy of corrosion to cell reaction. *L* is external load.

and some cathodic reaction is occurring at electrode C, for example, the hydrogen-evolution reaction:

$$H^+ + e_0^- \rightarrow \tfrac{1}{2}H_2 \tag{8.2}$$

on connecting the two electrodes externally through a load *L*. Thus, electrons released during dissolution of M pass through the external circuit and are consumed at C in the cathodic reaction. In Fig. 32, a corroding electrode is represented. No external circuit exists, but the anodic and cathodic reactions

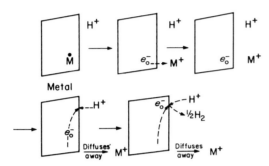

Figure 32 Representation of intermediate steps during corrosion.

are taking place on the same electrode. Wagner and Traud[95] discussed the situation at such an electrode when the anodic current is equal to the cathodic current. The main difference between such an electrode and a reversible electrode is that in the latter it is the *same* reaction which is proceeding at equal velocities in opposite directions. In corrosion, the anodic reaction is the dissolution of the metal [Eq. (8.1)], whereas the cathodic reaction may be hydrogen evolution (8.2) or oxygen reduction according to either:

$$O_2 + 2H^+ + 2e_0^- \rightarrow H_2O_2 \tag{8.3}$$

or

$$O_2 + 4H^+ + 4e_0^- \rightarrow 2H_2O \tag{8.4}$$

depending on the metal, oxygen pressure, pH of solution, etc.

Metal-dissolution reactions generally have higher exchange current densities than those for the hydrogen-evolution or the oxygen-dissolution reactions. Thus, it is usual to find one of these cathodic reactions controlling the rate of corrosion. Conversely, when the metal-dissolution reactions have low-rate constants, this situation is reversed and these determine the corrosion rates. Frequently, the mechanism of corrosion is further complicated by film formation on the metal, in which case, corrosion may proceed through the film, either by diffusion or by passage of ions through pores.

The problems of current distribution on a corroding electrode have been dealt with by several workers. In the simplest view, due to Wagner and Traud,[95] the surface may be assumed to be uniform with electron flow distributed homogeneously over the surface for both anodic and cathodic partial reactions. For this case, the anodic area A_a is equal to the cathodic area A_c which may be assumed to be of the same order as that of the overall surface area. An alternate view is expressed in the local cell theory.[96] Here, it is assumed that the anodic and cathodic reactions take place on only certain local sites (area A_a for anodic and area A_c for cathodic reactions). For this case,

$$A = A_a + A_c \tag{8.5}$$

The sites for the cathodic reaction may be few compared with the anodic ones ($A_c \ll A_a$) and may be caused by impurity atoms that accelerate the cathodic reaction. The net current through the corroding electrode is the algebraic sum of the anodic and cathodic currents ($i_a A_a + i_c A_c$) where i_a and i_c are the anodic and cathodic current densities. Hence,

$$i_a A_a + i_c A_c = 0 \tag{8.6}$$

The corrosion current is given by

$$I_p = i_a A_a = -i_c A_c \tag{8.7}$$

The local cell theory[96] is not different in principle from the theory of Wagner and Traud.[95] The only difference between the two is that in the former the surface is considered to be heterogeneous and in the latter to be homogeneous. Heterogeneity of the surface may be owing to the presence of impurity atoms or irregular films of oxide on the surface.

8.3   Expressions for Mixed Potential and Corrosion Current

It is possible, in principle, to calculate the corrosion rate using an idealized model. The basic assumption in the calculation is that there is a uniform potential on all parts of the surface, i.e., the surface is homogeneous. Such a calculation may first be visualized from Fig. 33, which shows the situation leading up to the attainment of a steady-state corrosion process. In the construction of Fig. 33, it is assumed for purposes of simplification that the activity of M^+ and of H^+ ions in solution is unity. Initially, net currents of the anodic (metal-dissolution) and cathodic (oxygen-dissolution or hydrogen-evolution) reactions are zero, and the potentials at the areas where the reactions take place may be assumed to be at the respective reversible potentials (for simplicity, anodic and cathodic areas are assumed to be equal). As each current increases, the potentials depart from their reversible values. The situation is reached when the anodic current due to metal dissolution is equal to the cathodic current due to hydrogen evolution or oxygen dissolution. The

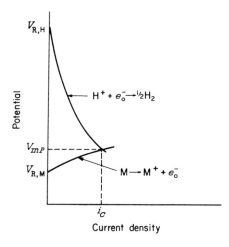

Figure 33 Potential–current-density relations for anodic ($M \rightarrow M^+ + e_o^-$) and cathodic ($H^+ + e_o^- \rightarrow \frac{1}{2}H_2$) reactions during attainment of corrosion.

value of the equal and opposite individual currents at this condition is the *corrosion current*. The potential at which this condition of equal magnitudes of anodic and cathodic currents is reached is referred to as the mixed potential.

This picture gives the basis of the method for obtaining expressions for the mixed potential and corrosion current density, assuming equal anodic and cathodic areas.

The mixed potential V_{mp} is defined as the steady-state metal-solution potential difference set up during corrosion of a metal. Assuming that the cathodic reaction during corrosion is hydrogen evolution, the mixed potential is given by the equation[36]

$$i_{0,\mathrm{H}} \left\{ \exp\left[-\beta_{\mathrm{H}}(V_{mp} - V_{\mathrm{R,H}}) \frac{F}{RT} \right] - \exp\left[(1 - \beta_{\mathrm{H}})(V_{mp} - V_{\mathrm{R,H}}) \frac{F}{RT} \right] \right\}$$

$$= i_{0,\mathrm{M}} \left\{ \exp\left[\beta_{\mathrm{M}}(V_{mp} - V_{\mathrm{R,M}}) \frac{F}{RT} \right] - \exp\left[-(1 - \beta_{\mathrm{M}})(V_{mp} - V_{\mathrm{R,M}}) \frac{F}{RT} \right] \right\}$$

$$(8.8)$$

for the case in which only activation polarization exists at each of the electrode reactions and assuming equal anodic and cathodic areas. The symbols have the usual meaning. The suffixes H and M refer to the hydrogen-evolution and metal-dissolution reactions, respectively. If the symmetry factors are equal to half, that is, $\beta_{\mathrm{M}} = \beta_{\mathrm{H}} = \frac{1}{2}$, the expression for V_{mp} is obtained in the relatively simple form:

$$V_{mp} = \frac{RT}{F} \ln \left[\frac{i_{0,\mathrm{H}} \exp (V_{\mathrm{R,H}}F/2RT) + i_{0,\mathrm{M}} \exp (V_{\mathrm{R,M}}F/2RT)}{i_{0,\mathrm{H}} \exp (-V_{\mathrm{R,H}}F/2RT) + i_{0,\mathrm{M}} \exp (-V_{\mathrm{R,M}}F/2RT)} \right] \qquad (8.9)$$

If in the numerator as well as in the denominator of the expression in square brackets the first term is much smaller than the second, which would be the case if the exchange current density for the metal-dissolution process is considerably larger than that for hydrogen evolution, V_{mp} would be approximately equal to $V_{R,M}$.

The corrosion current density is obtained by substituting for V_{mp}, according to Eq. (8.9), into the expression on either the left- or right-hand side of Eq. (8.8). For the case $i_{0,M} \gg i_{0,H}$, the corrosion current density i_c is given by

$$i_c = i_{0,H} \left\{ \exp\left[-\frac{(V_{R,M} - V_{R,H})F}{2RT} \right] - \exp\frac{(V_{R,M} - V_{R,H})F}{2RT} \right\} \qquad (8.10)$$

This is an expression for corrosion rate under the assumed ideal conditions. The corrosion rate is obtained quantitatively so long as the concentrations of the species in solution are known.

Some general trends may be seen from this equation. For example, there is (1) a linear dependence of the corrosion rate on the exchange current density of the slower of the constituent reactions and (2) an exponential dependence of i_c on the difference between the thermodynamic reversible potentials for the two reactions. Inspection of Eq. (8.10) shows that the basic condition for the commencement of corrosion is given by

$$V_{R,M} < V_{R,H} \qquad (8.11)$$

Alternately, this condition is expressed by

$$a_{H^+} > a_{M^+} \left[\exp\left(\frac{V_{R,M}{}^0 F}{RT} \right) \right] \qquad (8.12)$$

Equation (8.12) is consistent with the observation that acidic solutions tend to be more corrosive than alkaline solutions.

It is possible to treat many other situations in the theory of corrosion on the same lines as for the idealized treatment given above. For example, it is possible to treat the case where activation and concentration overpotentials exist for both partial reactions.[97] The assumption of homogeneity of the surface may be dropped. In all such treatments, however, it is necessary to know the rate constants for the individual reactions in pure systems.

8.4 Thermodynamic Considerations on the Stability of Metal Surfaces

8.4.1 Obtainable Information

A detailed calculation of the rate of corrosion is often not possible in real situations because of a lack of knowledge concerning heterogeneity of surface, particularly its impurity content. The concentration of impurity atoms may have a considerable effect on the corrosion rate. A simpler approach to determine some information on corrosion is a thermodynamic one, from which one is able to find out whether or not it is possible for corrosion to occur. From thermodynamic considerations, however, it is not possible to say whether corrosion will occur in a certain time.

From equations derived in Sec. 8.3, a necessary condition for corrosion to occur is that the reversible potential for the metal-dissolution reaction must be algebraically less than the reversible potential for the cathodic reaction which occurs during the corrosion process (e.g., hydrogen evolution). This condition can also be easily derived if one expresses the corrosion process by the reaction

$$M + nH^+ \rightarrow M^{n+} + \frac{n}{2} H_2 \qquad (8.13)$$

and notes that the free-energy change for the overall process must be negative if the corrosion is to proceed spontaneously.

In calculating the free-energy change of the reaction (8.13), it is necessary to know the hydrogen- and metal-ion concentrations, respectively. As was first done by Pourbaix,[98] the thermodynamic condition for the stability of metal surfaces may be obtained as a function of pH of the solution from potential-pH diagrams which represent variation in reversible potentials for reactions (8.1) and (8.2). Potential-pH diagrams are treated in the next subsection.

Thermodynamic considerations alone are not sufficient; for example, overpotential effects are neglected and thus no measure of the *rate* of corrosion can be obtained. Nevertheless, diagrams of the type mentioned are invaluable as indicating regions of pH and potential in which corrosion is impossible (i.e., free energy change of the overall process is positive).

8.4.2 *Pourbaix's Potential-pH Diagrams*

Pourbaix[98] expressed the basic thermodynamic condition ($V_{R,M} < V_{R,H}$) in terms of potential-pH diagrams for the M/M^{n+} and H^+/H_2 reactions. The former reaction is independent of pH, whereas the latter varies with pH. A plot of $V_{R,M}$ versus pH for varying metal-ion concentrations yields straight lines parallel to the pH axis, whereas a plot of $V_{R,H}$ versus pH is linear with a slope of $-2.3RT/F$. There is a parallel shift of the M/M^{n+} versus pH line with variation of M^{n+} concentration. Three types of diagrams are possible: (1) if for a metal the $V_{R,M}$-pH plot is above (more positive than) the $V_{R,H}$-pH plot, the metal is noncorrodible, as is the case for the noble metals; (2) if the line for the metal dissolution is completely below the line for hydrogen evolution (i.e., $V_{R,M}$ electrode potential is relatively negative), the metal is corrodible at all pHs; (3) if the $V_{R,M}$-pH and $V_{R,H}$-pH lines intersect one another, at pHs lower than that represented by the point of intersection, corrosion can occur, whereas at higher pHs the metal is stable. Potential-pH diagrams typifying the three cases are shown in Fig. 34. Thus, Ag is stable in the entire pH range. Pb is unstable in the pH range up to 5 (approximately) but stable in the higher range till pH 9.3. Mg is unstable over the entire pH range.

Pourbaix and his coworkers have constructed potential-pH diagrams for more complex situations.[98] In addition to metal-dissolution reactions, other

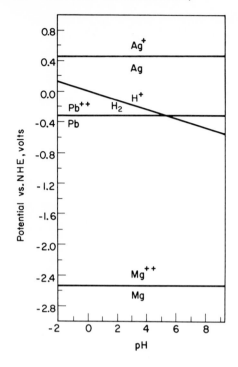

Figure 34 The three types of potential-pH diagrams showing the stability (Ag), partial stability (Pb), or instability (Mg) of some typical metals as a function of pH.

anodic reactions of metals such as

$$M + nH_2O \rightarrow M(OH)_n + nH^+ + ne_0^- \tag{8.14}$$

$$M + nH_2O \rightarrow MO_n^{n-} + 2nH^+ + ne_0^- \tag{8.15}$$

in acid medium and

$$M + nOH^- \rightarrow M(OH)_n + ne_0^- \tag{8.16}$$

$$M + 2nOH^- \rightarrow MO_n^{n-} + nH_2O + ne_0^- \tag{8.17}$$

in alkaline solution have been taken into consideration. Pourbaix diagrams have been prepared for most metals in the *Atlas D'Equilibres Electrochimiques*,[98] showing the regions of stability of the metal, their oxides, or complexes. In these diagrams, Pourbaix et al. made an assumption regarding the concentration of the metal ion. A value of 10^{-6} mole l^{-1} was arbitrarily chosen. Since the reversible potential varies with the logarithm of concentrations, according to the Nernst equation, even if the concentration of the metal ion increased or decreased by a factor of 10^2, the change in the reversible potential for a two-electron transfer M/M^{2+} reaction is only 0.06 volt at 25°C. The diagrams and thus the derived areas of thermodynamic stability are therefore relatively unaffected by the arbitrary value of c_{M^+} used.

For these more complex cases, three types of diagrams are obtained, depending on the possible reaction: (1) lines parallel to the potential axis, for reactions which are independent of potential, such as

$$Ni(OH)_2 + 2H^+ \rightarrow Ni^{2+} + 2H_2O \tag{8.18}$$

(2) lines parallel to the pH axis, for reactions which are independent of pH, such as

$$Fe \rightarrow Fe^{2+} + 2e_0^- \tag{8.19}$$

(3) lines showing a dependence of pH on potential, such as

$$Ni + 2OH^- \rightarrow Ni(OH)_2 + 2e_0^- \tag{8.20}$$

A typical potential-pH diagram for Fe is given in Fig. 35. From such a diagram, it is possible to determine the potential regions, at any pH, in which the different entities are stable. It may be seen from Fig. 35 that Fe does not corrode in alkaline solution, whereas it does so in acids. In alkaline solution, a passive layer forms on the metal in the potential region of the line dividing the Fe from the solid $Fe(OH)_2$ phase.

In the case of some metals in alkaline solution, the equilibrium is between the metal and a complex ion of the metal, for example, Zn and ZnO_2^{2-}. Thus, Zn corrodes in acid as well as in alkaline medium. In the intermediate range, Zn passivates.

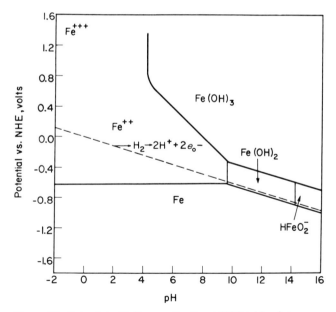

Figure 35 Potential-pH diagram for Fe at 25°C taking into consideration the oxide formation reactions in addition to the metal-dissolution reaction.[98]

Pourbaix diagrams are useful in selecting the pH regions under which corrosion cannot occur.   In practice, however, the question is more often whether the thermodynamically possible corrosion occurs at a significant rate.

8.5   Corrosion Inhibition

8.5.1   General

Corrosion inhibition is a very important field of electrochemical research, because many billions of dollars are lost annually by the corrosion of materials. As the term signifies, corrosion inhibition reduces the rate of corrosion.   Thus, during corrosion inhibition, the kinetics of the corrosion processes are reduced.

There are four distinct methods of corrosion inhibition.   The cheapest and the simplest method is the application of coatings on surfaces as used in the case of automobiles.   There is a severe problem encountered with this technique owing to the formation of cracks in the coating.   Corrosion occurs at these cracks and spreads beneath the coating to other areas.   However, this difficulty is being overcome by the use of electrochemical methods of coating, namely, the electrophoretic deposition of paints on metal surfaces.   Painting techniques are not applicable in several instances as, for example, for corrosion inhibition of pipes.   The other methods are inhibition by (1) adsorption, (2) cathodic protection, and (3) anodic protection.   These methods will be outlined in the following sections.

8.5.2   Inhibition by Adsorption

In this method, a small quantity of a substance, generally a large organic compound, is added to the solution.   Adsorption of this species occurs on the electrode.   An adsorption theory was suggested[99] following a study of inhibition by alkaloids, aromatic amines, and hydrocyanic acid in acid medium.   The inhibitor forms a protective layer and retards the metal-dissolution reaction. This theory was supported by some electron-diffraction studies.[100]

In a later theory,[101] it was proposed that the choice of the inhibitor depends on the corrosion potential of the metal with respect to that of its electrocapillary maximum (ecm) and hence on the charge on the metal at the corrosion potential. Thus, on Fe, which has a corrosion potential of about -0.03 volt in acid medium with respect to its ecm, the best inhibitors should be cationic or neutral substances, whereas anionic inhibitors should have no action.   This prediction is in good agreement with the evidence that cationic inhibitors are effective in acid media.[102]   However, in an oxidizing medium caused by addition of ferric ions to the solution, the corrosion potential is $+0.3$ volt with respect to the potential of the ecm, and cationic inhibitors are ineffective.   Conversely, anionic inhibitors are suitable in this medium.

Addition of certain compounds (alkaloids such as cinchonine and narcotine) to an electrolyte usually increases the hydrogen overpotential on a metal.[103] Upon adsorption, the inhibitor inactivates a number of cathodic sites and hence reduces the rate of the proton-discharge step [cf. Eq. (3.115)]. As a consequence, the corrosion current is also decreased, because during corrosion anodic and cathodic currents are equal. A corrosion diagram in the absence (corrosion rate i_{c_1}) and presence (corrosion rate i_{c_2}) of an inhibitor is shown in Fig. 36 ($i_{c_2} < i_{c_1}$). In the presence of an inhibitor, the corrosion potentials shift towards the reversible potential of the metal-dissolution reaction. In some cases, retardation of the anodic reaction may occur on addition of inhibitors. Adsorbents of the former type are referred to as cathodic and the latter as anodic inhibitors.

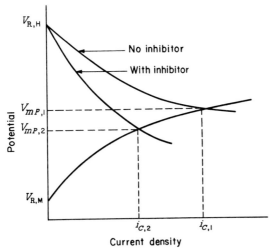

Figure 36   Corrosion diagram in the absence and in the presence of an inhibitor.

8.5.3   Cathodic Protection

The mechanism of cathodic protection to decrease corrosion may easily be understood from Fig. 37. *ABC* represents the hydrogen evolution and *DB* the metal-dissolution line. To the right of the point *B*, the net current is cathodic. At a point *G* on the cathodic line, where the potential is V_G, the net cathodic current is equal to the length *HG*. When the potential reaches $V_{R,M}$ the cathodic current is i_p and the anodic current (i.e., the metal dissolution or corrosion current) is zero. Thus, at any potential more negative than $V_{R,M}$ the metal is cathodically protected. The current necessary for cathodic protection may be fairly high, thus causing a high power consumption. An additional disadvantage of using these high current densities is that the surface concentration of hydrogen may be high enough to cause hydrogen embrittlement.

One way of reducing current densities necessary for cathodic protection is by addition of compounds which inhibit the hydrogen-evolution reaction, e.g., the hydrogen-evolution line becomes *AJK* in the presence of an inhibitor (Fig. 37).

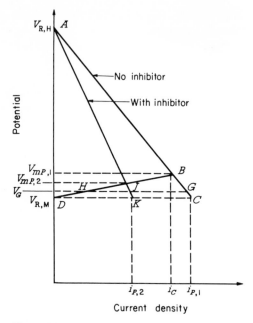

Figure 37 Method of corrosion inhibition by cathodic protection. Cathodic current must exceed $i_{P,1}$ in the absence of and $i_{P,2}$ in the presence of an inhibitor for stability of metal.

Under these conditions, the current density necessary for cathodic protection becomes i_M.

8.5.4 Anodic Protection

This method is somewhat different from the two preceding ones in that a new phase is introduced between the metal and the solution to hinder the spontaneous dissolution process of the metal.   There is some analogy between this method and that of painting the surface of a metal.

The new phase is introduced by increasing the anodic potential until it goes over into a passivating region.   In this passivation region, the anodic current becomes extremely small and thus excellent inhibition occurs.

A disadvantage of this method is that not all metals form passive films. For those which do not, increase of anodic potential merely increases the corrosion rate.

In recent times, the method of anodic protection has been used in the case of large steel tanks.   A disadvantage of cathodic protection is that a fairly high cathodic potential may be required to reduce the corrosion rate considerably (say by a factor of 10^3).   Hydrogen embrittlement problems occur. Further, electrical energy needs to be supplied continuously for cathodic protection.   In the case of anodic protection, it may sometimes be possible to reach the passivation potential by connecting the metal in question externally with a more electropositive metal placed in the same solution. Noncorrodible alloys (e.g., stainless steel) are like automated anodic protectors—local currents flow in a way to put them in a passivating region.

9 ESSENTIAL STEPS IN DETERMINATION OF REACTION MECHANISMS

Determination of mechanisms of electrochemical reactions is a prerequisite for a study of electrocatalysis. Increase of electrocatalytic activity is of primary importance for fuel-cell reactions and has the objective of increasing power generation in electrochemical energy conversion. In its historical development, determination of electrochemical reaction mechanisms follows that of classical chemical kinetics, in that it depended initially upon determination of reaction orders.[104] More work on mechanism determination has been done for the hydrogen electrode reaction[105,106] than for other reactions but an increasing amount of work is being done to elucidate mechanisms of metal deposition[107] and of electroorganic oxidation.[108,109]

Electrochemical mechanism-determination techniques use extra tools compared with those available in chemical kinetics. For example, variations of reaction rate with potential in the steady state or with time at constant potential in the non-steady state are additional mechanism-determining criteria for electrochemical reactions. It is noteworthy that transient methods[109a] (e.g., galvanostatic, potentiostatic, and potential sweep—cf. Chap. 9) have been used in electrode kinetics for considerably longer than those in chemical kinetics.[109b]

The determination of the mechanism of an electrochemical reaction involves five principal steps:

(i) Determination of overall reaction

This step can sometimes be omitted for simple reactions, e.g.,

$$Cu^{2+} + 2e_0^- \rightarrow Cu \tag{9.1}$$

$$2H^+ + 2e_0^- \rightarrow H_2 \tag{9.2}$$

because in these cases reaction products are obvious. The methods employed are analytic determinations of products and the relation of these to the current passed to determine coulombic efficiencies. Difficulties may arise when two overall reactions occur with the same order of magnitude of velocities.[110]

(ii) Determination of type of rate control

Three types of rate control are possible—activation control, mass-transfer control in solution, and mass-transfer control in the electrode. The methods to determine type of rate control involve steady-state and non-steady-state measurements.   They are described in detail in Chap. 9.   Most reactions of interest in electrochemical energy conversion are activation controlled on planar (i.e., nonporus) electrodes over a considerable current density range except near the limiting current.

(iii) Determination of the isotherm

It is necessary to know the dependence of surface concentration of reactants on their respective concentrations in solution and also on potential difference across the interface.   Such determinations are sparse for electrochemical reactions occurring at solid electrodes.   Without them, analysis of reaction mechanisms is difficult even in very simple cases.

(iv) Determination of the nature of adsorbed intermediates and their concentration variation as a function of potential

Except for relatively simple reactions where the nature of intermediates is unambiguous (e.g., the intermediate in the hydrogen-dissolution reaction), this aspect of mechanism determination is the most difficult one.   It may not be necessary to identify all reaction intermediates for a determination of the rate-determining step if it occurs early in the reaction sequence (as seems to be usually the case).   However, if the complete reaction sequence is required, all intermediates must be identified.

(v) Determination of kinetic parameters

Important mechanism-indicating parameters are (1) reaction orders with respect to reactants and products (Sec. 3.6.5); (2) stoichiometric number (Sec. 3.6.7); (3) Tafel slope and exchange current density (Sec. 3.6.6.6); (4) heat of activation at the reversible potential (Sec. 3.6.6.4).   Temperature effects of reaction rates yield information on the extent of tunneling in overall reactions. Another useful criterion in some cases is the isotope effect on reaction rates.[105] Isotopes may also be used to gain information on the participation or otherwise of a particular species in an electrochemical reaction.[111]

Only a brief description and exemplification of mechanism determinations is presented in this and the following sections, since this subject is dealt with in great detail in the chapter on techniques used in fuel-cell research (Chap. 9).

10   MECHANISMS OF SOME ELECTROCHEMICAL REACTIONS

10.1   Hydrogen-electrode Reaction

10.1.1   Cathodic Reaction

10.1.1.1   Overall reaction.   The most extensively studied electrode reaction is the hydrogen-evolution reaction.[36,106]   The overall reaction in acid solution is

$$2H_3O^+ + 2e_0^- \rightarrow H_2 + 2H_2O \tag{10.1}$$

and in alkaline solution is

$$2H_2O + 2e_0^- \rightarrow H_2 + 2OH^- \tag{10.2}$$

10.1.1.2 Probable Reaction Paths. Several reaction paths have been suggested for this reaction on different metals. In recent times, however, only two paths have been considered as most probable (Frumkin[106] and Bockris[36]). The first step—the discharge of hydroxonium ions (or water molecules, in the case of alkaline solutions) on the metal M with the formation of adsorbed hydrogen atoms MH—is common to both paths. The two paths differ in the mode of removal of the adsorbed hydrogen atoms. In one path, the removal of adsorbed hydrogen atoms is by a combination of hydrogen atoms (atomic hydrogen-desorption path) and in the other a hydroxonium ion discharges on the adsorbed atomic hydrogen to form molecular hydrogen. In acid solution, the two paths may be expressed by the following equations:

Discharge-recombination path:

$$H_3O^+ + e_0^- + M \rightarrow MH + H_2O \tag{10.3}$$

$$2MH \rightarrow 2M + H_2 \tag{10.4}$$

Discharge-electrochemical desorption path:

$$H_3O^+ + e_0^- + M \rightarrow MH + H_2O \tag{10.3}$$

$$H_3O^+ + e_0^- + MH \rightarrow M + H_2 + H_2O \tag{10.5}$$

In alkaline solutions, the discharging entity is the water molecule.

With mercury in alkaline solution, Bockris and Watson[112] showed that the charge-transfer reaction is the deposition of the alkali metal ion on the mercury to form an amalgam, which is followed by its irreversible reaction with water molecules to produce hydrogen.

$$Na^+ + e_0^- + xHg \rightarrow NaHg_x \tag{10.6}$$

$$2NaHg_x + 2H_2O \rightarrow 2NaOH + 2HgH + (2x - 2)Hg \tag{10.7}$$

$$2HgH \rightarrow 2Hg + H_2 \tag{10.8}$$

The above mechanism, for the hydrogen-evolution reaction in alkaline solution, probably applies to other high overpotential metals (for example, Pb, Sn, Tl) as well.

Horiuti and coworkers[113] proposed another path for the high overpotential metals (for example, Hg, Pb, Sn) in acid solution. The preliminary discharge step (10.3) is followed by the formation of a hydrogen-molecule ion. The final step of the discharge of the hydrogen-molecule ion was considered to be rate-determining. The reaction scheme may be represented by

$$H_3O^+ + e_0^- + M \rightarrow MH + H_2O \tag{10.3}$$

$$H_3O^+ + MH \rightarrow M + H_2^+ \tag{10.9}$$

$$H_2^+ + e_0^- \rightarrow H_2 \tag{10.10}$$

It has been shown that this reaction scheme is not thermodynamically feasible.[50]

In all the above reaction paths, it was assumed that the reaction is activation-controlled. Kandler, Knorr, and Schwitzer[114] suggested that on platinum and palladium in acid solution the activation processes are fast and the overall reaction is governed by the diffusion of molecular hydrogen away from the electrode. This view was also proposed for all platinum groups of metals.[115,116] The reaction path is as follows:

$$H_2O^+ + e_0^- + M \rightarrow MH + H_2O \tag{10.3}$$

$$2MH \rightarrow 2M + H_{2,e} \tag{10.4}$$

$$H_{2,e} \rightarrow H_{2,b} \tag{10.11}$$

where $H_{2,e}$ and $H_{2,b}$ refer to molecular hydrogen at the surface of the electrode and in the bulk of the solution, respectively. Recent work has shown that it is unlikely that step (10.11) is rate-determining on the noble metals[50] if they are activated to an extent corresponding to an $i_0 < 10^{-3}$ amp cm^{-2}. If i_0 is made higher than this, the electrode reactions become fast enough for reaction (10.11) to become rate-determining.

10.1.1.3 Present Position of Knowledge of Mechanisms. The theoretically forecast mechanism indicating criteria for the discharge-recombination [Eqs. (10.3) and (10.4)] and the discharge-electrochemical desorption paths [Eqs. (10.3) and (10.5)] are shown in Table 2. The detailed methods of deriving these predicted kinetic parameters have been treated either in Secs. 3.6.5 to 3.6.7 or elsewhere as indicated in the table.

The table shows that it is easy to distinguish the slow recombination mechanism from the other mechanisms. However, there are only a few mechanism-indicating criteria which distinguish the slow discharge from the slow electrochemical desorption mechanism.

A difficulty in some of the methods (viz., stoichiometric numbers and variation of coverage of hydrogen with potential) shown in Table 2 is that they involve measurements in the low-overpotential ($|\eta| \ll |RT/F|$) range or even anodic measurements. These are not possible in the case of a number of metals, particularly the transition metals in acid solution, because of competing reactions (metal dissolution, oxide formation). A method that has been found to be very useful in uniquely fixing the mechanism is by a determination of separation factors.[50,117–119] The advantage of this method is that separation factors can be determined over any desired range of potentials of the electrode. The hydrogen-tritium separation factor on an electrode is defined as the ratio

TABLE 2 Theoretically Forecast Kinetic Parameters for the Most Probable Mechanisms of the Hydrogen-evolution Reaction

Mechanism	Condition $\theta \to 0$ $\dfrac{\partial \eta}{\partial \ln i}$	$\dfrac{\partial \eta}{\partial \ln a_{H_3O^+}}$	$\dfrac{\partial \eta}{\partial \ln p_{H_2}}$	$\dfrac{\partial \eta}{\partial \ln \theta}$	Condition $\theta \to 1$ $\dfrac{\partial \eta}{\partial \ln i}$	$\dfrac{\partial \eta}{\partial \ln a_{H_3O^+}}$	$\dfrac{\partial \eta}{\partial \ln p_{H_2}}$	$\dfrac{\partial \eta}{\partial \ln \theta}$	ν	S_T
Slow discharge–fast recombination	$-\dfrac{RT}{\beta F}$	$\dfrac{RT}{F}$	$\dfrac{RT}{2F}$	0	$-\dfrac{RT}{\beta F}$	$\dfrac{RT}{F}$	$-\dfrac{RT}{2F}\dfrac{(1-\beta)}{\beta}$	0	2	$5^{[117]}$
Fast discharge–slow recombination	$-\dfrac{RT}{2F}$	0	$\dfrac{RT}{2F}$	$-\dfrac{RT}{F}$	∞	0	$\dfrac{RT}{2F}$	0	1	$11^{[119]}$
Coupled discharge–recombination	$-\dfrac{RT}{\beta F}$	$\dfrac{RT}{F}$	$\dfrac{RT}{2F}$	$\dfrac{2RT^{[121]}}{\beta F}$	$-\dfrac{RT}{\beta F}$	$\dfrac{RT}{F}$	$-\dfrac{RT}{2F}\dfrac{(1-\beta)}{\beta}$	$-\infty$	1	$5^{[117]}$
Slow discharge–fast electrochemical desorption	$-\dfrac{RT}{\beta F}$	$\dfrac{RT}{F}$	$\dfrac{RT}{2F}$	$+\dfrac{RT}{F}$	$-\dfrac{RT}{(1+\beta)F}$	$\dfrac{(1-\beta)}{(1+\beta)}\dfrac{RT}{F}$	$-\dfrac{RT}{2F}\dfrac{(1-\beta)}{(1+\beta)}$	0	1	$6^{[117]}$
Fast discharge–slow electrochemical desorption	$-\dfrac{RT}{(1+\beta)F}$	$\dfrac{(1-\beta)}{(1+\beta)}\dfrac{RT}{F}$	$\dfrac{RT}{2F}$	$\dfrac{RT}{F}$	$-\dfrac{RT}{\beta F}$	$\dfrac{RT}{F}$	$\dfrac{RT}{2F}$	0	1	$23^{[118]}$
Coupled discharge–electrochemical desorption	$-\dfrac{RT}{\beta F}$	$\dfrac{RT}{F}$	$\dfrac{RT}{2F}$	$0^{[121]}$	$-\dfrac{RT}{\beta F}$	$\dfrac{RT}{F}$	$\dfrac{RT}{2F}$	0	1	$7^{[117]}$
Slow molecular hydrogen-ion discharge	$-\dfrac{RT}{(1+\beta)F}$	$\dfrac{(1-\beta)}{(1+\beta)}\dfrac{RT}{F}$	$\dfrac{RT}{2F}$	$-\dfrac{RT}{F}$	$-\dfrac{RT}{\beta F}$	$\dfrac{RT}{F}$	$\dfrac{RT}{2F}$	0	1	$6^{[122]}$
Slow molecular hydrogen diffusion	$-\dfrac{RT}{2F}$	0		$-\dfrac{RT}{F}$	∞	0		0	1	$8^{[50]}$

TABLE 3 Experimental Kinetic Parameters and Mechanistic Conclusions for the Hydrogen-evolution Reaction on Some Metals in Acid Media

Metal	$\left(\dfrac{\partial \eta}{\partial \ln i}\right)_{T,\,a_{H^+},\,P_{H_2}}$	$\left(\dfrac{\partial \eta}{\partial \ln a_{H_3O^+}}\right)_{T,\,i,\,P_{H_2}}$	$\left(\dfrac{\partial \eta}{\partial \ln P_{H_2}}\right)_{T,\,i,\,a_{H_3O^+}}$	Stoichiometric number v	Hydrogen-tritium separation factor S_T at current density of $10^{-2}\ amp\ cm^{-2}$	Mechanistic conclusions[50]
Hg	$-\dfrac{2RT}{F}$	$\dfrac{RT}{F}$	$\dfrac{RT}{2F}$		5.8 ± 0.3	Slow discharge–fast electrochemical desorption
Pb	$-\dfrac{2RT}{F}$	$\dfrac{RT}{F}$	$\dfrac{RT}{2F}$		6.7 ± 0.7	Slow discharge–fast electrochemical desorption
Cu	$-\dfrac{2RT}{F}$	$\dfrac{RT}{F}$	$\dfrac{RT}{2F}$		18.1 ± 2.4	Fast discharge–slow electrochemical desorption
Ni	$-\dfrac{2RT}{F}$	$\dfrac{RT}{F}$	$\dfrac{RT}{2F}$		18.0 ± 0.9	Fast discharge–slow electrochemical desorption
Pt	$-\dfrac{RT}{2F}$		$\dfrac{RT}{2F}$	1	9.6 ± 0.4	Fast discharge–slow recombination
Rh	$-\dfrac{RT}{2F}$		$\dfrac{RT}{2F}$	1	10.7 ± 0.4	Fast discharge–slow recombination

of atomic concentrations of hydrogen to tritium in the electrolytically evolved hydrogen on the electrode to that in the electrolyte that contains the two isotopic species.

The experimentally determined values of the kinetic parameters in the case of some typical metals are presented in Table 3. The last column of Table 3 also shows the probable mechanisms in these cases as predicted from the theoretically forecast kinetic parameters for the various mechanisms (Table 2). As stated previously, the separation-factor method is the single most useful method in uniquely fixing the mechanism. The technique of determining separation factors is also relatively simple[50a] (Chap. 9).

The dependence of overpotential (at a constant current density) on the strength of the M-H bond (where M represents a metal) for a number of metals is a useful mechanism-indicating criterion[120] (Fig. 38). In the case of the slow

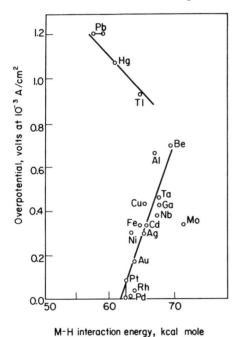

Figure 38 Overpotential for hydrogen evolution at 10^{-3} amp cm^{-2} vs. M-H bond strength for some metals.[120]

discharge mechanism, the M-H bond is being formed during this slow step. Thus, increase in bond strength should lower the overpotential at a constant current density (Chap. 6). The opposite behavior should be expected for the slow electrochemical desorption mechanism where the M-H bond is being broken. Figure 38 shows this predicted behavior.

10.1.2 Anodic Reaction

The theoretically forecast kinetic parameters for the most probable mechanisms are found in Table 4. Hydrogen dissolution is the commonest anodic reaction

TABLE 4 Theoretically Forecast Kinetic Parameters for the Most Probable Mechanism of the Hydrogen-dissolution Reaction

Mechanism	Condition $\theta \to 0$			Condition $\theta \to 1$			ν
	$\dfrac{\partial \eta}{\partial \ln i}$	$\dfrac{\partial \eta}{\partial \ln p_{H_2}}$	$\dfrac{\partial \eta}{\partial \ln \theta}$	$\dfrac{\partial \eta}{\partial \ln i}$	$\dfrac{\partial \eta}{\partial \ln p_{H_2}}$	$\dfrac{\partial \eta}{\partial \ln \theta}$	
Slow discharge–fast recombination	$\dfrac{RT}{(1-\beta)F}$	$\dfrac{RT}{2F(1-\beta)}$	0	$\dfrac{RT}{(1-\beta)F}$	$\dfrac{RT}{2F}$	0	2
Fast discharge–slow recombination	∞		$-\dfrac{RT}{F}$	$\dfrac{RT}{2F}$	0	0	1
Slow discharge–fast electrochemical desorption	$\dfrac{RT}{(2-\beta)F}$	$-\dfrac{RT}{2F}\dfrac{\beta}{(2-\beta)}$	$+\dfrac{RT}{F}$	$\dfrac{RT}{(1-\beta)F}$	$\dfrac{RT}{2F}$	0	1
Fast discharge–slow electrochemical desorption	$\dfrac{RT}{(1-\beta)F}$	$\dfrac{RT(1+\beta)}{2F(1-\beta)}$	$-\dfrac{RT}{F}$	$\dfrac{RT}{(2-\beta)F}$	$-\dfrac{RT}{2F}\dfrac{\beta}{(2-\beta)}$	0	1
Slow molecular hydrogen-ion discharge	$\dfrac{RT}{(1-\beta)F}$	$\dfrac{RT(1+\beta)}{2F(1-\beta)}$	$-\dfrac{RT}{F}$	$\dfrac{RT}{(2-\beta)F}$	$-\dfrac{RT}{2F}\dfrac{\beta}{(2-\beta)}$	0	1
Slow molecular hydrogen diffusion	∞		$-\dfrac{RT}{F}$	$\dfrac{RT}{2F}$		0	1

in electrochemical energy conversion. However, studies of it have been limited mainly because there are competing anodic reactions (corrosion, oxide formations) in the case of many metals, particularly in acid solution. The noble metals may be used both in acid and alkaline medium, since for them the potentials at which these irrelevant anodic reactions take place are more anodic than, and clearly separated from, those in which the hydrogen-dissolution reaction takes place at rates less than the limiting current density for this reaction. It is possible to carry out this reaction on several nonnoble metals (including some transition metals) in *alkaline* solution.

The question arises whether any conclusions of the mechanism of the anodic dissolution reaction for hydrogen may be drawn from the large amount of work done for the corresponding cathodic reaction on many metals. From the principle of microscopic reversibility,[123] it follows that the mechanism of the cathodic and anodic reactions must be the same at the reversible potential. Further, since the cathodic and anodic Tafel lines intersect at the thermodynamic reversible potential for the overall reaction in the case of the few systems[124,125] where both reactions have been studied, the mechanisms of both reactions must be the same for these metals over the potential range of the Tafel lines. Until more direct determinations are made of the mechanism of the anodic dissolution of hydrogen, one may tentatively extend this assumption to other metals and to potential regions outside the reversible one, and hence infer rate-determining steps in dissolution on them from results such as those of Table 3.

10.2 Mechanism of Iron Deposition and Dissolution

10.2.1 Overall Reaction

A clear demonstration of the elucidation of a rate-determining step is given by the reaction of iron deposition and dissolution.[126] The overall dissolution reaction is

$$Fe \rightarrow Fe^{2+} + 2e_0^- \tag{10.12}$$

which has been verified by allowing the reaction to proceed in a solution of dilute sulfuric acid and quantitatively analyzing the solution thereafter for its Fe^{2+} concentration. The number of electrons transferred in the overall reaction was shown to be two by the relation of the quantity of electricity passed to the amount of Fe^{2+} formed (Faraday's law). The deposition reaction is represented by the reverse of Eq. (10.12).

10.2.2 Theoretically Forecast Parameters for Various Possible Mechanisms and the Experimentally Observed Values

The theoretically forecast parameters for the various proposed mechanisms are tabulated in Table 5.[126] The experimentally observed parameters are shown in Table 6.[126]

TABLE 5 Theoretically Forecast Kinetic Parameters for Various Possible Mechanisms of the Iron-deposition Reaction[126]

Reaction path	Rate-determining step	Cathodic Tafel slope $\left(\dfrac{\partial\eta}{\partial\ln i}\right)$	Reaction order with respect to Fe²⁺ $\left(\dfrac{\partial\ln i}{\partial\ln a_{Fe^{2+}}}\right)_{V,\,a_{OH^-}}$	Reaction order with respect to OH⁻ $\left(\dfrac{\partial\ln i}{\partial\ln a_{OH^-}}\right)_{V,\,a_{Fe^{2+}}}$	Variation of potential with OH⁻ concentration $\left(\dfrac{\partial V}{\partial\ln a_{OH^-}}\right)_{a_{Fe^{2+}}}$
$Fe^{2+} + OH^- \rightleftharpoons FeOH^+$ $FeOH^+ + e_0^- \rightarrow FeOH$ $FeOH + e_0^- \rightleftharpoons Fe + OH^-$	$FeOH^+ + e_0^- \rightarrow FeOH$	$-\dfrac{2RT}{F}$	1	$-\dfrac{1}{2}$	$\dfrac{RT}{F}$
$Fe^{2+} + OH^- + e_0^- \rightleftharpoons FeOH$ $Fe^{2+} + FeOH + 2e_0^- \rightarrow Fe_2OH$ $Fe_2OH \rightleftharpoons 2Fe + OH_{ads}$ $OH_{ads} + e_0^- \rightleftharpoons OH^-$	$Fe^{2+} + FeOH + 2e_0^- \rightarrow Fe_2OH$	$-\dfrac{RT}{2F}$	2	$-\dfrac{3}{5}$	$-\dfrac{4RT}{5F}$
$Fe^{2+} + H_2O + e_0^- \rightleftharpoons FeOH + H^+$ $Fe^{2+} + FeOH + e_0^- \rightleftharpoons Fe_2OH^+$ $Fe_2OH^+ \rightarrow FeOH^+ + Fe$ $FeOH^+ + e_0^- \rightleftharpoons FeOH$ $FeOH + H^+ + e_0^- \rightleftharpoons Fe + H_2O$	$Fe_2OH^+ \rightarrow FeOH^+ + Fe$	$-\dfrac{RT}{2F}$	2	$-\dfrac{3}{5}$	$-\dfrac{4RT}{5F}$
$Fe^{2+} + OH^- \rightleftharpoons FeOH^+$ $FeOH^+ + 2e_0^- \rightarrow Fe + OH^-$	$FeOH^+ + 2e_0^- \rightarrow Fe + OH^-$	$-\dfrac{RT}{F}$	1	$-\dfrac{1}{3}$	$-\dfrac{4RT}{3F}$
$Fe^{2+} + 2OH^- \rightleftharpoons Fe(OH)_2$ $Fe(OH)_2 + 2e_0^- \rightarrow Fe + 2OH^-$	$Fe(OH)_2 + 2e_0^- \rightarrow Fe + 2OH^-$	$-\dfrac{RT}{F}$	1	0	$-\dfrac{2RT}{F}$
$Fe^{2+} + 2OH^- \rightleftharpoons Fe(OH)_2$ $Fe(OH)_2 + OH^- \rightleftharpoons HFeO_2^- + H_2O$ $HFeO_2^- \rightleftharpoons FeO + OH^-$ $FeO + H_2O + e_0^- \rightarrow FeOH + OH^-$ $FeOH + e_0^- \rightleftharpoons Fe + OH^-$	$FeO + H_2O + e_0^- \rightarrow$ $FeOH + OH^-$	$-\dfrac{2RT}{F}$	1	$-\dfrac{1}{4}$	$\dfrac{3RT}{2F}$

Table 6   Some Experimental Parameters for the Iron-deposition Reaction[126]

Tafel slope $\left(\dfrac{d\eta}{d\ln i}\right)$	*Reaction order with respect to* Fe^{2+} $\left(\dfrac{\partial \ln i}{\partial \ln a_{a_{Fe^{2+}}}}\right)_{V,\,a_{OH^-}}$	*Reaction order with respect to* OH^- $\left(\dfrac{\partial \ln i}{\partial \ln a_{OH^-}}\right)_{V,\,a_{Fe^{2+}}}$	*Variation of potential with* a_{OH^-} $\left(\dfrac{\partial V}{\partial \ln a_{OH^-}}\right)_{a_{Fe^{2+}}}$
$-\dfrac{2RT}{F}$	0.8	$-\dfrac{1}{2}$	$-\dfrac{RT}{F}$

10.2.3   Mechanistic Conclusions

From Tables 5 and 6, it is readily seen that the pH effect is an important mechanism-indicating criterion for this reaction. Mechanism 1 in Table 5 is the only one in agreement with experiment.

10.3   Electrochemical Mechanisms of Some Chemical Reactions

10.3.1   General

There are a number of reactions catalyzed by metal or semiconductor catalysts which are generally regarded as proceeding by a chemical path, but which take place via an electrochemical path, as will be seen in the reactions considered in the following sections.

10.3.2   Reduction of Nitrobenzene by Hydrogen

Nitrobenzene is reduced by bubbling hydrogen through an aqueous solution of nitrobenzene in the presence of platinum black as a catalyst. In the electrochemical reduction, products are found to depend on the potential of the platinum electrode.[127] In the chemical case, the reaction probably proceeds by ionization of hydrogen on the platinum black catalyst yielding hydrogen ions and electrons. The latter are supplied to the nitrobenzene causing its reduction.

10.3.3   Reduction of Titanium Chloride by Magnesium

Addition of magnesium to a molten salt eutectic of KCl-LiCl containing $TiCl_3$ reduces the latter. It is probable that this reaction proceeds by the scheme

$$Mg \rightarrow Mg^{2+} + 2e_0^- \tag{10.13}$$

$$TiCl_3 + 3e_0^- \rightarrow Ti + 3Cl^- \tag{10.14}$$

$$Mg^{2+} + 2Cl^- \rightarrow MgCl_2 \tag{10.15}$$

10.3.4   Oxidation of Ti^{3+} Ions by Iodine

When an iodine solution (I_3^-) is added to a solution containing Ti^{3+} ions, no reaction is apparent. However, if a graphite electrode is introduced into solution, reaction occurs rapidly.[128] The reaction rate is increased even further if powdered graphite is used as catalyst, which is due to an increase in surface area of the catalyst. The isolated graphite electrode probably assumes a mixed potential at which the rate is fast (Fig. 39).

10.3.5   Reductions by Hypophosphorous Acid

The reaction

$$H_3PO_2 + H_2O \rightarrow H_3PO_3 + 2H^+ + 2e_0^- \qquad (10.16)$$

has a standard reversible potential of -0.5 volt and thus H_3PO_2 should be a very strong reducing agent.   The reducing power of H_3PO_2 is slow in the absence of metallic catalysts.   Addition of a small quantity of Pd to a solution of H_3PO_2 in water makes the above reaction proceed with generation of H_2.[128]

Further, mercuric salts are reduced very slowly by hypophosphorous acid. The addition of a small quantity of Ag^+ ion accelerates the rate considerably. It is probable that the acid reduces Ag^+ ion to silver and the silver then acts as a catalyst for the reduction of the mercuric ions which proceeds by an electrochemical mechanism according to the scheme

$$Ag^+ + e_0^- \rightarrow Ag \qquad (10.17)$$

$$\left\{ \begin{array}{l} Ag \rightarrow Ag^+ + e_0^- \qquad (10.18) \\ 2Hg^{2+} + 2e_0^- \rightarrow Hg_2^{2+} \qquad (10.19) \end{array} \right.$$

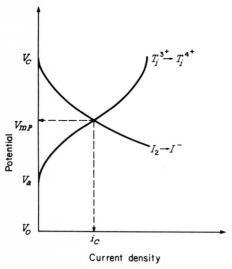

Current density

Figure 39   Mixed potentials arising from simultaneous reduction of I_2 and oxidation of Ti^{3+} on graphite electrode.[128]

11 PARASITIC PHENOMENA—EFFECTS OF TRACE IMPURITIES

Traces of impurities, which are electrochemically active, are generally present in solutions, normally regarded as pure. In studying some electrochemical reactions with a low exhange current density, e.g., hydrogen evolution on lead and oxygen evolution on platinum, impurities have a marked effect on the over-potential–current-density relations for these reactions. For example, in the presence of oxygen (concentration 10^{-4} mole l^{-1}), there is considerable depolarization caused by this impurity on the overpotential–current-density relation for hydrogen evolution on a lead electrode at current densities below 10^{-4} amp cm^{-2} (Fig. 40).

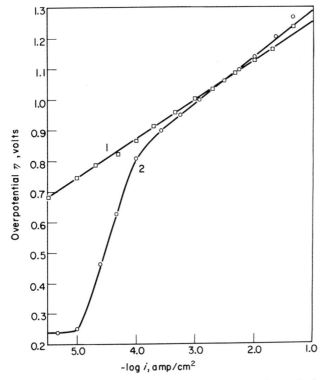

Figure 40   Tafel lines for the hydrogen-evolution reaction on lead from 0.5 N H_2SO_4 at 25°C in the absence (curve 1) and in the presence (curve 2) of an electroactive impurity (oxygen).[29]

One may make a calculation of the extent of purification necessary to avoid depolarization effects. Suppose the reaction under study is one that is activation-controlled with a low exchange current density and the lowest value of the current density at which the Tafel measurements are commenced is i_m. Thus, it is necessary to have

$$i_{L,i} \ll i_m \tag{11.1}$$

assuming that the electrode reaction of the impurity is taking place at its limiting current density $i_{L,i}$, which is given by Eq. (3.127):

$$i_{L,i} = \frac{DnFc_i}{\delta} \tag{11.2}$$

where D is the diffusion coefficient of the impurity in the electrolyte, c_i is its concentration, and δ is the diffusion-layer thickness. Using Eq. (11.2) in inequality (11.1),

$$c_i \ll \frac{\delta}{DnF} i_m \tag{11.3}$$

With $i_m = 10^{-9}$ amp cm^{-2}, $D = 10^{-5}$ cm^2 sec^{-1}, $n = 4$ (say impurity is O_2 in studies of hydrogen evolution on lead), $F = 10^5$ coul, and $\delta = 10^{-3}$ cm (an approximate estimate in mildly stirred solutions), it is necessary for c_i to be less than 2.5×10^{-13} mole cm^{-3} (that is, 2.5×10^{-10} mole l^{-1}) to eliminate de-polarization effects. The concentration of oxygen in air-saturated solutions is of the order of 10^{-4} mole l^{-1}. Thus, for the case exemplified, a purification factor of over 10^6 is necessary.

Electroactive impurities are most commonly removed by preelectrolysis on a scavenger electrode of the same material as the test electrode. The expression for the variation of impurity concentration with time of preelectrolysis[36] may be derived in the following manner. Suppose the impurity is being electrolytically removed from solution at its limiting current density. Thus

$$Ai_{L,i} = -nFV \frac{dc_i}{dt} \tag{11.4}$$

where A is the area of the scavenger electrode and V is the volume of the solution in the scavenger electrode compartment. Using Eq. (11.2) in (11.4) and integrating the resulting equation,

$$c_{i,t} = c_{i,0} \exp\left(-\frac{ADt}{\delta V}\right) \tag{11.5}$$

where $c_{i,0}$ and $c_{i,t}$ are the impurity concentrations in solution at times $t = 0$ and $t = t$, respectively. Thus, in order that the impurity concentration may be reduced by a factor of 10^6 (i.e., from 10^{-4} mole l^{-1} to 10^{-10} mole l^{-1}), on an electrode of area 10 cm^2 and in a cell containing 100 cm^3 of solution, it is necessary to preelectrolyze for a period of at least 4 hr. In practice, pre-electrolysis times of 16 to 72 hr have been used. In some cases, where both the oxidizable and reducible impurities are present, it has been found necessary to use cathodic preelectrolysis followed by anodic preelectrolysis, or vice versa.

From Eq. (11.5), it follows that the conditions necessary for efficient pre-electrolysis are large areas of scavenger electrodes, small volumes of solution, and efficient stirring of solution.

Impurities may also have another type of effect. They may be strongly adsorbed at the active sites and thus reduce the exchange current density of the desired reaction. Impurities may also influence the free energy of adsorption of reactants or intermediates and thereby alter the exchange current density. Bockris and Conway[129] found that concentrations of adsorbable impurities as low as 10^{-10} mole l^{-1} affect the rate of hydrogen evolution on mercury (Fig. 41). Adsorbable impurities (e.g., organic compounds) may also be removed by preelectrolysis. In these cases, it is best to carry out the preelectrolysis at potentials close to the adsorption maximum of the electrode.

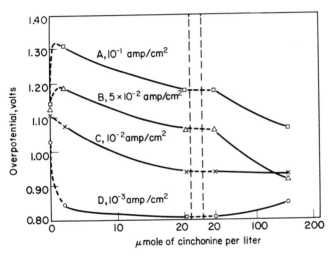

Figure 41 Overpotential as a function of concentration of adsorbable species (cinchonine) at various current densities for the hydrogen-evolution reaction on mercury at 25°C from 0.1 N HCl.[29]

REFERENCES

1. Vetter, K. J.: "Electrochemische Kinetik," Springer-Verlag, Berlin, 1961; English translation, K. J. Vetter, "Electrochemical Kinetics, Theoretical and Experimental Aspects," Academic Press Inc., New York, 1967.
2. Frumkin, A. N.: *J. Electrochem. Soc.*, **107**, 461 (1960).
3. Gierst, L.: Chap. 5, in E. Yeager (ed.), "Transactions of the Symposium on Electrode Processes," John Wiley & Sons, Inc., New York, 1961.
4. Parsons, R., and M. A. V. Devanathan: *Trans. Faraday Soc.*, **49**, 404 (1953).
5. Parsons, R.: Chap. 3, in J. O'M. Bockris and B. E. Conway (eds.), "Modern Aspects of Electrochemistry," Butterworth & Co. (Publishers), Ltd., London, 1954.

6. Delahay, P.: "Double Layer and Electrode Kinetics," Interscience Publishers, Inc., New York, 1965.

7. Grahame, D. C.: *Chem. Rev.*, **41**, 441 (1947).

8. Quincke, G.: *Pogg. Ann.*, **113**, 513 (1861).

9. Helmholtz, H.: *W. Abhandl. Physik. Tech. Reichsanstalt*, **1**, 925 (1879).

10. Devanathan, M. A. V.: *Trans. Faraday Soc.*, **50**, 373 (1954).

11. Gouy, A.: *Ann. Chim. Phys.*, **29**, 145 (1903); *Compt. Rend.*, **149**, 654 (1909).

12. Chapman, D. L.: *Phil. Mag.*, **25**, 475 (1913).

13. Bockris, J. O'M., and A. K. N. Reddy: "Essentials of Modern Electrochemistry," Plenum Press, New York, 1969.

14. Stern, O.: *Z. Elektrochem.*, **30**, 508 (1924).

15. Essin, O. A., and B. F. Markov: *Zh. Fiz. Khim.*, **13**, 318 (1939).

16. Grahame, D. C.: *J. Electrochem. Soc.*, **98**, 313 (1951).

17. Devanathan, M. A. V.: *Trans. Faraday Soc.*, **50**, 373 (1954).

18. Lange, E., and K. P. Mischenko: *Z. Physik. Chem.*, **149**, 1 (1930).

19. Bockris, J. O'M., and E. C. Potter: *J. Chem. Phys.*, **20**, 614 (1952).

20. Bockris, J. O'M., M. A. V. Devanathan, and K. Müller: *Proc. Roy. Soc., Ser. A*, **274**, 55 (1963).

21. Kober, F. P., and D. D. Fitts: *Electrochim. Acta*, **11**, 641 (1966).

22. Butler, J. A. V.: *Proc. Roy. Soc., Ser. A*, **122**, 399 (1929).

23. Wroblowa, H., Z. Kovac, and J. O'M. Bockris: *Trans. Faraday Soc.*, **61**, 511 (1965).

23a. Bockris, J. O'M., E. Gileadi, and K. Müller: *Electrochim. Acta*, **12**, 1301, 1967.

23b. Wroblowa, H., and K. Müller: *J. Phys. Chem.*, in press.

24. Bockris, J. O'M., M. Green, and D. A. J. Swinkels: *J. Electrochem. Soc.*, **111**, 743 (1964).

25. Bockris, J. O'M., and D. A. J. Swinkels: *J. Electrochem. Soc.*, **111**, 736 (1964).

26. Brattain, W. H., and C. G. B. Garret: *Ann. N.Y. Acad. Sci.*, **58**, 951 (1954).

27. Johnson, J. W., H. Wroblowa, and J. O'M. Bockris: *Electrochim. Acta*, **9**, 639 (1964).

27a. Bagotzky, V. S., and Yu. B. Vassilyev: *Electrochim. Acta*, **12**, 1323 (1967); M. W. Breiter, *J. Electroanal. Chem.*, **14**, 407 (1967); **15**, 221 (1967); **19**, 131 (1968).

28. Buck, R. P., and L. R. Griffith: *J. Electrochem. Soc.*, **109**, 1005 (1962).

29. Srinivasan, S.: Doctoral dissertation, University of Pennsylvania, Philadelphia, 1963.

30. Christiansen, J.: *Z. Physik. Chem., Ser. B*, **33**, 145 (1936); *Ser. B*, **37**, 374 (1937).

31. Glasstone, S., K. J. Laidler, and H. Eyring: "The Theory of Rate Processes," McGraw-Hill Book Company, New York, 1941.

32. Parsons, R.: *J. Chim. Phys.*, **49**, C82 (1952).

33. Laidler, K. J.: "Chemical Kinetics," McGraw-Hill Book Company, New York, 1966.

34. Bockris, J. O'M.: *J. Electrochem. Soc.*, **98**, 153c (1951).

35. Bowden, F. P., and E. K. Rideal: *Proc. Roy. Soc., Ser. A*, **120**, 59 (1928).

36. Bockris, J. O'M.: Chap. 4, in J. O'M. Bockris and B. E. Conway (eds.), "Modern Aspects of Electrochemistry," vol. 1, Butterworth & Co. (Publishers), Ltd., London, 1954.

37. Gileadi, E.: *J. Electroanal. Chem.*, **11**, 137 (1966).

38. Eyring, H., S. Glasstone, and K. J. Laidler: *J. Chem. Phys.*, **7**, 1053 (1939).

39. Horiuti, J., and M. Polanyi: *Acta Physicochim. USSR.*, **2**, 505 (1935).

40. Butler, J. A. V.: *Proc. Roy. Soc., Ser. A*, **157**, 423 (1936).

41. Parsons, R., and J. O'M. Bockris: *Trans. Faraday Soc.*, **46**, 914 (1951).

41a. Conway, B. E., and J. O'M. Bockris: *Proc. Roy. Soc., Ser. A*, **248**, 1394 (1958); *Electrochim. Acta*, **3**, 340 (1961).

42. Vetter, K. J.: *Z. Physik. Chem.*, **194**, 284 (1950); *Z. Elektrochem.*, **55**, 121 (1951).

42a. Parsons, R.: *Trans. Faraday Soc.*, **47**, 1332 (1951).

43. McDonald, J. J., and B. E. Conway: *Proc. Roy. Soc., Ser. A*, **269**, 419 (1962).

44. Tafel, J.: *Z. Physik. Chem.*, **50**, 641 (1905).

45. Horiuti, J., and M. Ikusima: *Proc. Imp. Acad. Tokyo*, **15**, 39 (1939).

45a. Mohilner, D.: *J. Phys. Chem.*, **68**, 623 (1964); D. B. Matthews and J. O'M. Bockris, in J. O'M. Bockris and B. E. Conway (eds.), "Modern Aspects of Electrochemistry," vol. 5, Plenum Press, New York, 1969.

46. Frumkin, A. N.: *Z. Physik Chem.*, **164A**, 121 (1933).

47. Bockris, J. O'M., I. A. Ammar, and A. K. M. S. Huq: *J. Phys. Chem.*, **61**, 879 (1957).

48. Gierst, L.: "Cinétique d'approche et réactions d'électrodes irreversibles," thèse d'agrégation, University of Brussels, Belgium, 1958.

49. Frumkin, A. N.: Chap. 5, in P. Delahay and C. W. Tobias (eds.), "Advances in Electrochemistry and Electrochemical Engineering," vol. 3, Interscience Publishers, Inc., New York, 1963.

50. Bockris, J. O'M., and S. Srinivasan: *Electrochim. Acta*, **9**, 31 (1964).

50a. Bockris, J. O'M., S. Srinivasan, and M. A. V. Devanathan: *J. Electroanal. Chem.*, **6**, 205 (1963).

51. Despic, A., and J. O'M. Bockris: *J. Chem. Phys.*, **32**, 389 (1960).

52. Gurney, R. W.: *Proc. Roy. Soc., Ser. A*, **134**, 137 (1931).

53. Hush, N. S.: *J. Chem. Phys.*, **28**, 962 (1958).

54. Marcus, R. A.: *J. Chem. Phys.*, **24**, 966 (1956); Chap. 13, in E. Yeager (ed.), "Transactions of the Symposium on Electrode Processes," John Wiley & Sons, Inc., New York, 1961.

55. Bockris, J. O'M., and D. B. Matthews: *Proc. Roy. Soc., Ser. A*, **292**, 479 (1966).

56. Richardson, O. W.: *Phil. Mag.*, **23**, 601 (1912); **24**, 740 (1912); **28**, 633 (1914).

57. Moelwyn-Hughes, E. A.: Chap. 4, in "Physical Chemistry," Pergamon Press, New York, 1961.

58. Wigner, E. P.: *Z. Physik. Chem.*, **B19**, 903 (1932).

59. Eckart, C.: *Phys. Rev.*, **35**, 1303 (1930).

60. Bockris, J. O'M., and D. B. Matthews: *J. Chem. Phys.*, **44**, 298 (1966).

60a. Levich, V. G.: Chap. 4, in P. Delahay (ed.), "Advances in Electrochemistry and Electrochemical Engineering," vol. 4, Interscience Publishers, Inc., New York, 1966.

60b. Christov, S. G.: *Electrochim. Acta*, **4**, 306 (1961).

61. Bockris, J. O'M., and D. B. Matthews: *Electrochim. Acta*, **11**, 143 (1966).

62. Nernst, W., and E. S. Merriam: *Z. Physik. Chem.*, **53**, 235 (1905).

63. Delahay, P.: "New Instrumental Methods in Electrochemistry," Interscience Publishers, Inc., New York, 1954.

63a. Bockris, J. O'M., D. Inman, A. K. N. Reddy, and S. Srinivasan: *J. Electroanal. Chem.*, **5**, 476 (1963).

64. Levich, V. G.: "Physicochemical Hydrodynamics," Prentice-Hall, Inc., Englewood Cliffs, N.J., 1962.

64a. Vielstich, W.: *Z. Electrochem.*, **57**, 646 (1953).

65. Green, M.: Chap. 5, in J. O'M. Bockris and B. E. Conway (eds.), "Modern Aspects of Electrochemistry," vol. 2, Butterworth & Co. (Publishers), Ltd., London, 1959.

66. Dewald, J. F.: Chap. 17, in N. B. Hannay (ed.), "Semiconductors," Reinhold Publishing Corporation, New York, 1959.

67. Gerischer, H.: Chap. 4, in P. Delahay and C. W. Tobias (eds.), "Advances in Electrochemistry and Electrochemical Engineering," vol. 1, Interscience Publishers, Inc., New York, 1961.

68. Schokley, W.: "Electrons and Holes in Semiconductors," chap. 12, D. Van Nostrand Company, Inc., Princeton, N.J., 1950; *Bell System Tech. J.*, **28**, 435 (1949).

69. Langmuir, I.: *J. Am. Chem. Soc.*, **40**, 1361 (1918).

70. Henry, W.: *Phil. Trans. Roy. Soc. London*, **29**, 274 (1803).

71. Frumkin, A. N.: *Z. Physik.*, **35**, 792 (1926).

72. Temkin, M. I.: *Zh. Fiz. Khim.*, **15**, 296 (1941).

73. Thomas, J. A.: *Trans. Faraday Soc.*, **57**, 1603 (1961).

74. Conway, B. E., and E. Gileadi: *Trans. Faraday Soc.*, **58**, 2493 (1962).

75. Conway, B. E., and P. L. Bourgault: *Can. J. Chem.*, **40**, 1690 (1962).

76. Dolin, P., and B. Ershler: *Acta Physicochim, USSR*, **13**, 747 (1940).

77. Grahame, D. C.: *J. Electrochem. Soc.*, **99**, 370c (1952).

78. Bockris, J. O'M., and H. Kita: *J. Electrochem. Soc.*, **108**, 676 (1961).

79. Frumkin, A. N., P. Dolin, and B. Ershler: *Acta Physicochim. USSR*, **13**, 779, 793 (1940).

80. Gileadi, E., and B. E. Conway: *J. Chem. Phys.*, **39**, 3420 (1963).

81. Bockris, J. O'M., H. Wroblowa, E. Gileadi, and B. J. Piersma: *Trans. Faraday Soc.*, **61**, 2531 (1965).

82. Delahay, P., and I. Trachtenberg: *J. Am. Chem. Soc.*, **79**, 2355 (1957).

83. Reinmuth, W. H.: *Anal. Chem.*, **65**, 473 (1961).

84. Reddy, A. K. N.: Chap. 4, in E. Gileadi (ed.), "Electrosorption," Plenum Press, New York, 1966.

85. Blomgren, E., J. O'M. Bockris, and C. Jesch: *J. Phys. Chem.*, **65**, 2000 (1961).

86. Gileadi, E., B. T. Rubin, and J. O'M. Bockris: *J. Phys. Chem.*, **69**, 3335 (1965).

87. Wilson, H. A.: "Modern Physics," chap. 4, Blackie & Son Ltd., Glasgow, 1928.

87a. Bailey, D. N., D. M. Hercules, and D. K. Roe: *J. Electrochem. Soc.*, **116**, 190 (1969).

88. Copeland, A. W., O. D. Black, and A. B. Garrett: *Chem. Rev.*, **31**, 177 (1942).

89. Moser, J.: *Mol. Chem.*, **8**, 373 (1887); Rigollof, H.: *Compt. Rend., Acad. Sci. Paris*, **116**, 873 (1893).

90. Thomphson, G. E.: *Phys. Rev.*, **5**, 43 (1915); Stora, C.: *J. Chim. Phys.*, **29**, 168 (1932) and *Compt. Rend. Acad. Sci. Paris*, **202**, 2152 (1936).

91. Eisenberg, M., and H. P. Silverman: *Electrochim. Acta*, **5**, 1 (1961).

92. Fraenkel, W., and H. Heinz: *Z. Anorg. Allgem. Chem.*, **133**, 153 (1924).

93. Zaromb, S. (to Philco Corp.), U.S., 3, 114, 658 (Cl. 136-6), Dec. 17, 1963, Appl. Oct. 22, 1959.

94. Hoar, T. P., and U. R. Evans: *Proc. Roy. Soc., Ser. A*, **137**, 343 (1932).

94a. Fontana, M., and N. D. Greene: "Corrosion Engineering," McGraw-Hill Book Company, New York, 1967.

95. Wagner, C., and W. Traud: *Z. Electrochem.*, **44**, 391 (1938).

96. Uhlig, H.: "Corrosion Handbook," John Wiley & Sons, Inc., New York, 1948.

97. Gellings, P. J.: *Ber. Bunsenges. Physik. Chem.*, **67**, 167 (1963).

98. Pourbaix, M.: "Atlas D'Equilibres Electrochimiques," Gauthier-Villars, Paris,

1963; English translation, M. Pourbaix, "Atlas of Electrochemical Equilibria in Aqueous Solutions," Pergamon Press, New York, 1966.

99. Sieverts, A., and P. Lueg: *Z. Anorg. allgem. Chem.*, **126**, 193 (1923).

100. Hackerman, N., and H. Schmidt: *Corrosion*, **5**, 7, 23 (1949).

101. Antropov, L. I.: "Kinetics of Electrode Processes and Null Points of Metals," Council of Scientific and Industrial Research, New Delhi, 1960.

102. Elze, J., and H. Fisher: *Arch. Metal.*, **12**, 127 (1952).

103. Conway, B. E., J. O'M. Bockris, and B. Lovrecek: *Compt. Rend. CITCE*, **6**, 207 (1955).

104. Vetter, K. J.: Chap. 3, in E. Yeager (ed.), "Transactions of the Symposium on Electrode Process," John Wiley & Sons, Inc., New York, 1961.

105. Bockris, J. O'M., S. Srinivasan, and D. B. Matthews: *Discussions Faraday Soc.*, **39**, 239 (1965).

106. Frumkin, A. N.: Chap. 2, vol. 1, and chap. 5, vol. 3, in P. Delahay and C. W. Tobias (eds.), "Advances in Electrochemistry and Electrochemical Engineering," Interscience Publishers, Inc., New York, 1961 and 1963.

107. Bockris, J. O'M., and A. Damjanovic: Chap. 4, in J. O'M. Bockris and B. E. Conway (eds.), "Modern Aspects of Electrochemistry," vol. 3, Butterworth & Company (Publishers), Ltd., London, 1964.

108. Piersma, B. J., and E. Gileadi: Chap. 4, in J. O'M. Bockris (ed.), "Modern Aspects of Electrochemistry," vol. 4, Plenum Press, New York, 1966.

109. Bagotski, V. S., and U. B. Vasylev: *Electrochim. Acta*, **9**, 869 (1964).

109a. Bowden, F. P., and E. K. Rideal: *Proc. Roy. Soc.*, *Ser. A*, **120**, 59, 80 (1928).

109b. Norrish, R. G. W., and G. Porter: *Discussions of Faraday Society*, **17**, 40 (1954).

110. Gileadi, E., and S. Srinivasan: *J. Electroanal. Chem.*, **7**, 452 (1964).

111. Davis, M. O., M. Clark, E. Yeager, and F. Horvoka: *J. Electrochem. Soc.*, **106**, 56 (1959).

112. Bockris, J. O'M., and R. G. H. Watson: *J. Chim. Phys.*, **49**, 1 (1952).

113. Horiuti, J., T. Keii, and K. Hirota: *J. Res. Inst. Catalysis, Hokkaido Univ.* **2**, 1 (1951–53).

114. Kandler, L., C. A. Knorr, and C. Schwitzer: *Z. Physik. Chem.*, **180**, 281 (1937).

115. Breiter, M., and R. Clamroth: *Z. Elektrochem.*, **58**, 493 (1954).

116. Breiter, M.: Chap. 17, in E. Yeager (ed.), "Transactions of the Symposium on Electrode Processes," John Wiley & Sons, Inc., New York, 1961.

117. Bockris, J. O'M., and S. Srinivasan: *J. Electrochem. Soc.*, **111**, 844 (1964).

118. Bockris, J. O'M., and S. Srinivasan: *J. Electrochem. Soc.*, **111**, 853 (1964).

119. Bockris, J. O'M., and S. Srinivasan: *J. Electrochem. Soc.*, **111**, 858 (1964).

120. Conway, B. E., and J. O'M. Bockris: *J. Chem. Phys.*, **26**, 532 (1957).

121. Devanathan, M. A. V., J. O'M. Bockris, and W. Mehl: *J. Electroanal. Chem.*, **1**, 143 (1959/60).

122. Horiuti, J.: *J. Res. Inst. Catalysis, Hokkaido Univ.*, **4**, 55 (1956).

123. Frost, A. A., and R. G. Pearson: "Kinetics and Mechanism," John Wiley & Sons, Inc., New York, 1965.

124. Schuldiner, S.: *J. Electrochem. Soc.*, **106**, 891 (1959).

125. Schuldiner, S.: *J. Electrochem. Soc.*, **107**, 452 (1960).

126. Drazic, D., A. Despic, and J. O'M. Bockris: *Electrochim. Acta*, **4**, 325 (1961).

127. Haber, F.: *Z. Elektrochem.*, **4**, 506 (1898).

128. Goursier, J.: thesis, Masson, Paris, 1954.

129. Bockris, J. O'M., and B. E. Conway: *Nature*, **159**, 711 (1947).

CHAPTER THREE

Thermodynamic Aspects of Electrochemical Energy Conversion

1 ESSENTIALS OF BASIC THERMODYNAMICS

1.1 General

The field of chemical thermodynamics is a well-developed one. Since it has been treated excellently in several books,[1-6] basic thermodynamics will not be dealt with in detail in this chapter. In the succeeding subsections, a brief summary of the essentials in basic thermodynamics, required by the fuel-cell worker, is outlined. The references quoted above are useful for the reader interested in a further knowledge of this field.

1.2 Thermodynamic Functions

The basic functions in thermodynamics are internal energy E, enthalpy H, entropy S, Helmholtz free energy A, and Gibbs free energy G. The relations between these quantities are given by

$$H = E + PV \tag{1.1}$$

$$A = E - TS \tag{1.2}$$

$$G = H - TS \tag{1.3}$$

where P, V, and T denote pressure, volume, and temperature of the system, respectively. The thermodynamic functions E, H, S, A, and G are extensive properties of a system. Extensive properties of a system are first-order homogeneous functions of the corresponding properties of the components of the system (i.e., they depend on the quantity of matter specified in the system). P and T are intensive properties of a system. Intensive properties are zero-order homogeneous functions of the corresponding properties of the components of a system (i.e., they do not depend on the quantity of matter specified in the system).

1.3 The Laws of Thermodynamics

The essence of thermodynamics is contained in the three laws of thermodynamics. Several formulations have been given for these laws. They appear to be best stated in the following:

The first law of thermodynamics: The total energy of an isolated system must remain constant, although there may be changes from one form to another.

The second law of thermodynamics: It is impossible to construct a machine, operating in cycles, which can convert heat into an equivalent amount of work.

The third law of thermodynamics: Every substance has a finite positive entropy, but at the absolute zero of temperature the entropy may become zero and does so become in the case of a perfectly crystalline substance.

1.4 Chemical Potential

Since thermodynamic functions are extensive properties of the system, they would depend on the composition of the system. Thus, in a system that consists of n_1 moles of species 1, n_2 moles of species 2, etc., the free energies A and G may be expressed by

$$A = f(V, T, n_1, n_2, \ldots) \tag{1.4}$$

$$G = f(P, T, n_1, n_2, \ldots) \tag{1.5}$$

and the chemical potential μ_i of the ith species is given by

$$\mu_i = \left(\frac{\partial A}{\partial n_i} \right)_{T,V,n_j} \qquad \neq i \tag{1.6}$$

$$\mu_i = \left(\frac{\partial G}{\partial n_i} \right)_{T,P,n} \qquad j \neq i \tag{1.7}$$

Another name for the chemical potential of the ith species is partial molar free energy of the ith species, and it represents the increase in Helmholtz free energy or Gibbs free energy of the mixture at constant temperature and volume (or pressure) with the addition of 1 mole of the ith constituent of the mixture while the composition of the other constituents remains unchanged.

1.5 Thermodynamics of Chemical Reactions

1.5.1 Free-energy Change of a Chemical Reaction

Since it is more practical to carry out reactions at a constant temperature and pressure rather than at constant temperature and volume, the change in Gibbs free energy is more useful than the change in Helmholtz free energy.

The Gibbs free-energy change ΔG of the reaction

$$a\mathrm{A} + b\mathrm{B} \rightarrow c\mathrm{C} + d\mathrm{D} \tag{1.8}$$

is given by the equation

$$\Delta G = c\mu_C + d\mu_D - a\mu_A - b\mu_B \tag{1.9}$$

where the μ's are the chemical potentials of the indicated species.

The free-energy change of a chemical reaction is a measure of the maximum net work obtainable from the reaction.   It is equal to the enthalpy change of the reaction only if the entropy change of the reaction ΔS is zero, as may be seen from the equation

$$\Delta G = \Delta H - T \Delta S \tag{1.10}$$

In this connection, it is interesting to note that if in a chemical reaction the number of moles of gaseous products and reactants are equal, the entropy change of such a reaction is effectively zero.   This is because the main contribution to the entropy change in a reaction is due to changes in translational entropies, and this is zero for a reaction involving no change in the number of molecules in the gas phase during the reaction.   An example of a chemical reaction of this type is the oxidation of carbon to carbon dioxide:

$$C + O_2 \rightarrow CO_2 \tag{1.11}$$

If the number of moles of gaseous products exceeds that of the gaseous reactants, the entropy change of the reaction is positive as a result of the increase in translational modes.   Oxidation of carbon to carbon monoxide serves as a good example of this type:

$$2C + O_2 \rightarrow 2CO \tag{1.12}$$

For such a reaction, it follows from Eq. (1.10) that the free-energy change is more negative than the enthalpy change of the reaction.

More common are reactions in which the number of moles of gaseous reactants exceeds that of products.   In such cases, the entropy change is negative.   The free-energy change is less negative than the enthalpy change for such a reaction.   The gas-phase reaction between hydrogen and oxygen to produce water is one of this type:

$$2H_2 + O_2 \rightarrow 2H_2O \tag{1.13}$$

(The free-energy and enthalpy changes for the various types of reactions are presented in Table 2, page 158.)

1.5.2   Standard Free-energy Change of a Chemical Reaction

The chemical potential of any substance may be expressed by an equation of the form

$$\mu = \mu^0 + RT \ln a \tag{1.14}$$

where a is the activity of the substance and μ has the value μ^0 when a is unity. The standard free-energy change ΔG^0 of the reaction (1.9) is then given by

Eq. (1.9), with the chemical potentials of all species replaced by their standard chemical potentials:

$$\Delta G^0 = c\mu_C^0 + d\mu_D^0 - a\mu_A^0 - b\mu_B^0 \tag{1.15}$$

Substitution of Eq. (1.14) for each of the reactants and products and Eq. (1.15) into Eq. (1.9) gives

$$\Delta G = \Delta G^0 + RT \ln \frac{a_C^c a_D^d}{a_A^a a_B^b} \tag{1.16}$$

For a process at constant temperature and pressure at equilibrium, the free-energy change is zero. Thus, with the free-energy change as zero in Eq. (1.16), it follows that

$$\Delta G^0 = -RT \ln \frac{a_{C,e}^c a_{D,e}^d}{a_{A,e}^a a_{B,e}^b} \tag{1.17}$$

$$= -RT \ln K \tag{1.18}$$

The suffixes e in the activity terms indicate the values of the activities at equilibrium, and K is the equilibrium constant for the reaction.

The importance of a knowledge of ΔG^0 is that it allows ΔG to be calculated for any composition of a reaction mixture. Knowledge of ΔG indicates whether a reaction will occur or not. If ΔG is positive, a reaction cannot occur for the assumed composition of reactants and products. If ΔG is negative, a reaction can occur.

1.5.3 Effect of Temperature on Free-energy Change

At any temperature, the free-energy change of a chemical reaction is given by Eq. (1.10). Using the relation

$$\left(\frac{\partial \Delta G}{\partial T}\right)_P = -\Delta S \tag{1.19}$$

Eq. (1.10) becomes

$$\Delta G = \Delta H + T\left(\frac{\partial \Delta G}{\partial T}\right)_P \tag{1.20}$$

Another useful form of Eq. (1.20) can be obtained by utilizing Eq. (1.19) and remembering that ΔS is almost independent of temperature. Dividing Eq. (1.20) by T and subsequent differentiation with respect to T gives

$$\left(\frac{\partial \Delta G/T}{\partial T}\right)_P = -\frac{\Delta H}{T^2} \tag{1.21}$$

Equations (1.20) and (1.21) are referred to as the Gibbs-Helmholtz equations.

The standard free-energy change of a reaction may easily be expressed as a function of temperature by the substitution of $\Delta G = \Delta G^0$ and $\Delta H = \Delta H^0$ in Eqs. (1.20) and (1.21). Since $\Delta G^0 = -RT \ln K$, the variation of the equilibrium constant K with temperature is also obtained.

1.5.4   *Effect of Pressure on Free-energy Change*

From Eq. (1.9), it follows that

$$\left(\frac{\partial \Delta G}{\partial P}\right)_T = c\left(\frac{\partial \mu_C}{\partial P}\right)_T + d\left(\frac{\partial \mu_D}{\partial P}\right)_T - a\left(\frac{\partial \mu_A}{\partial P}\right)_T - b\left(\frac{\partial \mu_B}{\partial P}\right)_T \tag{1.22}$$

Also,

$$\left(\frac{\partial \mu_i}{\partial P}\right)_T = \left(\frac{\partial}{\partial P}\right)_T\left(\frac{\partial G}{\partial n_i}\right) = \left(\frac{\partial^2 G}{\partial P\, \partial n_i}\right)_{T,n_j} = \left(\frac{\partial^2 G}{\partial n_i\, \partial P}\right)_{T,n_j} \qquad n_j \neq n_i \tag{1.23}$$

and

$$\left(\frac{\partial G}{\partial P}\right)_T = V \tag{1.24}$$

Thus, using Eq. (1.24) in Eq. (1.23),

$$\left(\frac{\partial \mu_i}{\partial P}\right)_T = \left(\frac{\partial V}{\partial n_i}\right)_{n_j} = \bar{V}_i \qquad n_j \neq n_i \tag{1.25}$$

where $\bar{V}_i$ is the partial molar volume of the ith constituent of the mixture.   Thus, introducing Eq. (1.25) into Eq. (1.22),

$$\left(\frac{\partial \Delta G}{\partial P}\right)_T = c\bar{V}_C + d\bar{V}_D - a\bar{V}_A - b\bar{V}_B \tag{1.26}$$

If the reactants are gases and the products liquids ($\bar{V}_C$ and $\bar{V}_D \ll \bar{V}_A$ and $\bar{V}_B$, as for the H_2-O_2 fuel cell), the net change in partial molar volumes will be considerable, i.e., there will be a significant pressure dependence of ΔG.

If in a gaseous reaction reactants and products behave ideally, it follows that

$$V = (n_A + n_B + n_C + n_D)\frac{RT}{P} = \sum n_i \frac{RT}{P} \tag{1.27}$$

Thus, the partial molar volume of any component, i, of an ideal gas mixture is given by

$$\left(\frac{\partial V}{\partial n_i}\right)_{n_j} = \frac{RT}{P}$$

$$= \bar{V}_i \qquad \text{where } i = \text{A, B, C, or D and } j \neq i \tag{1.28}$$

Substitution of an equation of the form (1.28) for each of the species into Eq. (1.26) gives

$$\left(\frac{\partial \Delta G}{\partial P}\right)_T = \Delta n \frac{RT}{P} \tag{1.29}$$

where:

$$\Delta n = c + d - a - b$$
$$= n_C + n_D - n_A - n_B \tag{1.30}$$

Integration of Eq. (1.29) gives

$$\Delta G_{P_2} = \Delta G_{P_1} + \Delta n\, RT \ln \frac{P_2}{P_1} \tag{1.31}$$

Thus, if ΔG_{P_1} is known at a pressure P_1, ΔG_{P_2} at pressure P_2 may be calculated.

If the reactants and products are all liquids or solids, the influence of pressure on the free-energy change is small. The effect of pressure on the standard free-energy change of a reaction is expressed by an equation similar to (1.26) but with the substitutions $\Delta G = \Delta G^0$ and $\bar{V}_i = \bar{V}_i^0$ where $\bar{V}_i^0$ is the partial molar volume of the ith component when all the reactants and products are in their standard states.

2 THEORETICAL EFFICIENCY FOR CONVERSION OF HEAT LIBERATED IN A CHEMICAL REACTION INTO MECHANICAL ENERGY

2.1 Physical Picture of Heat Engine: Simple Derivation of the Theoretical Efficiency

At the present time, the commonest method of obtaining electrical energy is by first converting the heat evolved during a chemical reaction to mechanical energy, which is then transformed into electrical energy. It is thus worthwhile deriving the theoretical limitations of this method of energy conversion before making similar considerations for the electrochemical method.

It is necessary to visualize the way in which this conversion takes place. A chemical reaction (say, the combustion of a hydrocarbon to carbon dioxide) occurs, and a certain amount of heat is evolved because the heat content of the products is less than that of the reactants. This evolved heat (the enthalpy change of the reaction) causes a rise in temperature of the products and of any unconverted reactants. Since most of these are gases, they expand—the physical expression of the increase in translational energy. In a heat engine, this expansion of gases produces mechanical work by making pistons move whereby the mechanical energy is communicated to the wheels.

The fact that the efficiency of this conversion is less than unity, even assuming an approach to an ideal system of limitingly low friction, can be seen from the following model. The essential act in the conversion of the heat energy to work is the collision of gas molecules, which possess a high translational energy due to the enthalpy of the reaction, with the piston. However, when two bodies collide, they do not transfer to each other all their translational energy (cf. problems in elementary mechanics in terms of colliding billiard balls). The energy that is not transferred to the piston in a heat engine appears as heat energy of the rejected gases. Hypothetically, the efficiency of a heat engine could be unity, only if the kinetic energy of the rebounding gas molecules were zero. If this were so, the gases would leave the system at the absolute zero.

A simple derivation of the expression for the theoretical efficiency of a heat engine may be obtained in the following manner. The translational energy per mole of gas entering the piston is $3RT_1/2$, where T_1 is the source temperature; the energy per mole of gas leaving the piston after the expansion is $3RT_2/2$, where T_2 is the sink temperature. Thus, the amount of energy converted to useful work W_u during the expansion of the piston per mole of gas is given by

$$W_u = \frac{3R(T_1 - T_2)}{2} \tag{2.1}$$

The energy input per mole of gas (W_i) is given by

$$W_i = \frac{3RT_1}{2} \tag{2.2}$$

Therefore, the theoretical efficiency ϵ of a heat engine—the Carnot efficiency—is given by

$$\epsilon = \frac{W_u}{W_i}$$

$$= \frac{T_1 - T_2}{T_1} \tag{2.3}$$

Thus, the efficiency can be unity only if T_2 is at the absolute zero.

2.2 Thermodynamic Derivation of the Theoretical Efficiency of a Heat Engine

The thermodynamic deduction of the theoretical, i.e., the maximum, efficiency of a heat engine is well-known and is derived in every classical thermodynamics textbook.[1-6] In essence, the derivation is made assuming that the gas inside the piston first expands isothermally from a volume V_1 to V_2 at a temperature T_1 and then adiabatically from V_2 to V_3 during which process the gas cools from temperature T_1 to T_2. The gas returns to its original state in two stages again, i.e., first isothermal contraction at T_2, followed by adiabatic contraction (Fig. 1). The theoretical efficiency for the entire process was derived first by Carnot[7] and shown to be that expressed by Eq. (2.3).

In general, it is difficult to have high source temperatures because of materials problems. Further, it is not practicable to have T_2 much less than T_1 because of conduction of heat between the high- and low-temperature zones of the machine. Thus, from these practical considerations, the maximum Carnot efficiency generally is found to be between 40 and 50 percent. The observed efficiencies of heat engines are about half these values.

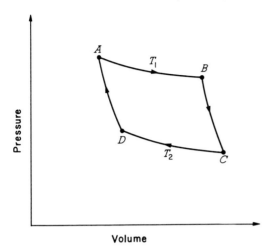

Pressure

Volume

Figure 1 The intermediate steps in a Carnot cycle for derivation of theoretical efficiency of a heat engine. Steps *A* to *B* and *C* to *D* are carried out isothermally; steps *B* to *C* and *D* to *A* are carried out adiabatically.

2.3 Carnot Limitation for Some Direct-energy-conversion Devices

The conventional form of a heat engine, which is used to produce electrical energy, works indirectly in the sense that mechanical energy is first produced which is then used to drive a generator and hence produce electrical energy.

As seen from Chap. 1, there are several types of energy converters that produce electrical energy directly from heat energy—thermoelectric, thermionic, and magnetohydrodynamic energy-conversion devices. These systems are also subject to the Carnot limitation for the same reason as are conventional heat engines, where the gas molecules enter and leave the system with average kinetic energies per mole of $3RT_1/2$ and $3RT_2/2$, respectively. Thus, all the heat energy cannot be converted to electrical energy since T_2 can never be zero.

The only direct-energy-conversion methods that are free of the Carnot limitation are those using photovoltaic, electrochemical, and gravitational devices.

3 THE RELATION BETWEEN THE FREE-ENERGY CHANGE IN A CELL REACTION AND THE CELL POTENTIAL

3.1 Essence of Electrochemical Energy Conversion

For a reaction that is carried out isothermally and at a constant pressure in a reversible way, its free-energy change expresses the maximum useful obtainable work.   A reaction of the type

$$C_3H_8 + 5O_2 \rightarrow 3CO_2 + 4H_2O \tag{3.1}$$

can be carried out electrochemically under the conditions of a constant temperature and pressure (Fig. 2).

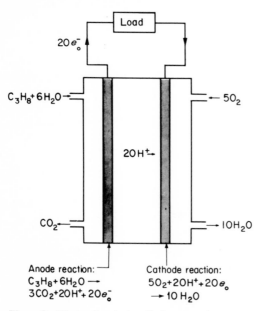

Anode reaction:
$C_3H_8 + 6H_2O \longrightarrow$
$3CO_2 + 20H^+ + 20e_o^-$

Cathode reaction:
$5O_2 + 20H^+ + 20e_o$
$\longrightarrow 10\,H_2O$

Figure 2 Electrochemical cell for carrying out reaction $C_3H_8 + 5O_2 \rightarrow 3CO_2 + 4H_2O$.

Before evaluating the electromotive force developed in the cell, it is interesting to reconsider how this chemical reaction is used in a combustion engine. The essential mode of operation in this case is that the chemical energy [the heat of the reaction (3.1)] is transformed into ordered translational energy of the products—mechanical energy.   The heat input Q_1 is the heat of the reaction ΔH, and a part of it is used in expanding the gas and pushing the cylinder (i.e., creating mechanical work), whereas the balance, which is usually the major

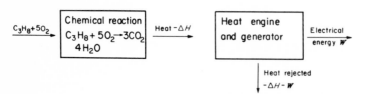

Figure 3 Representation of conversion of chemical energy of reaction $C_3H_8 + 5O_2 \rightarrow 3CO_2 + 4H_2O$ into electrical energy by conventional method.

portion, is rejected as heat given off at a lower temperature (Fig. 3). The theoretical efficiency ϵ is given by Eq. (2.3).

The main difference in the electrochemical path is that the particles which react do so in two partial reactions occurring at different locations; each partial reaction involves electron transfer. For example, the reaction (3.1) takes place according to the partial reactions

$$C_3H_8 + 6H_2O \rightarrow 3CO_2 + 20H^+ + 20e_0^- \tag{3.2}$$

and

$$5O_2 + 20H^+ + 20e_0^- \rightarrow 10H_2O \tag{3.3}$$

at the electrodes M_1 and M_2.

The difference in energy of reactants and products at the interfaces $M_1/$ solution and $M_2/$ solution is required. Instead of being expressed as a difference in increase or decrease of translational motion of molecules and associated entropy changes, the free-energy change of the reaction (3.1), when carried out electrochemically, is expressed as a difference of *electron pressure* (i.e., electric cell potential). It is the electrons in the outer circuit of the cell which have more energy as a result of the reaction taking place. When it comes to converting into mechanical work the energy change of the overall chemical reaction, which takes place as a sum of the two partial electrode reactions in the cell, the process is no longer a *partial* using up of translational or heat energy of gas molecules (which hold in themselves the energy of the reaction in the form of translational motions) but rather a complete utilization of the energy of the electrons. These, for example, pass into an electric motor, across which there is a potential difference almost equal to the cell potential. In passing through this potential gradient, the electrons give up all the electrical energy that they obtain at the two electrodes in the cell to the electric motor and cause it to operate. There is no partial transfer of energy as in heat engines. Instead of there being an *intrinsically* incomplete conversion as in heat engines (where all the heat of the chemical reactions *cannot* be used up), there can be a complete conversion of the free energy released in the reaction, diminished only by mechanical losses of the motor (which can, in practice, be reduced to about 5 percent).

Hence, the essential difference between the two methods of obtaining electrical energy from the difference in total energy of products and reactants of a chemical reaction is as follows: if the method of carrying out the reaction is thermal ("hot" combustion), it is, for intrinsic reasons, only possible to get a fraction of the chemical energy change converted to electrical energy. But if the method of carrying out the reaction is electrochemical ("cold" combustion[8]), the total free-energy change of the reaction, which is for the combustion of many fuels nearly equal to the total energy change in the reaction, can be converted, as far as intrinsic considerations are concerned, to electrical energy. Table 1 illustrates the steps involved in the two methods. Thus the basic

TABLE 1   Essential Steps in the Production of Energy by the "Hot" (Heat Engine) and "Cold" (Electrochemical Energy Converter) Combustion of Propane

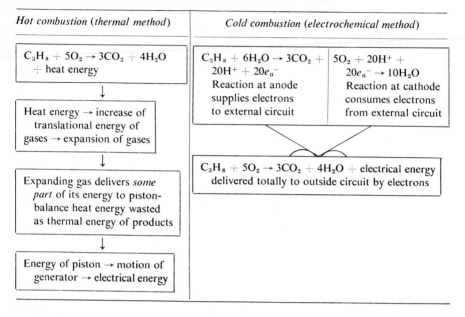

Hot combustion (thermal method)	*Cold combustion (electrochemical method)*	
$C_3H_8 + 5O_2 \rightarrow 3CO_2 + 4H_2O$ + heat energy	$C_3H_8 + 6H_2O \rightarrow 3CO_2 +$ $20H^+ + 20e_0^-$ Reaction at anode supplies electrons to external circuit	$5O_2 + 20H^+ +$ $20e_0^- \rightarrow 10H_2O$ Reaction at cathode consumes electrons from external circuit
Heat energy $\rightarrow$ increase of translational energy of gases $\rightarrow$ expansion of gases		
Expanding gas delivers *some part* of its energy to piston-balance heat energy wasted as thermal energy of products	$C_3H_8 + 5O_2 \rightarrow 3CO_2 + 4H_2O$ + electrical energy delivered totally to outside circuit by electrons	
Energy of piston $\rightarrow$ motion of generator $\rightarrow$ electrical energy		

advantages of the electrochemical method are twofold: the possibility of an approach to 100 percent conversion of the free energy, and that the product is *directly* energy in the form of electricity.

In the chemical reaction carried out in a combustion engine, there is heat transfer; and in the electrochemical reaction, there is charge transfer. In charge transfer, the whole energy of the electrons can be used up, i.e., the electrons fall through the total potential difference (the electromotive force of the cell), as in the case of the potential energy of a falling body of mass m from h_2 to h_1 which is completely used up. $mg(h_2 - h_1)$ is analogous to $e(V_2 - V_1)$, where e is the charge on the electron and $V_2 - V_1$ is the potential drop across the load. The latter is equal to the electromotive force of the cell, if the internal resistance of the cell is negligible. As a result of the potential difference between the two electrodes in the cell, the extra energy of the electrons is completely used up by the time they get around the circuit work. On the contrary, since the temperature of the sink in a heat engine cannot be reduced to zero in practice, the energy conversion is incomplete, and thus the molecules still possess some energy from the enthalpy change in the reaction, after collision with a piston. A heat engine cannot therefore extract all the energy released in a chemical reaction, but an electrochemical energy converter could approach close to doing so.

The difference in the intrinsic efficiencies of electrochemical and heat engines in the conversion of the energy of chemical reactions is a fundamental one. One might say that the delay by about a century in utilizing the electro-chemical path for energy conversion was a "false step" in the development of technology. Thus, it gave rise to a consumption of more than twice the fuel which would have been used electrochemically to produce the same energy; and secondarily, many of the negative consequences of our present technology (smog, smoke, vibration, and noise) would have been avoided.

3.2 Derivation of Relation

The enthalpy change of the reaction may be written as

$$\Delta H = \Delta E + P\,\Delta V$$
$$= Q - W + P\,\Delta V \tag{3.4}$$

where ΔE, Q, and W are the internal energy of, heat absorbed by, and work done by the system, respectively. Suppose reaction (3.1) were carried out in a heat engine. The only work done by the system would be the work of expansion, and Eq. (3.4) thus reduces to

$$\Delta H = Q \tag{3.5}$$

The enthalpy change of the reaction is therefore equal to the heat evolved by the reaction, i.e., the heat absorbed by the system.

If the same reaction is carried out electrochemically, W in Eq. (3.4) is then, not only the work of expansion done by gases produced, but also the electrical work involved in transporting the charges around the circuit from the anode to the cathode—at which the potentials are $V_{rev,a}$ and $V_{rev,c}$, respectively. The maximum electrical work that can be done per act of an overall reaction (W') carried out in a cell and that involves transfer of n electrons per act of the overall reaction is

$$W'_{el} = ne(V_{rev,c} - V_{rev,a}) \tag{3.6}$$

for a hypothetical case in which the internal resistance of the cell and over-potential losses are negligible. For converting to molar quantities, it is necessary to multiply W'_{el} by N, the Avogadro number; and since the product of the electronic charge and Avogadro's number is the Faraday,

$$W_{el} = nF(V_{rev,c} - V_{rev,a}) \tag{3.7}$$

Since the only forms of work involved in the working of the electrochemical cell are electrical work and work of expansion,

$$W = W_{el} + P\,\Delta V \tag{3.8}$$

If, in addition, the process is carried out reversibly,

$$Q = T\,\Delta S \tag{3.9}$$

Using Eqs. (3.4) and (3.7) to (3.9), it follows that

$$\Delta H = T\,\Delta S - nF(V_{rev,c} - V_{rev,a}) \tag{3.10}$$

By comparison of Eq. (3.10) with Eq. (1.10), which holds for an isothermal process, the important relation

$$\Delta G = -nF(V_{rev,c} - V_{rev,a}) \tag{3.11}$$

arises.

Writing

$$V_{rev,c} - V_{rev,a} = E \tag{3.12}$$

Eq. (3.11) becomes

$$\Delta G = -nFE \tag{3.13}$$

where E is the electromotive force of the cell.

If the reactants and products are all in their standard states, it follows that

$$\Delta G^0 = -nFE^0 \tag{3.14}$$

where E^0 is the standard electromotive force (commonly referred to as the standard reversible potential) of the cell.

3.3   Temperature and Pressure Coefficients of Thermodynamic Reversible Cell Potentials

The variation of E with temperature at constant pressure can easily be obtained from Eqs. (1.20), (3.13), and (3.14):

$$E = -\frac{\Delta H}{nF} + T\left(\frac{\partial E}{\partial T}\right)_P \tag{3.15}$$

From Eqs. (1.19), (1.20), and (3.15) it is seen that the second term in Eq. (3.15) is related to the entropy change of the cell reaction by the equation

$$nF\left(\frac{\partial E}{\partial T}\right)_P = \Delta S \tag{3.16}$$

Equations (3.15) and (3.16) show that cell potentials at any temperature can be calculated theoretically if entropy changes of the corresponding cell reactions are available.

Using Eqs. (1.31) and (3.13), the thermodynamic reversible cell potential may be expressed as a function of pressure:

$$E_P = E_{P_0} - \Delta n \frac{RT}{nF} \ln \frac{P}{P_0} \tag{3.17}$$

where E_P and E_{P_0} are the cell potentials at (total) pressures of P and P_0, respectively. Δn is the change in number of gaseous molecules during the reaction. It is assumed that the gaseous reactants and products obey the ideal gas laws. The more general expression for the thermodynamic reversible cell potential as a function of pressure, as obtained from Eqs. (1.24) and (3.13), is

$$E_P = E_{P_0} - \frac{1}{nF} \int_{P_0}^{P} \Delta V \, dP \qquad (3.18)$$

where ΔV is the volume change of the reaction. According to this equation, it follows that the effect of pressure on the thermodynamic reversible cell potentials is small for reactions involving only liquids and solids. However, in the cases where gaseous reactants and products are involved and if the volume change is significant (e.g., the hydrogen-oxygen fuel cell), pressure effects are significant. For example, in the H_2-O_2 fuel cell, increasing the total pressure from 1 to 10 atm changes the cell potential by 45 mv.

3.4 Standard Reversible Potentials and Their Temperature and Pressure Coefficients for Some Fuel-cell Reactions

Calculations of standard thermodynamic reversible cell potentials are relatively simple. It is the first step in determining the usefulness or otherwise of potential fuels. In this section, these calculations will be exemplified in two cases. The overall reaction in the hydrogen-oxygen fuel cell is

$$2H_2 + O_2 \rightarrow 2H_2O \qquad (1.13)$$

The standard free-energy change of this reaction is -113.38 kcal mole^{-1} of oxygen. The overall reaction involves the transfer of four electrons, as may be seen by writing down the partial reactions

$$2H_2 \rightarrow 4H^+ + 4e_0^- \qquad (3.19)$$

$$O_2 + 4H^+ + 4e_0^- \rightarrow 2H_2O \qquad (3.20)$$

Using $\Delta G^0 = -113.38$ kcal mole^{-1} of O_2 consumed and $n = 4$ in Eq. (3.14) and noting that 1 ev is equal to 23.05 kcal mole^{-1}, the standard thermodynamic reversible potential of the hydrogen-oxygen fuel cell at 25°C is 1.229 volts.

A second fuel-cell reaction which may be considered is that in the propane-oxygen fuel cell. The overall reaction here is given by Eq. (3.1), which takes place according to the partial reactions (3.2) and (3.3). The standard free-energy change of the reaction (3.1) is 503.93 kcal per mole of propane. The number of electrons transferred in the overall reaction is 20. Thus, using these values for ΔG^0 and n in Eq. (3.14), the standard thermodynamic reversible cell potential for the propane-oxygen fuel cell is 1.093 volts.

Temperature and pressure coefficients of the standard reversible potentials may be easily calculated from Eqs. (3.16) and (3.17), respectively. The standard thermodynamic reversible cell potentials, and the temperature and pressure coefficients of the standard thermodynamic reversible potentials for a number of fuel-cell reactions, are given in Table 2. The lithium-halogen fuel cells have the highest values for the standard thermodynamic reversible cell potential, being about three times higher than those for hydrogen-oxygen or organic

TABLE 2 Thermodynamic Data for Some Fuel-cell Reactions†

Reaction	$\Delta G°$, kcal mole⁻¹	$\Delta H°$, kcal mole⁻¹	n	Δn	$E_r°$, volts	$\partial E_r°/\partial T$, mv/°C	$\partial E_r/\partial \log P$, mv	ϵ_i
Temperature, 25°C								
1. $H_2 + \frac{1}{2}O_2 \rightarrow H_2O$	−56.69	−68.32	2	−1.5	1.229	−0.84	45	0.830
2. $CH_4 + 2O_2 \rightarrow CO_2 + 2H_2O$	−195.50	−212.80	8	−2	1.060	−0.31	15	0.919
3. $C_2H_6 + \frac{7}{2}O_2 \rightarrow 2CO_2 + 3H_2O$	−350.73	−372.82	14	−2.5	1.087	−0.23	10.7	0.941
4. $C_3H_8 + 5O_2 \rightarrow 3CO_2 + 4H_2O$	−503.93	−530.61	20	−3	1.093	−0.19	9	0.950
5. $C_4H_{10} + \frac{13}{2}O_2 \rightarrow 4CO_2 + 5H_2O$	−656.74	−687.99	26	−3.5	1.095	−0.17	8	0.955
6. $C_5H_{12} + 8O_2 \rightarrow 5CO_2 + 6H_2O$	−809.48	−845.17	32	−4	1.097	−0.16	7.5	0.958
7. $C_8H_{18}(g) + \frac{25}{2}O_2 \rightarrow 8CO_2 + 9H_2O$	−1268.43	−1317.46	50	−5.5	1.100	−0.14	6.6	0.963
$C_8H_{18}(l) + \frac{25}{2}O_2 \rightarrow 8CO_2 + 9H_2O$	−1265.87	−1307.54	50	−4.5	1.098	−0.12	5.4	0.968
8. $C_{10}H_{22}(g) + \frac{31}{2}O_2 \rightarrow 10CO_2 + 11H_2O$	−1574.42	−1632.35	62	−6.5	1.101	−0.13	6.3	0.965
9. $CH_3OH(g) + \frac{3}{2}O_2 \rightarrow CO_2 + 2H_2O$	−168.05	−182.61	6	−1.5	1.215	−0.35	15	0.920
$CH_3OH(l) + \frac{3}{2}O_2 \rightarrow CO_2 + 2H_2O$	−167.91	−173.67	6	−0.5	1.214	−0.13	5	0.967
10. $NH_3 + \frac{3}{4}O_2 \rightarrow 1/2N_2 + 3/2H_2O$	−85.04	−91.44	3	−1.25	1.225	−0.31	25	0.930
11. $N_2H_4 + O_2 \rightarrow N_2 + 2H_2O$	−143.83	−148.69	4	−1	1.560	−0.18	15	0.967
12. $C + \frac{1}{2}O_2 \rightarrow CO$	−32.81	−26.42	2	+0.5	0.711	+0.46	−15	1.24
13. $C + O_2 \rightarrow CO_2$	−94.26	−94.05	4	0	1.022	0	0	1.002
14. $CO + \frac{1}{2}O_2 \rightarrow CO_2$	−61.45	−67.63	2	−0.5	1.333	−0.44	15	0.909
15. $Li + \frac{1}{2}Cl_2 \rightarrow LiCl(g)$	−58	−53.00	1	0.5	2.515	−0.72	−30	1.094

Temperature, 150°C

Reaction								
1. $H_2 + \tfrac{1}{2}O_2 \rightarrow H_2O$	−52.94	−58.142	2	−0.5	1.14799	−0.25	21	0.911
2. $CH_4 + 2O_2 \rightarrow CO_2 + 2H_2O$	−191.29	−191.42	8	0	1.03702	0	0	0.999
3. $C_2H_6 + \tfrac{1}{2}O_2 \rightarrow 2CO_2 + 3H_2O$	−346.99	−340.66	14	0.5	1.07491	+0.04	−3	1.019
4. $C_3H_8 + 5O_2 \rightarrow 3CO_2 + 4H_2O$	−499.54	−487.82	20	1	1.08324	+0.05	−4.2	1.024
5. $C_4H_{10} + \tfrac{13}{2}O_2 \rightarrow 4CO_2 + 5H_2O$	−651.94	−634.29	26	1.5	1.08747	+0.06	−4.9	1.028
6. $C_5H_{12} + 8O_2 \rightarrow 5CO_2 + 6H_2O$	−804.98	−781.19	32	1	1.09099	+0.07	−5.4	1.030
7. $C_8H_{18} + \tfrac{25}{2}O_2 \rightarrow 8CO_2 + 9H_2O$	−1263.72	−1221.70	50	3.5	1.09614	+0.08	−5.9	1.034
8. $C_{10}H_{22}(g) + \tfrac{31}{2}O_2 \rightarrow 10CO_2 + 11H_2O$	−1569.62	−1515.37	62	4.5	1.09796	+0.08	−6.2	1.036
9. $NH_3 + \tfrac{3}{4}O_2 \rightarrow 1/2N_2 + 3/2H_2O$	−47.28	−77.28	3	0.25	0.6835	−0.96	−7.1	0.612
10. $C + \tfrac{1}{2}O_2 \rightarrow CO$	−36.09	−26.31	2	0.5	0.782	0.47	−21	1.372
11. $C + O_2 \rightarrow CO_2$	−94.36	−94.08	4	0	1.02309	0	0	1.003
12. $CO + \tfrac{1}{2}O_2 \rightarrow CO_2$	−58.26	−67.77	2	−0.5	1.26335	−0.46	21	0.860
13. $Li + \tfrac{1}{2}Cl_2 \rightarrow LiCl(g)$	−81.38	−52.01	1	0.5	3.52942	+2.84	−42	1.565

† Thermodynamic data are presented for the oxidation of one mole of fuel.

compound–oxygen fuel cells.   It is a noteworthy fact that for practically every cell in the latter group, the thermodynamic reversible cell potentials are of the order of 1 volt.

3.5   Heat Changes in an Ideally Operating Fuel Cell

3.5.1   Origin of Heat Changes

It has been stressed heavily that the chemical energy in thermal engines is first released as heat, which then causes the expansion of the working gases thereby doing mechanical work, and is then transformed into electrical energy by an engine generator.   This is the normal "hot" combustion.   It has been equally stressed that electrochemical energy conversion avoids the intermediate stage of production of heat in the transformation of chemical energy to electrical energy and this has been called, following Justi and Winsel,[8] "cold" combustion.

It is not true, however, that electrochemical energy conversion takes place completely without temperature change even when working under ideal conditions.   Thus, an ideal electrochemical energy converter yields electrical energy to the extent of the free-energy change of the reaction, as given by Eq. (3.13).   However, the *total* energy released in a chemical reaction corresponds to the enthalpy change of the reaction; and so long as the enthalpy change is more negative than the free-energy change of the reaction, a part of the total energy change of the reaction which cannot be converted to electrical energy is given out as heat.   This part is represented by $(\Delta H - \Delta G)$, which is equal to $T \Delta S$, as seen from Eq. (1.10).   Thus, heating effects occur even in the hypothetical ideal operation of a fuel cell if ΔS is negative.   Of course, such heating effects are very small compared to those associated with a heat engine.

There are some reactions that have positive entropy changes.   In these cases, the free-energy changes of the corresponding reaction are more negative than the enthalpy changes.   Under these conditions, the electrochemical energy converter, in which such a reaction occurs, cools and extracts heat from the atmosphere, which is also converted into electrical energy.   An example of this type of reaction is the oxidation of carbon to carbon monoxide.   The ideal efficiency in this case is about 137 percent at 150°C (cf. Sec. 4.1).

3.5.2   Location of Heat Changes in an Ideal Electrochemical Energy Converter

In most of the existing fuel cells, the heating effects observed within the electrolyte are due to ohmic losses.   The rate of heat liberation is given by $I^2 R_i$, where I is the current and R_i is the ohmic resistance of the electrolyte.   In an ideal electrochemical energy converter this loss is zero, but there is still heat evolved if the entropy change of the cell reaction is negative.   The heat evolved is numerically equal to $T \Delta S$ per mole of fuel consumed.   Since ΔS is equal to $nF(dE/dT)$, this heat change may be broken up into three components:

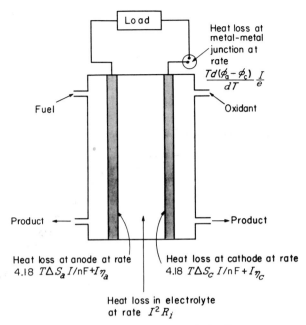

Figure 4 Location of heat losses in a fuel cell.

heat evolved at (1) each of the two metal-solution junctions and (2) the metal-metal junctions (Fig. 4). It is likely that the major contribution to the heat evolved occurs at the two metal-solution interfaces. Thus the heating effect at the metal-metal junctions is small because the potential difference across this junction is equal to the difference in work functions of the two metals and the temperature coefficients of work functions are small.

It must be carefully noted that the above discussion of the relation between the free-energy change of an overall reaction and the potential developed in a cell assumes extrapolation of a real case to an ideal one—namely, the electrochemical reaction is carried out sufficiently slowly so that it may be regarded as behaving thermodynamically reversibly. Realization of the ideal situation, treated above, is equivalent to the case in which an electrochemical energy converter works at an efficiency of 80 to 90 percent or even greater but at a negligible *rate* of doing work, i.e., at a negligible power.†

† The maximum intrinsic ideal efficiency of most fuel cells is in the range 80–96 percent at room temperature and not 100 percent as sometimes stated. Thus, 100 percent of the free energy change could be recovered as electrical energy in an ideally operating fuel cell, but this free energy change is generally numerically less than the enthalpy change of the reaction. Conversely, in the rare case when $|\Delta G| > |\Delta H|$, the ideally operating fuel cell could produce electrical energy in excess of the enthalpy change of the reaction. The extra energy comes from the heat energy of the surrounding atmosphere.

3.6   Departure of Cell Potential from Reversible Value

In certain electrochemical reactions[9-11], for example, hydrogen-bromine fuel cell (room temperature), lithium-chlorine fuel cell ($\sim 700°C$)—thermodynamic reversibility can be so nearly attained in practice that such reactions are quoted as realistic examples of a very near approach to this condition in actuality. However, in the normal operation of an electrochemical energy-conversion device, it is clear that the electrical energy must be supplied at a significant rate, and under these conditions the current densities drawn from the system are too high for the state of thermodynamic reversibility to be maintained.   The cell potential under load is found to be less than that given by Eq. (3.13).   However, Eq. (3.13) must be regarded as the bedrock of the entire subject of electrochemical energy conversion.   It not only gives the ideal attainment that is theoretically possible but also serves as the reference state for measurement of departures due to extrinsic causes from the maximally efficient conversion of energy which it indicates.

In practice, the cell potential, E, of an electrochemical energy converter working at an appreciable rate is given by

$$E = E_r - \sum \eta \tag{3.21}$$

where $\sum \eta$ is the sum of all the overpotentials that exist at the electrode-electrolyte interfaces and electrodes and in the electrolytes.   The types of overpotentials that arise have been treated in Chap. 2.   Thus, in electrochemical energy conversion, increased *power* (hence current density and overpotential) is associated with departure from the ideal high conversion efficiency of the enthalpy change of the reaction that is intrinsically attainable.

4   EFFICIENCY OF ELECTROCHEMICAL ENERGY CONVERSION

4.1   The Intrinsic Maximum Efficiency

In the case of a heat engine, the loss in conversion efficiency has been described in detail and stressed as being intrinsic.   In the case of an electrochemical energy converter working ideally, it has been shown that the free-energy change of the reaction may be totally converted to electrical energy.   Thus, an electrochemical energy converter has an intrinsic maximum efficiency given by

$$\epsilon_i = \frac{\Delta G}{\Delta H} = 1 - \frac{T \Delta S}{\Delta H} \tag{4.1}$$

It is perhaps not appropriate to regard this equation as indicative of an intrinsic maximum efficiency of less than 100 percent because there is a possibility in the case of some reactions for ΔG to exceed ΔH.   Table 2 gives the *intrinsic maximum efficiencies* for a number of fuel-cell reactions under standard conditions.   It shows that the intrinsic maximum efficiencies for nearly all the reactions in the table are greater than 90 percent† (cf. the intrinsic maximum efficiencies of heat engines, working ideally between practical operating temperatures of source and sink, which are nearly always less than 40 percent).

An interesting fact must be noted concerning the efficiencies of hydrocarbon-air fuel cells. At temperatures below 100°C, water, a product of the cell reactions, is in the liquid form. This causes the entropy changes in the corresponding reaction to be negative, and thus the intrinsic maximum efficiencies are less than 100 percent. At temperatures above 100°C, however, water is liberated, as one of the products, in vapor form. The entropy changes are thus positive under these conditions (Table 2), corresponding to intrinsic maximum efficiencies of over 100 percent. At the present time, overpotential losses reduce the practical efficiencies of these fuel cells to values much less than the intrinsic maximum efficiencies. However, were sufficient advances in electrocatalysis made (hence, overpotential reduced) it might be possible to attain practical efficiencies of over 100 percent and close to maximum intrinsic efficiencies, particularly in situations in which the power density does not have to be high, so that the current density and hence overpotential can be low.

4.2 Effect of Temperature on Intrinsic Maximum Efficiency

If the entropy change of a reaction is negative, it follows from Eq. (4.1) that (recalling the negative sign of ΔH) the intrinsic maximum efficiency would *decrease* with increase of temperature. Thus, a hydrogen-oxygen fuel cell has intrinsic maximum efficiencies of 0.83 at 25°C and of 0.78 at 100°C. An important difference from this result to the corresponding one for a thermal engine must be made here. As the temperature of the hot stage of the thermal energy converter increases, the difference between the temperatures of the heat source and the heat sink also increases and the corresponding Carnot efficiency consequently *increases* with temperature. In making any theoretical forecast on the variation of efficiency of a thermal engine with temperature, however, one has to be somewhat cautious. One cannot simply assume that the temperature of the heat sink (T_2) is always at the surrounding temperature and is independent of temperatures of the heat source. Increasing the temperature of the heat source would automatically cause some increase in temperature of the heat sink. Thus, the increase in intrinsic maximum efficiency of thermal engines with temperatures of heat source in these practical cases would be less than if one makes the assumption that the heat-sink temperature is constant and equal to the temperature of the surroundings. In Fig. 5, the variations of intrinsic maximum efficiency of a hydrogen-oxygen fuel cell and of heat engines with temperature are shown.

The opposite behavior of variation of the intrinsic maximum efficiency with temperature of thermal engines and of fuel cells reduces some of the advantages

† In Eq. (4.1), it must be remembered that ΔH is usually negative and ΔS is also usually negative. Thus, ϵ_i is less than unity for these cases.

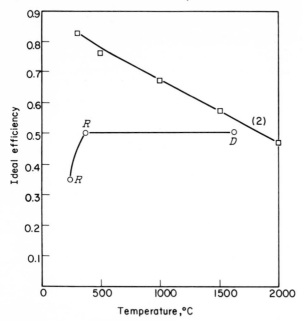

Figure 5   Variation of (1) theoretical efficiency of heat engines (R, Rankine cycle; D, diesel engine) and (2) intrinsic maximum efficiency of hydrogen-oxygen fuel cell with temperature.

of fuel cells at high temperatures.   At higher temperatures, however, the need for expensive electrocatalysts is diminished because the temperature itself increases the reaction rate and hence makes the overpotential necessary for a given current density, or power, less than that at lower temperatures.

The entropy change for the oxidation of carbon to carbon monoxide is positive.   For this case, ϵ_i, according to Eq. (4.1), exceeds unity and ϵ_i increases with temperature.   For the complete oxidation of carbon to carbon dioxide, ΔS is approximately equal to zero and ϵ_i is nearly unity with hardly any temperature variation.   The entropy changes in the overall reaction for several hydrocarbon-oxygen fuel cells operating at temperatures of over 100°C are also greater than zero (Table 2).

4.3   Voltage Efficiency

The cell voltage E under load is less than the thermodynamic reversibly potential E_r, calculated according to Eq. (3.13).   Factors affecting this departure of E from E_r are dealt with in Sec. 5.   The voltage efficiency is defined as

$$\epsilon_e = \frac{E}{E_r} \tag{4.2}$$

Voltage efficiencies observed in some fuel cells (e.g., hydrogen-oxygen) are as high as 0.9 at low current densities and decrease only slowly with increasing current drawn from the cell,[12] until a limiting value is reached.

4.4   Faradaic Efficiency

The faradaic efficiency is defined as

$$\epsilon_f = \frac{I}{I_m} \tag{4.3}$$

I is the observed current from the fuel cell. I_m is the theoretically expected current on the basis of the amount of reactants consumed, assuming that the overall reaction in the fuel cell proceeds to completion. Faradaic efficiency is analogous to current efficiency in conventional electrochemical cells. In most fuel cells ϵ_f is unity. ϵ_f may be less than 1 because of: (1) parallel electrochemical reactions yielding fewer electrons per mole of reactant consumed,[13] (2) chemical reaction of reactants, catalyzed by electrodes,[14] and (3) a direct chemical reaction of the two electrode reactants.[15]

4.5   Overall Efficiency

The overall efficiency ϵ in electrochemical energy conversion is the product of the efficiencies worked out in the preceding subsections:

$$\epsilon = \epsilon_i \epsilon_e \epsilon_f \tag{4.4}$$

For an electrochemical reaction [say, of the type (3.1)], under the chosen conditions of temperature, pressure, and concentration of reactants and products, ϵ_i is a definite quantity, and the maximum possible value of ϵ is ϵ_i. A main goal in electrochemical energy conversion is to make both ϵ_e and ϵ_f tend to unity. It is not difficult to make ϵ_f tend to unity in the case of many fuel-cell reactions.

5   FACTORS AFFECTING EFFICIENCY OF ELECTROCHEMICAL ENERGY CONVERSION

5.1   Activation Overpotential

As stated in the previous chapter, activation overpotential results from the slowness of one or more of the intermediate steps in either one or both of the electrode reactions. Details of methods by which one may attempt a reduction of activation overpotential are found in Chap. 6. A typical plot of terminal cell voltage E vs. current density i of an operating electrochemical energy converter is shown in Fig. 6. The open-circuit voltage E_a is generally less than the thermodynamically reversible potential E_r for the specified conditions of temperature, pressure, activities of reactants, and products because of interference caused by adventitous reactions of impurities. When the net current drawn from the cell is small, cell potentials may tend to be

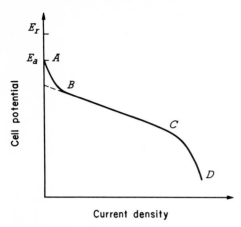

Figure 6 A typical cell-potential–current-density relation for a fuel cell.

controlled by these impurity reactions. However, due to their low concentrations, at higher currents generated from the cell impurity effects are small. Further, it is found that at low current densities there is a very sharp decrease of E with i, as represented by the portion AB of the curve. This type of behavior is characteristic of highly irreversible processes and is caused by activation overpotential (Chaps. 2 and 4).

5.2   Ohmic Overpotential

The linear portion in Fig. 6 corresponds to a relatively high current density region in which some part of the decrease in cell potential with increase of current density is due to ohmic overpotential. Ohmic overpotential is a result of the resistance of the solution and is sometimes due to the electrical resistance in the electrodes. It is given by

$$\eta_r = ir_i \tag{4.5}$$

where r_i is the internal resistance per square centimeter of cross section of the cell. Resistivities of aqueous, molten, and solid electrolytes (the last, for example, as in solid oxide electrolyte cells[16]) are of the order of 1.0, 0.1, and 10 ohms cm, respectively. When porous electrodes are used, as in the case of most electrochemical energy converters, not only the layer of electrolyte between the anode and the cathode but also resistance of the electrolyte within the pores contributes to the electrolyte resistance (Chap. 5).

The ohmic overpotential is the simplest cause of loss of potential in an electrochemical energy converter. It may be thought that reduction in the thickness of the electrolyte layer between anode and cathode would eliminate ohmic   overpotential.   However,   "thin"   electrolyte   layers   may   cause the problem of intermixing of anodic and cathodic reactants, which would thereby reduce faradaic efficiencies. Further, however thin the distance between the outside surface of the two electrodes, these are sections inside porous electrodes in which ohmic overpotential always arises. In the case of high-temperature fuel cells, ohmic overpotential may be a necessary part of the heat balance in the cell. (The rate of heating effect due to ohmic overpotential is $i^2 r_i$ watt cm^{-2}.)

5.3   Mass-transfer Overpotential

At sufficiently high rates, most heterogeneous reactions pass over into a region where they are controlled by the rate of transport of reactants to, or products away from, the electrode (Chap. 2). This is shown by region CD in Fig. 6.

There are two causes of mass-transport control in electrochemical energy converters, which most often use porous electrodes. The first is common to all electrode systems. The potential of one of the electrodes (rarely both together) reaches a value at which it demands a greater rate of supply of its reactant (Chap. 2) than the rate that diffusional and convectional processes can supply. Under these conditions, the current can no longer increase with change of potential. The other cause of mass-transfer polarization is characteristic only of porous gas-diffusion electrodes (Chap. 5). It is caused by a holdup in the supply of gas to the electrode-electrolyte interface. This occurs when the rate of diffusion of the gas through the electrolyte-free part of the pores becomes equal to or less than the subsequent steps, viz., dissolution of gaseous reactant in the electrolyte and electrochemical reaction of the dissolved reactant at the electrode-electrolyte interface within the pore.

6   EFFICIENCIES OF REGENERATIVE FUEL CELLS

6.1   General

A regenerative fuel cell is one in which the fuel-cell product (e.g., water in the hydrogen-oxygen fuel cell) is reconverted into its reactants (e.g., hydrogen and oxygen in the hydrogen-oxygen fuel cell) by one of several possible methods—thermal, chemical, photochemical, electrical, or radiochemical. Details of this type of fuel cell are found in Chap. 10.

Since there are two stages in a regenerative fuel cell—(1) conversion of fuel-cell reactants into products while producing electrical energy and (2) reconversion of fuel-cell products into reactants—it is clear that the overall efficiency of a regenerative fuel cell is the product of the efficiencies of these two stages. In the following subsections, efficiency aspects of regenerative fuel cells will be considered.

6.2   Thermally Regenerative Fuel Cells

The four stages involved in a thermally regenerative fuel cell (Fig. 7) are found in Table 3. A and B are the fuel-cell reactants (e.g., H_2 and O_2); AB is the fuel-cell product (e.g., H_2O); T_2 is the low temperature at which the fuel-cell reaction is carried out, and T_1 is the high temperature at which AB is decomposed.

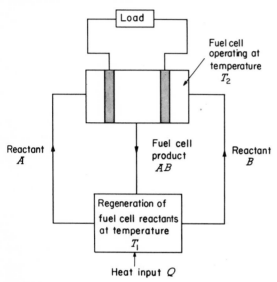

Figure 7   The mode of operation of a thermally regenerative fuel cell.

The efficiency expression of the thermally regenerative system, assuming that stages I to IV are carried out reversibly and at a constant pressure, was worked out by de Bethune[17] in the following manner.

Stage I: Since this process is carried out reversibly, isothermally, and at a constant pressure,

$$\Delta G_I = -W_{u,I} \tag{6.1}$$

$$Q_I = T_2 \, \Delta S_I \tag{6.2}$$

where ΔG_I, W_{u_I}, Q_I, and ΔS_I are the free-energy change, useful work obtained, heat rejected or absorbed, and entropy change, respectively, during stage I.

Stages II and IV combined: The steps II and IV should be carried out in a heat exchanger to achieve higher efficiencies.   The heat absorbed Q_{II} in step II is

$$\int_{T_2}^{T_1} C_{P,AB} \, dT$$

TABLE 3 Intermediate Stages during Operation of a Thermally Regenerative Fuel Cell

Stage no.	Intermediate stage	Initial temperature	Final temperature
I	Fuel-cell reaction: A + B → AB	T_2	T_2
II	Increase of temperature of fuel-cell products: AB → AB	T_2	T_1
III	Regeneration of fuel cell reactants: AB → A + B	T_1	T_1
IV	Decrease of temperature of fuel-cell reactants: A + B → A + B	T_1	T_2

whereas the heat rejected Q_{IV} in stage IV is

$$\int_{T_1}^{T_2} (C_{P,A} + C_{P,B})\, dT$$

C_P's are the specific heats at constant pressure of the appropriate species indicated by the suffixes. Thus, the net heat absorbed $(Q_{II} + Q_{IV})$ in the heating and cooling steps is given by

$$Q_{II} + Q_{IV} = Q_{II+IV} = \Delta H_{II+IV} = \int_{T_2}^{T_1} \Delta C_P\, dT \qquad (6.3)$$

where

$$\Delta C_P = C_{P,AB} - (C_{P,A} + C_{P,B}) \qquad (6.4)$$

Since stages II and IV are carried out at constant pressure, the useful work output of these two steps is zero.

Stage III: Since this step is carried out reversibly, isothermally, and at a constant pressure, the heat absorbed Q_{III} and the free-energy change ΔG_{III} are given by

$$Q_{III} = T_1 S_{III} \qquad (6.5)$$

$$\Delta G_{III} = -W_{u,III} \qquad (6.6)$$

where $W_{u,III}$ is the useful work output for this step.

Since stage III is the reverse of step I but at a temperature of T_1 instead of T_2,

$$\Delta H_{III} = -\left(\Delta H_I + \int_{T_2}^{T_1} \Delta C_P\, dT\right) \qquad (6.7)$$

and

$$\Delta S_{III} = -\left(\Delta S_I + \int_{T_2}^{T_1} \Delta C_P\, d\ln T\right) \qquad (6.8)$$

Using Eqs. (1.10), (6.1), and (6.6) to (6.8), the total work output W_u for the whole cycle is

$$W_u = \sum \Delta G = -\Delta G_I - \Delta G_{III}$$

$$= -\Delta S_I(T_1 - T_2) + \int_{T_2}^{T_1} \Delta C_P\, dT - T_1 \int_{T_2}^{T_1} \Delta C_P\, d\ln T \qquad (6.9)$$

Since a thermally regenerative fuel cell is a system which absorbs heat at a high temperature T_1 and converts some of it to electricity and rejects the balance at a lower temperature, its efficiency is given by the useful work output divided by the heat input at the higher temperature. The useful work output (W_u) is expressed by Eq. (6.9). The net heat input at the higher temperature is given by Eq. (6.5) and hence by Eq. (6.8). Thus, the efficiency of the regenerative fuel cell is given by

$$\epsilon = \frac{-\Delta S_1\,(T_1 - T_2) + \displaystyle\int_{T_2}^{T_1} \Delta C_P\, dT - T_1 \displaystyle\int_{T_2}^{T_1} \Delta C_P\, d\ln T}{- T_1\left(\Delta S_1 + \displaystyle\int_{T_2}^{T_1} \Delta C_P\, d\ln T\right)} \tag{6.10}$$

An alternative deduction assuming Carnot's theorem leads to the same expression for the efficiency. In the derivation given here, the limitation of Carnot's theorem is proved. Thus, just as in the case of heat engines, the Carnot limitation applies to regenerative fuel cells as well. This limitation in the latter case is seen more clearly if one assumes that ΔC_P is zero. Under these conditions, the expression (6.10) for the efficiency reduces to

$$\epsilon = \frac{T_1 - T_2}{T_1} \tag{6.11}$$

The assumption made here, that all steps are thermodynamically reversible, is not correct in practice. Generally, the chief causes of irreversibility are in the heating and cooling stages (II and IV) only. According to this treatment, the desirable thermodynamic properties for a thermally regenerative system are that ΔG_1 is negative, ΔS_{I} is negative [only then is useful work done by the system, as seen from Eq. (6.9)], and ΔC_P is as close as possible to zero.

A more detailed analysis of the efficiency of thermally regenerative systems has also been carried out.[18] This treatment differs from that of de Bethune[17] mainly in that θ, the degree of reaction, is not constant during the heating and cooling steps II and IV and also that the conversion may not be complete in steps I and III. The conclusion reached is that $d(\theta\,\Delta H)/dT$ and not $d(\Delta H)/dT$ (that is, ΔC_P) should be zero for the Carnot efficiency to be obtained. Further, two cases can be distinguished depending on whether or not there is a change in the number of molecules during step I and hence step III. In the former case the efficiency ϵ is pressure-dependent, whereas in the latter ϵ is pressure-independent.

6.3   Chemically Regenerative Fuel Cells

In this type of fuel cell, the products of the fuel-cell reaction are converted into its reactants chemically by the action of oxidizing or reducing agents. A typical case is illustrated in Fig. 8,[19] where the half-cell reactions in the fuel cell are

Anode: $Sn^{2+} \rightarrow Sn^{4+} + 2e_0^-$ (6.12)

Cathode: $Br_2 + 2e_0^- \rightarrow 2Br^-$ (6.13)

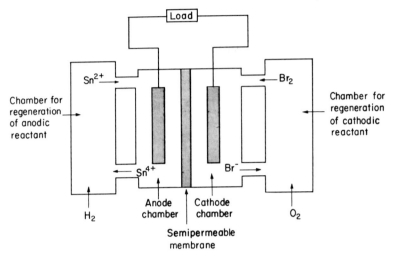

Figure 8   The mode of operation of a chemically regenerative fuel cell.[19]

and the regeneration reactions are

$Sn^{4+} + H_2 \rightarrow Sn^{2+} + 2H^+$ (6.14)

$2H^+ + 2Br^- + \frac{1}{2}O_2 \rightarrow H_2O + Br_2$ (6.15)

Since the overall reaction is

$H_2 + \frac{1}{2}O_2 \rightarrow H_2O$ (6.16)

the cell electromotive force is governed by that for a primary hydrogen-oxygen fuel cell. Thus, the ideal efficiency, with respect to the free-energy change of reaction (6.16), is that of hydrogen-oxygen cell multiplied by the efficiency of solution-phase regenerative reactions (6.14) and (6.15), which may have a theoretical value of unity.   Thus, the efficiencies of these systems can attain high values close to unity, unlike thermally regenerative fuel cells which are limited by the Carnot efficiency.

Although there are no intrinsic efficiency losses in homogeneous-phase redox reactions, extrinsic efficiency losses occur when reactions take place at finite rates, i.e., not reversibly.   Such a case will be associated with rise or fall of temperature in the solution.

The disadvantage of such systems is that the anolyte and catholyte compartments have to be separated by a membrane to prevent direct chemical reaction of electrode reactants, but inclusion of a membrane increases the ohmic losses in the cell.

6.4   Photochemically Regenerative Fuel Cells

There are basically two types of photochemically regenerative systems (Figs. 9 and 10).   In one, the product of the electrochemical reaction AB is converted to

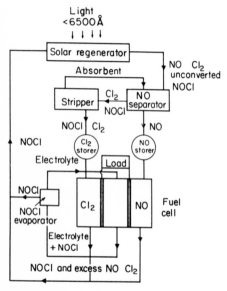

Figure 9   The mode of operation of the first type of photochemically regenerative fuel cell.[20]

the reactants A and B by photochemical dissociation.   These reactions may be represented by

Electrochemical: $A + B \rightarrow AB + \text{electricity}$ (6.17)

Photochemical: $AB + \text{light} \rightarrow A + B$ (6.18)

Overall: $\text{Light} \rightarrow \text{electricity}$ (6.19)

An example is the nitric oxide–chlorine cell, in which the product of the fuel-cell reaction, nitrosyl chloride, is decomposed photochemically.[20]

In the other type, a dye D and a compatible reducing agent HR react chemically in the presence of light in the anode compartment of an "illuminated" cell.[21]

$D + HR + \text{light} \rightarrow DH + R$ (6.20)

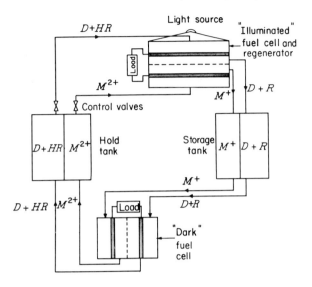

Figure 10 The second type of photochemically regenerative fuel cell.[21]

DH diffuses to the anode, where it is oxidized:

$$DH \rightarrow D + H^+ + e_0^-$$ (6.21)

The cathode reaction is:

$$M^{2+} + e_0^- \rightarrow M^+$$ (6.22)

where M^+/M^{2+} represents the two valence states of a suitable oxidation-reduction couple. Thus, the overall reaction in the illuminated cell is

$$HR + M^{2+} + light \rightarrow R + H^+ + M^+ + electricity$$ (6.23)

The products of the illuminated cell are led to a dark cell, where the anodic and cathodic reactions are

$$M^+ \rightarrow M^{2+} + e_0^-$$ (6.24)

$$R + H^+ + e_0^- \rightarrow HR$$ (6.25)

The overall reaction in the dark cell is

$$R + H^+ + M^+ \rightarrow HR + M^{2+} + electricity$$ (6.26)

The two reactions (6.23) and (6.26) again add up to

$$Light \rightarrow electricity$$ (6.27)

There are two reactions yielding electrical energy. The efficiency of conversion of chemical and light energy to electrical energy of the first reaction, represented by Eq. (6.23), is $\epsilon_1 \varphi$. The efficiency of the second reaction [Eq. (6.26)] depends on that of the first and is $\epsilon_2\epsilon_1\varphi$. Thus, the overall efficiency ϵ of this type of photochemical regenerative fuel cell may be expressed by

$$\epsilon = \epsilon_1\varphi + \epsilon_1\epsilon_2\varphi \qquad (6.28)$$

where φ is the quantum yield for the photochemical reaction (6.20) and ϵ_1 and ϵ_2 are the overall efficiencies of the illuminated and dark fuel cells, respectively.

6.5   Electrically Regenerative Fuel Cells

In an electrically regenerative fuel cell, the products of the fuel-cell reaction are reconverted into its reactants electrically. As the name of this type of cell suggests, it is in effect like a storage battery. However, storage batteries are always sealed units and the charging and discharging processes are carried out in the battery itself. In the case of an electrically regenerative fuel cell, this is not necessarily the case, and the fuel-cell reaction may occur in one cell and its products led into another cell where regeneration occurs.

A good example of an electrically regenerative fuel cell is the lithium-chlorine fuel cell.[10]   The fuel-cell reaction is

$$2Li + Cl_2 \rightarrow 2LiCl \qquad (6.29)$$

The regeneration reaction is represented by the reverse of Eq. (6.29). Another example is the hydrogen-bromine fuel cell.[9]

The efficiency of an electrically regenerative fuel cell is the product of the efficiencies in the fuel and regenerative cells.

6.6   Radiochemically Regenerative Fuel Cells

Nuclear energy is available in large quantities. At the present time, the most common way of converting this energy to electricity is via the intermediate of heat. Thus, the Carnot limitation applies in this approach.

A better method of conversion of nuclear energy to electrical energy may appear to be the development of radiochemically regenerative fuel cells. In addition to the absence of the Carnot limitation, there are other advantages to be compared with those of conventional nuclear reactors such as absence of moving parts and of high temperatures. Here, the products of the fuel-cell reaction are reconverted into its reactants by α, β, or γ radiation from a radioactive source. One may consider the hydrogen-oxygen fuel cell. The regeneration may be expressed by[22]

$$2H_2O + \gamma \rightarrow 2H_2 + O_2 \qquad (6.30)$$

Another example is the hydrogen-halogen (Cl_2 or Br_2) fuel cell, in which case γ radiation may also be used to decompose the hydrogen halides.[23]

The efficiency of a radiochemically regenerative fuel cell is the product of the fuel-cell efficiency and that of the radiochemical process. The efficiency loss due to the recombination process (ϵ_r) at the present time is fairly high (more than 80 percent). Since the practical efficiencies of hydrogen-oxygen and of hydrogen-halogen fuel cells are quite high (over 70 percent), overall efficiencies are about 14 percent. With further research on the mechanism of the recombination processes, it may be possible to reach high overall efficiencies.

REFERENCES

1. Glasstone, S.: "Thermodynamics for Chemists," D. Van Nostrand Company, Inc., Princeton, N.J., 1963.
2. Kirkwood, J. A., and I. Oppenheim: "Chemical Thermodynamics," McGraw-Hill Book Company, New York, 1961.
3. Lewis, A. N., and M. Randall: "Thermodynamics and the Free Energy of Chemical Substances," McGraw-Hill Book Company, New York, 1928.
4. Klotz, I. M.: "Introduction to Chemical Thermodynamics," W. A. Benjamin, Inc., New York, 1964.
5. Guggenheim, E. A.: "Thermodynamics," 14th ed., Interscience Publishers, Inc., New York, 1957.
6. Wall, F. T.: "Chemical Thermodynamics," 2d ed., W. H. Freeman and Company, San Francisco, 1965; W. F. Ludher, "A Different Approach to Thermodynamics," Reinhold Publishing Corporation, New York, 1967; R. S. Benson, "Advanced Engineering Thermodynamics," Pergamon Press, New York, 1967.
7. Carnot, S.: Reflections on Motive Power of Heat (English translation by R. H. Thurston), American Society Mechanical Engineers, 1953.
8. Justi, E., and A. W. Winsel: "Kalte-Verbrennung," Franz Steiner Verlag, Wiesbaden, 1962.
9. Berger, C.: Fuel Cells, *Advan. Chem. Ser. 47*, chap. 14, American Chemical Society, Washington, D.C., 1965.
10. Swinkels, D. A. J.: *J. Electrochem. Soc.*, **113**, 6 (1966).
11. Henderson, R. E.: Fuel Cells, *Am. Inst. Chem. Eng. Progr. Tech. Manual* 17 (1963).
12. Morrill, C. C.: *Proc. Ann. Power Sources Conf.*, **19**, 38 (1965).
13. Gileadi, E., and S. Srinivasan: *J. Electroanal. Chem.*, **7**, 452 (1964).
14. Grubb, W. T.: *Nature*, **198**, 883 (1963).
15. Shropshire, J. A., and B. L. Tarmy: Fuel Cells, *Advan. Chem. Ser. 47*, chap. 12, American Chemical Society, Washington, D.C., 1965.
16. Archer, D. H., J. J. Alles, W. A. English, L. Elikan, E. F. Sverdrup, and R. L. Zahradnik: *Advan. Chem. Ser. 47*, chap. 24, American Chemical Society, Washington, D.C., 1965.
17. De Bethune, A. J.: *J. Electrochem. Soc.*, **107**, 937 (1960).
18. Friauf, J. B.: *J. Appl. Phys.*, **32**, 616 (1961).
19. Posner, A. M.: *Fuel*, **43**, 330 (1955).
20. McKee, W. E., E. Findl, J. D. Margerum, and W. B. Lee: *Proc. Ann. Power Sources Conf.*, **14**, 68 (1960).
21. Eisenberg, M., and H. P. Silverman: *Electrochim. Acta.*, **5**, 1 (1961).
22. Rosenblum, L., and R. E. English: Advanced Energy Sources and Conversion Techniques, *Off. Tech. Serv. Dept. Comm. Rept.*, PB 151461 (Astia No. AD 209301), 1, 243.
23. Gomberg, J., and R. A. Lee: Private communication (1966).

CHAPTER FOUR

Some Electrode Kinetic Aspects of Electrochemical Energy Conversion

1 GENERAL

The present chapter consists of a collection of only partly connected topics, but all of which deal with attempts to attain a more mathematical formulation of electrode kinetic aspects of electrochemical energy conversion. Hitherto, not many published contributions[1,2,2a] in electrode kinetic theory, applied to cells, exist.

In some respects, equational treatments presented in this chapter are too much those of principle and not yet developed toward practice in that they do not take into account electrode kinetic formulations in terms of porous electrodes. However, they may serve as a basis for more realistic formulations in future years, at least in terms of computer-evaluated solutions to the complicated equations to which porous-electrode theory gives rise (Chap. 5).

Among topics treated in this chapter are initial and simplified analyses of various types of unconventional electrode systems, some of which have not yet been realized in practice.

2 BASIC SIMILARITIES AND DISSIMILARITIES AMONG THE THREE ELECTROCHEMICAL DEVICES[1]

Until recently, attention was paid too strongly to the differences between driven and spontaneously acting electrochemical devices. During the past few years, the connections of the chemistry of spontaneously acting electrochemical energy conversion processes to electrode kinetics occurring under driven conditions at individual interfaces became clear; and now there is perhaps too much identification of the driven with the spontaneously acting surface.

Although there is a large degree of truth in the view that in electrochemical reactors it is simply the electrode reactions which function in a way made familiar from experimental work under driven conditions, the differences between driven and spontaneously acting electrochemical cells should be formulated. At the same time, the rechargeable battery and its relation to fuel cells should be considered. It is suggested that the terminology in the field would be more understandable to those beginning its study if the principal terms were more literal. Thus, one may suggest:

Fuel cell = Electrochemical electricity producer (ecep) or electrochemical energy converter (ecec)

Driven cell = Electrochemical substance producer (ecsp)

Rechargeable or secondary battery = Electrochemical electricity storer (eces)

The usual grouping together of primary and secondary batteries seems inappropriate: primary cells are simply "fuel cells" that have internal fuel storage. It is the secondary cell which has a unique function, which distinguishes it from the other devices grouped together here. It *stores electricity*, i.e., it accepts it and redelivers it. This electrochemical device is the only known way of storing electricity and having it available on demand.

The similarities and differences of the three types of electrochemical devices are shown in Table 1.

3 IMPORTANCE OF ELECTRODE KINETICS IN ELECTROCHEMICAL ENERGY CONVERSION

At the present time, considerable (nonohmic) overpotential losses occur in nearly all working fuel cells, the exceptions being certain high- and medium-temperature fuel cells (for example, the lithium-chlorine and high-temperature hydrogen-oxygen fuel cells) and the low-temperature hydrogen-bromine fuel cell. Significant overpotential losses are observed not only in low-temperature cells. For example, these losses exist in cells involving oxidation of CO at temperatures of about 600°C (Chap. 10, Sec. 2.3.2).

Potential losses may be classified under activation, mass transfer, and ohmic overpotential, which quantities are the central foci of interest in the field of electrochemical energy conversion. A goal in electrochemical energy conversion is to attain high efficiencies at practical current densities, which is possible only by solving the problems of reduction in overpotential at any desired current density. In a wider sense, the attainment of satisfactory electrochemical energy conversion depends on (1) an understanding of electrode kinetics, at a molecular level of mechanism, by which overpotential losses arise; (2) realization of the fundamental electrode kinetics upon which practical

TABLE 1   Similarities and Dissimilarities among the Three Basic Electrochemical Devices

Electrochemical substance producer (driven cell)	Electrochemical electricity producer (fuel cell or electrochemical energy converter)	Electrochemical electricity storer (secondary battery)
Accepts electricity and produces substance	Accepts substances and produces electricity	Accepts electricity and produces electricity
Cathode is negative; anode is positive	Cathode is positive; anode is negative	During discharge, cathode is positive, anode is negative; vice versa during charging
Reaction is forced to occur against spontaneous free energy tendency by external power source	Reaction spontaneous	Reaction spontaneous during discharge
The driving cell is tacit, inexplicit; the thermodynamic potential and the electrocatalytic properties of the substrate are economically important but are subject to potential of driving cell	The load is tacit, but explicit; the thermodynamic potential is a central point	The load is tacit, explicit; the thermodynamic potential is a central point during discharge
In principle, can operate ad infinitum	In principle, can operate ad infinitum	Intrinsically limited to store certain amount of electric energy
Can be regarded in terms of a single electrode at which substance in question is produced	Behavior determined importantly by both electrodes	Behavior determined importantly by both electrodes during discharge
Potential of driving cell shifts potentials of electrodes in driven cell till desired current is reached. *Current* increases with increase of activation overpotential	Thermodynamic potential of cell reaction creates current, which in turn sets up overpotential. *Overpotential* increases with increase of current	During charge, cf. substance producer. During discharge cf. electricity producer

devices are based; (3) an understanding at the molecular level of the instability of materials under prolonged use, particularly under electric fields; and (4) engineering solutions to the problems of heat transfer in multicell electrochemical electricity producers.

The overpotential losses are caused by some or all of the consecutive processes occurring at the electrodes and in solution. An ultimate aim of electrochemical energy conversion, from the economic side, is to use cheap fuels, e.g., hydrocarbons. With such fuels, as with many others, the major losses are due to activation overpotential (Chap. 2, Sec. 3) associated with the slow step in the electrochemical reaction at the interface. Further, the best electrocatalyst, hitherto known, for the electrochemical oxidation of hydrocarbons is platinum. It is vital to develop electrocatalysts considerably cheaper than this metal for the efficient utilization of hydrocarbons in electrochemical electricity producers (Chap. 6, Sec. 1). In view of the importance of the development of fuel cells using electroorganic fuels, Chap. 7 is entirely devoted to this field.

The optimization of the mass-transfer conditions in fuel cells is an important field. It determines the maximum rate at which the reactor can work. The upper limit of current at which mass-transfer control prevents further gain of power by increase of current density is considerably affected by the use of porous gas-diffusion electrodes (Chap. 5). The present chapter deals with the theory of electrode kinetics special to problems encountered in electrochemical energy conversion, excluding those using porous electrodes (which are dealt with in Chap. 5), and with the elementary theory of some possible methods of increasing power density.

4 THE BASIC CELL POTENTIAL-CURRENT RELATION OF AN ELECTROCHEMICAL ENERGY CONVERTER

In the kinetic study of electrode reactions, the relation of fundamental importance is that between the current density, i.e., a measure of the reaction rate, and the potential of the test electrode versus a reference electrode. In an electrochemical energy converter, the important relation is between the terminal cell potential and the current. The basic equation which represents it is presented in this section, with the simplifying assumptions that the reactions occur at *planar* surfaces to avoid the mathematical complexities of porous electrodes, which prevents analytical solutions.[1] All trends and tendencies indicated here for planar electrodes remain true if kinetic equations for porous electrodes are used. Positions of maximum power density, optimum working conditions, etc., will, of course, change somewhat. Calculations for porous electrode situations similar to the ones presented in this chapter may be made with equations presented in Chap. 5 but mainly with numerical solutions.

As can be seen in Table 1, the current across a driven cell is the result of the overpotentials forced upon electrodes by outside sources. The independent variable is the overpotential. In the converter, the independent variable is the external load. Thus, the current I is given by

$$I = \frac{(V_c - V_a) - \eta_{\text{ohm}}}{R_e} \tag{4.1}$$

where V is the electrode potential of either cathode or anode (as indicated by the suffixes c or a). The ohmic loss in the cell is η_{ohm}, and R_e is the resistance of the external load. The potential of the cathode V_c is positive with respect to that of the anode V_a. This is the first condition which must be fulfilled in examining potential fuel-cell reactions. This condition corresponds to a negative free-energy change for the overall fuel-cell reaction (Chap. 3, Sec. 3).

The potential of the cathode is given by

$$V_c = V_{r,c} - \sum \eta_c$$
$$= V_{r,c} - \eta_{c,act} - \eta_{c,conc} \tag{4.2}$$

Similarly, for the anode,

$$V_a = V_{r,a} + \sum \eta$$
$$= V_{r,a} + \eta_{a,act} + \eta_{a,conc} \tag{4.3}$$

The suffixes "act" and "conc" denote activation and concentration overpotentials, respectively (Chap. 2, Sec. 3). Since cathodic and anodic processes are associated with negative and positive overpotentials, respectively, the cathode potential is its reversible potential ($V_{r,c}$) diminished by the overpotential, and the anode potential is correspondingly its reversible potential ($V_{r,a}$) enhanced by its overpotential. [η's in Eqs. (4.2), (4.3), and the rest of this section represent the magnitudes of the overpotential without sign.]

If one considers a situation in which both cathodic and anodic reactions of the cell are in the linear Tafel region (cf. Chap. 2, Sec. 3),

$$\eta_{c,act} = -\frac{RT}{\alpha_c F} \ln i_{0,c} + \frac{RT}{\alpha_c F} \ln \frac{I}{A_c} \tag{4.4}$$

$$\eta_{c,conc} = -\frac{RT}{nF} \ln \left(1 - \frac{I}{A_c i_{L,c}}\right) \tag{4.5}$$

$$\eta_{a,act} = -\frac{RT}{\alpha_a F} \ln i_{0,a} + \frac{RT}{\alpha_a F} \ln \frac{I}{A_a} \tag{4.6}$$

$$\eta_{a,conc} = -\frac{RT}{nF} \ln \left(1 - \frac{I}{A_a i_{L,a}}\right) \tag{4.7}$$

A's and α's with the appropriate suffixes denote the areas of the respective electrodes and the transfer coefficients for the respective electrode reactions; n is the number of electrons transferred per act of overall reaction.

In addition, the ohmic potential loss between the electrodes is given by

$$\eta_{ohm} = IR_i \tag{4.8}$$

where R_i is the internal resistance of the cell.
Use of Eqs. (4.4) and (4.5) in Eq. (4.2) yields

$$V_c = V_{r,c} - \frac{RT}{\alpha_c F} \ln \frac{I}{A_c i_{0,c}} + \frac{RT}{nF} \ln \left(1 - \frac{I}{A i_{L,c}}\right) \tag{4.9}$$

Similarly, using Eqs. (4.6) and (4.7) in Eq. (4.3) gives

$$V_a = V_{r,a} + \frac{RT}{\alpha_a F} \ln \frac{I}{A i_{0,a}} - \frac{RT}{nF} \ln \left(1 - \frac{I}{A i_{L,a}}\right) \tag{4.10}$$

Substituting for V_c and V_a from Eqs. (4.9) and (4.10) and for η_{ohm} from (4.8) in Eq. (4.1), one has

$$IR_e = E = \left[E_r - \frac{RT}{\alpha_c F} \ln \frac{I}{A_c i_{0,c}} + \frac{RT}{nF} \ln \left(1 - \frac{I}{A_c i_L} \right) - \frac{RT}{\alpha_a F} \ln \frac{I}{A_a i_{0,a}} \right.$$

$$\left. + \frac{RT}{nF} \ln \left(1 - \frac{I}{A_a i_{L,a}} \right) - IR_i \right] \quad (4.11)$$

where E_r is the thermodynamic reversible potential of the cell and is given by

$$E_r = V_{r,c} - V_{r,a} \quad (4.12)$$

The quantity IR_e is the potential that the reactor has available for impelling the current through the external load R_e. It can be referred to as the "cell potential" E and is the total thermodynamic cell potential, diminished by the internal potential losses, i.e., the overpotentials and the internal ohmic potential drop, which is caused by the passage of current between the electrodes in the cell.

Assuming for the plot in Fig. 1 that the internal ohmic potential drop IR_i is small, one may examine the relationship of E to V_c and V_a. In Fig. 1, V_c and V_a

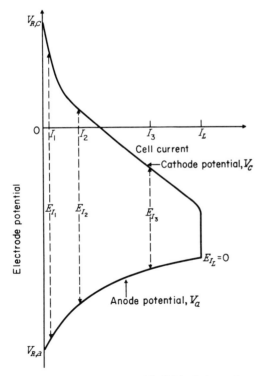

Figure 1 Typical relation of individual electrode potentials V to cell potential E and to current I in an electrochemical energy converter.

are plotted as a function of current for a typical case. Under the assumed conditions of negligible internal resistance of the cell, the difference between V_c and V_a is the cell potential (i.e., the potential difference across the load R_e). When the current tends towards the limiting current I_L for one of the partial reactions, the cell potential approaches zero.

Figure 2 is a typical cell potential-current density (assuming anodic and cathodic areas are equal) curve for an electricity producer showing the regions of influences of the various factors—i.e., activation, concentration, and ohmic overpotential.

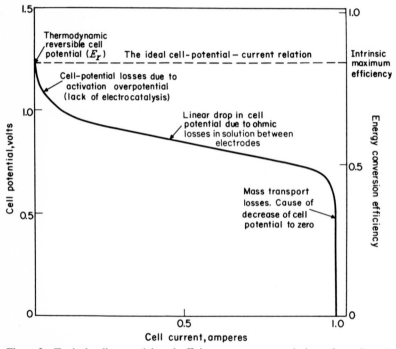

Figure 2 Typical cell potential and efficiency vs. current relation of an electro-chemical electricity producer showing regions of major influence of various types of overpotential losses.

Equation (4.11) allows one, from a knowledge of fundamental electrochemical parameters ($i_{0,c}$, $i_{0,a}$, $i_{L,c}$, $i_{L,a}$, and E_r), to calculate the cell potential corresponding to a given current. This calculation has been carried out varying the parameters, as indicated in Table 2. Figure 3 shows the effect of variation of Ai_0 keeping Ai_L and R constant for two extreme values of R_i. Initially there is a marked decrease in E; thereafter, the E-I relation is nearly linear until the limiting current. The lower the exchange current density for one of the partial electrode reactions, the sharper is the initial drop in the cell potential. When $R_i = 1$ ohm, because of the significant ohmic drop in the cell, the cell potential reaches zero at currents less than the limiting current.

TABLE 2   Assumed Electrode Kinetic Parameters in the Theoretical Analysis of their Effects on the Performance of Electrochemical Reactor

Calculation number	$A_a i_{0,a}$, amp	$A_c i_{0,c}$, amp	$A_a i_{L,a}$, amp	$A_c i_{L,c}$, amp	α_a	α_c	R_i, ohms
I	10^{-3}	10^{-9}	1	1	$\frac{1}{2}$	$\frac{1}{2}$	1
II	10^{-3}	10^{-3}	1	1	$\frac{1}{2}$	$\frac{1}{2}$	1
III	>1	10^{-3}	1	1	∞	$\frac{1}{2}$	1
IV	10^{-3}	10^{-3}	1	1	$\frac{1}{2}$	$\frac{1}{2}$	0.1
V	>1	10^{-3}	1	1	∞	$\frac{1}{2}$	0.1
VI	10^{-3}	10^{-3}	1	1	$\frac{1}{2}$	$\frac{1}{2}$	0.01
VII	>1	10^{-3}	1	1	∞	$\frac{1}{2}$	0.01
VIII	10^{-3}	10^{-6}	1	1	$\frac{1}{2}$	$\frac{1}{2}$	1
IX	10^{-3}	10^{-6}	1	1	$\frac{1}{2}$	$\frac{1}{2}$	0.1
X	>1	10^{-6}	1	1	∞	$\frac{1}{2}$	0.1
XI	>1	10^{-3}	0.1	0.1	∞	$\frac{1}{2}$	0.01
XII	>1	10^{-6}	0.1	0.1	∞	$\frac{1}{2}$	1

The linear portions of these curves have approximately the same slopes, which correspond to the ohmic resistance. The effect of exchange current density is seen even more clearly when $R_i = 0.01$ ohm. There is a steeper initial drop in curve VI than in curve VII. When $R_i = 0.01$ ohm, the cell potential reaches zero at the limiting current, i.e., the influence of the ohmic drop in the cell on

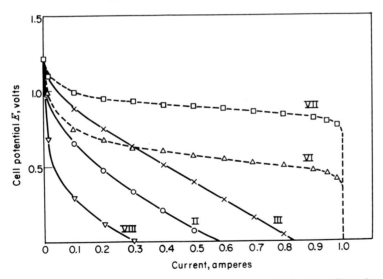

Figure 3   Plots of terminal cell potential E vs. current I showing effect of variation of $A i_0$ at constant values of $A i_L$ and R_i (see Table 2 for assumed kinetic parameters).[1]   Solid lines are for $R_i = 1$ ohm and broken lines are for $R_i = 0.01$ ohm.

the cell potential at this value of the current density is negligible.   This may also be easily seen from curves VI and VII in that the linear portions are nearly parallel to the current axis.

In Fig. 4, the effect of variation of Ai_L while Ai_0 and R_i are constants is shown.   The range of current is reduced by a decade for a reduction of i_L by a factor of 10.   Otherwise, the shape of the E-I curve is essentially independent of i_L.

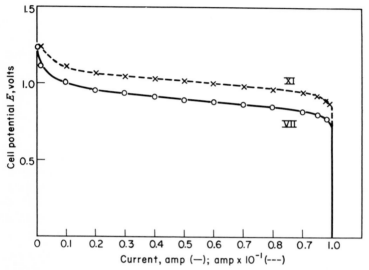

Figure 4   Plots of terminal cell potential E vs. current I showing effect of variation of Ai_L at constant values of Ai_0 and R_i (see Table 2 for assumed kinetic parameters).[1]

Figure 5 shows the marked effect of the internal resistance of the cell on the slope of linear E-I region while maintaining Ai_0 and Ai_L constant.   Two cases are considered here.   When the electrode reactions have high exchange current densities [curves III, V, and VII (see Table 2)], the initial drop in cell potential is small.   It is followed by the resistance-dependent linear portion.   The lower the internal resistance of the cell, the smaller is the slope of the linear portion. For curve III, where $R_i = 1$ ohm, the slope of the curve is so sharp that E reaches zero before the limiting current is reached.   This is not so for the other values of R_i (curves V and VII).   In the second case, where the exchange current densities are not too high (curves VIII and IX), the initial drop in cell potential is quite high.   Thus, the linear portion intersects the current axis corresponding to $E = 0$ for currents less than the limiting current.   This figure shows the importance of reducing the internal resistance of the cell.   However, as seen from Fig. 3, the linear region is approximately parallel to the I axis when

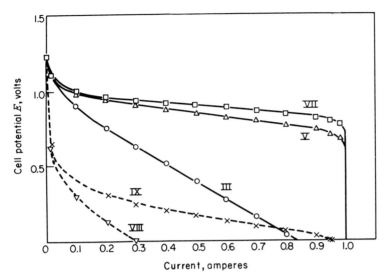

Figure 5 Plots of terminal cell potential E vs. current I showing effect of variation of R_i at constant values of Ai_0 and Ai_L; solid and broken lines are for two sets of values of Ai_0 (see Table 2 for assumed kinetic parameters).[1]

$R_i = 0.01$ ohm, and it can be raised considerably in a parallel direction only by increasing the exchange current densities significantly.

5 THE DIFFERENTIAL RESISTANCE OF AN ELECTROCHEMICAL ENERGY CONVERTER AS A FUNCTION OF CURRENT

The differential resistance of an electrochemical energy converter (dE/dI) is given by[1] [cf. Eq. (4.11)]

$$\frac{dE}{dI} = -\frac{RT}{\alpha_c FI} - \frac{RT}{\alpha_a FI} - \frac{RT}{nF(A_c i_{L,c} - I)} - \frac{RT}{nF(A_a i_{L,a} - I)} - R_i \qquad (5.1)$$

It is plotted as a function of current density in Figs. 6 to 8.

The effect of concentration overpotential on the slope dE/dI is seen only close to the limiting current. The importance of the activation overpotential on the slope of the differential-resistance–current relations (Figs. 6 to 8) is predominant in the low current density region. At intermediate current densities, however (i.e., at values of current densities such that $(IR_i)/(RT/F) > 10$), the effect of activation overpotential on dE/dI is less than 10 percent of R_i. If R_i is unity, this value of I is 0.25 amp. This would account for the near constancy of dE/dI with current density in the middle range of I in a number of the cases (cf. Chap. 10).†

† This deduction would apply even more so to the real situation in which porous electrodes (Chap. 5) are used. Here the ohmic drop is intrinsic because it occurs in the pores of the electrodes.

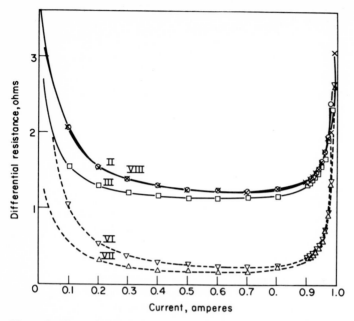

Figure 6 Plots of differential resistance dE/dI vs. current I corresponding to E-I curves in Fig. 3.[1]

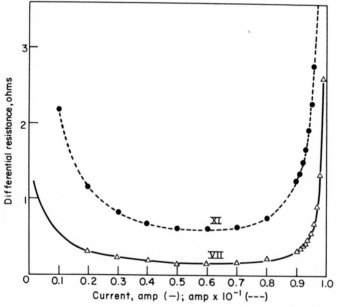

Figure 7 Plots of differential resistance dE/dI vs. current I corresponding to E-I curves in Fig. 4.[1]

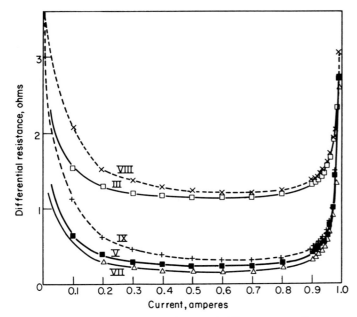

Figure 8   Plots of differential resistance dE/dI vs. current I corresponding to E-I curves in Fig. 5.[1]

6   OVERALL EFFICIENCY OF AN ELECTROCHEMICAL ENERGY CONVERTER AS A FUNCTION OF CURRENT

The efficiency of an electrochemical electricity producer is given by (Chap. 3, Sec. 4)

$$\epsilon = -\frac{nF}{\Delta H} E \tag{6.1}$$

From Eqs. (4.11) and (6.1) together with

$$E = IR_e \tag{6.2}$$

it follows that[1]

$$\epsilon = -\frac{nF}{\Delta H}\left[E_r - \frac{RT}{\alpha_c F}\ln\frac{I}{A_c i_{0,c}} + \frac{RT}{nF}\left(1 - \frac{I}{A_c i_{L,c}}\right)\right.$$
$$\left. -\frac{RT}{\alpha_a F}\ln\frac{I}{A_a i_{0,a}} + \frac{RT}{nF}\ln\left(1 - \frac{I}{A_c i_{L,c}}\right) - IR_i\right] \tag{6.3}$$

It follows from Eqs. (4.11) and (6.3) that ϵ and E vary in the same way with I.   Thus, an analysis of the effect of the various kinetic and physical parameters on the efficiency is similar to the one found in the preceding section.   Plots of efficiency vs. current for the various cases corresponding to the *E-I* plots (Figs. 3 to 5) are shown in Figs. 9 to 11.   The efficiency is close to unity at limitingly low values of current density and decreases monotonously with increasing *I*.

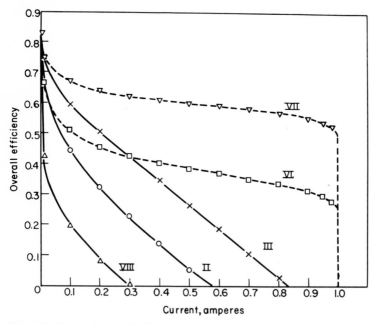

Figure 9 Plots of overall efficiency ε vs. current *I* corresponding to *E-I* curves in Fig. 3.[1]

7 POWER OF AN ELECTROCHEMICAL ENERGY CONVERTER AS A FUNCTION OF CURRENT

The power *P* of an electrochemical reactor is given by

$$P = IE \tag{7.1}$$

Power is expressed in watts. If *I* is the current density, power density is in watts cm^{-2}.   Qualitatively, one can examine the nature of the *P-I* relation.   When *I* is low, *E* is high; and, conversely, when *I* is high, *E* is low. Thus, the *P-I* curve should pass through a maximum.   Figure 12 is a qualitative representation of the power-density–current-density relation in a hypothetical fuel cell.   The hypothetical curve, corresponding to no overpotential losses in the fuel cell, is also shown.   Explanations for the decreased power in the various regions of the *P*-versus-*I* curve are indicated.   The *P-I* curves pass through the origin, since when *I* = 0, *P* = 0.   If one compares the *P-I* and ε-*I* curves, it will be seen that the efficiency is a maximum when *P* = 0 and the ε-*I* curve

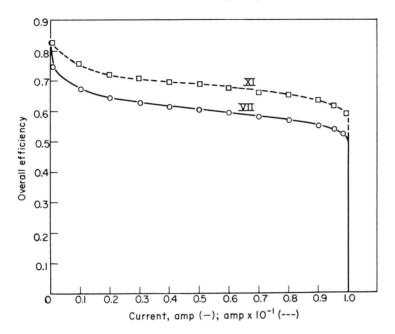

Figure 10 Plots of overall efficiency ϵ vs. current I corresponding to $E\text{-}I$ curves in Fig. 4.[1]

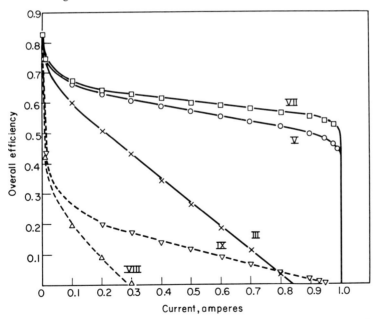

Figure 11 Plots of overall efficiency ϵ vs. current I corresponding to $E\text{-}I$ curves in Fig. 5.[1]

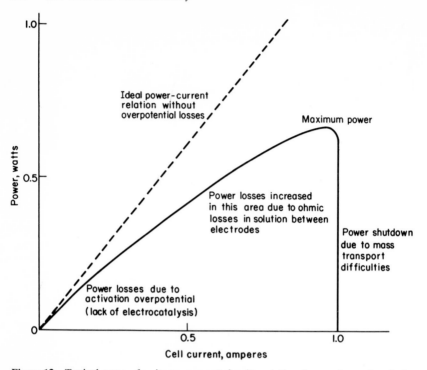

Figure 12   Typical power density vs. current density relation for an electrochemical electricity producer showing reasons for power losses in various regions.

steadily decreases with increasing I, whereas the P-I curve first increases, passes through a maximum, and then decreases to a power of zero when E reaches 0.

From Eqs. (4.11) and (7.1), it follows that[1]

$$P = I \left[E_r - \frac{RT}{\alpha_c F} \ln \frac{I}{A_c i_{0,c}} + \frac{RT}{nF} \ln \left(1 - \frac{I}{A_c i_{L,c}} \right) \right.$$

$$\left. - \frac{RT}{\alpha_a F} \ln \frac{I}{A_a i_{0,a}} + \frac{RT}{nF} \ln \left(1 - \frac{I}{A_a i_{L,a}} \right) - IR_i \right] \quad (7.2)$$

The power is plotted as a function of I in Figs. 13 to 15 for the same variations in kinetic parameters as in Figs. 3 to 5, respectively. At any particular value of I, the power is significantly increased with increase of $A i_0$. P is also increased by decrease of R_i. In most of the cases calculated, except when the internal resistance is high or when $A i_0$, even for one of the electrodes, is low, the maximum power is close to the limiting current.

In cases where the cell voltage tends to zero before the limiting current is reached, the P-I plots are parabolic.

It must be stressed that the deductions and corresponding plots refer to

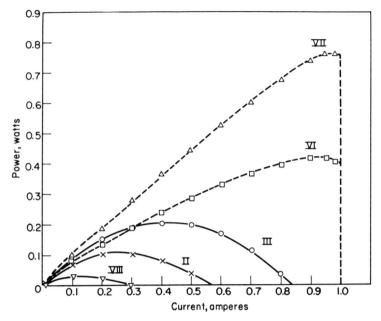

Figure 13 Plots of power *P* vs. current *I* corresponding to *E-I* curves in Fig. 3.[1]

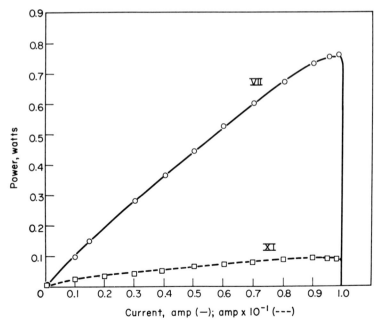

Figure 14 Plots of power *P* vs. current *I* corresponding to *E-I* curves in Fig. 4.[1]

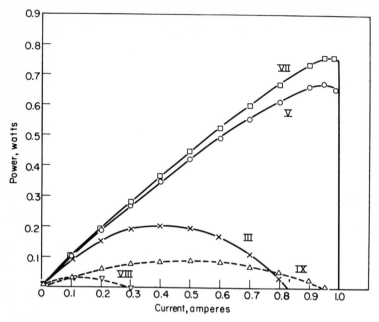

Figure 15   Plots of power P vs. current I corresponding to E-I curves in Fig. 5.[1]

ideal "single-cell" fuel cells in which *planar electrodes* of effective area A_a and A_c are used. Hence, such expressions will not quantitatively apply to real situations where porous electrodes (Chap. 5) are used, but the trends that are observed with variations of i_0, i_L, and R_i are similar.

By combining the E-I curves with the corresponding P-I ones, the power may be plotted as a function of the cell potential. The P-E curves for the variations in kinetic parameters according to Table 2 are shown in Figs. 16 to 18. The maximum power is found in most of these cases at low cell potentials, which occurs near the limiting current. However, in the cases where the cell potential drops to zero before the limiting current is reached, the P-E curves are parabolic and the maximum power occurs at nearly half the reversible cell potential (see below).

A general analytical expression for the cell potential or current at which the power is a maximum is difficult to obtain even for the great simplification introduced by considering an idealized fuel-cell element with planar, instead of the usual porous, electrodes. This may, however, be done for some limiting cases as shown below.

(i) Conditions under which the E-I relation is linear

Under the condition when the electrode reactions are fast, the sum of the activation overpotentials η_{act} at both electrodes varies linearly with the current

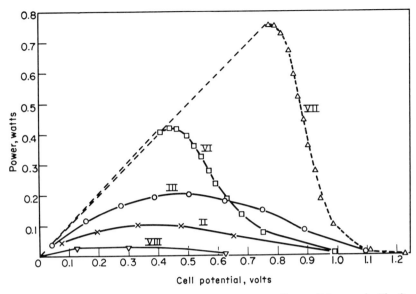

Figure 16 Plots of power P vs. cell potential E corresponding to E-I curves in Fig. 3.

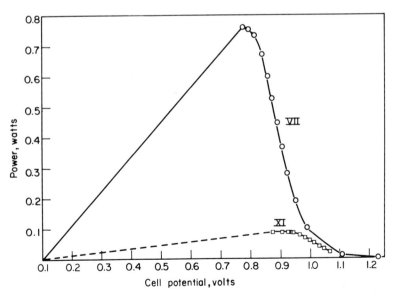

Figure 17 Plots of power P vs. cell potential E corresponding to E-I curves in Fig. 4.

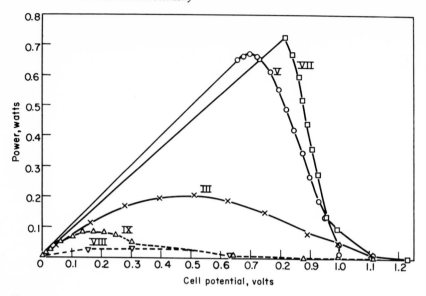

Figure 18   Plots of power P vs. cell potential E corresponding to E-I curves in Fig. 5.

according to the equation (cf. Chap. 2, Sec. 3.6.6)

$$\eta_{act} = \frac{RT}{F}\left(\frac{I}{A_a i_{0,a}} + \frac{I}{A_c i_{0,c}}\right) \tag{7.3}$$

This is a case seldom obtained; an example would be hydrogen-bromine fuel cells. Further, if $I \ll A_a i_{L,a}$ and $I \ll A_c i_{L,c}$, the total concentration over-potential η_{conc} is given by (cf. Chap. 2, Sec. 3.7.3)

$$\eta_{conc} = \frac{RT}{F}\left(\frac{I}{A_c i_{L,c}} + \frac{I}{A_a i_{L,a}}\right) \tag{7.4}$$

Thus, all forms of polarization vary linearly with the current and the terminal cell potential is given by

$$E = E_r - IR_t \tag{7.5}$$

where

$$R_t = \frac{RT}{F}\left[\frac{1}{A_c}\left(\frac{1}{i_{0,c}} + \frac{1}{i_{L,c}}\right) + \frac{1}{A_a}\left(\frac{1}{i_{0,a}} + \frac{1}{i_{L,a}}\right)\right] + R_i \tag{7.6}$$

R_t is the total effective resistance of the cell.   For this case, it follows from Eqs. (6.1) and (6.5) that

$$P = I(E_r - R_t I) \tag{7.7}$$

The condition for maximum power is

$$\frac{dP}{dI} = E_r - 2R_tI_m = 0 \tag{7.8}$$

that is,

$$I_m = \frac{E_r}{2R_t} \tag{7.9}$$

$$P_m = \frac{E_r{}^2}{4R_t} \tag{7.10}$$

$$E_m = E_r - I_mR_t = \frac{E_r}{2} \tag{7.11}$$

According to Eq. (7.9), the power is a maximum when the external load is equal to R_t. As seen from Eqs. (7.6) and (7.10), in order that P_m may be as high as possible, it is necessary for the exchange current densities and the limiting current densities of the relevant reactions to be as high as possible and to have low internal resistances of the cell.

Using Eqs. (6.5) and (7.5) in (6.1), the power may also be expressed in terms of R_i and R_e by the relation

$$P = E_r{}^2 \frac{R_e}{(R_e + R_i)^2} \tag{7.12}$$

(ii) Conditions under which the current-potential relation at each electrode is in the Tafel region

The mass transfer and ohmic polarizations are assumed to be negligible. The power–current-density relation is given by

$$P = I[E_r + (a_1 + a_2) - (b_1 + b_2) \log I] \tag{7.13}$$

from Eqs. (4.11) [with $R_i = 0$ and η_{conc}, as expressed by Eq. (7.4), also zero] and (7.1). In Eq. (7.13),

$$a_1 = \frac{RT}{\alpha_c F} \ln A_c i_{0,c} \tag{7.14}$$

$$a_2 = \frac{RT}{\alpha_a F} \ln A_a i_{0,a} \tag{7.15}$$

$$b_1 = \frac{RT}{\alpha_c F} \tag{7.16}$$

$$b_2 = \frac{RT}{\alpha_a F} \tag{7.17}$$

The condition for maximum power is obtained by differentiating Eq. (7.13) and equating the resulting equation to zero:

$$\frac{dP}{dI} = E_r + (a_1 + a_2) - (b_1 + b_2) \log (I_m) - (b_1 + b_2) = 0 \tag{7.18}$$

Hence,

$$\log I_m = \frac{E_r + (a_1 + a_2) - (b_1 + b_2)}{b_1 + b_2} \tag{7.19}$$

$$E_m = (b_1 + b_2) \tag{7.20}$$

$$P_m = (b_1 + b_2) \exp \frac{E_r + (a_1 + a_2) - (b_1 + b_2)}{b_1 + b_2} \tag{7.21}$$

Using Eqs. (7.14) to (7.17), Eqs. (7.19) to (7.21) may be expressed in terms of the exchange current densities and transfer coefficients. Thus

$$\log I_m$$

$$= \frac{E_r + (RT/\alpha_c F) \ln (A_c i_{0,c}) + (RT/\alpha_a F) \ln (A_a i_{0,a}) - (RT/\alpha_c F) - (RT/\alpha_a F)}{(RT/\alpha_c F) + (RT/\alpha_a F)} \tag{7.22}$$

$$E_m = \frac{RT}{\alpha_c F} + \frac{RT}{\alpha_a F} \tag{7.23}$$

$$P_m = \left(\frac{RT}{\alpha_c F} + \frac{RT}{\alpha_a F} \right)$$

$$\times \exp \left[\frac{E_r + (RT/\alpha_c F) \ln (A_c i_{0,c}) + RT/\alpha_a F \ln (A_a i_{0,a}) - (RT/\alpha_c F) - (RT/\alpha_a F)}{(RT/\alpha_c F) + (RT/\alpha_a F)} \right] \tag{7.24}$$

Equations (7.22) and (7.24) show that I_m and P_m increase as the exchange current densities increase. The effect of exchange current density on the maximum power may be seen more clearly if one makes the further simplifying assumption that activation overpotential is predominant only at one electrode (i.e., the exchange current density for the half-cell reaction at the other electrode is extremely high—say of the order of 1 amp cm^{-2}). Under these conditions, P_m is expressed by

$$P_m = \frac{RT}{\alpha_c F} A_c i_{0,c} \exp \left(\frac{E_r \alpha F}{RT} - 1 \right) \tag{7.25}$$

8 BASIC ELECTRODE KINETIC PARAMETERS AND THE PERFORMANCE OF ELECTROCHEMICAL ENERGY CONVERTERS

8.1 Influence of Exchange Current Densities

The utility of a fuel cell is determined by its efficiency at reasonable power outputs and by its maximum power. These in turn depend centrally on the cell potential-current relation for the fuel cell. From the results presented graphically in the preceding sections, the exchange current densities of the partial reactions play a leading role in determining the performance of a fuel cell. The initial drop in the cell potential-current relation is determined mainly by the exchange current density—the lower the exchange current density, the greater is this drop (Fig. 3), and hence the greater the loss of efficiency and power.

The influence of exchange current densities on the performance of fuel cells is better seen by plotting the maximum power and efficiency at the maximum power as a function of the exchange current density for constant values of limiting current densities of the half-cell reactions and of the ohmic resistance of the electrolyte. This is done for the cases corresponding to II, III, and VIII, of Table 2 in Figs. 19 and 20, respectively. (The exchange current density for one of the half-cell reactions is maintained at 10^{-3} amp cm^{-2} and the i_0 for the other half-cell reaction is varied.) The importance of using electrocatalysts with high i_0's[2b] to obtain good performance in fuel cells can be readily seen.

8.2 Influence of Thermodynamic Reversible Cell Potential

The importance of this factor has been neglected in fuel-cell discussions. Its influence on the performance of a fuel cell can be seen in some simple cases in the following way:

(*i*) If we suppose the cell potential-current relation is linear, the maximum power occurs at half the thermodynamic reversible cell potential and is given by Eq. (7.10). This equation shows that the maximum power varies linearly with the square of the thermodynamic reversible cell potential.

(*ii*) Another case is where concentration and ohmic overpotential are absent and activation overpotential exists only at one of the electrodes. For this case, according to Eq. (7.25), the maximum power varies exponentially with the reversible potential.

Thus, it is important to attempt to use electrode reactions having the highest possible thermodynamic reversible cell potentials. As seen from Table 2 in Chap. 3, alkali metal halogen cells possess the greatest advantage in this direction.

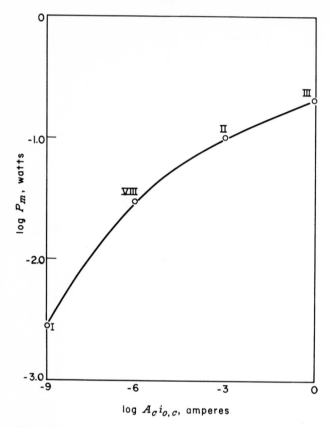

Figure 19   Maximum power vs. exchange current density for constant values of limiting current density and internal resistance of cell (see Table 2 for assumed kinetic parameters and Fig. 13 for maximum power).

8.3   Influence of Limiting Current Densities

The limiting current densities of the partial reactions play a significant role in determining the performance of a fuel cell. This is particularly so if the exchange current densities of the electrode reactions are fairly high and the ohmic resistance of the cell is low. Under these conditions, the maximum power occurs at current densities nearly equal to the limiting current density. From Fig. 17, it can be seen that the maximum power varies nearly linearly with the limiting current. The influence of concentration overpotential on the performance of a cell is seen at current densities close to i_L (Figs. 3 to 5).

Here is the origin, in the simple planar-electrode case, for the great effect of the *structure* of porous electrodes upon the power produced in a fuel cell (Chap. 5). Thus the principal difference between planar and porous electrode

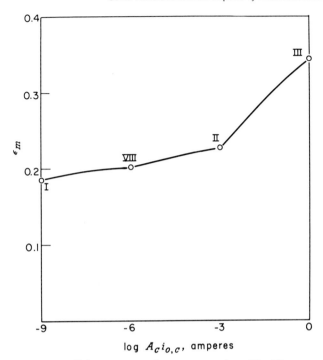

Figure 20 Efficiency at maximum power (see Fig. 19) vs. exchange current density for constant values of limiting current density and internal resistance of cell (see Table 2 for assumed kinetic parameters, Fig. 9 for efficiency, and Fig. 13 for maximum power).

situations is not so much due to the greater real area of a porous electrode per geometric square centimeter but more to the higher value of the limiting current density per real square centimeter engendered by the lowered diffusion-layer thicknesses in the thin menisci present in the pores.[2c]

8.4 Influence of Internal Resistance of the Cell

The slope of the linear region of the *E-I* curve is largely determined by the internal resistance of the cell. (Again, in porous electrodes, this is determined largely by the resistance of the solution in menisci and pores: it is hence electrode *structure* dependent.) If the slope is high, it can make the cell potential reduce to zero at currents less than the limiting current (curves II, III, and VIII in Fig. 3). The influence of the internal resistance of the cell on the maximum power may be seen by considering Eqs. (7.6) and (7.10). Suppose activation and concentration overpotentials are negligible; in Eq. (7.6), R_i is then the predominant term, and it follows from Eq. (7.10) that the maximum power varies inversely with the ohmic resistance of the cell.   In Fig. 21, the maximum power is plotted as a function of R_i, corresponding to curves III, V, and VII of Fig. 18.   The reason for the slower increase of P_m with decrease of R_i for

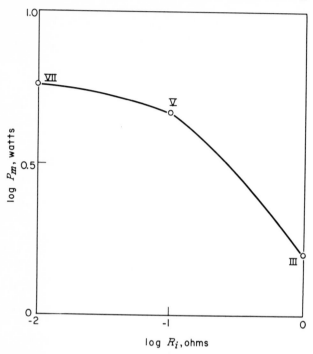

Figure 21   Maximum power as a function of internal resistance of cell for constant values of exchange and limiting current densities (see Table 2 for assumed kinetic parameters and Fig. 15 for maximum power).

$R_i \leqslant 0.1$ ohm is because the influence of i_L sets in.   In Fig. 22, the efficiency at maximum power is plotted as a function of R_i.   Here, too, the efficiency increases with decrease of R_i.   The efficiency at the maximum power level is independent of R_i for the case of negligible activation and concentration over-potentials [Eqs. (6.1) and (7.11)].

9   BASIC ELECTRODE KINETIC FACTORS AND CERTAIN APPLICATIONS

9.1   Space Applications

Much fuel-cell research activity is oriented in the direction of space applications. For these applications, two of the important criteria are the minimizing of

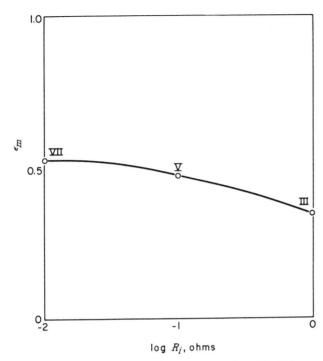

Figure 22 Efficiency at maximum power (see Fig. 21) vs. internal resistance of cell for constant values of exchange and limiting current densities (see Table 2 for assumed kinetic parameters, Fig. 11, for efficiency, and Fig. 15 for maximum power).

weight and volume of the system (including fuel, oxidant) for the required power output of the system P and the mission duration t.

The energy/weight ratio of the fuel-cell system is given by

$$\frac{\text{Energy}}{\text{Weight}} = \frac{Pt}{W_1 + Pt/\epsilon\xi} \tag{9.1}$$

where W_1 is the weight of the electrochemical energy converter and accessories, t is the time of operation, and ξ is the ratio of the energy to the weight of fuel and oxidant, assuming a 100 percent efficiency. At short times, $W_1 \gg Pt/\epsilon\xi$. Under these conditions,

$$\frac{\text{Energy}}{\text{Weight}} = \frac{Pt}{W_1} \tag{9.2}$$

that is, the energy/weight ratio increases linearly with time. At longer times, when the above approximation does not hold, the rate of increase of the energy/

weight ratio with time decreases until $Pt/\epsilon\xi \gg W_1$, whereupon:

$$\frac{\text{Energy}}{\text{Weight}} = \epsilon\xi \tag{9.3}$$

that is, there is no further increase in the energy/weight ratio with time.   This is clearly seen in Fig. 23, which is a plot of energy/weight vs. time for a hydrogen-oxygen fuel cell, for silver-zinc and lead-acid batteries, and for an engine

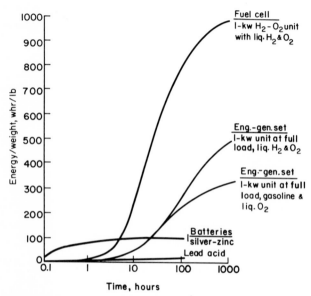

Figure 23   Plots of energy/weight ratio as a function of time for some energy converters.   (*By permission of W. Mitchell, Jr.,* "*Fuel Cells,*" *Academic Press Inc., New York*, 1963.)

generator set using hydrogen and oxygen.   At long times the curves flatten out. Figure 23 is constructed assuming a power output of 1 kW.   For this case, the advantages of the hydrogen-oxygen fuel cell over the other systems is striking. Similar plots may be made for different power outputs.   One can then make a plot of the areas of applicability of the various power sources for the different power output levels as a function of the mission duration.   Such a plot was shown in Fig. 11 of Chap. 1 ("map of the Balkans").   Fuel cells are optimal energy-conversion systems up to power levels of 100 kW for mission durations ranging from 10 hr to 1 month, if energy density is the principal criterion of goodness.

For very long missions, primary fuel cells are not suitable because of the excessive weight of the fuel and oxidant.   Even for these missions, however, regenerative (secondary) fuel cells may provide the power.   Solar or nuclear energy may be used for the regeneration of the fuel-cell reactants from the products.

The energy/volume-vs.-time-of-operation plots show characteristics similar to the energy/weight-vs.-time relations.

From Eqs. (9.1) and (9.3), it follows that the efficiency must be as high as possible to maximize the energy/weight ratio for the energy-conversion system. The efficiency of a fuel cell is given by Eq. (6.1). From the results presented in Sec. 6, it is clear that high values of efficiency are obtained if the exchange current densities and the limiting current densities of the electrode reactions have relatively high values ($i_0 > 10^{-3}$ amp cm^{-2} and $i_L > 1$ amp cm^{-2}). The numerical values quoted refer to the calculations presented in this chapter and do not have quantitative meaning for porous electrodes. As will be seen (Chap. 5), there is no single value of i_L, and a series of values exist, depending upon the position of the meniscus and pore considered.

For very short missions, the energy/weight ratio of the fuel-cell system is given by Eq. (9.2). Under these conditions, a plot of the energy/weight ratio versus time is linear and the slope is given by P/W_1. P/W_1 is simply the power/weight ratio of the system. The power of a fuel cell is expressed by Eq. (7.2). In Sec. 7, it was shown that the power is also maximized when the exchange current densities and limiting current densities of the electrode reactions are as high as possible and the internal resistance of the cell is as low as possible.

The energy/volume ratio of an energy-conversion system may also be obtained as a function of mission-duration time by a similar method. The same factors (viz., exchange current densities, limiting current densities, internal resistance of the cell) are important in maximizing the performance of the energy-conversion system.

One of the major requirements of energy-conversion systems for space applications is the reliability of the system. Thus, considerations of initial and running costs are not severe, when compared with ground applications.

9.2 Mobile Ground Applications

Because of the problem of air pollution, the demand for electrically powered automobiles will probably increase. The most important criteria from a commercial viewpoint are the initial and running costs. For mobile applications, the principal requirements are high power/weight and power/volume ratios. It is interesting to consider the variation of the weight/power ratio as a function of time. This is given by [cf. Eq. (9.3)]

$$\frac{W}{P} = \frac{W_1}{P} + \frac{t}{\epsilon \xi} \tag{9.4}$$

where W is the total weight of the fuel cell, accessories, and fuel, and is equal to $(W_i + Pt/\epsilon \xi)$.

Thus, when W/P is plotted as a function of t, at a constant P, a straight line should be obtained. The slope of this line decreases with increasing ϵ as well as for higher values of ξ. The hydrogen-oxygen fuel-cell system should be the best, since ξ and ϵ are the highest for this system.   An equation similar to (9.4) would apply for other energy-conversion methods as well.   Figure 24 shows the plot of W/P as a function of t for a number of systems.   The advantage of hydrogen-oxygen fuel cells over other systems is striking.   In the plot of W/P versus t, it is necessary to have the intercept at as low a value as possible; thus, for a given weight of the fuel-cell system, exclusive of the weight of the fuel, it

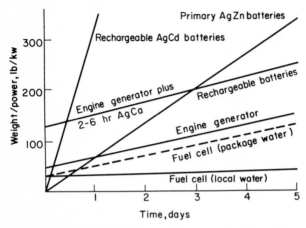

Figure 24   Plots of weight/power ratios as a function of time for some energy converters.

is necessary to operate under maximum power conditions so that the dependence on limiting current considerations, hence porous-electrode structure, is great. The question of the extent to which fuel cells (rather than secondary batteries) may be used in electric automobiles depends upon several factors in addition to the power/weight ratio and its dependence on electrode-kinetic factors.   In particular, the cost of hydrogen† dominates the situation: its present cost makes fuel cells uneconomic for private cars, although probably economic for delivery trucks and other larger vehicles undergoing frequent stops.   Hydrocarbon cells which charge regenerative molten-salt cells seem possible, with respect to power density and cost, for automotive application (high i_0 for the molten-salt cell, low cost of hydrocarbon).

9.3   Stationary Ground Applications

Many possible applications of electrochemical energy converters in ground situations exist, and each has its own series of features which determine its competitive situation.   One generalization in respect to the influence of an electrode-kinetic aspect can be made: In most stationary applications, because

† The weight of the hydrogen container is also a vital point.   Here advances may be made. Plastic containment, storage in metals such as zirconium, and even solid hydrogen have all to be considered and probably researched.

the maximization of power per unit weight is less important than a high efficiency of conversion, the mass-transport aspects will be less important than for situations in which maximum power per unit weight (depending directly upon i_L, cf. Sec. 7) is dominant. The electrocatalytic situation dominates the low-temperature devices just as the corrosion resistance and ionic conductance of solids dominate the high-temperature ones.

10 HEAT GENERATION IN FUEL CELLS

There are three sources of heat generation in fuel cells: (1) The heat loss due to the entropy change of the reaction, which is equal to $T \Delta S$. A few exceptional reactions, for example, $C + \frac{1}{2}O_2 \rightarrow CO$, are accompanied by a positive entropy change with which there is a cooling rather than a heating effect. (When the entropy change for a reaction is positive, the numerical value of the free-energy change of the reaction exceeds its enthalpy change. Thus, during the reaction, the cell cools and consequently extracts heat from the surroundings). (2) The heating caused by the irreversibility of the reaction, which is equal to $i \sum \eta$ per unit area where $\sum \eta$ is the sum of the activation and concentration overpotential losses at the anode and cathode. (3) The resistance heating effect in the bulk of the electrolyte and at electrical contacts or within the electrode equal to i^2R per unit cross-sectional area of the cell.

Expressed mathematically, the total heat loss per second is equal to

$$Q = - \left(\frac{4.18T \Delta S}{nF} \right) i + i \sum \eta + i^2 R \qquad \text{watt cm}^{-2} \tag{10.1}$$

for unit cross section of the electrode.

In Eq. (10.1), the first term on the right-hand side is the heating effect due to the entropy change of the reaction and arises when ΔS is negative. During the oxidation of 1 mole of fuel for which nF coul of electricity are required, $-4.18T \Delta S$ joule is the heat *liberated* into the surroundings assuming that the cell is working reversibly. Thus, when the current density is i amp cm^{-2} (which is the same as i coul cm^{-2} sec^{-1}), the heat liberated under reversible conditions is given by the first term on the right of Eq. (10.1). The second and third terms on the righthand side are the heating effects caused by the irreversibility of the reaction. Since $T \Delta S$ is generally small, the overall heating effect depends largely on electrodic and ohmic losses in the cell. It is essential, therefore, to have a heat-removal system to operate the cell under constant-temperature conditions. Investigation of heat removal began in the early sixties with the development of electrochemical energy converters for space applications.

It is interesting to examine the influence of electrode kinetic parameters on the heat generated in cells as a function of current density. It is convenient to do this in the same way as was done in Secs. 4 to 7, where the dependences

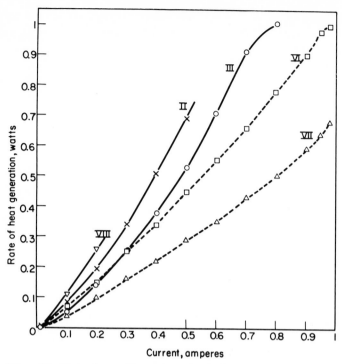

Figure 25 Plots of rate of heat generation in fuel cells Q vs. current I corresponding to E-I curves in Fig. 3.

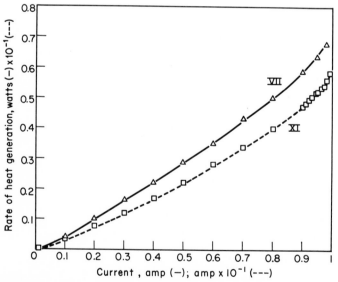

Figure 26 Plots of rate of heat generation in fuel cells Q vs. current I corresponding to E-I curves in Fig. 4.

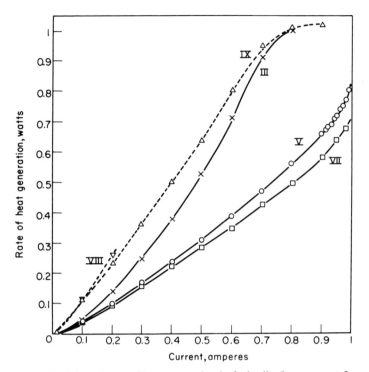

Figure 27 Plots of rate of heat generation in fuel cells Q vs. current I corresponding to E-I curves in Fig. 5.

of the E versus I, dE/dI versus I, ϵ versus I, and P versus I on the various electrode kinetic parameters were determined. Using the variation of electrode kinetic parameters as in Table 2, Q versus I is plotted for these cases in Figs. 25 to 27. In these cases, $T \Delta S$ is assumed to be that for the hydrogen-oxygen fuel cell at 25°C. The same limitation of planar-electrode calculations applies here as in the earlier calculations.

Figure 25 shows the effect of variation of i_0 on the heat generated in a fuel cell for two values of R_i. The lower the i_0, the higher is the slope of the Q-versus-I plot. In Fig. 26, which shows the effect of variation of i_L, it is seen that the Q-versus-I plots are similar for the two chosen values of i_L but the curve for the lower limiting current is displaced by a decade in current density as well as in the rate of heat generation. The effect of variation of R_i is seen in Fig. 27. Two sets of values of i_0's are chosen. The lower the value of R_i, the lower is the slope of the Q-versus-I line. This is more apparent when the i_0's are high for both the electrode reactions. When i is low for even one of the electrode reactions, the initial slopes are practically the same with variation of R_i; but at higher current densities, the slopes show a similar dependence on R_i, as when i_0's are high.

11 KINETICS OF CERTAIN SYSTEMS RELEVANT TO ELECTROCHEMICAL ENERGY CONVERSION

11.1 Fast Reactions: Reactions in the Li-LiCl-Cl$_2$ Cell

11.1.1 General

Systems that are advantageous from an electrode kinetic point of view in electrochemical energy conversion are those in which the electrode reactions are fast. If they also have a high energy density, they are even more advantageous. An example of such a system is the lithium-chlorine cell, which consists of a molten lithium electrode, a molten lithium chloride electrolyte, and a porous carbon electrode.[3] The electrode reactions of this system will be considered in the following sections.†

11.1.2 Lithium-electrode Reaction

(i) Overall reaction

The reaction which occurs at the lithium electrode is

$$Li \rightarrow Li^+ + e_0^- \tag{11.1}$$

(ii) Current-potential relation

The current-potential relation on a lithium anode is linear between 0 and 40 amp cm^{-2} and passes through the origin.[3] The same behavior is also observed for the reverse reaction, and the current-potential plot has the identical slope as for the anodic reaction (Fig. 28). If activation overpotential were important, the $\eta - i$ relation would be nonlinear above 100 mv at the temperature concerned, so that the behavior is ohmic in the entire region.

(iii) Conclusions

The lithium-electrode reaction is therefore an ideal half-cell reaction for a fuel cell. The overpotential is only due to the resistance of the electrolyte. High current densities are easily obtainable without polarization losses at the electrode.

11.1.3 Chlorine-electrode reaction

(i) Overall reaction

The reaction that occurs at the chlorine electrode is

$$Cl_2 + 2e_0^- \rightarrow 2Cl^- \tag{11.2}$$

† The Li-LiCl-Cl$_2$ cell is discussed here as though it were a fuel cell because its use in practice promises to be one in which it is charged electrically and then discharged (i.e., an electrically regenerative fuel cell); it may also be classed as a secondary battery, i.e., an electrochemical electricity storer.

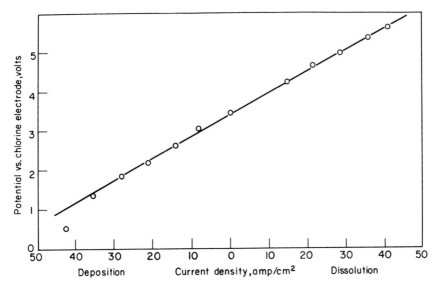

Figure 28 Current-potential relations for the lithium dissolution and deposition reactions at 650°C.[3]

(*ii*) *Mechanism of chlorine dissolution in aqueous media at low temperatures*

Significant activation overpotential exists in this medium and the Tafel relation is obeyed. It has been proposed that the electron-transfer step

$$\text{MCl}_{\text{ads}} + e_0^- \rightarrow \text{M} + \text{Cl}^- \tag{11.3}$$

controls the rate of the overall reaction.

(*iii*) *Mechanism of chlorine dissolution on graphite electrodes in molten lithium chloride*

(*a*) Experimental findings

This reaction and also the corresponding anodic reaction have been studied by Triaca, Solomons, and Bockris.[4] Since this reaction is fast, transient methods (Chap. 9) were used for its mechanism investigation. The current-potential behavior for the cathodic reaction showed only a short Tafel region with a slope of $2.3RT/F$ (Fig. 29). A limiting current density of a little over 1 amp cm^{-2} at 1-atm pressure of chlorine was observed. The limiting current density varied linearly with partial pressure of chlorine. The cathodic and anodic Tafel slopes intersected at the reversible potential, corresponding to an exchange current density of 0.1 amp cm^{-2} at 650°C. The anodic Tafel slope is $2.3RT/2F$ over the current density range of 0.3 to 10.0 amp cm^{-2}. The temperature effect of the exchange current density yielded an energy of activation at the reversible potential of 7.1 kcal mole^{-1}. From the temperature-dependence of the limiting current density, an energy of activation of 5.7 kcal mole^{-1}

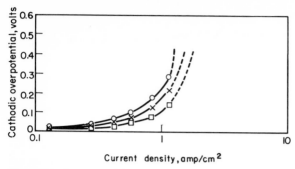

Figure 29 Overpotential–current-density plots for the chlorine-dissolution reaction on graphite electrodes in molten LiCl at three temperatures: ○—657°; x—715°; □—767°C.[4]

was obtained for the rate-limiting diffusional process. The stoichiometric number for the reaction was found to be close to unity. The decay of anodic overpotential with time had a slope of $-2.3RT/4F$ and was shown to be independent of current density. Conversely, the slope of the line for the decay of cathodic overpotential with time depends on current density.

(*b*) Mechanistic conclusions

From the experimental results stated briefly in the preceding subsection, Triaca et al. were led to the view that the chlorine-dissolution reaction proceeds by the following path:

$$Cl_2 + 2M \rightarrow 2MCl_{ads} \tag{11.4}$$

$$MCl_{ads} + e_0^- \rightarrow M + Cl^- \tag{11.3}$$

with step (11.4) controlling the rate of the overall reaction.

The adsorption of the intermediate Cl, formed in the first step (11.4), occurs under Temkin conditions (Chap. 2, Sec. 5). Its surface concentration c_0, as calculated according to the equation[4a]

$$\frac{d\eta}{dt} = \frac{RT}{(nF)^2} \frac{i}{c_0} \tag{11.5}$$

where i is the current density before starting the decay measurements, was estimated at 2×10^{-10} mole cm^{-2}, corresponding to a degree of coverage of over 0.2 when $i = 1$ amp cm^{-2}.

Under Temkin conditions, the degree of coverage θ may be expressed as a function of potential η by

$$r\theta = \eta F + \text{const} \tag{11.6}$$

where r is an interaction energy parameter. Thus, the cathodic current-density–overpotential relation is of the form

$$i = k p_{Cl_2} \exp\left(-\frac{\eta F}{RT}\right) \tag{11.7}$$

Hence, the Tafel slope is given by

$$\frac{d\eta}{d \log i} = -\frac{2.3RT}{F} \tag{11.8}$$

which is the experimentally observed one. All the experimental results are consistent with this mechanism.

11.2 Redox Systems

11.2.1 General

The redox systems find application in chemically regenerative fuel cells (Chap. 3, Sec. 6.3). The advantage is that their electrode reactions have high exchange current densities and thus they replace the electrodic reactions of the fuel and/or oxidant. The fuel and/or oxygen is used chemically to generate the electro-active species, as, for example, in the following reaction scheme:

Electrode reaction: $\quad 6Mo^{5+} \rightarrow 6Mo^{6+} + 6e_0^-$ $\tag{11.9}$

Chemical reaction: $\quad CH_3OH + H_2O + 6Mo^{6+} \rightarrow CO_2 + 6H^+ + 6Mo^{5+}$

$$\tag{11.10}$$

Overall reaction: $\quad CH_3OH + H_2O \rightarrow CO_2 + 6H^+ + 6e_0^-$ $\tag{11.11}$

For a redox fuel cell to be effective, there are three essential criteria.

(*i*) The reversible potential of the redox couple should be slightly more cathodic than that for the overall reaction in the cathode compartment and for an anodic reaction the converse should hold. This criterion is necessary (*a*) to obtain open-circuit potentials close to that for the fuel cell operating in the absence of the redox system and (*b*) for the spontaneous regeneration of the electroactive species in each of the compartments.

(*ii*) The electrode reactions of the respective redox couples must be considerably faster than the direct electrode reaction of fuel and oxidant in the respective compartments.

(*iii*) The homogeneous chemical regenerations in solution must be suffi-ciently fast to supply the reactants for the electrode reactions.

Two systems that have been used with some degree of success in the development of the methanol-air fuel cell are the Mo^{5+}/Mo^{6+} redox couple for methanol oxidation (Heath[5]) and the HNO_3/NO redox couple for oxygen reduction (Shropshire and Tarmy[6]).

11.2.2   Current-potential Relations for a Reaction Using the Principle of Intermediate Redox Catalysis

For simplicity, the current-potential relation will be derived for a reaction of the following types:

Electrode reaction: $M^+ \rightarrow M^{2+} + e_0^-$ (11.12)

Chemical reaction: $A + M^{2+} \rightarrow A^+ + M^+$ (11.13)

Overall reaction: $A \rightarrow A^+ + e_0^-$ (11.14)

The rate of the overall reaction is the rate of consumption of the reactant A in the chemical step (11.13).   In units of current this rate (i_2) may be written as

$$i_2 = k_2[A][M^{2+}] - k_{-2}[A^+][M^+] \tag{11.15}$$

k_2 and k_{-2} are the rate constants for the forward and reverse reactions of the chemical step.   Using the stationary-state hypothesis for the intermediate species M^{2+}, it follows that

$$(\vec{i_1} - \overleftarrow{i_1}) - (\vec{i_2} - \overleftarrow{i_2}) = 0 \tag{11.16}$$

The rate of the electrode reaction (11.12), i_1, may be expressed by an equation of the form

$$i_1 = \left\{ k_1[M^+] \exp\left(\frac{\beta VF}{RT}\right) - k_{-1}[M^{2+}] \exp\left[-(1-\beta)\frac{VF}{RT}\right] \right\} \tag{11.17}$$

Using Eqs. (11.15) to (11.17),

$$M^{2+} = \frac{[M^+]\{k_1 \exp(\beta VF/RT) + k_{-2}[A^+]\}}{\{k_2[A] + k_{-1} \exp[-(1-\beta)VF/RT]\}} \tag{11.18}$$

Using (11.18) in (11.15),

$$i_2 = \frac{[M^+]\{k_1 k_2[A] \exp(\beta VF/RT) - k_{-1}k_{-2}[A^+] \exp[-(1-\beta)VF/RT]\}}{\{k_2[A] + k_{-1} \exp[-(1-\beta)VF/RT]\}} \tag{11.19}$$

There are two limiting cases for this expression.   If

$$k_2[A] \gg k_{-1} \exp\left[-(1-\beta)\frac{VF}{RT}\right] \tag{11.20}$$

which corresponds to the chemical step (11.13) being considerably faster than the electrochemical step (11.12), the expression for i_2 reduces to

$$i_2 = [M^+]\left\{ k_1 \exp\left(\frac{\beta VF}{RT}\right) - \frac{k_{-1}k_{-2}[A^+]}{k_2[A]} \exp\left[-(1-\beta)\frac{VF}{RT}\right] \right\} \tag{11.21}$$

The second case is one in which the rate of the chemical step (11.13) is slow compared with that of the electrochemical step (11.12). Thus

$$k_{-1} \exp \left[-(1 - \beta) \frac{VF}{RT} \right] \gg k_2[A] \tag{11.22}$$

Under these conditions,

$$i_2 = [M^+] \left\{ \frac{k_1}{k_{-1}} k_2[A] \exp \left(\frac{VF}{RT} \right) - k_{-2}[A^+] \right\} \tag{11.23}$$

Comparing the rate expressions (11.21) and (11.23) for the two cases, the dependence of (1) i_2 on V and (2) i_2 on A can be used to distinguish between a rate-determining chemical (11.13) and an electrochemical (11.12) step.

This indirect catalysis will succeed only if

$$k_2, k_{-2} \gg k_d, k_{-d} \tag{11.24}$$

where the latter rate constants are those for the direct electrooxidation of the fuel A. The rate i_d of the direct electrooxidation of A is given by

$$i_d = k_d[A] \exp \left(\frac{\beta VF}{RT} \right) - k_{-d}[A^+] \exp \left[-(1 - \beta) \frac{VF}{RT} \right] \tag{11.25}$$

The Tafel slope for the direct electrooxidation of A [Eq. (11.14)] is the same as that for the indirect case when the electrochemical step [Eq. (11.12)] is slow compared to the chemical one [cf. Eqs. (11.21) and (11.25)]. However, were indirect catalysis to be advantageous, the exchange current density for the direct electrooxidation of A would be considerably less than that for the indirect reaction. Little experimental data is as yet available about the rates of such homogeneous oxidation reactions.

One of the problems encountered by this indirect catalysis is the migration of the electroactive anodic reactant to the cathode, or vice versa, which would obviously affect the fuel-cell efficiency. This transport could be greatly reduced, as will be seen in Sec. 12.

11.3 Effect of Specific Adsorption of Ions on the Rates of Reactions

The specific adsorption of ions† may influence the kinetics of electrode processes by its effect on (1) the double-layer structure at the metal-solution interface; (2) the available free surface for the reaction; (3) the free energy of adsorption of reactants, intermediates, or products; and (4) the properties of the electrode material (e.g., work function of the metal).

The relative importance of these effects depends on the reaction concerned. The maximum surface coverage due to specific adsorption of ions on mercury

† Knowledge of the adsorption of ions on solid electrodes is extremely sparse. It has been shown to be obtainable by ellipsometric means.[7a]

is about 20 percent.   Thus, the effect of specific adsorption of ions on mercury due to surface coverage is generally rather small.   It would, however, tend to reduce the rate at a constant overpotential.

Information concerning specific adsorption of ions on solid metals is relatively sparse.   There is some indication that surface coverages of ions are higher on solid metals than on mercury.[7]   If this were the case, the rates of fuel-cell reactions may be reduced by a reduction in the electroactive area of the electrode.   If the reactant of an electrode reaction in a fuel cell is an ion, the effect of the double-layer structure can be seen in two ways—the concentration of the reactant ions undergoing charge transfer is altered and so also is the potential drop across the interface.[8]   In general, specific adsorption of an anion increases the rate of a cathodic reaction, and, conversely, specific adsorption of a cation increases the rate of an anodic reaction due to their respective effects on the double-layer structure.[8]

The third possible effect of specific adsorption is on the free energy of adsorption of reactants, intermediates, or products.   No quantitative data on this is available.

The last possible effect is on the electronic properties (e.g., work function) of the electrode.   This effect may be exemplified by the influence of specific adsorption of alkali cations on the oxygen-evolution reaction.[9]   Oxygen evolution takes place through the intermediate formation of chemisorbed oxygen.   The formation of chemisorbed oxygen creates a dipole with the negative end towards the solution.   This orientation therefore helps the specific adsorption of cation.   But the specific adsorption of cations increases the stability of the chemisorbed layer (i.e., the M-O bond strength).   Increase in the M-O bond strength results in an increase in the coverage of the surface with O, which reduces the free sites on the electrode and hence also the rate of the overall reaction.   The effect is most with cesium and least with lithium.   Specific adsorption of ions can also alter the surface properties of the electrocatalyst.   There is evidence[10] that the adsorption of cesium ions on tungsten in the gas phase alters the work function of W.   The same effect may be expected for specific adsorption from solutions.   Changes in work function can also affect the rate of the electrode reaction.   Though it has been shown[11] that there is no direct influence of the work function of a metal on the rate of an electrode reaction at it, indirect effects exist due to the influence of work function on the energy of the chemisorbed bond of the reactant to the metal.

This field of effects of ionic adsorption on reaction rates on solid catalysts is largely unexplored.   It is of great relevance because of the possibility of increasing reaction rates by the correct choice of supporting electrolyte and also because of the probability that anions are highly adsorbed on electrocatalysts.   Work has recently been started in this direction[12] to determine the effects of specific adsorption of anions such as SO_4^{2-}, F^-, and Cl^- and cations such as Cs^+, Ba^{2+}, and La^{2+} on the electroreduction of oxygen on platinum electrodes.

11.4   Slurry Electrodes

11.4.1   Slurry-electrode Design

A novel method of obtaining high current densities (per geometric area) is by using slurry electrodes. In this approach, the electrode system essentially consists of a suspension of catalytically active particles that have intermittent contact with a collector electrode. While in solution, the catalyst particles adsorb the electroactive fuel (e.g., hydrogen, hydrocarbons), which is then discharged during contact with the collector electrode. The idea of the slurry electrode was first introduced by Schwabe[13] and subsequently used by Boutry et al.[14] and by Gerischer and coworkers[15,16] to study the hydrogen- and oxygen-dissolution reactions.

The current obtainable, using this arrangement, depends mainly on: (1) the mechanism of the reaction on the slurry electrode; (2) the size of the particles; (3) the frequency of contact of the particles with the collector; and (4) the time of contact of the particles with the collector surface. An arrangement that appears suitable for maximizing factors (3) and (4) is a double-sandwich arrangement (Fig. 30). The anolyte and catholyte compartments are on either

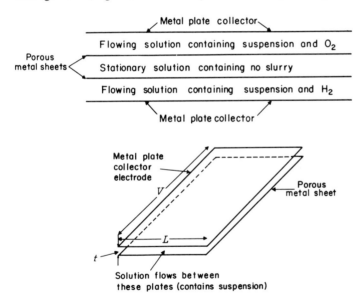

Figure 30   A proposed model for a slurry-electrode cell.

side of a central bridge compartment. The electrolyte in the central compartment is stationary, whereas the electrolyte containing the catalyst particles and the fuel or oxidant stream through the other two compartments. The walls of the anode and cathode compartments serve as the respective collector electrodes. The outer walls of each of these compartments are metal plates.

Their inner walls are of porous metal sheets, which allow transport of ions but not the fuel, oxidant, or catalyst particles.

11.4.2   Mode of Operation of Slurry Electrodes and Their Advantages

For simplicity, one may consider the hydrogen-dissolution reaction

$$H_2 + 2H_2O \rightarrow 2H_3O^+ + 2e_0^- \qquad (11.26)$$

occurring on a slurry electrode.   The first step in the electrode reaction is the dissociative adsorption of hydrogen on the particles in suspension according to

$$H_2 + 2M \rightarrow 2MH \qquad (11.27)$$

The preceding step of diffusion of hydrogen in solution to the catalyst in suspension is considerably faster than diffusion of hydrogen to a planar electrode because the catalyst particles are small.   Following the adsorption step, ionization of hydrogen takes place

$$MH + H_2O \rightarrow M + H_3O^+ + e_0^- \qquad (11.28)$$

Thus, a charge is imparted to the catalyst particles and a double layer is set up across the slurry particle-solution interface.   The next step is collision of these charged particles with the collector electrode during which process they lose their charge.   Transfer of charge from the slurry particles to the collector electrode provides the current in the external circuit.

It is not yet clear which step controls the rate of the overall reaction, although the work of von Held and Gerischer[16] suggests that the rate-determining step is probably the electron transfer from the slurry particles to the metal surface.   Despite lack of knowledge in this direction, it can be qualitatively seen that this method could give rise to considerable increase in power per unit volume and power per unit weight because the steps (11.27) and (11.28) take place in solution at highly accelerated rates compared with those on smooth or porous electrodes.   The acceleration of reaction rates obtained by use of this method is significant, as seen from Fig. 31.   It remains to be shown that the power per gram of catalyst is improved over that obtained with porous electrodes if expensive catalyst materials are used (e.g., platinum).   So far, no improvement in this direction has been obtained.   However, it would perhaps be possible to coat inert particles of cheap materials with thin films of the expensive catalysts.

11.5   Jet Electrodes

11.5.1   A Proposed Model

In this model, the electrolyte solution saturated with fuel or oxidant is forced through a jet at high speeds and aimed at a metal plate that acts as one electrode. A horizontal cross section of the model is shown in Fig. 32.   Alternate small tubes are the jets that carry the electrolyte and hydrocarbon.   The remaining

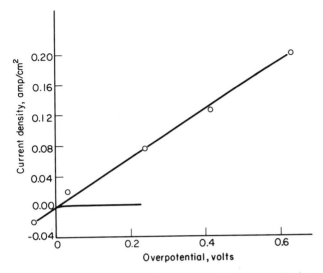

Figure 31 Comparison of the overpotential–current-density relations for the hydrogen-dissolution reaction on slurry ($\bigcirc$) and planar platinum electrode in 1 N H_2SO_4 at 25°C.[15]

tubes contain the electrolyte, oxidant (for example, O_2), and serve as electrodes for the electrochemical reduction process. Due to the close spacing between the metal-plate anode and the tubular cathodes, such an arrangement would minimize the ohmic drop within the cell.

The layer adjacent to the metal-electrode plane is not affected by the turbulence caused by the streaming jet. This layer is more or less stationary. Its thickness depends on the velocity of the streaming jet. Beyond this layer turbulence exists, and the concentration of the hydrocarbon can be assumed to be effectively a constant and equal to the saturation value. The diffusion layer is therefore equal to the thickness of the stationary sublayer.

The thickness of this sublayer is not altered by rotating the metal electrode, which may be considered in the shape of a disk. Further, the effective anodic area is not increased by this rotation, since in calculating the current a consideration of both the area of the portion of the disk exposed to the jet electrode and

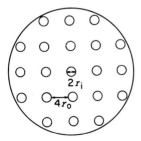

Figure 32 Horizontal cross section of a jet electrode model.

the time for which it is exposed should be taken into account in the calculation of the current. The product of these two factors, which enters the expression for the current, is a constant. Thus, in the present arrangement, the metal electrode is considered stationary.

11.5.2 Calculation of Limiting Current Density

Suppose the inner radius of the jet is r_i and outer radius r_0. The same radii are also assumed for the tubes that serve as the cathodes. If the distance between the centers of two adjacent tubes is equal to $4r_0$, then the distance between the centers of two neighboring cathodes or fuel jets is $8r_0$, assuming a cubic array for the cross section of the tubes (Fig. 32).

It is assumed that the effective anodic area, caused by one jet, is the projection of its inner area on the metal plate, that is, πr_i^2. This assumption is valid because the diffusion-layer thickness (δ_j) increases rapidly outside this area on the metal plate (Fig. 33) so that only the area directly underneath the jet is active.

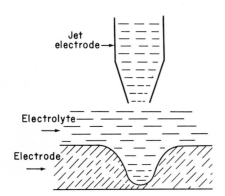

Figure 33   Variation of diffusion-layer thickness with distance from center of projection of jet on the metal plate.

The number of jets N which may be arranged at a distance $8r_0$ apart and project on to the metal electrode of radius R is given by

$$N = \frac{\pi}{64} \frac{R^2}{r_0^2} \tag{11.29}$$

as may be seen from Fig. 32. Thus, the effective anodic area, A_a, is

$$A_a = \frac{\pi}{64} \frac{R^2}{r_0^2} \pi r_i^2$$

$$= \frac{\pi^2 R^2}{64 r_0^2} r_i^2 \tag{11.30}$$

The limiting current for the jet model is therefore given by

$$I_{L,j} = i_{L,j} \frac{\pi^2}{64} \frac{R^2}{r_0^2} r_i^2$$

$$= \frac{DnFc_0}{\delta_j} \frac{\pi^2}{64} \frac{R^2}{r_0^2} r_i^2 \tag{11.31}$$

The limiting current for a plane electrode of area equal to that of disk is

$$I_{L,p} = i_{L,p} \pi R^2$$

$$= \frac{DnFc_0}{\delta_p} \pi R^2 \tag{11.32}$$

where δ_p is the diffusion-layer thickness at a planar electrode.

Thus, the ratio of the currents, obtainable from the jet model to the planar model, is

$$\frac{I_{L,j}}{I_{L,p}} = \frac{\pi}{64} \frac{r_i^2}{r_0^2} \frac{\delta_p}{\delta_j} \tag{11.33}$$

Suppose $r_i \approx r_0$, $\delta_p = 10^{-3}$ cm, and $\delta_j = 10^{-6}$ cm,

$$I_{L,j} = 50 I_{L,p} \tag{11.34}$$

An improvement of about 50 times over the planar situation can be obtained. A further increase by a factor of about 4 times may be obtained by having the tubes practically touching each other. Though the values of the calculated limiting current densities for this device are lower than those obtained on porous gas-diffusion electrodes, the jet electrode model appears promising for *liquid* fuels.

11.6 Spaghetti-tube Model

The model[1] consists of a number of parallel tubes, through which the fuel and oxidant flow in adjacent ones (Fig. 34). The external surface of each tube is coated with a catalyst. Hitherto, tubes permeable to fuel and oxygen and possessing a metallic conducting layer have not been realized but seem to be attainable.

Let the outer and inner diameters of the tubes be R and r, respectively. The current drawn from each pair of tubes is $2\pi RLi$, where i is the current density for operation at a reasonably small polarization loss and L is the length of the cubic nodule. The number of electrode pairs per nodule N is given by

$$N = \frac{L^2}{32R^2} \tag{11.35}$$

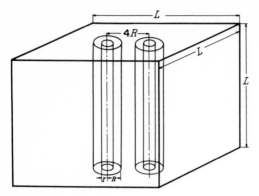

Figure 34 Spaghetti-tube model for a fuel cell. Only two adjacent spaghetti-tube electrodes are shown.[17]

Hence, the total current drawn from the nodule (I_T) is

$$I_T = 2\pi \frac{RL^3}{32R^2} i$$

$$= \frac{\pi L^3 i}{16R} \tag{11.36}$$

and the current per cubic centimeter (i_v) is

$$i_v = \frac{\pi i}{16R} \tag{11.37}$$

Using $i = 10^{-2}$ amp cm^{-2} and $R = 10^{-2}$ cm, $i_v \approx 2 \times 10^{-1}$ amp cm$^{-3} \approx 5 \times 10^3$ amp ft^{-3}. This value of i_v compares favorably with nearly the best available fuel-cell systems. Losses due to ohmic polarization in the solution and in the electrodes were considered but shown to be negligible for this arrangement.[17] To maintain the assumed value of current density, it is necessary to have a pressure differential of about 3 atm for a tube of length 10 cm.

12 PROBLEMS OF DIFFUSION OF FUEL-TO-CATHODE COMPARTMENT (OR OF OXIDANT-TO-ANODE COMPARTMENT)

12.1 General

One of the problems encountered in some fuel-cell systems is that of migration of the fuel through the electrolyte to the cathode or of oxygen to the anode. This migration is often observed if the fuel or oxidant is quite soluble in the electrolyte, as, for example, when using methanol in aqueous acid solution.[18] Such a transport of fuel or oxidant has two deleterious effects: (1) it reduces the efficiency of utilization of the fuel or oxidant; (2) it reduces the performance of the "opposite" electrode by its electrochemical reaction at this electrode. Possible ways of reducing this transport in a cell are by use of a membrane or of a scavenger electrode between its anode and cathode.

12.2 Effect of a Membrane between Anode and Cathode on the Diffusion Process

The effect of the membrane on the migration of the fuel from anode to cathode is considered. A rectangular cell arrangement (Fig. 35) is assumed in the following calculation.

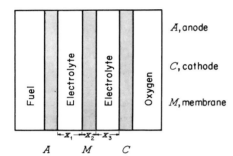

A, anode

C, cathode

M, membrane

Figure 35 Cell arrangement and coordinate system for reducing the problem of diffusion of fuel from anode to cathode using either a membrane or a porous scavenger electrode.

Let x_1 be the closest distance between the anode and membrane, x_2 the thickness of the membrane, and x_3 the closest distance between the membrane and the cathode. It is further assumed that the concentration of the fuel at the end of the anode, closer to the membrane, is c_0 and that at a similar position of the cathode is 0. The latter assumption corresponds to the fuel being consumed at the cathode at the limiting current. Expressed mathematically, the boundary conditions are at

$$x = 0 \qquad\qquad c = c_0 \tag{12.1}$$

$$x = x_1 \qquad\qquad c = c_1 \tag{12.2}$$

$$x = x_1 + x_2 \qquad c = c_2 \tag{12.3}$$

$$x = x_1 + x_2 + x_3 \quad c = 0 \tag{12.4}$$

A linear concentration gradient is assumed in the regions $0 < x < x_1$, $x_1 < x < x_1 + x_2$, and $x_1 + x_2 < x < x_1 + x_2 + x_3$.

The flux between the anode and the membrane (N_1) is given by

$$N_1 = -D_1 \frac{c_1 - c_0}{x_1} \tag{12.5}$$

where D_1 is the diffusion coefficient of fuel in the electrolyte. The flux of fuel through the membrane (N_2) is expressed by

$$N_2 = -D_2 \frac{c_2 - c_1}{x_2} \tag{12.6}$$

where D_2 is the diffusion coefficient of fuel in the membrane. The diffusional flux from the membrane to the cathode (N_3) is

$$N_3 = -D_1 \frac{(0 - c_2)}{x_3} \tag{12.7}$$

Under steady-state conditions,

$$N_1 = N_2 = N_3 = N_m \tag{12.8}$$

where N_m is the flux of electrolyte from anode to cathode through the membrane.

Using Eqs. (12.5) to (12.8), the diffusional flux in the presence of the membrane (N_m) may be expressed by

$$N_m = \frac{D_1 c_0}{x_1 + x_3 + (D_1/D_2)x_2} \tag{12.9}$$

In the absence of the membrane but with the same distance between the anode and cathode and also assuming the same boundary conditions, the diffusional flux (N_0) is given by

$$N_0 = \frac{D_1 c_0}{x_1 + x_2 + x_3} \tag{12.10}$$

Assuming that

$$x_1 = 3x_2 = x_3 \tag{12.11}$$

and

$$D_1 = 100 D_2 \tag{12.12}$$

$$\frac{N_m}{N_0} = \frac{7}{106} \tag{12.13}$$

Thus, in the present example the diffusional flux is reduced by about 15 times by introducing a membrane whose thickness is one-seventh that of the distance between the anode and cathode and in which the diffusion coefficient of methanol is 100 times smaller than that in the electrolyte.

12.3 Effect of a Scavenger Electrode between Anode and Cathode on the Diffusion Process

The same type of cell arrangement as that of the preceding case is assumed but with a grid electrode replacing the membrane. Equations (12.5) to (12.7) hold for this case. In addition, the rate of the reaction on the scavenger electrode (u) may be written as

$$u = k \frac{c_1 + c_2}{2} \tag{12.14}$$

where k is the rate constant for the reaction on the scavenger electrode and

$$N_1 = N_2 + u \tag{12.15}$$

$$N_2 = N_3 = N_s \tag{12.16}$$

where N_s is the net flux from anode to cathode through the porous scavenger electrode. The other terms are as defined in the preceding subsection.

In Eq. (12.14), the average concentration of the fuel at the scavenger electrode is taken, since the reaction may occur in any part of the electrode. From Eqs. (12.5) to (12.7) and from (12.14) to (12.16), it follows that the flux of fuel from anode to the cathode N_s is

$$N_s = \frac{D_1 c_0}{x_1 + x_3 + (D_1/D_2)x_2 + kx_1(x_2/2D_2 + x_3/D_1)} \tag{12.17}$$

Assuming, as in the last case, Eqs. (12.11) and (12.12) and also

$$kx_2 = 100 D_2 \tag{12.18}$$

which means that the rate of the reaction on the scavenger electrode is 100 times the rate of diffusion of fuel through it, it follows from Eqs. (12.10) and (12.17) that

$$\frac{N_s}{N_0} = \frac{7}{255} \tag{12.19}$$

With the assumed values of the constants, it follows that the rate of diffusion of fuel from the anode to the cathode compartment may be reduced by about 33 times using a scavenger electrode. The use of a scavenger electrode is thus more effective than that of a membrane, as seen from Eqs. (12.9) and (12.17).

13   TIME EFFECTS IN ELECTRODE KINETICS

13.1   General

Electrode reactions are often studied under steady-state conditions in mechanism determinations. However, if the current-time behavior is observed under potentiostatic conditions (or the potential time under galvanostatic conditions), the transient behavior is characteristic of the reaction and its mechanism. Such time effects are short in duration (e.g., less than 1 sec) and are due to the attainment of the steady-state radical concentration.

Much longer time effects have been found in overpotential studies on the hydrogen[19] and on the oxygen[20] electrode reactions. The observed time effects of hydrogen overpotential on Pt were explained as being due to (1) progressive inactivation of the substrate and (2) the slow rate of adsorption equilibrium. Similar explanations have been put forward for the time effects observed in oxygen overpotential studies on Pt. A commonly suggested explanation of time effects is impurity adsorption on active sites. In some cases, it may also be due to diffusion of hydrogen or oxygen atoms into the substrate.

Time effects observed in the case of electroorganic oxidation are more marked than in the case of the hydrogen- or oxygen-electrode reactions. Times of the order of 10 min for formic acid[21] oxidation, 30 to 60 min for oxalic acid[22] or acetylene[23] oxidation, and several hours for ethylene[24] oxidation in alkaline solution are required to attain steady state. A detailed study of time effects has been made only in the case of oxidation on unsaturated hydrocarbons on platinized-platinum electrodes in sulfuric acid.[24,25]

13.2 Time Effects in the Oxidation of Unsaturated Hydrocarbons

13.2.1 Experimental Observations

The experimental observations under potentiostatic conditions in ethylene oxidation on activated platinized platinum may be summarized as follows: (1) The current decreases with time till a steady state is reached (Fig. 36). (2) Both the transient and steady-state currents decrease with an increase in stirring rate. (3) The coverage of ethylene on Pt changes with time, requiring about 15 min to reach steady state. (4) The electrode can be activated by superimposing a pulse, with a pulse height of greater than $+0.9$ volt. (5) The current-time behavior depends on the length of time the electrode is maintained in a

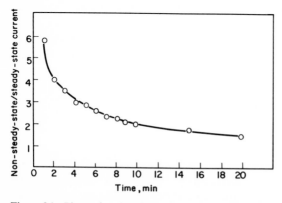

Figure 36 Plots of ratio of non-steady-state to steady-state current i/i_e vs. time for the electrooxidation of ethylene in $1\ N\ H_2SO_4$ at 80°C under potentiostatic conditions at 0.42 volt (NHE).[25]

hydrocarbon atmosphere, at open circuit, prior to the measurement. However, the steady-state current is unchanged. There is no appreciable effect on the steady-state current if a nitrogen atmosphere is substituted for the hydrocarbon atmosphere when the electrode is under open circuit prior to the experiment. (6) The rate of current decay increases as the partial pressure of the hydrocarbon decreases.

13.2.2 Probable Mechanisms

The steady-state mechanism of the electrooxidation reactions of unsaturated hydrocarbons on platinized platinum in sulfuric acid involves a rate-determining water-discharge step on the free sites.[24,25] Since the transient current decreases with time, the indications are that there is a gradual filling up of sites by the organic compound, thereby reducing the sites for the water-discharge step and hence the current. Several possible mechanisms have been examined to explain the time-dependence of the current. Two mechanisms, one for short and the other for long times, appear most plausible. The observed stirring dependence points to a diffusion-controlled mechanism at short times (10 to 15 min). At longer times, adsorption of the organic compound probably becomes activated, which may be owing to the heterogeneity of the surface, and this process also causes a further, but slower, reduction in the number of sites for the water-discharge step. Such a mechanism may then raise the question as to why this adsorption step is not the rate-determining step in the steady state. The pressure effects observed in the reaction under steady state cannot be explained on the basis of a slow adsorption of the organic compound. A probable explanation for this theory is that the organic molecules which are adsorbed at longer times cannot be oxidized in the linear region of the Tafel line at an appreciable rate and are susceptible to oxidation only at higher anodic potentials (e.g., by anodic activation). The molecules oxidized in the Tafel region are those which are adsorbed on the electrode at shorter times by a process which does not require a high activation energy.

The process of adsorption of the organic compound under diffusion control and its subsequent oxidation will now be examined.† The kinetics of the first step was treated by Delahay and Trachtenberg[26] and it was briefly presented in Chap. 2, Sec. 6.4. In this theory, it was shown that the variation of surface concentration Γ_t with time is given approximately by

$$\Gamma_t = \Gamma_e\left[1 - \exp\left(-\frac{Dt}{k\delta}\right)\right] \tag{13.1}$$

where D is the diffusion coefficient of the organic compound in the electrolyte,

---

† The theory presented involves the assumption that there is nondissociative adsorption, with diffusion in the solution rate controlling in respect to the buildup of the adsorbed layer towards the steady state. It is also possible that dissociative adsorption, e.g., $C_3H_8 \rightarrow C_3H_{7ads} + H^+ + e_0^-$, occurs.[26a]

δ is the diffusion layer thickness, and k is the adsorption coefficient, which is given by

$$k = K\Gamma_m \tag{13.2}$$

K is the equilibrium constant for the adsorption process and Γ_m is the saturation surface concentration. Γ_e is the equilibrium surface concentration. Equation (13.1) is obtained by assuming the *linear isotherm*, which applies only at *low coverages*.

Assuming that the water-discharge step is rate-determining, even under non-steady-state conditions, the current density i is given by

$$i = k_0 c_{H^+}{}^{-0.5}(1 - \theta_t) \exp\left(\frac{\alpha VF}{RT}\right) \tag{13.3}$$

where θ_t is the total coverage on the electrode due to adsorption of the hydrocarbon θ_{RH} and of hydrogen θ_H.

Since $\theta_H \ll \theta_t$, it may be further assumed that $\theta_t \approx \theta_{RH}$. Equation (13.1) may easily be transformed into the θ_{RH}-versus-t relation by using the simple relation

$$\frac{\Gamma_t}{\Gamma_m} = \theta_t \tag{13.4}$$

and

$$\frac{\Gamma_e}{\Gamma_m} = \theta_e \tag{13.5}$$

where θ_e is the equilibrium surface coverage. Using the resulting expression for θ_t in Eq. (13.3), it follows that

$$i = k c_{H^+}{}^{-0.5} \left\{ 1 - \theta_e \left[1 - \exp\left(-\frac{Dt}{k\delta}\right) \right] \right\} \exp\left(\frac{\alpha VF}{RT}\right) \tag{13.6}$$

Differentiating the above equation, at constant V, with respect to t,

$$\frac{di}{dt} = \frac{D}{k\delta} k_0 c_{H^+}{}^{-0.5} \theta_e \exp\left(-\frac{Dt}{k\delta}\right) \exp\left(\frac{\alpha VF}{RT}\right) \tag{13.7}$$

Hence

$$\frac{d \ln (-di/dt)_v}{dt} = -\frac{D}{k\delta} \tag{13.8}$$

The equilibrium constant K for electroadsorption of ethylene on platinum has been found[27] to be $(7.5 \pm 2.5)10^8$ cm^3 mole^{-1}. With $D = 2 \times 10^{-5}$ cm^2 sec^{-1} at 80°C, $\Gamma_m = 6 \times 10^{-10}$ mole cm^{-2}, and $\delta = 5 \times 10^{-3}$ cm, $D/k\delta = 9 \times 10^{-3}$ sec^{-1}, which is in good agreement with the experimental value of 4.4×10^{-3} sec^{-1} obtained from a plot of log $(-di/dt)$ versus t (Fig. 37).

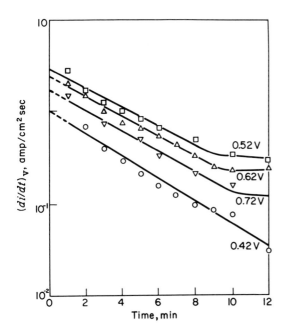

Figure 37 Plot of log $(-di/dt)$ versus t for ethylene oxidation on Pt in 1 N H$_2$SO$_4$ at 80°C under potentiostatic conditions at 0.42, 0.52, 0.62, and 0.72 volt (NHE).[25]

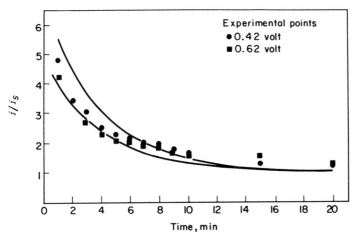

Figure 38 Theoretical plots of i/i_s versus t for two potentials.[25]

It is interesting to compare the experimental i-t curve with that expected from theory, at constant V, according to Eq. (13.6). In Fig. 38, the theoretical plots of i/i_s (i_s is the steady-state current density) versus t are made for two different potentials. The points on the curve represent the experimental observations for the respective cases. According to theory, a steady state should be reached in 10 to 15 min, which is of the order of the time taken to reach adsorption equilibrium in direct adsorption measurements.

At longer times, a slower variation of current is observed than indicated theoretically for the slow diffusion process. The explanation of an activated adsorption in this region is supported.[24,25] There is analogous behavior in gas-phase adsorption studies, where fast nonactivated adsorption is observed at low temperatures on part of the surface and slow activated adsorption on other parts of the surface at higher temperatures.[10]

REFERENCES

1. Bockris, J. O'M., and S. Srinivasan: *J. Electroanal. Chem.*, **11**, 350 (1966).
2. Greene, S. B., and N. D. Greene: *J. Electrochem. Tech.*, **1**, 276 (1963).
2a. Bockris, J. O'M., and A. K. N. Reddy: "The Essentials of Modern Electrochemistry," Plenum Press, New York, 1969.
2b. Srinivasan, S., H. Wroblowa, and J. O'M. Bockris: Chap. 6, in D. D. Eley, H. Pines, and P. B. Weisz (eds.), "Advances in Catalysis," vol. 17, Academic Press Inc., New York, 1967.
2c. Bockris, J. O'M., B. D. Cahan, and S. Srinivasan: *Adv. Energ. Conv.* (1969).
3. Swinkels, D. A. J.: *J. Electrochem. Soc.*, **113**, 6 (1966); D. A. J. Swinkels and R. N. Seefurth, *J. Electrochem. Soc.*, **115**, 995 (1968).
4. Triaca, W., C. Solomons, and J. O'M. Bockris: *Electrochim. Acta*, **13**, 1949 (1968).
4a. Mehl, W., and J. O'M. Bockris: *Can. J. Chem.*, **37**, 190 (1959).
5. Heath, C. E.: *Proc. Ann. Power Sources Conf.*, **18**, 33 (1964).
6. Shropshire, J. A., and B. L. Tarmy: *Advan. Chem. Ser.*, **47**, 153 (1965).
7. Balashova, N. A., and V. E. Kazarinov: *Elektrokhimiya*, **1**, 512 (1965); M. Genshaw and Y. C. Chiu, *J. Phys. Chem.*, **72**, 4325 (1968).
8. Frumkin, A. N.: Chap. 1, in E. Yeager (ed.), "Transaction of the Symposium on Electrode Processes," John Wiley & Sons, Inc., New York, 1961; P. Delahay, "Double Layer and Electrode Kinetics," Interscience Publishers, Inc., New York, 1965.
9. Erdey Gruz, T., and I. Shafarik: *Proc. 4th Conf. Electrochem.*, *Moscow*, 1956, Moscow, Academy of Science, 1959.
10. Trapnell, B. M. W.: "Chemisorption," Butterworth & Co. (Publishers), Ltd., London, 1955.
11. Damjanovic, A., M. Paunovic, and J. O'M. Bockris: *Electrochim. Acta*, **10**, 111 (1965); J. O'M. Bockris, A. Damjanovic, and R. J. Mannan, *J. Electroanal. Chem. and Inter. Electrochem.*, **18**, 349 (1968); J. O'M. Bockris, R. J. Mannan, and A. Damjanovic, *J. Chem. Phys.*, **48**, 1898 (1968).
12. Damjanovic, A., and M. K. Y. Wong: *J. Electrochem. Soc.*, **114**, 592 (1967).
13. Schwabe, K.: *Z. Elektrochem.*, **61**, 744 (1957).

14. Boutry, P., O. Bloch, and J. C. Balaceanu: *Comptes Rend.*, **254**, 2583
M. Bonnemay, G. Bronoel, and D. Doniat, Extended Abstracts, 1968 C.I.'I.
Meeting, Detroit, U.S.A.
15. Gerischer, H.: *Ber. Bunsenges Physik. Chem.*, **67**, 164 (1963).
16. von Held, J., and H. Gerischer: *ibid.*, **67**, 621 (1963).
17. Bockris, J. O'M.: "Introduction to Electrochemical Energy Conversion," Institute
for Defense Analysis, Washington, D.C., 1965.
18. Heath, C. E., G. Ciprios, and B. L. Tarmy: Extended Abstracts, 1968 C.I.T.C.E.
Meeting, Detroit, U.S.A.
19. Bockris, J. O'M.: *Trans. Faraday Soc.*, **43**, 417 (1946).
20. Busing, W. R., and W. Kauzmann: *J. Chem. Phys.*, **20**, 1129 (1952).
21. Brummer, S. B., and A. C. Makrides: *J. Phys. Chem.*, **68**, 1448 (1964).
22. Johnson, H., H. Wroblowa, and J. O'M. Bockris: *Electrochim. Acta*, **9**, 639 (1964).
23. Johnson, H., H. Wroblowa, and J. O'M. Bockris: *J. Electrochem. Soc.*, **111**, 863
(1964).
24. Wroblowa, H., B. J. Piersma, and J. O'M. Bockris: *J. Electroanal. Chem.*, **6**, 401
(1963).
25. Wroblowa, H., E. Gileadi, J. O'M. Bockris, and B. J. Piersma: *Trans. Faraday
Soc.*, **61**, 2531 (1965).
26. Delahay, P., and I. Trachtenberg: *J. Am. Chem. Soc.*, **79**, 2355 (1957).
26a. Bockris, J. O'M., E. Gileadi, and G. Stoner: *J. Phys. Chem.*, (1969).
27. Gileadi, E., B. T. Rubin, and J. O'M. Bockris: *J. Phys. Chem.* **69**, 3335 (1965).

1 ESSENTIAL ROLE OF POROUS ELECTRODES IN ELECTROCHEMICAL ENERGY CONVERSION

The exchange current densities (i.e., current per apparent unit area) of most reactions of interest for application in electrochemical energy converters, as, for example, the oxidation of hydrocarbons and the reduction of oxygen, are relatively low (about 10^{-8} amp cm^{-2} or less) on the presently available catalysts at low and medium temperatures. A desirable cell performance is obtained in cells which generate current densities of about 1 amp cm^{-2} at cell voltages of 0.5 volt or higher. With an exchange current density of 10^{-8} amp cm^{-2} for each electrode in a hydrocarbon-oxygen fuel cell using planar electrodes, the maximum current density obtainable at a cell potential of 0.5 volt is 10^{-5} amp cm^{-2} (assuming that the thermodynamic reversible cell potential is 1.2 volts) under the conditions of absence of mass transfer and ohmic overpotential. Even if the overpotential at one of the electrodes of the cell were negligible, the maximum current density attainable at the other electrode would be about 10^{-2} amp cm^{-2}.

The power density under the latter conditions is 5×10^{-3} watt cm^{-2}, which is about 100 times less than that desirable for practical applications. Even at such power levels, however, another limitation sets in. The solubilities of the common fuels and of oxygen are of the order of 10^{-4} mole l^{-1}. It is easy to show [cf. Chap. 2, Eq. (3.127)] that these solubilities imply a limiting current density at a planar electrode of the order of 10^{-4} amp cm^{-2}. There is thus a necessity of using some other electrode arrangement to reduce activation overpotential at desired output currents and to facilitate mass transfer to the reactant sites.

The first approach might be to use electrodes with rough surfaces (e.g., platinized platinum). Here, the current under activation control at any over-potential per apparent square centimeter will be increased by a factor equal to the ratio of the real area of the roughened surface to its apparent area. The maximum increase in apparent current density obtainable with roughened surfaces is by a factor of about 100. The rates of diffusional processes to roughened surfaces are not greatly enhanced, unless the depths of roughness are at least of the order of magnitude of diffusion-layer thickness. Even in this case, an increase in limiting currents by only about 10 could be obtained.

It is thus essential to have electrode designs radically different from those of planar electrodes, and this necessity is independent of possible substantial progress in the field of electrocatalysis. It depends mainly on the limits of mass transport. An obvious solution to the problem is to use porous media, as was first suggested in the late nineteenth century.[1] A porous electrode generally consists of a catalyst (e.g., platinum), distributed in the form of small particles, in a porous substrate (e.g., porous carbon). The original, simple idea was that such porous electrodes possess a greater area which results in an increase in current density at any overpotential. Thus, the higher power densities were interpreted as being purely due to an area effect. One may estimate the increase in surface area in the following way: suppose the porous electrode consists of uniform pores of radius of 1 μ, its porosity is 50 percent, and the thickness of the electrode is 1 mm. The effective area of this electrode per apparent square centimeter of the electrode is 1,000 cm^2. This is equivalent to a roughness factor of 1,000, and hence in this way it was thought that desired power outputs of 0.1 to 1.0 watt cm^{-2} at reasonable cell potentials could be obtained.

This simple view on the enhanced activity of porous electrodes was the basis of much work, particularly in U.S. government and company research laboratories, between 1958 and 1965. With more and more research in this field, it was gradually realized that the reason for the much greater power densities afforded by porous electrodes, as compared with planar electrodes, was only partly due to its high ratio of real to apparent area. As will be seen in Secs. 5 to 7, current densities are not uniform within the porous media because of mass transfer and ohmic hindrances so that far less than the total area is available. The fact that there is in practice a greatly increased power density is due to another reason as well: porous electrodes permit a limiting current much higher than do planar electrodes. This is due to the fact that the diffusion-layer thicknesses, when using porous electrodes, are considerably less than when using planar electrodes. Within many pores there is a thin film or meniscus of the electrolyte, and the reactant gases can reach the electrode by diffusion of the dissolved gas through this film or meniscus. In these cases, the diffusion-layer thickness is of the order of the thickness of the film, perhaps about 1 μ (but see Sec. 7), enabling one to obtain very high limiting currents compared with those at planar electrodes. Another advantage of porous electrodes is that the catalyst, in the form of very small particles (1 μ), is dispersed uniformly within the pores of an inert conducting substrate. The quantity of catalyst thus is considerably reduced as compared with sheet electrodes made entirely of catalyst or with electrodeposited materials.

Compared with the kinetics of heterogeneous gas-phase reactions, the field of electrode kinetics is a relatively new one, having had only some fifteen years development at the fundamental level. The theory of electrode reactions in porous media is even more recent (less than five years old). One overriding complexity with porous electrodes, as compared with planar electrodes, is that it is generally difficult to consider only one form of rate control for reactions in porous electrodes, as can be done with planar electrodes.

The difficulty referred to arises because, in a porous electrode, the part played by diffusion control and ohmic control, as additions to activation control, varies throughout a pore. At each distance from the three-phase boundary, one of these forms of overpotential contributes more or less dominatingly to determine the current at the site concerned.   At a planar electrode, each contributes always to the same degree, and one can speak clearly of activation control, diffusion control, etc.

Two fallacies sometimes arise in this connection.   Firstly, in a situation in which the ohmic overpotential is large (perhaps greater in total amount than the activation overpotential), these two forms of overpotential are still additive. Hence, one must still have a good electrocatalyst; otherwise the total overpotential will be large and hence power and efficiency of conversion small.

A second fallacy† concerns the concept of rate-determining step in porous electrode discussions.   This remains entirely valid in its application to the reaction sequence.   The step concerned still controls the rate of electrocatalytic reaction to the degree to which its rate is much smaller than that of any other in the sequence.   Reactions in which two steps have rates which are more or less equal are hypothetically possible (whereupon there would be no rate-controlling step) but appear fairly unlikely.   If there is negligible ohmic and diffusion overpotential, the reaction step with the smallest rate simply controls the reaction rate and costs the engineer a given overpotential and hence efficiency loss.   If there are significant diffusion and ohmic contributions (as there are in all porous electrode situations), then the rate-determining step within the reaction sequence of the reaction determines the activation overpotential contribution to the overpotential.   The process (the transport of reaction material or the electric transport) which contributes most to the overpotential then varies, as stated, within a pore.   The equations developed from (3.2) onward describe implicitly this variation.

The present chapter deals with a theoretical analysis of the various models proposed for porous electrodes.   It is mainly concerned with the theory of porous gas-diffusion electrodes, which are used in practically all fuel-cell systems.   The experimental work on porous electrodes, including model pore studies, is treated in Chap. 9.

TYPES OF POROUS ELECTRODE SYSTEMS

Basically two types of porous electrodes systems may be considered.   They are the two-phase and the three-phase systems.   The phases present in the former are the liquid and solid state, whereas in the latter all three phases—gas, liquid,

---

† Thus, it is sometimes stated that there can be no rate-determining step because in the steady state all the reaction steps occur at the same rate.   Such a fallacy is printed explicitly in a 1968 book on fuel cells[1a] and thus removes the understanding of the central chemical aspect of fuel cells, the dependence of the overpotential loss on the particular intermediate step in the overall reaction at the electrode.   All the consecutive steps in a reaction sequence at steady state must indeed occur at the same velocity.   However, this velocity is a *net* velocity. In the non-rate-determining reaction, there is also a back reaction which takes place at a velocity sufficiently high so that (Chap. 2, Sec. 3.3)

$$v_i - v_{-i} = v_j - v_{-j}$$

where i is a non-rate-determining step and j is rate determining in the sense that $v_j \ll v_i$ and $v_{-j} \ll v_{-i}$ and that $v_i \approx v_{-i}$; that is, all steps other than the rate-determining step are virtually in equilibrium.

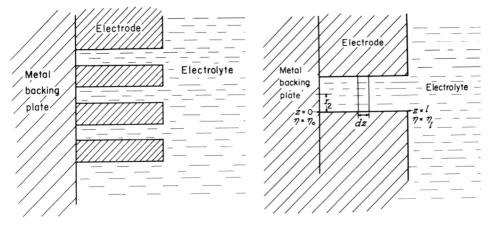

Figure 1 Idealized model of a porous electrode, consisting of parallel cylindrical pores, in a two-phase system.

Figure 2 Representation of single pore for analysis of current distribution and current-potential relations in a two-phase porous electrode.

and solid—exist. As examples of the first type, one may consider porous electrodes at which the oxidation of dissolved methanol or a redox reaction like $Sn^{2+} \rightarrow Sn^{4+} + 2e_0^-$ takes place. Most of the systems of interest in electrochemical energy conversion belong to the second type because these use gaseous reactants. In a two-phase system, the reactant is dissolved in the electrolyte and is transported to the active sites of the electrode by diffusion and electrolytic migration (the latter in the case of charged species). In the case of a three-phase system, the reactant gas dissolves in the electrolyte at the gas-electrolyte interface and diffuses through the electrolyte to the active sites of the electrodes. The current carriers in solution are ions of some reactants, products, or inert electrolytes.

3   ANALYSIS OF STEADY-STATE BEHAVIOR IN TWO-PHASE SYSTEMS

3.1   Description of the Model

For simplifying the treatment, the following assumptions are made: (1) A reaction of the type

$$M^{z+} \rightarrow M^{(z+1)^+} + e_0^- \qquad (3.1)$$

occurs at the porous electrode. (2) The porous electrode consists of uniform parallel cylindrical pores, blocked by a metal backing plate at one end and open to the electrolyte at the other end (Fig. 1). All the pores are filled with the electrolyte. (3) The conductivity of the porous electrode matrix is high enough such that there is no potential drop in the metal. (4) The concentrations of the reactant M^{z+} and of the product $M^{(z+1)^+}$ are high enough so that there are no mass-transfer limitations. This assumption may not be valid at very high current densities.

An analysis of the current–potential relation and the current distribution has been carried out in a single pore.[2,3]   The apparent current density (i.e., current per unit cross-sectional area of the electrode) is obtained by multiplying the total current generated in a single pore by the number of pores per square centimeter of the cross-sectional area of the electrode.

3.2   Mathematical Formulations and Solutions

The kinetics of reactions in two-phase systems were treated in detail by Newman and Tobias[2] and by Micka.[3]   Consider a single pore, as represented in Fig. 2. A system of cylindrical coordinates is chosen with O as the origin.   Let the radius of the pore be r_2.†   The rate (dI_z) of an electrode reaction of the type $R \rightarrow O + ne_0^-$ in an element dz of the electrode is given by

$$dI_z = 2\pi r_2 dz i_0 \left\{ \exp\left(\frac{\alpha \eta F}{RT}\right) - \exp\left[-(1-\alpha)\frac{\eta F}{RT}\right] \right\} \tag{3.2}$$

where i_0 is the exchange current density of the reaction (3.1); α is the transfer coefficient; and η is the overpotential at $z = z$.   The change in overpotential $(d\eta)$ from $z = z$ to $z = z + dz$ is expressed by representing Ohm's law for the passage of current through the solution over the distance dz across which occurs the potential difference $d\eta$.   One has

$$d\eta = I_z \frac{dz}{\kappa \pi r_2^2} \tag{3.3}$$

where I_z is the current generated in one pore from $z = 0$ to $z = z$ and κ is the specific conductivity of the electrolyte.   Differentiating Eq. (3.3) and combining the resulting equation with (3.2), it follows that

$$\frac{d^2\eta}{dz^2} = \left(\frac{2}{\kappa r_2}\right) i_0 \left\{ \exp\left(\frac{\alpha \eta F}{RT}\right) - \exp\left[-(1-\alpha)\frac{\eta F}{RT}\right] \right\} \tag{3.4}$$

The boundary conditions for this problem are (Fig. 2):

$$\eta = \eta_0 \quad \text{at } z = 0 \tag{3.5}$$

$$I_{z=0} = \kappa \pi r_2^2 \left(\frac{d\eta}{dz}\right)_{z=0} = 0 \quad \text{at } z = 0 \tag{3.6}$$

where the current begins to be generated.

It must be noted that the measured overpotential is η_l (i.e., value of η at $z = l$).   The difference $(\eta_l - \eta)$ represents the ohmic-potential drop in the solution from $z = z$ to $z = l$.

The total current generated in the pore (I_t) is obtained from Eq. (3.3) but evaluated at the solution end of the pore (that is, $z = l$).   Thus

$$I_{z=1} = I_t = \kappa \pi r_2^2 \left(\frac{d\eta}{dz}\right)_{z=l} \tag{3.7}$$

† The symbol r_1 is used in the thin-film model (Secs. 4.3 and 6) for the radius of the pore excluding the film.   This is the reason for the use of the symbol r_2 here.

To find I_z as well as the potential distribution in the pore, it is necessary to solve the differential equation (3.4) with boundary conditions (3.5) and (3.6). It is not possible to obtain a general analytic solution for Eq. (3.4). However, an analytic solution is possible either when $\alpha = \frac{1}{2}$ or under the conditions when the rate of the reverse reaction of (3.1) is so small compared with the forward rate that it may be neglected.

With $\alpha = \frac{1}{2}$, the current distribution I_z/I_t (see also Fig. 2) and the total current may be shown to be[3]

$$\frac{I_z}{I_t} = \frac{\tan (\psi)_{x=x}}{\tan (\psi)_{x=1}} \tag{3.8}$$

$$I_t = \kappa \pi r_2{}^2 \frac{2RT}{lF} (4a)^{\frac{1}{2}} \sinh \frac{y_0}{2} \tan (\psi)_{x=1} \tag{3.9}$$

where:
$$\cos (\psi) = \frac{\sinh (y_0/2)}{\sinh (y/2)} \tag{3.10}$$

$$kf(k,\psi) = a^{\frac{1}{2}}x \tag{3.11}$$

$$f(k,\psi) = \int_0^{\psi} \frac{d\psi}{(1 - k^2 \sin^2 \psi)^{\frac{1}{2}}} \tag{3.12}$$

$$a = \frac{2i_0 l^2 F}{\kappa RT r_2} \tag{3.13}$$

$$x = \frac{z}{l} \tag{3.14}$$

$$y = \frac{\eta F}{2RT} \tag{3.15}$$

$$k = \frac{1}{\cosh (y_0/2)} = \sin \theta \tag{3.16}$$

$f(k,\psi)$ is the elliptic integral of the first kind and tables of this integral are available as a function of θ and ψ.

It is necessary to use the expressions (3.8) and (3.9) for the current distribution and total current only when η_0 is less than 100 mv. A more convenient result is obtained when η_0 exceeds this value.[4] Under these conditions, the backward current of reaction (3.1) is negligible compared with the forward one for $0 < z < l$. For this case, the current distribution and total current are given by

$$\frac{I_z}{I_t} = \frac{\tan [(a^{\frac{1}{2}}/2) \exp (y_0/2) x]}{\tan [(a^{\frac{1}{2}}/2) \exp (y_0/2)]} \tag{3.17}$$

$$I_t = \kappa \pi r_2{}^2 \frac{2RT}{lF} a^{\frac{1}{2}} \exp \left(\frac{y_0}{2}\right) \tan \left[\left(\frac{a^{\frac{1}{2}}}{2}\right) \exp \left(\frac{y_0}{2}\right)\right] \tag{3.18}$$

The potential variation in the pore is given by

$$\eta_z - \eta_0 = \frac{4RT}{F} \ln \sec \left[\left(\frac{a^{\frac{1}{2}}}{2} \right) \exp \left(\frac{y_0}{2} \right) x \right]$$ (3.19)

Equation (3.19) is the expression for the ohmic-potential drop in the solution from $z = 0$ to $z = z$. According to this equation and Eqs. (3.13) to (3.15), it follows that the ohmic-potential drop in the solution depends on the parameters i_0, κ, η_0, r_2, and l.

Expressions (3.8), (3.9), (3.17), and (3.18) are greatly simplified if i_0 is very low ($< 10^{-9}$ amp cm^{-2}) or κ very high (greater than 10 ohm^{-1} cm^{-1}). In these cases, there is hardly any potential variation in the pore, the current distribution is linear with distance in the pore, and the predicted Tafel slope is the same as on a smooth electrode. For the more general case, where Eqs. (3.17) to (3.19) must be used, I_z/I_t is initially linear with x, having a slope of 45° with the x axis; but as η_0 increases it varies rapidly with x. The overpotential–current-density plot shows two sections depending on the current density—at lower current densities the normal Tafel slope is observed, whereas at higher current densities the Tafel slope is double the normal value (see Sec. 3.3.1 for derivation).

3.3   Numerical Calculations

3.3.1   *Elliptic Integral Calculations*

The elliptic integral solutions [Eqs. (3.8) and (3.9)] are necessary in the region where η_0 is less than 0.1 volt. For the elliptic integral calculations, it is first necessary to use some values of k in Eq. (3.11). Each value of k corresponds to a certain η_0 [Eq. (3.16)]. The tables of elliptic integrals are given in terms of the parameters θ and ψ. The chosen θ values are given in Table 1. Though this calculation is only necessary for η_0 values less than 0.1 volt, the higher values

TABLE 1 θ Values for Elliptic Integral Calculation (Case of Activation and Ohmic Overpotential for Two-phase Porous Electrode and Corresponding η_0 values

θ	η_0, *volts*
5	0.312
10	0.243
20	0.174
40	0.101
60	0.055
80	0.018
85	0.009

may be used as a check on the calculations made for the limiting case according to the Tafel approximation. The first stage of the calculation is to obtain $f(k,\psi)$ for each value of k and of z. This is done by using Eq. (3.11) for $f(k,\psi)$. The values of i_0, κ, and r_2 used in this calculation are given in Table 2. The next

TABLE 2 Kinetic and Physical Parameters for Elliptic Integral Calculations under Activation and Ohmic-overpotential Conditions for a Two-phase Porous Electrode

i_0, *amp cm*$^{-2}$	10^{-3}	10^{-6}	10^{-9}
κ ohm^{-1} cm^{-1}	0.1	1	2
r_2 cm	10^{-4}	2×10^{-4}	5×10^{-4}

step is to obtain the value of ψ corresponding to the value of k (that is, θ) and the calculated value of $f(k, \psi)$. The value of ψ is read off from the table of $f(k,\psi)$ as a function of θ and ψ. Once ψ is known, η is calculated using Eq. (3.10).

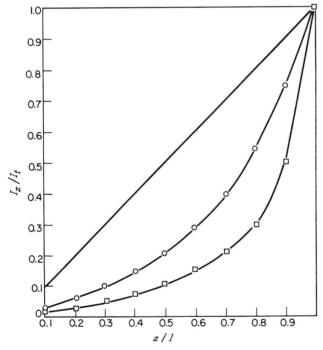

Figure 3 Current distribution relations for case of small activation and ohmic overpotential (elliptic integral calculation) at a two-phase porous electrode. $i_0 = 10^{-3}$ amp cm^{-2}; $\kappa = 1.0$ ohm^{-1} cm^{-1}; $r_2 = 10^{-4}$ cm; $\bigcirc - \eta_0 = 0.009$ volt; $\square - \eta_0 = 0.018$ volt.

Use of the value of ψ in Eqs. (3.8) and (3.9) gives the current distribution and total current per pore. All these calculations were carried out on a computer (IBM 7090). The results obtained are presented graphically in Figs. 3 to 8 and may be summarized as follows:

(*i*)   For an exchange current density as great as 10^{-3} amp cm^{-2}, ohmic overpotential plays an important role, leading to an uneven current distribution even at low values of η_0. For example, as seen from Fig. 3 with $\kappa = 1$ ohm^{-1} cm^{-1} and $r = 10^{-4}$ cm, even when η_0 is as low as 0.018 volt, only 10 percent of the current is generated from $z = 0$ to $z = 0.05$ ($l = 10^{-1}$ cm). For $\eta_0 = 0.055$ volt, practically all the current is generated at $z = l$. However, for $\kappa = 2$ ohm^{-1} cm^{-1} and $r = 5 \times 10^{-4}$ cm, practically all the current commences to be generated at $z = l$ only when η_0 exceeds 0.17 volt (Fig. 4).

(*ii*)   When the exchange current density is in the medium range of 10^{-6} amp cm^{-2}, the current distribution becomes more uniform; for example, with $\kappa = 0.1$ ohm^{-1} cm^{-1} and $r_2 = 5 \times 10^{-4}$ cm, 10 percent of the current is generated in the first half of the pore only, when η_0 is 0.312 volt (Fig. 5). When the conductivity is increased by a factor of 10, the current distribution is nearly

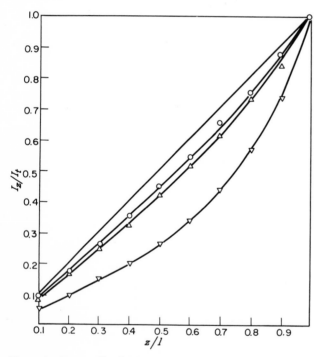

Figure 4   Current-distribution relations for case of small and intermediate activation and ohmic overpotential (elliptic integral calculation) at a two-phase porous electrode. $i_0 = 10^{-3}$ amp cm^{-2}; $\kappa = 2$ ohm^{-1} cm^{-1}; $r_2 = 5 \times 10^{-4}$ cm; $\bigcirc - \eta_0 = 0.018$ volt; $\triangle - \eta_0 = 0.055$ volt; $\triangledown - \eta_0 = 0.101$ volt.

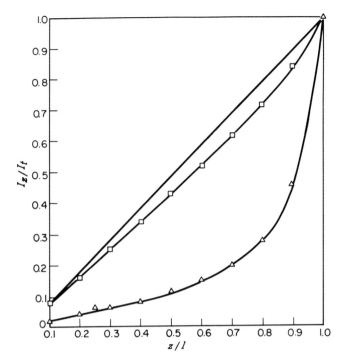

Figure 5 Current-distribution relations for case of activation and ohmic overpotential (elliptic integral calculation) at a two-phase porous electrode. $i_0 = 10^{-6}$ amp cm^{-2}; $\kappa = 0.1$ ohm^{-1} cm^{-1}; $r_2 = 5 \times 10^{-1}$ cm; $\square - \eta_0 = 0.243$ volt; $\triangle - \eta_0 = 0.312$ volt.

uniform even at this value of η_0 (Fig. 6). The calculation at the higher η_0 values agrees well with the Tafel case calculations as should be expected. The over-potential-vs.-current-density relations (η–log i) when $\kappa = 0.1$ ohm^{-1} cm^{-1} does not show any linear section for any value of r_2 (Fig. 7). However, when κ is increased to 1 ohm^{-1} cm^{-1} the linear section is fairly long (over 2 decades of current) with a Tafel slope of approximately $2RT/F$ (Fig. 8).

(*iii*) When i_0 is 10^{-9} amp cm^{-2} or smaller, the current distribution is uniform for all values of κ and r_2 even when $\eta_0 = 0.312$ volt.

A limitation in this calculation is when the $f(k,\psi)$ values calculated are small corresponding to values of ψ less than $10°$. This difficulty arises because the $f(k,\psi)$ values are tabulated to within a degree of ψ, and thus when $f(k,\psi)$ is small the selection of the ψ value is accurate to only within this figure. In this range (0 to $10°$), cos ψ is practically unity.

3.3.2   Tafel-region Calculations

3.3.2.1   Current and Potential Distribution Relations. From Eqs. (3.17) and (3.18), evaluated for high overpotential conditions (cf. Chap. 2, Sec. 3.6),

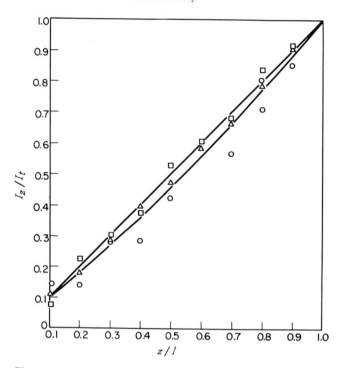

Figure 6 Current-distribution relations for case of activation and ohmic overpotential (elliptic integral calculation) at a two-phase porous electrode. $i_0 = 10^{-6}$ amp cm^{-2}; $\kappa = 1$ ohm^{-1} cm^{-1}; $r_2 = 10^{-4}$ cm; $\Delta - \eta_0 = 0.312$ volt.

one can obtain[4]

$$I_z = \left(\frac{4RT}{lF} \kappa\pi r_2{}^2\right) A \tan Ax \tag{3.20}$$

and

$$I_t = \left(\frac{4RT}{lF} \kappa\pi r_2{}^2\right) A \tan A \tag{3.21}$$

where

$$A = \frac{a^{\frac{1}{2}}}{2} \exp\left(\frac{y_0}{2}\right) \tag{3.22}$$

Also

$$\frac{I_z}{I_t} = \frac{\tan Ax}{\tan A} \tag{3.23}$$

The maximum value of A is $\pi/2$, because otherwise the current would tend to infinity at $z = l$ (where $x = 1$). Because of the simple nature of the relation

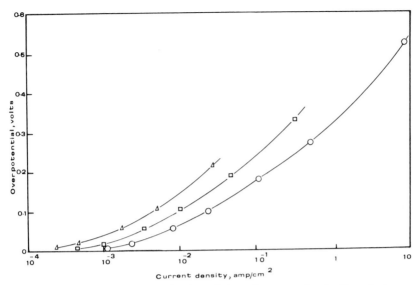

Figure 7 Overpotential–current density relations for case of activation-ohmic over-potential (elliptic integral calculation) at a two-phase porous electrode. $i_0 = 10^{-6}$ amp cm^{-2}; $\kappa = 0.1$ ohm^{-1} cm^{-1}; r_2 is in (1) $\bigcirc - 5 \times 10^{-4}$; (2) $\square - 2 \times 10^{-4}$; (3) $\triangle - 10^{-4}$ cm.

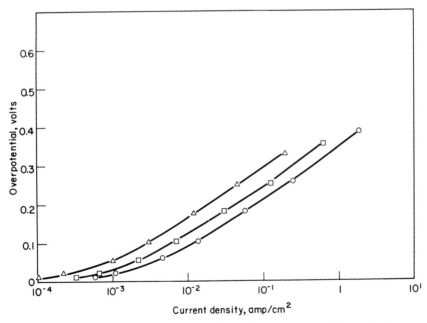

Figure 8 Overpotential–current density relations for case of activation-ohmic over-potential (elliptic integral calculation) at a two-phase porous electrode. Same param-eters as in Fig. 7 except $\kappa = 1$ ohm^{-1} cm^{-1}.

(3.23), it is therefore possible to construct a set of I_z/I_t versus x ($x = z/l$) curves choosing various values of A below $\pi/2$. For $A < 0.2$ rad, $\tan A \simeq A$. Under these conditions Eq. (3.23) reduces to

$$\frac{I_z}{I_t} = x \tag{3.24}$$

Thus, a plot of I_z/I_t versus x is a straight line passing through the origin, with a slope of $45°$, for all values of $A < 0.2$ rad. Hence, under the conditions stated, the current density is uniform. The dependence of I_z/I_t for other conditions is shown in Fig. 9. For $A < 0.4$, the I_z/I_t versus x plots are approximately linear. For larger values of A (e.g., $A > 1.30$), initially the I_z/I_t versus x relation has a small slope that is followed by the remaining region with a very high slope. An increase in the value of A above $A = 0.4$ rad corresponds, therefore, to an increase in the departure from an even-current distribution in the pore. For $A = 1.55$, nearly 90 percent of the current is generated from $x = 0.9$ to $x = 1.0$.

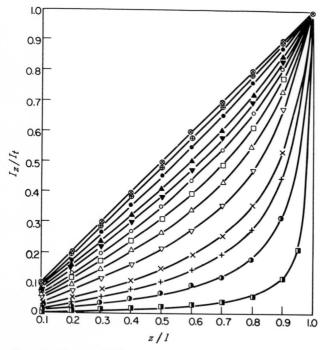

Figure 9 Current-distribution relations for case of activation and ohmic overpotential as a function of the parameter A. Curves apply for two-phase porous electrodes and for simple-pore[4] and thin-film[11] models of porous gas-diffusion electrodes. A is given by Eq. (3.22) for first two cases and by Eq. (6.16) for third case. A values are for ⊗ 0.5; ⊕ 0.6; ● 0.7; ▲ 0.8; ▼ 0.9; ○ 1.0; □ 1.1; △ 1.2; ▽ 1.3; × 1.4; + 1.45; ◑ 1.50; ◪ 1.55 volts.

Using Eqs. (3.19) and (3.22), the potential variation in the pore is expressed by the equation

$$\eta_z - \eta_0 = \left(\frac{4RT}{F}\right) \ln \sec Ax \tag{3.25}$$

Plots of $\eta - \eta_0$ versus x using the above values of A are shown in Fig. 10. In this case, for small values of A (<0.4) there is hardly any potential variation in the pore, whereas for $A > 1.3$ there is a significant potential variation in the pore.

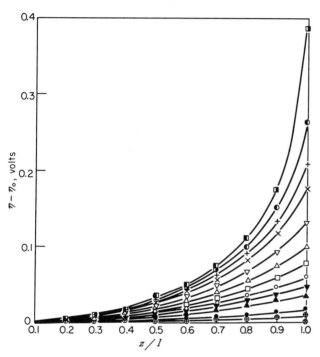

Figure 10 Potential distribution relations for case of activation and ohmic overpotential as a function of the parameter A. Curves apply for two-phase porous electrodes and for simple-pore[4] and thin-film[11] models of porous gas-diffusion electrodes. Symbols for A values are given in Fig. 9.

Construction of curves I_z/I_t and of $\eta_z - \eta_0$ versus x in terms of the parameter A gives a convenient way of analyzing the current- and potential-distribution problems as a function of the exchange current density, overpotential at the end $z = 0$, the specific conductivity of the electrolyte, the radius of the pore, the length of the pore, and temperature. This may be seen easily from the equation

$$A = \left(\frac{i_0 l^2 F^{1/2}}{2\kappa r_2 RT}\right)^{1/2} \exp \frac{\eta_0 F}{4RT} \tag{3.26}$$

which is obtained from Eqs. (3.22) and (3.13).   In Table 3 are shown the various η_0 values, corresponding to the chosen values of A, for some selected values of i_0.   An increase of i_0 favors an uneven-current distribution.   Thus, from these η_0 values and the η versus x plots, one can easily obtain the potential distribution in the pore for each value of A.   In these calculations (Table 3), κ was taken as 1 ohm^{-1} cm^{-1} and r_2 as 10^{-4} cm.   Similarly, one may find the effect of

TABLE 3 A-η_0 **Relation, Assuming** $\kappa = 1$ **ohm^{-1} cm^{-1},** $r_2 = 10^{-4}$ **cm, and** $l = 10^{-1}$ **cm, for Two Values of** i_0 **in the Case of Activation and Ohmic Overpotential for a Two-phase Porous Electrode** [A **Is Expressed by Eq. (3.26)**]

A	η_0, volts for $i_0 = 10^{-6}$ amp cm^{-2}	η_0, volts for $i_0 = 10^{-9}$ amp cm^{-2}
0,2	0.150	0.495
0.3	0.190	0.536
0.4	0.219	0.565
0.5	0.241	0.587
0.6	0.260	0.605
0.7	0.275	0.620
0.8	0.289	0.634
0.9	0.300	0.645
1.0	0.311	0.656
1.1	0.320	0.666
1.2	0.329	0.674
1.3	0.336	0.682
1.4	0.344	0.690
1.45	0.348	0.693
1.50	0.351	0.697
1.55	0.354	0.700

κ from the curves.   Table 4 shows the η_0 values calculated for $i_0 = 10^{-6}$ amp cm^{-2} and for two values of κ (0.1 and 10 ohm^{-1} cm^{-1}).   As seen from this table, a reduction in κ tends to an increase in uneven-current distribution in the pore. The effect of change of radius of the pore is shown in Table 5.   In this case too, i_0 was taken as 10^{-6} amp cm^{-2} and κ as 1 ohm^{-1} cm^{-1}.

3.3.2.2   Overpotential–Current-density Relations.   One may also obtain the current-potential relation from this useful parameter A.   Equation (3.21) may be written in the form

$$\ln I_t = \ln \left(\frac{4RT}{lF} \kappa \pi r_2 \right) + \ln A + \ln \tan A \tag{3.27}$$

The potential required for this plot is the one at $z = l$ (i.e., the measured overpotential)

$$\eta_l = \eta_0 + \eta_{\text{ohm},0 \to l)} \tag{3.28}$$

TABLE 4 A-η_0 Relation, Assuming $i_0 = 10^{-9}$ amp cm^{-2}, $r_2 = 10^{-4}$ cm, and $l = 10^{-1}$ cm, for Two Values of κ in the Case of Activation and Ohmic Overpotential for a Two-phase Porous Electrode [A Is Expressed by Eq. (3.26)]

A	η_0, volts for $\kappa = 0.1$ ohm^{-1} cm^{-1}	η_0, volts for $\kappa = 1.0$ ohm^{-1} cm^{-1}
0.2	0.380	0.495
0.3	0.421	0.536
0.4	0.450	0.565
0.5	0.472	0.587
0.6	0.490	0.605
0.7	0.504	0.620
0.8	0.517	0.634
0.9	0.529	0.645
1.0	0.539	0.656
1.1	0.549	0.666
1.2	0.558	0.674
1.3	0.567	0.682
1.4	0.574	0.690
1.45	0.577	0.693
1.50	0.581	0.697
1.55	0.584	0.700

TABLE 5 A-η_0 Relation, Assuming $i_0 = 10^{-6}$ amp cm^{-2}, $\kappa = 1$ ohm^{-1} cm^{-1}, and $l = 10^{-1}$ cm, for Two Values of r_2 in the Case of Activation and Ohmic Overpotential for a Two-phase Porous Electrode [A Is Expressed by Eq. (3.26)]

A	η_0, volts for $r_2 = 10^{-4}$ cm	η_0, volts for $r_2 = 5 \times 10^{-4}$ cm
0.2	0.150	0.230
0.3	0.190	0.271
0.4	0.219	0.300
0.5	0.241	0.322
0.6	0.260	0.340
0.7	0.275	0.356
0.8	0.289	0.369
0.9	0.300	0.381
1.0	0.311	0.391
1.1	0.320	0.401
1.2	0.329	0.410
1.3	0.336	0.418
1.4	0.344	0.425
1.45	0.348	0.428
1.50	0.351	0.432
1.55	0.354	0.435

where $\eta_{\text{ohm } 0 \to l}$ is the ohmic drop from $z = 1$ to $z = 0$ [cf. paragraph following Eq. (3.19)]. The latter is obtained from Eq. (3.25) evaluated at $x = 1$. Thus

$$\eta_l = \eta_0 + \frac{4RT}{F} \ln \sec A \tag{3.29}$$

η_0 may be expressed analytically in terms of A using Eq. (3.26). Using this expression in Eq. (3.29),

$$\eta_l = \frac{4RT}{F} \left(\ln A + \ln \sec A - \frac{1}{2} \ln \frac{i_0 l^2 F}{2 \kappa r_2 RT} \right) \tag{3.30}$$

Thus, from Eqs. (3.27) and (3.30) a plot of η_l versus $\ln I_t$ could be made for some chosen values of i_0, κ, r_2, and l. The current density *for the electrode* (current generated per unit cross-sectional area of the porous electrode) is given by

$$i = N_p I_t \tag{3.31}$$

where N_p is the number of pores per centimeter of cross-sectional area of the porous electrode. Assuming that the pores are touching each other in a cubic array,

$$N_p = \frac{1}{4 r_2^2} \tag{3.32}$$

The η_l versus $\log i$ plots are shown in Fig. 11 (both these calculated quantities now represent quantities subject to experimental measurement). It is interesting to see that there is a lower linear section with a slope of $2RT/F$ passing over into an upper linear section of double this slope. This behavior can be predicted easily from Eqs. (3.21) and (3.26) to (3.30). When A [as represented by Eq. (3.26)] is small (<0.2) $\tan A \simeq A$. Thus

$$I_t = 2\pi r_2 l i_0 \exp \frac{\eta_0 F}{2RT} \tag{3.33}$$

and

$$\eta_0 = \eta_l \tag{3.34}$$

This case corresponds to one of an even-current distribution in the pore (Fig. 9), and there is no potential drop in the pore. For very large values of A (>1.40),

$$\tan A \simeq \sec A \tag{3.35}$$

Under these conditions, combining Eqs. (3.27) to (3.30) results in

$$\ln I_t = \frac{\eta_l F}{4RT} + \frac{1}{2} \ln \frac{8 i_0 RT \kappa r_2^3}{F} \tag{3.36}$$

which shows that for $A > 1.4$, the Tafel slope is $4RT/F$.

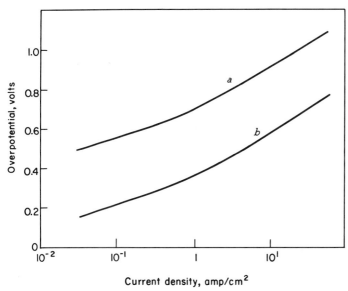

Figure 11 Overpotential–current density relations for case of activation and ohmic overpotential at a two-phase porous electrode or at a porous gas-diffusion electrode using the simple-pore[4] model (Tafel approximation calculation). $\kappa = 1$ ohm^{-1} cm^{-1}; $r_2 = 10^{-4}$ cm; i_0 is in (a) 10^{-9} and in (b) 10^{-6} amp cm^{-2}.

Expressions for equations for I_t and η_l in the form (3.27) and (3.30) are interesting from several points of view. Thus, an increase of i_0 by 1 decade will cause only a parallel shift downwards by $2RT/F$. Examination of the effect of change of κ and r_2 is somewhat more complex. Their effect may be seen more easily from the limiting equations (3.33) and 3.36). At low values of η_l, when condition (3.34) holds, there is no effect of κ on I_t but I_t varies directly with r_2. At high values of η_l, I_t varies linearly with $\kappa^{\frac{1}{2}}$ and with $r_2^{\frac{3}{2}}$.

4 SOME PROPOSED PHYSICAL MODELS FOR POROUS GAS-DIFFUSION ELECTRODES

4.1 General

Since most of the fuels or oxidants used in fuel cells are gases, some of the models proposed for porous gas-diffusion electrodes are presented in this section. Sections 5 to 9 deal with the theoretical analysis of these models.

For an analysis of the behavior of three-phase systems, it is necessary to understand the mode of operation of the porous electrode system. The choice of the model depends largely on the manner of preparation of the electrode. For instance, in some cases teflon is added to the catalyst particles, which have an effect of decreasing the wetting character of the electrode. There is a view that the gas adsorbs on the electrode where it is not covered with electrolyte and thereafter diffuses to the solution-covered region where it ionizes.

An actual porous electrode is more complex than is a model of uniform-parallel cylindrical pores. Firstly, pores are not uniformly straight but tortuous. A simple correction may be made for the model of uniform-parallel cylindrical pores by assuming a multiplying tortuosity factor for the length of the pore. Secondly, a more serious defect of the simple model is that the actual porous electrode consists of pores of different radii and some of these may be interconnected as well. A more advanced model has taken into consideration this distribution of pore radii and interconnection of pores (Secs. 4.6 and 8).

4.2   The Simple-pore Model for Nonwetting Electrodes

A model which appears feasible for nonwetting electrodes is the simple-pore model.[3] The condition for nonwetting is given by the Dupres equation:

$$\cos \theta = \frac{\gamma_{s,g} - \gamma_{s,l}}{\gamma_{l,g}} < 0 \tag{4.1}$$

where θ is the contact angle and the γ's are the surface tensions between the appropriate interfaces gas (g), liquid (l), and solid (s), as indicated by the subscripts. Thus for this case $\theta > 90°$. For the purpose of simplifying the mathematical treatment that follows, the electrode is assumed to consist of uniform parallel cylindrical pores in which $\theta = 90°$ (Fig. 12). Thus, it is possible to analyze the total-current–overpotential relation and the current distribution in a single pore and from the former obtain the apparent current-density–overpotential relation, as shown in the preceding section.

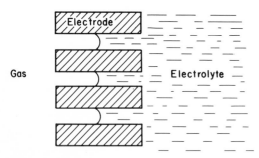

Figure 12   Idealized model of parallel cylindrical pores for a porous gas-diffusion electrode.

A single pore of this system is illustrated in Fig. 13 with a gas-electrolyte interface at $z = 0$. As in the preceding problem, a cylindrical coordinate

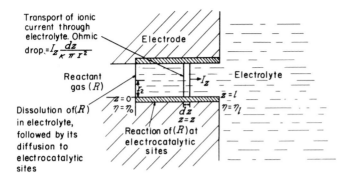

Figure 13 Mode of operation in a single pore of a porous gas-diffusion electrode using the simple-pore model.[4]

system may be used. Let the overall reaction occurring in the pore be

$$R \rightarrow P + ne_0^-$$ (4.2)

where R represents a gaseous reactant and P the product. As examples of reactions of this type, one may consider the anodic reactions

$$H_2 \rightarrow 2H^+ + 2e_0^-$$ (4.3)

$$C_3H_8 + 6H_2O \rightarrow 3CO_2 + 20H^+ + 20e_0^-$$ (4.4)

or a corresponding cathodic reaction such as

$$O_2 + 4H^+ + 4e_0^- \rightarrow 2H_2O$$ (4.5)

In this model, the reaction is assumed to occur in the following manner: the reactant gas R diffuses through the pore to the gas-electrolyte interface at $z = 0$, where it dissolves in the electrolyte, and the dissolved gas diffuses through the electrolyte to the various electrocatalytic sites along the pore, where the electrochemical reaction occurs. It is further assumed that the electrode reaction occurs in the following sequence:

$$R_{soln} \leftrightharpoons R_{ads}$$ (4.6)

$$R_{ads} \xrightarrow{rds} R_{ads}^+ + e_0^-$$ (4.7)

$$R_{ads}^+ \xrightarrow{fast} P + (n-1)e_0^-$$ (4.8)

The rate-determining step (rds) of the electrode reaction is assumed to be the one represented by Eq. (4.7). For simplicity, the many steps that follow the rate-determining step are represented by a single equation (4.8).

4.3 The Thin-film Model for Wetting Electrodes

In the thin-film model,[5] the basic assumption is that a comparatively lengthy thin film of liquid extends above the meniscus and is in contact with the solid phase in the pore (Fig. 14.) It is assumed that the thickness of the film, Δr, is a constant and is equal to $r_2 - r_1$ where r_1 is the radius of the pore excluding the film. For a theoretical analysis, a cylindrical coordinate system may be used as with the simple-pore model. Since Δr is small compared with the radius of the pore including the thin film, it may be assumed that the film forms a right-angle edge with the meniscus of the electrolyte. Another assumption generally made

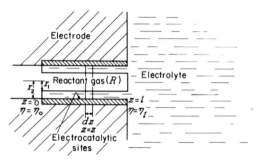

Figure 14   Schematic representation of a single pore of a porous gas-diffusion electrode using the thin-film model.[11]   Thickness of film is largely exaggerated.

is that all the current is generated on the electrode surface in the film region (i.e., from $z = 0$ to $z = l$ in Fig. 14). One may consider the reaction (4.2) again. The gas dissolves at the gas-electrolyte interface in the region of the thin film. The dissolved gas diffuses across the film and reaches the electrode-electrolyte interface where the reaction (4.2) occurs via the intermediate steps (4.6) to (4.8). Ionic transport occurs through the film and the bulk electrolyte to the counter electrode.

4.4   The Finite-contact-angle Meniscus Model for Partially Wetting Electrodes

The finite-contact-angle meniscus model[6] is intermediate between the simple-pore and thin-film models. It arose from work on reactions carried out in single pores (Chap. 9, Sec. 8). This model is schematically represented in Fig. 15. Interferometric and reflection studies were used (Cahan[6]) to show that the meniscus makes a finite contact angle with the electrode surface. The gas dissolves at the gas electrolyte interface along AB, and the dissolved gas diffuses through the electrolyte to the electrode-electrolyte interface. One may qualitatively predict that close to the region at the upper end of the meniscus, A, the current density should be high, since the diffusion path length is quite small. At the same time, the ohmic drop in this region is also high, since the cross-sectional area for ionic transport is small. Conversely, near the bottom end of the meniscus, the diffusion path length is high but the ohmic drop is small.

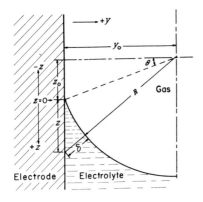

Figure 15 Finite-contact-angle model for a porous gas-diffusion electrode.[6] Coordinate system for theoretical calculations is shown.

Consequently there is a maximum in the current density in the intermediate region.

4.5 The Double-porous and Cone Models for Electrodes with a Stable Meniscus

In the models described in the preceding section, it has been assumed that the pores are cylindrical and of uniform radius. A disadvantage of this type of model is that the pressure of reactant in the gas phase is quite critical. Thus, within each pore there is an equilibrium at the gas-electrolyte interface due to the gas pressure, which tends to force the electrolyte out of the pore, and due to the capillary forces of the electrolyte, which tends to flood the pore. Expressed mathematically, the condition for a stable meniscus is given by

$$P = \frac{2\gamma}{r_2} \cos \theta \qquad (4.9)$$

where P is the pressure of the gas R, γ is the surface tension of the electrolyte, and θ is the contact angle of the electrolyte with the electrode surface. If pores have radii (r) less than the critical radius (r_2), as defined by Eq. (4.9), they get flooded with the electrolyte. On the other hand, if $r > r_2$, the gas passes through these pores and they are dry. The basic difficulty with nonhomoporous electrodes is that many of the pores are not active.

There are two ways of overcoming these difficulties of obtaining a stable meniscus within a pore. In the first, a double-porous structure is used with the large pores on the gas side and the small pores on the solution side. This model was first introduced by Bacon[7] and is used in the Apollo fuel cells.[4a] The meniscus is stabilized at the junction of the small and large pores. A single pore of this electrode is schematically represented in Fig. 16a.

In the second type, the porous electrode consists of conical pores. Here again, the larger part of the pores face the gas side and the smaller part the solution side, as seen in Fig. 16b. This model was first suggested by Justi.[8]

In both these models, one can visualize a flat meniscus, a meniscus with a

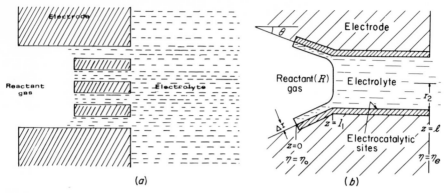

Figure 16 (*a*) Single pore of a double-porous structure of a porous gas-diffusion electrode; (*b*) cone model for a porous gas-diffusion electrode. Only a single pore is shown.

finite contact angle of a thin film. From considerations of construction, the double-porous electrodes appear more practical than conical-porous electrodes.

4.6   The Intersecting Pore Model for Practical Electrodes

In the preceding models, considerations of the pore distribution have been suppressed by making the oversimple assumption that the porous electrode consists of parallel cylindrical pores, all of the same radius. A detailed analysis is then made of the current distribution, potential distribution, and total current generated in a pore. There is an alternative approach. It is to neglect the aforementioned detailed considerations within a single pore but consider a model which concentrates on the pore distribution, shape, tortuosity, pore interconnections, etc. The latter approach has been adopted by Burstein et al. in their intersecting pore model.[9]

It is assumed here that a porous electrode consists of an intersection of micropores with macropores (Fig. 17). Due to the gas pressure, capillary forces, and the multitude of intersection of micropores with macropores, it is assumed that the entire surface of the macropore is covered with a film of electrolyte, and that the micropores are filled with electrolyte and the macropores with the reactant gas. The reactant gas dissolves at the gas-electrolyte

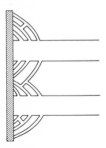

Figure 17 Intersecting pore model for a porous gas-diffusion electrode.[9] Only a single macropore is shown.

film interface, and the dissolved gas diffuses through the film to the electrolytic sites on the surface of the macropores where the reaction occurs. Ionic conduction occurs through the electrolyte film and then through the electrolyte in the micropores. To obtain optimum electrocatalytic activity, it is necessary to have a critical ratio of the total cross-sectional area of the micropores to the total surface area of the macropores.

5 THEORETICAL ANALYSIS FOR NONWETTING POROUS GAS-DIFFUSION ELECTRODES USING THE SIMPLE-PORE MODEL

5.1 Case Where all Forms of Overpotential May Be Present

5.1.1 Two-dimensional Treatment—Difficulties in Obtaining a Solution

This model was treated in detail by Srinivasan, Hurwitz, and Bockris.[1] In this work, analytic and/or numerical solutions were obtained for the current and potential distribution relations within a pore and for the overpotential–current-density relations, taking into consideration all forms of overpotentials (viz., activation, concentration, and ohmic). In addition, the effects of variations of electrode kinetic and physical parameters on these relations were thoroughly examined. The treatment presented here differs from the one in Sec. 3, where it was assumed that concentration overpotential is absent which may also apply in the case of liquid fuels dissolved in electrolyte. A rigorous analysis of the solution to this problem (viz., obtaining the overpotential–current-density and current-distribution relations) should be made by using a two-dimensional model where a concentration gradient of the reactant gas must be assumed both in the z and r directions (Fig. 13). In this section, it will be shown that this is not possible and that it is necessary to make some approximations. Since the step (4.7) is rate-determining, the rate of the electrode reaction in the element dz is given by

$$dI = 2\pi r_2 dz i_0 \left\{ \frac{c}{c^\circ} \exp\left(\frac{\beta \eta F}{RT}\right) - \exp\left[-(1-\beta)\frac{\eta F}{RT}\right] \right\} \tag{5.1}$$

The assumption is made that concentration overpotential is due only to the reactant species R. η represents the local overpotential at z, i_0 is the exchange current density, c/c° represents the ratio of concentration of R at (z, r_2) to that at $z = 0$, and β is the symmetry factor.

The boundary conditions for η are

$$\eta = \eta_0 \quad \text{at } z = 0 \tag{5.2}$$

and

$$\eta = \eta_l \quad \text{at } z = l \tag{5.3}$$

η_t is the *measured* overpotential of the porous electrode with respect to a reversible electrode, at which point the reaction (4.2) is at equilibrium and the reactants and products are at concentrations of $c_R{}^0$ and $c_P{}^0$, respectively. Another boundary condition results from the condition that when $z = 0$, one comes to the end of the current-producing region:

$$I = \kappa \pi r_2{}^2 \frac{d\eta}{dz} = 0 \qquad \text{at } z = 0, \tag{5.4}$$

The ohmic drop in the solution $d\eta$ is given by

$$d\eta = I \frac{dz}{\kappa \pi r_2{}^2} \tag{5.5}$$

In order that an expression may be obtained for I as a function of distance in a pore, limitations due to mass transport of the reactant through the pore must be considered. To obtain the concentration of the reactant as a function of the distance both along the pore and in the radial direction, it is necessary to solve Laplace's equation:

$$\nabla^2 c = 0 \qquad \text{for } 0 \leqslant z \leqslant l \qquad \text{and} \qquad 0 \leqslant r < r_2 \tag{5.6}$$

The boundary conditions for Eq. (5.6) are

$$c = c^\circ \qquad \text{at } z = 0 \qquad \text{for } 0 \leqslant r < r_2 \tag{5.7}$$

$$\left(\frac{\partial c}{\partial z}\right) = 0 \qquad \text{at } z = l \qquad \text{for } 0 \leqslant r < r_2 \tag{5.8}$$

$$dI = -2\pi r_2 dz\, DnF \left(\frac{\partial c}{\partial r}\right) \qquad \text{at } r = r_2 \qquad \text{for } 0 < z < l \tag{5.9}$$

and

$$I_t = -2\pi DnF \int_0^{r_2} r \left(\frac{\partial c}{\partial z}\right)_{z=0} dr \tag{5.10}$$

c° is the saturation solubility of R in the electrolyte at the gas-electrolyte interface.

The boundary condition (5.8) means that the reactant R, which enters the solution, is totally consumed at the electrode within the pore. Although it may not always be valid, this condition is an ideal one for an electrochemical energy converter from the point of view of complete utilization of the fuel. This condition is complementary with condition (5.10), which explicitly states that the total flux of reactant gas at $z = 0$ is equal to the total current, owing to the oxidation of R, generated in the entire pore. The boundary condition (5.9) denotes that the current generated in an element dz of the electrode is equal to the radial flux of R towards the electrode within this element (Fig. 13).

The mathematical objective of the system of equations is to solve Eq. (5.1), which in turn depends on the solution of Eq. (5.6). It is not possible to obtain an analytic solution to the differential equation (5.6) with boundary conditions (5.7) to (5.10) due to the variation of η along the pore.   A numerical solution to this equation is also quite difficult because the system of equations involves obtaining (1) η as a function of z and (2) c as a function of r and z.

Two attempts[4] have been made to overcome this problem.   In the first (Sec. 5.1.2), it is assumed that there is a concentration gradient of the reactant only in the axial direction of the pore and not in the radial direction.   Thus, any limiting current that may be observed under these conditions is due to a limiting rate of supply of reactant through the electrolyte free part of the pore and is determined using Poiseuille's law.[10]   The assumption of a unidirectional concentration gradient (i.e., one which exists only along z direction and that $dc/dr = 0$) is valid under the conditions that the local activation-controlled current density is less than the limiting current density owing to radial diffusion. Expressed mathematically, this condition is

$$i_0 \exp\left(\frac{\beta \eta F}{RT}\right) \ll \left(\frac{DnFc^0}{r_2}\right) \tag{5.11}$$

In expressing condition (5.11), it is assumed that the rate of the reverse reaction is much less than the corresponding forward rate in obtaining the above condition.   The above condition would still hold even if the reverse rate were taken into account.

In the second attempt (Sec. 5.2) to solve the difficulties encountered in solving Eqs. (5.1) and (5.6), it is assumed that the potential is constant along the pore.   Under these conditions, a solution of the Laplace equation (5.6) with the boundary conditions (5.7) to (5.10) is possible.

5.1.2   Treatment Neglecting Radial Diffusion—One-dimensional Treatment

5.1.2.1   Mathematical Formulations and Solutions.   In order that the diffusion equation for the one-dimensional treatment may be derived, consider the cylindrical element dz (Fig. 13).   In the steady state, the net flux into the element is equal to the current generated in this element.   Thus

$$dI_z = \pi r_2^2 DnF\left(\frac{d^2c}{dz^2}\right) dz \tag{5.12}$$

Another expression for dI_z/dz may be obtained by considering the ohmic drop within the element dz.   Thus, differentiating Eq. (5.5),

$$\left(\frac{dI_z}{dz}\right) = \kappa \pi r_2^2\left(\frac{d^2\eta}{dz^2}\right) \tag{5.13}$$

Combining Eqs. (5.12) and (5.13) results in

$$\left(\frac{d^2\eta}{dz^2}\right) = \left(\frac{DnF}{\kappa}\right)\frac{d^2c}{dz^2} \tag{5.14}$$

In Eqs. (5.12) and (5.14), c denotes the concentration of R dissolved in the electrolyte as a function of distance. The boundary conditions for the differential equations (5.14) are expressed by Eqs. (5.2), (5.3), and by

$$c = c^\circ \qquad \text{at } z = 0 \tag{5.15}$$

$$\pi r_2{}^2 DnF\left(\frac{dc}{dz}\right) = -I_t \qquad \text{at } z = 0 \tag{5.16}$$

$$\left(\frac{dc}{dz}\right) = 0 \qquad \text{at } z = l \tag{5.17}$$

A differential equation in η and z is obtained by substitution of Eq. (5.13) in (5.1):

$$\left(\frac{d^2\eta}{dz^2}\right) = \left(\frac{2}{\kappa r_2}\right) i_0 \left\{\left(\frac{c}{c^\circ}\right) \exp\left(\frac{\beta \eta F}{RT}\right) - \exp\left[-(1-\beta)\frac{\eta F}{RT}\right]\right\} \tag{5.18}$$

The boundary conditions for this equation are expressed by Eqs. (5.2) and (5.4).

Methods used for solving the above system of equations are involved and found in the original paper.[4]   The current distribution and total current are per pore are given by

$$\frac{I_z}{I_t} = \frac{(a'b' \exp y_0)^{1/2} \exp (mx/2)(dc/d\alpha) + m}{m} \tag{5.19}$$

$$I_t = 2\kappa \pi r_2{}^2 \frac{m}{lF} \tag{5.20}$$

where:

$$\frac{dc}{d\alpha} = [1 - \exp(-2y_0)] \frac{K_1(\alpha_2)I_1(\alpha) - I_1(\alpha_2)K_1(\alpha)}{K_0(\alpha_1)I_1(\alpha_2) + I_0(\alpha_1)K_1(\alpha_2)} \tag{5.21}$$

$$m = -(a'b' \exp y_0)^{1/2} \left(\frac{dc}{d\alpha}\right)_{\alpha_1} \tag{5.22}$$

$$= 2\left(ua' \frac{\exp y_0}{b'm^2}\right)^{1/2} \tag{5.23}$$

$$u = \exp mx \tag{5.24}$$

$$x = \frac{z}{l} \tag{5.25}$$

$$a' = \frac{i_0 l^2 F}{\kappa r_2 RT} \tag{5.26}$$

$$b' = \frac{DnF^2 c^\circ}{2\kappa r_2 RT} \tag{5.27}$$

In Eq. (5.21), K's and I's are the Bessel function solutions of order indicated by the respective suffixes.

5.1.2.2 Numerical Calculations. Under the conditions that m is small ($<10^{-2}$), there is only activation and concentration overpotential. For this case, the current distribution and total current per pore may be expressed by[4]

$$\frac{I_z}{I_t} = \frac{\sinh K - \sinh [K(1-x)]}{\sinh K} \tag{5.28}$$

and

$$I_t = \frac{\pi r_2^2 DnFc^\circ}{l} [1 - \exp(-2y_0)] K \tanh K \tag{5.29}$$

where

$$K^2 = \frac{a'}{b'} \exp y_0 \tag{5.30}$$

Calculations for the current distribution as a function of x have been carried out, according to Eq. (5.28), varying the parameter K. (The parameter K in this section resembles the parameter A in Sec. 3.) They are presented graphically in Fig. 18. Plots in terms of the parameter K are quite interesting, since from a few plots one may easily predict the nature of the curve for variations in

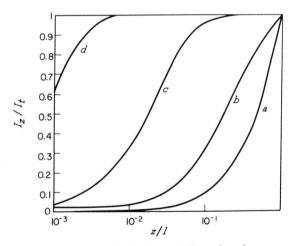

Figure 18 Current-distribution relations for the case where all forms of overpotential are considered using the simple-pore model for a porous gas-diffusion electrode as a function of K.[4] $DnFc^0 = 10^{-7}$ amp cm^{-1}; $\kappa = 1$ ohm^{-1} cm^{-1}. Some variations of i_0 and η_0 corresponding to different values of K which give rise to the different curves a to d are shown in Table 6.

i_0, η_0, D, c^0, and r_2.   Some variations which correspond to the different values of the parameter K are given in Table 6.   The significant part played by mass

TABLE 6   Values of i_0 and η_0 Corresponding to Current Distribution Plots and K Values in Fig. 18 [K Is Expressed by Eq. (5.30)]

Curve	K	i_0, amp cm^{-2}	η_0, volts
a	1	10^{-12}	0.10
b	3.8	10^{-9}	0.10
c	40.5	10^{-12}	0.65
c	40.5	10^{-6}	0.01
d	122.0	10^{-9}	0.65
	$DnFc^0 = 10^{-7}$ for all cases		

transfer is seen from these curves.   Thus, with $i_0 = 10^{-9}$ amp cm^{-2}, $r_2 = 10^{-4}$ cm, $\kappa = 1$ ohm^{-1} cm, and $l = 10^{-1}$ cm, curve b is obtained for an overpotential of 0.1 volt, whereas curve d is obtained for an overpotential of 0.65 volt.   Even at 0.1 volt, 80 percent of the current is generated at less than 10 percent of the total length of the pore because of diffusional holdup in the pore.

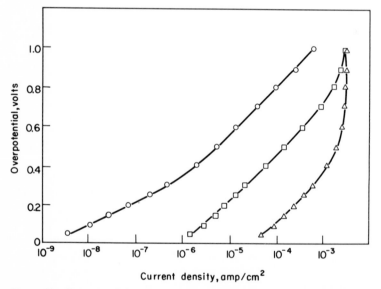

Figure 19   Overpotential–current density relations at a porous gas-diffusion electrode using the simple-pore model for the case where all forms of overpotential are considered.[4]   Values of $DnFc^0$ and κ are same as in Fig. 18. i_0 values are for $\bigcirc - 10^{-12}$; $\square - 10^{-9}$; $\triangle - 10^{-6}$ amp cm^{-2}.

At 0.65 volt, only 0.17 percent of the pore length is required to generate 80 percent of the current. An increase in the concentration of the reactant c^0 or the diffusion coefficient shifts the curves towards a uniform distribution of current generated in the pore (the dotted line gives the curve for the uniform distribution of current). For these cases, where the assumption $\tanh K \simeq 1$ holds, the Tafel slope is twice the normal Tafel slope. From Eqs. (5.26), (5.27), and (5.30) it follows that high K values correspond to low values of $DnFc^0$ and medium-to-high values of η_0 and of i_0. Typical numerical values may be obtained from the plots in Fig. 19.

The current density (current generated per unit cross-sectional area of the porous electrode) is obtained by combining Eqs. (5.29) with (3.31) and (3.32). The current-density–potential relations for three values of i_0, using the same values of $DnFc^0$, are represented in Fig. 19. For $i_0 = 10^{-12}$ amp cm^{-2}, a two-section Tafel plot is obtained. For the other i_0 values, only the higher slope is obtained. Thus, the important result is obtained that for the usual values of solubilities of gases in electrolytes (about 10^{-4} mole l^{-1}), mass transport determines the active area of a pore even if reactions have as low an exchange current density as 10^{-9} amp cm^{-2}.

5.2 Case of Activation and Concentration Overpotential (i.e., Negligible Ohmic Overpotential)—Two-dimensional Treatment

5.2.1 Mathematical Formulations and Solutions

As stated in Sec. (5.1.1), the second approach to the solution of the problem is to neglect ohmic overpotential within the pore. Under these conditions, the concentration of the gas R in the pore must satisfy the Laplace equation (5.6) in cylindrical coordinates, assuming a symmetry around the z axis and with boundary conditions expressed by Eqs. (5.7) to (5.10). Also, dI in Eq. (5.9) is expressed by Eq. (5.1) with the assumption that η is constant in the pore.

The following expressions are obtained for the current distribution and the total current per pore:

$$\frac{I_t - I_z}{I_t} = \frac{\sum\limits_{n=1}^{\infty} \dfrac{\sinh\left[(l-z)\alpha_n\right]}{\alpha_n(h^2 + \alpha_n^2)\cosh l\alpha_n}}{\sum\limits_{n=1}^{\infty} \dfrac{\tanh l\alpha_n}{\alpha_n(h^2 + \alpha_n^2)}} \tag{5.31}$$

and

$$I_t = 4\pi i_0 \left\{ \exp\left(\frac{\beta\eta F}{RT}\right) - \exp\left[-(1-\beta)\frac{\eta F}{RT}\right] \right\} \sum_{n=1}^{\infty} \frac{h}{\alpha_n(h^2 + \alpha_n^2)} \tanh l\alpha_n \tag{5.32}$$

where α's are the roots of the Bessel function equation

$$\alpha r_2 J_1(\alpha r_2) = h r_2 J_0(\alpha r_2) = 0 \tag{5.33}$$

and

$$h = \frac{i_0}{DnFc^0} \exp\left(\frac{\beta\eta F}{RT}\right) \tag{5.34}$$

For small values of hr_2, Eqs. (5.31) and (5.32) reduce to Eqs. (5.28) and (5.29), respectively.

The other extreme case is for large values of the parameter hr_2. One then gets an expression for the limiting current

$$I_{t,l} = 4\pi DnFc^0 r_2 \tag{5.35}$$

Use of Eqs. (3.31) and (3.32) in (5.35) gives the expression for the *limiting current density* for the whole porous *electrode*, rather than the limiting current for one pore

$$i_L = \frac{\pi DnFc^0}{r_2} \tag{5.36}$$

Equation (5.36) shows one of the distinct advantages of porous electrodes over planar electrodes—radial rather than planar diffusion. Thus, the limiting current density i_L varies linearly with the diffusion coefficient and with the solubility of the gaseous reactant in the electrolyte and inversely with the radius of the pore.

5.2.2 Numerical Calculations

Only over a small region of current density, above 25 percent of i_L, is it necessary to use the general equations [Eqs. (5.31) and (5.32)] for the current distribution and overpotential–current-density relations.[4] These calculations are quite tedious, since they involve solutions of the Bessel function equation (5.33). An approximate method may be used for this region of current density by combining the expressions of the one-dimensional treatment (Sec. 5.1.2) and of the limiting current of the two-dimensional treatment given here for values of i_0, as seen in Fig. 19. The two-dimensional treatment is necessary, however, to obtain the limiting current density.

5.3   Case of Activation and Ohmic Overpotential (i.e., Negligible Concentration Overpotential)

5.3.1   *Mathematical Formulations and Solutions*

This case is similar to the one of activation and ohmic overpotential in two-phase systems. Thus, equations for the current distribution and for the overpotential–current-density relations are identical with those found in Sec. 3.

5.3.2   *Numerical Calculations*

The effect of variation of kinetic and physical parameters on the current (and potential) distribution and on the overpotential–current-density relations may be seen from the calculations presented graphically in Sec. 3.3.

5.4   Elimination of Concentration Overpotential (e.g., by Circulation of Electrolyte) and Significant Improvement in Performance

An important result arises from a comparison of the equation in Sec. 5.1.2 for the current as a function of activation, ohmic, and concentration overpotentials, together with that of the equations in Sec. 3.3, which neglect mass-transport effects. A comparison of Figs. 11 and 19 shows that elimination of concentration overpotential increases the current density *by a factor of about* 10^3 *at any over-potential.* Concentration overpotential may be eliminated by using fuels which have high solubilities or diffusion coefficients in the electrolyte. In the cases where the solubility and diffusion coefficient are low, the same effect may be obtained by *circulation of the electrolyte, saturated with the reactant fuel, through the porous electrode* at a rate such that no concentration gradient exists within the pore.

6   THEORETICAL ANALYSIS FOR WETTING POROUS GAS-DIFFUSION ELECTRODES USING THE THIN-FILM MODEL

6.1   Case Where All Forms of Overpotential Are Present

6.1.1   Mathematical Formulations and Solutions

Considering again the electrode reaction (4.2), taking place in the reaction sequence expressed by Eqs. (4.6) to (4.8), the rate of the electrode reaction in the element dz of the thin-film model (Fig. 14) is given by

$$dI_z = 2\pi r_2 dz i_0 \left[\frac{c_e}{c^0} \exp\left(\frac{\eta F}{2RT}\right) - \exp\left(-\frac{\eta F}{2RT}\right) \right] \tag{6.1}$$

All symbols refer to the same parameters as in the preceding section. β is taken as $\frac{1}{2}$.

The potential drop in the element dz is given by

$$d\eta = I_z \frac{dz}{\kappa\pi(r_2{}^2 - r_1{}^2)} \tag{6.2}$$

In order to ascertain the concentration c_e at the electrode surface in the steady state, Srinivasan and Hurwitz[11] assumed that the reactant gas has a flux only in the r direction and that the reactant is only consumed at the electrode surface:

$$dI_z = -2\pi r_2 dz \, DnF\left(\frac{\partial c}{\partial r}\right) \tag{6.3}$$

From Fig. 14, it is clear that the concentration of the reactant R on the electrolyte side of the gas-electrolyte interface always corresponds to its saturation solubility.   Thus, integrating Eq. (6.3) with the boundary condition that

$$c = c^0 \qquad\qquad \text{at } r = r_1 \qquad\qquad (6.4)$$

$$c_e = c^0 + \frac{1}{2\pi DnF} \frac{dI_z}{dz} \ln \frac{r_1}{r_2} \qquad\qquad (6.5)$$

Using Eqs. (6.1), (6.2), and (6.5), Srinivasan and Hurwitz[11] arrived at the equation

$$\frac{d^2\eta}{dz^2} = \frac{[4r_2 i_0/\kappa(r_2{}^2 - r_1{}^2)] \sinh(\eta F/2RT)}{1 + (r_2 i_0/DnFc^0)\ln(r_2/r_1)\exp(\eta F/2RT)} \qquad (6.6)$$

Making the substitutions,

$$\frac{\eta F}{2RT} = y \qquad\qquad (6.7)$$

and

$$\frac{z}{l} = x \qquad\qquad (6.8)$$

Eq. (6.6) reduces to

$$\frac{d^2 y}{dx^2} = \frac{a \sinh y}{1 + b \exp y} \qquad\qquad (6.9)$$

where

$$a = \frac{2r_2 i_0 l^2 F}{\kappa RT(r_2{}^2 - r_1{}^2)} \simeq \frac{i_0 l^2 F}{\kappa RT \Delta r} \qquad\qquad (6.10)$$

and

$$b = \frac{r_2 i_0}{DnFc^0} \ln \frac{r_2}{r_1} \simeq \frac{i_0 \Delta r}{DnFc^0} \qquad\qquad (6.11)$$

In terms of the dimensionless parameters x and y, the current generated from $z = 0$ to $z = z$ (Fig. 14) is given by [cf. Eq. (6.2)]

$$I_z = 2\kappa\pi(r_2{}^2 - r_1{}^2) \frac{RT}{lF}\left(\frac{dy}{dx}\right)_{x=x} \qquad\qquad (6.12)$$

and the total current generated from $z = 0$ to $z = l$ by

$$I_t = 2\kappa\pi(r_2{}^2 - r_1{}^2) \frac{RT}{lF}\left(\frac{dy}{dx}\right)_{x=1} \qquad\qquad (6.13)$$

The ratio of the current at z to the total current is thus

$$\frac{I_z}{I_t} = \frac{(dy/dx)_{x=x}}{(dy/dx)_{x=1}} \tag{6.14}$$

It is not possible to solve Eq. (6.9) analytically in a general case. A numerical solution is, therefore, necessary to study the influence of the various parameters $(i_0, \kappa, D, c^0, r_2, r_1, \text{ and } \eta_0)$ on the $I_z - z$ and $I_t - \eta_l$ ($\eta = \eta_l$ at $z = l$) relations. For some special cases, analytic solutions of Eq. (6.11) are, however, possible, as shown in Sec. 6.2.

6.1.2 Numerical Calculations

Numerical solutions have been made using an exchange current density of 10^{-6} amp cm^{-2} but varying (1) the product $DnFc^0$, (2) the specific conductance of the electrolyte κ, (3) the radius of the pore r_2, and (4) the thickness of the film Δr. The values of these parameters for this calculation are shown in Table 7.

TABLE 7 Kinetic and Physical Parameters for Numerical Calculations in the Case Where All Forms of Overpotential Are Considered, Using the Thin-film Model of Porous Gas-diffusion Electrodes (See Figs. 20 to 22)

Curve number in Figs. 20 to 22	$DnFc^0$, amp cm^{-1}	κ, ohm^{-1} cm^{-1}	r_2, cm	Δr,† cm
1	10^{-4}	1	10^{-4}	10^{-5}
2	10^{-4}	0.1	10^{-4}	10^{-5}
3	10^{-9}	1	10^{-4}	10^{-5}
4	10^{-9}	0.1	10^{-4}	10^{-5}
5	10^{-6}	1	10^{-4}	10^{-5}
6	10^{-6}	1	10^{-4}	10^{-6}
7	10^{-6}	1	10^{-3}	10^{-5}

‡ Values of the film thickness may appear too low but they are reasonable for pores with radii of the order of 1μ.

Equation (6.9) shows that a limiting current is obtained when the overpotential reached fairly high values and i_L is proportional to a/b. From this condition and Eqs. (6.10) and (6.11), it follows that the limiting current is independent of the exchange current density. In the lower overpotential range, the current-density–overpotential relation is similar to that for the activation-ohmic overpotential case (Sec. 6.3) (cf. Figs. 20 to 24). Thus, it follows that if the exchange current densities are smaller than 10^{-6} amp cm^{-2}, the shape of the overpotential–current-density curve is similar to that shown for 10^{-6} amp cm^{-2} with the same values of $DnFc^0$, r_2, Δr, and κ but with a parallel shift in the lower

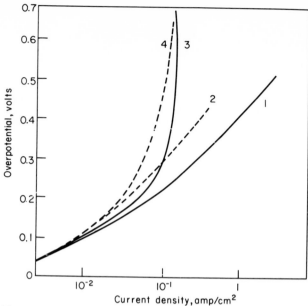

Figure 20 Overpotential–current density relations at a porous gas-diffusion electrode, using the thin-film model, for the case where all forms of overpotential are taken into account showing effect of variation of κ or product $DnFc^0$.[11] Kinetic parameters used in the calculations, yielding the curves 1–4, are given in Table 7.

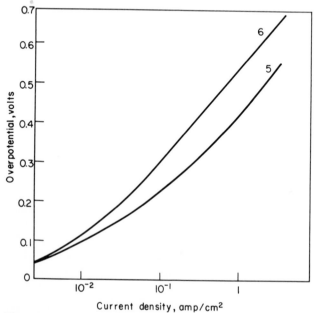

Figure 21 Overpotential–current density relations at a porous gas-diffusion electrode, using the thin-film model, for the case where all forms of overpotential are taken into account showing effect of variation of Δr.[11] Kinetic parameters used in the calculations, yielding curves 5 and 6, are given in Table 7.

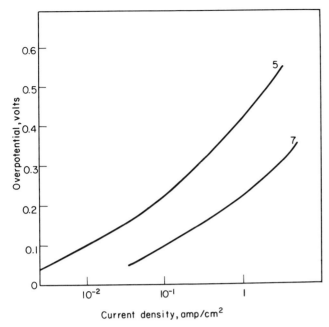

Figure 22 Overpotential–current density relations at a porous gas-diffusion electrode, using the thin-film model, for the case where all forms of overpotential are taken into account, showing effect of variation of r_2.[11] Kinetic parameters used in the calculations, yielding curves 5 and 7, are given in Table 7.

overpotential region and tending towards the same limiting current density. The relations for lower exchange current densities show longer Tafel regions than those for higher exchange current densities. The overpotential–current-density relations for the various cases considered in Table 7 with $i_0 = 10^{-6}$ amp cm^{-2} are shown in Figs. 20 to 22. The noteworthy features of these curves are that: (1) The initial shape of these curves corresponds to the case of activation-ohmic overpotential, considered in the next section, i.e., the role of diffusion overpotential is negligible. (2) The length of the portion corresponding to the case of activation-ohmic overpotential depends on the magnitude of $DnFc^0$, r_2, Δr, and κ in the following manner. The higher the value of $DnFc^0$, the longer is this region. This is also the case for the lower values of κ, Δr, and r_2. (3) When b, which is expressed by Eq. (6.11), is less than 10^{-4}, a limiting current density is not reached in the practical overpotential range (less than 0.7 volt). This is particularly true if the exchange current density is lower than 10^{-6} amp cm^{-2}. Low values of b correspond to low values of i_0, Δr and to medium or high values of $DnFc^0$. (4) The limiting current density is higher for lower values of Δr, and the higher values of $DnFc^0$, or r_2. The limiting current density is independent of the value of κ. However, for lower values of κ, the limiting current is reached at higher values of the overpotential for the same

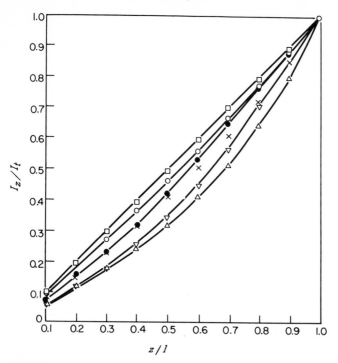

Figure 23   A typical current-distribution relation at a porous gas-diffusion electrode using the thin-film model for case where all forms of overpotential are considered and in which limiting current is observed.[11]   Figure corresponds to curve 4 of Fig. 20. η_l values are for $\bigcirc$ — 0.062; $\times$ — 0.140; $\triangle$ — 0.286; $\bigtriangledown$ — 0.458; $\bullet$ — 0.631; and $\square$ — 0.890 volts.

values of the kinetic and physical parameters; one sees readily that the thin-film model gives current densities greater than that for the simple-pore model at the same overpotential throughout the entire range (Figs. 19 and 20).   The general shape of the current-density–overpotential relation is the same in both cases. At low overpotentials, there is a short region showing the normal Tafel slope of $2RT/F$ which passes over into a region where the Tafel slope is $4RT/F$ and finally the region where the current density varies slowly with increase of overpotential close to the limiting current density of the electrode.

The current-distribution plots [I_z-x (or z) relations] show a special type of behavior.   In previous cases, with increase of overpotential, the current distribution tends to become more nonuniform with concentration of current generation increasing at either one or the other end of the pore.   In the present cases, where the product $DnFc^0$ is not too high and a limiting current is observed in the overpotential region of interest, the current generation becomes non-uniform with increase of overpotential at lower overpotentials, but the behavior

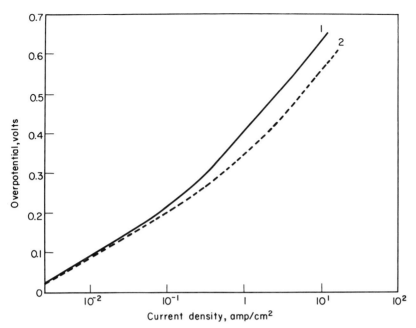

Figure 24 Overpotential–current density relation at a porous gas-diffusion electrode, using the thin-film model, for the case of activation and ohmic overpotential (Tafel approximation calculation).[11] $i_0 = 10^{-6}$ amp cm^{-2}; $\kappa = 1$ ohm^{-1} cm^{-1}; $r_2 = 10^{-4}$ cm; $\triangle r = 10^{-5}$ cm.   For comparison, corresponding relation for simple-pore model (broken line) is also shown.

is reversed at higher overpotentials in the regions where the current is close to the limiting current.   A typical current-distance relation is shown in Fig. 23.   At the limiting current, there is a uniform current distribution within the pore as is observed at low overpotentials.

6.2   Case of Activation and Ohmic Overpotential (i.e., Negligible Concentration Overpotential)

6.2.1   *Mathematical Formulations and Solutions*

When concentration overpotential is absent, $b \exp y \ll 1$ and Eq. (6.11) becomes

$$\frac{d^2y}{dx^2} = a \sinh y \tag{6.15}$$

This equation is identical in form with Eq. (3.4) using $\beta = \frac{1}{2}$.   The current distribution and total current per pore are expressed by Eqs. (3.8) and (3.9) with all the symbols represented by Eqs. (3.10) to (3.16) except a, which is given by Eq. (6.10).

6.2.2   Numerical Calculations

At low overpotentials, the elliptic integral calculations (cf. Sec. 3.3.1) are necessary. They have been carried out varying i_0, r_2, r_1, and κ, as indicated in Table 8. The only parameter which one finds in addition to those for the

TABLE 8   Kinetic and Physical Parameters for Elliptic Integral Calculations under Activation and Ohmic Overpotential Conditions Using the Thin-film Model of Porous Gas-diffusion Electrodes

i_0, amp cm^{-2}	10^{-3}	10^{-6}	10^{-9}
κ, ohm^{-1} cm^{-1}	0.1	1	2
r_2, cm	10^{-3}	10^{-4}	
Δr, cm	10^{-4}	10^{-5}	10^{-6}

calculations in Sec. 3.3 is Δr, which is equal to $r_2 = r_1$, the thickness of the thin film. Δr was also varied in the calculations for this model. Values of η_0 for this calculation are found in Table 1. An analysis of the results of the present calculation may be best made by comparing it with the results of the similar calculation for the simple-pore model and may be summarized as follows: (1) The current distribution becomes more nonuniform at lower overpotentials for the thin-film model. This effect is due to ionic conduction having to occur only through the film for the present model, whereas through the entire pore in the simple-pore model, this effect is obviously less the higher the thickness of the film. (2) In the present calculation, even with $i_0 = 10^{-9}$ amp cm^{-2}, there is an effect of the ohmic overpotential at small values of the overpotential. This was not so with the simple-pore model.

At higher overpotentials, the current and potential distribution relations are represented by the same figures as for the simple-pore model (Figs. 9 and 10). However, A in this case is given by

$$A = \frac{1}{2} \left(\frac{i_0 l^2 F}{\kappa \, \Delta r RT} \right)^{\frac{1}{2}} \exp \left(\frac{y_0}{2} \right) \tag{6.16}$$

and I_t by

$$I_t = 8 \kappa \pi r_2 \Delta r \, \frac{RT}{lF} \, A \tan A \tag{6.17}$$

As in the elliptic integral calculation, the current distribution becomes more nonuniform at lower overpotentials for the thin film than for the simple-pore model for the same values of i_0, r_2, and κ. This trend is seen by a comparison of Tables 3 and 9, which show the η_0 values corresponding to the A values used in the calculations (and hence the different curves in Figs. 9 and 10) for various values of i_0, κ, r_2, and Δr.

TABLE 9 A-η_0 Relation, Assuming $\kappa = 1$ ohm^{-1} cm^{-1}, $\Delta r = 10^{-5}$ cm, $l = 10^{-1}$ cm, for Two Values of i_0 in the Case of Activation and Ohmic Overpotential Using the Thin-film Model of Porous Gas-diffusion Electrodes [A Is Expressed by Eq. (6.16)]

A	η_0, volts for $i_0 = 10^{-6}$ amp cm^{-2}	η_0, volts for $i_0 = 10^{-9}$ amp cm^{-2}
0.2	0.069	0.415
0.3	0.110	0.456
0.4	0.139	0.485
0.5	0.161	0.507
0.6	0.179	0.525
0.7	0.195	0.541
0.8	0.208	0.554
0.9	0.220	0.566
1.0	0.230	0.576
1.1	0.240	0.586
1.2	0.248	0.594
1.3	0.256	0.602
1.4	0.264	0.610
1.45	0.267	0.613
1.50	0.271	0.617
1.55	0.274	0.620

The current-density–overpotential relation is again similar in form to that obtained for the simple-pore model and is simply obtained from the useful parameter A, except for a parallel shift both vertically and horizontally depending on the values of the kinetic parameters. A typical total current-potential relation is shown in Fig. 24, using $i_0 = 10^{-6}$ amp cm^{-2}, $\kappa = 1$ ohm^{-1} cm^{-1}, $r_2 = 10^{-4}$ cm, and $r_1 = 9 \times 10^{-5}$ cm. This figure also shows the corresponding current-density–overpotential relation for the simple-pore model using the same values of the kinetic parameters. Thus, when concentration overpotential is absent, the current density for the simple-pore model is higher than that for the thin-film model at higher overpotentials.

7 THEORETICAL ANALYSIS FOR PARTIALLY WETTING POROUS GAS-DIFFUSION ELECTRODES USING THE FINITE-CONTACT-ANGLE MENISCUS MODEL[6]

7.1 Mathematical Formulations and Solutions

The two models discussed above represent hypotheses and examples of what configurations exist in porous electrodes. Few of these have been determined. More recent interferometric techniques have shown that when a platinum electrode is in contact with a sulfuric acid, the contact angle is finite and has a value of a few degrees.[6] These experiments also showed that no thin film existed beyond the intrinsic meniscus.

Bockris and Cahan[6] set up the basic differential equations in the case of the finite-angle meniscus model; the coordinate system shown in Fig. 15 was used. The current flow through an element of the electrolytic solution in the meniscus region is illustrated in Fig. 25.

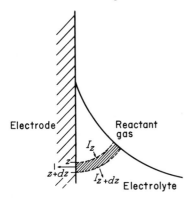

Figure 25 Schematic representation of the flow of current through the solution of a porous gas-diffusion electrode for the finite-contact-angle meniscus model.[6]

The current dI_z generated in a strip of length dz and width 1 cm (width is measured in a direction perpendicular to paper) during reaction (4.1) is given by

$$dI_z = i_0 \left\{ \frac{c}{c^0} \exp\left(\frac{\alpha \eta F}{RT}\right) - \exp\left[-(1-\alpha)\frac{\eta F}{RT}\right] \right\} dz \qquad (7.1)$$

The potential drop in the element dz is given by

$$d\eta = \frac{I_z\, dz}{\kappa\, \delta_z} \qquad (7.2)$$

The concentration of the reactant at the electrode within the element dz may be obtained using the assumption that the flux of reactant gas is perpendicular to the gas-electrolyte interface (which direction gives the shortest distance between the gas-electrolyte interface and the electrode surface in an element within the region of the meniscus) and that the dissolved gas is only consumed at the electrode. Thus

$$dI_z = DnF\,\frac{c^0 - c}{\delta_z}\, dz \qquad (7.3)$$

Hence

$$\frac{c}{c^0} = 1 + \frac{\delta_z}{DnFc^0}\frac{dI}{dz} \qquad (7.4)$$

Use of Eq. (7.4) in Eq. (7.1) and rearranging it results in

$$\frac{dI_z}{dz} = \frac{i_0 \{\exp(\alpha\eta F/RT) - \exp[-(1-\alpha)\eta F/RT]\}}{1 + (i_0\delta_z/DnFc^0)\exp(\alpha\eta F/RT)} \tag{7.5}$$

Differentiating Eq. (7.2), one obtains

$$\frac{dI_z}{dz} = \kappa\frac{d\delta_z}{dz}\frac{d\eta}{dz} + \delta_z\frac{d^2\eta}{dz^2} \tag{7.6}$$

One can easily show that

$$\frac{d\delta_z}{dz} = \frac{z - z_0}{\delta_z + R} \tag{7.7}$$

R and x_0 are constants, as seen in Fig. 15.
      Use of Eqs. (7.6) and (7.7) in (7.5) yields

$$\frac{d^2\eta}{dz^2} = \frac{1}{\delta_z}\frac{z - z_0}{\delta_z + R}\frac{d\eta}{dz} + \frac{1}{\kappa\delta_z}\frac{i_0\{\exp(\alpha\eta F/RT) - \exp[-(1-\alpha)\eta F/RT]\}}{1 + (i_0\delta_z/DnFc^0)\exp(\alpha\eta F/RT)} \tag{7.8}$$

The boundary conditions for this equation are

$$\eta = \eta_0 \qquad \text{at } z = 0 \tag{7.9}$$

and

$$\frac{d\eta}{dz} = 0 \qquad \text{at } z = 0 \tag{7.10}$$

      It is not possible to obtain analytic solutions for Eq. (7.8). Numerical solutions, however, may be obtained.

7.2 Numerical Calculations

A large number of computer calculations have been made (Cahan[6]) to determine the influence of electrode kinetic and physical parameters on the overpotential versus total current and on the current-distribution relations. The parameters, which are varied, are (1) the Tafel parameters i_0 and α; (2) solubility of reactant gas c^0; (3) specific conductivity κ; (4) diffusion coefficient of reactant gas in electrolyte D; (5) contact angle θ; and (6) the pore size.
      The results of the calculations are presented graphically in Figs. 26 to 43. The parameters used for the calculations were chosen to correspond to those for the hydrogen- and oxygen-dissolution reactions because experimental work was carried out on these reactions at single-slit electrodes. These parameters are found in Table 10. In order that the effect of variation of these parameters may be obtained, all but the one in question were maintained at the values in Table 10. The results of the effect of variation of these parameters are best summarized as follows:

(i)   Variation of Tafel slope

Tafel slopes of 120 mv (A), 60 mv (B), and 30 mv (C) were used.   If the exchange current density is high (as for the hydrogen-dissolution reaction), most of the current is generated near the top of the meniscus even at small overpotentials (Fig. 26).   There is an approximate parallel shift with Tafel slope

TABLE 10   Kinetic and Physical Parameters for the Hydrogen- and Oxygen-dissolution Reactions Used in the Theoretical Calculations for the Finite-contact-angle Meniscus Model (Variations Seen in Figs. 26 to 41)

	Value of parameter for	
Kinetic or physical parameter	*Hydrogen-dissolution reaction*	*Oxygen-dissolution reaction*
Tafel slope, mv	120	120
Exchange current density, amp cm^{-2}	10^{-3}	10^{-9}
Number of electrons transferred in overall reaction	2	4
Concentration of reactant, moles cm^{-3}	7.6×10^{-7}	9.3×10^{-7}
Diffusion coefficient, cm^2 sec^{-1}	3.1×10^{-5}	1.5×10^{-5}
Specific resistance, ohm cm	4.65	4.65
Contact angle	$2°$	$2°$
Pore radius, cm	0.05	0.05

in the overpotential-versus-total-current relation (Fig. 27).   For the case of high i_0, this relation is practically linear over a considerable range.

For a reaction with low exchange current density (e.g., the oxygen-dissolution reaction) there is again a parallel shift with Tafel slope in the overpotential-vs.-current relation (Fig. 28) with variation of the Tafel slopes, but the effects are

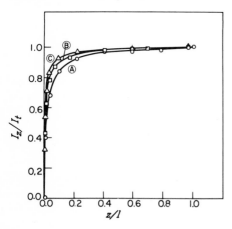

Figure 26   Current–distribution relations at a porous gas-diffusion electrode using the finite-contact-angle meniscus model for the hydrogen-dissolution reaction at an overpotential of approximately 450 mv, showing the effect of variation of Tafel slope.[6]   Tafel slopes are 120, 60, and 30 mv in curves A, B, and C, respectively.

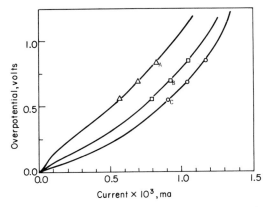

Figure 27   Overpotential vs. total current per pore[6] corresponding to parameters in Fig. 26.

more pronounced.   Even for this case, the curves tend to become linear at appreciable currents (say, above 50 ma cm^{-1}).   The current-distribution relations for this case are shown in Fig. 29.

(ii)   Variation of exchange current density

In Fig. 30, exchange current densities are 10^{-3}, 3×10^{-3}, and 10^{-2} amp cm^{-2} in curves *A*, *B*, and *C*, respectively.   In Fig. 31, the corresponding values are 10^{-6} (curve *A*), 10^{-8} (curve *B*), and 10^{-10} (curve *C*) amp cm^{-2}.   The total-current–overpotential relations are parallel with variation of exchange current density.   The effect of increasing i_0 becomes less with increase of i_0.   The current-distribution relations show that the higher the exchange current density,

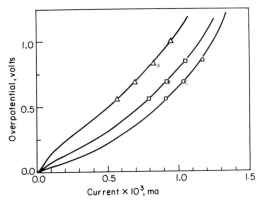

Figure 28   Overpotential vs. total current per pore at a porous gas-diffusion electrode using the finite-contact-angle meniscus model for the oxygen-dissolution reaction showing effect of variation of Tafel slope.[6]   Tafel slopes are 120, 60, and 30 mv in Curves *A*, *B*, and *C*, respectively.

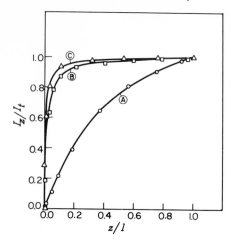

Figure 29 Current-distribution relations at an overpotential of approximately 600 mv corresponding to parameters in Fig. 28.

the more is localization of current near the top of the meniscus at any overpotential.

(iii) Variation of concentration of reactants

There is a marked influence of variation in concentrations of reactant gases. Figure 32 shows concentrations corresponding to 7.6×10^{-6} in curve A, 7.6×10^{-7} in curve B, and 7.6×10^{-8} mole cm^{-3} in curve C for the hydrogen-dissolution reaction. In Fig. 33 for the oxygen-dissolution reaction, concentration values of 9.3×10^{-6}, 9.3×10^{-7}, and 9.3×10^{-8} mole cm^{-3} are used. There is a marked effect of variation of concentrations on the current-distribution relations as well (Figs. 34 and 35).

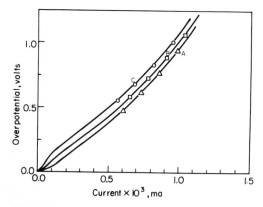

Figure 30 Overpotential vs. total current per pore at a porous gas-diffusion electrode using the finite-contact-angle meniscus model for the hydrogen-dissolution reaction showing the effect of variation of exchange current density.[6] i_0's are 10^{-3}, 3×10^{-3}, and 10^{-2} amp cm^{-2} in curves A, B, and C, respectively.

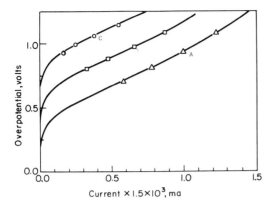

Figure 31 Overpotential vs. total current per pore at a porous gas-diffusion electrode using the finite-contact-angle meniscus model for the oxygen-dissolution reaction showing the effect of variation of exchange current density.[6] i_0's are 10^{-6}, 10^{-8}, and 10^{-10} amp cm^{-2} in curves *A*, *B*, and *C*, respectively.

(iv) Variation of specific resistance of electrolyte

Specific resistances of 1.16 (*A*), 2.32 (*B*), 4.65 (*C*), and 9.3 (*D*) ohm cm were used for both the hydrogen- and oxygen-dissolution reactions. Curves for variation of specific resistances (Figs. 36 and 37) are somewhat similar to those for variation of concentations. The current-distribution relations show

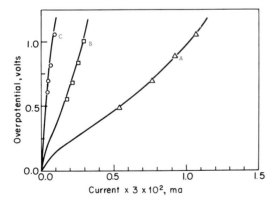

Figure 32 Overpotential vs. total current per pore relations at a porous gas-diffusion electrode using the finite-contact-angle meniscus model for the hydrogen-dissolution reaction showing the effect of variation of concentration of reactant $(c^0)^6$. c^0's are 7.6×10^{-6}, 7.6×10^{-7}, and 7.6×10^{-8} mole cm^{-3} in curves *A*, *B*, and *C*, respectively.

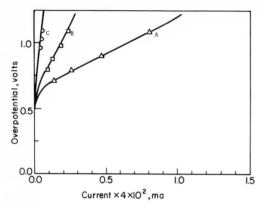

Figure 33 Overpotential vs. total current per pore relations at a porous gas-diffusion electrode using the finite-contact-angle meniscus model for the oxygen-dissolution reaction showing the effect of variation of concentration of reactant $(c^0)^6$. c^0's are 9.3×10^{-6}, 9.3×10^{-7}, and 9.3×10^{-8} mole cm^{-3} in curves A, B, and C, respectively.

that the greater the specific resistivity, the more is the localization of the current near the top (i.e., fuel side) of the meniscus.

    (v) Variation of contact angle

    Figures 38 and 39 show that variation of the contract angle from 1 to 4° has only a small influence on the total current at any overpotential; the smaller the contact angle, the higher is the current.   Likewise, variation of contact angle has little effect on the current-distribution relations.

    (vi) Variation of pore size

    Pore sizes of 5×10^{-5} to 5×10^{-2} cm with an incremental factor of 10 were chosen for both reactions.   The higher the pore size, the higher is the

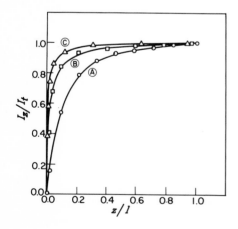

Figure 34 Current-distribution relations at an overpotential of approximately 400 mv^6 corresponding to parameters in Fig. 32.

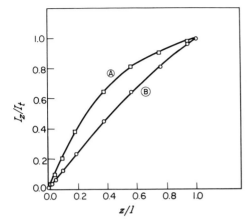

Figure 35 Current-distribution relations at an overpotential of approximately 600 mv[6] corresponding to parameters in Fig. 33.

current at any overpotential (Figs. 40 and 41). However, there is an optimum in pore size when one considers the current density and not the total current pore. The current density at any overpotential is a product of two factors [cf. Eq. (3.31)], viz., total current per pore and number of pores per square centimeter. The former increases with pore size, but the latter decreases. The smaller the pore size, the more is the localization of current in a pore.

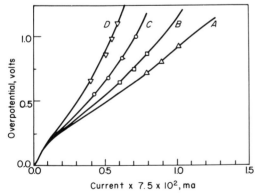

Figure 36 Overpotential vs. total current per pore relations at a porous gas-diffusion electrode using the finite-contact-angle meniscus model for the hydrogen-dissolution reaction showing the effect of variation of specific resistance of the electrolyte.[6] Specific resistances are 1.16, 2.32, 4.65, and 9.3 ohm cm in curves *A*, *B*, *C*, and *D*, respectively.

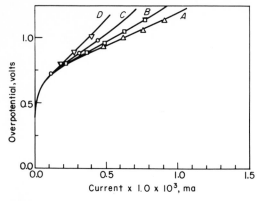

Figure 37 Overpotential vs. total current per pore relations at a porous gas-diffusion electrode using the finite-contact-angle meniscus model for the oxygen-dissolution reaction showing the effect of variation of specific resistance of the electrolyte.[6] Specific resistances are 1.16, 2.32, 4.65, and 9.3 ohm cm in curves *A*, *B*, *C*, and *D*, respectively.

7.3   Concluding Remarks

Figures 42 and 43, obtained by using the appropriate kinetic and physical parameters in Table 10, show the total current-potential relations for the hydrogen- and oxygen-dissolution reactions on platinum, respectively.   The corresponding experimental curves are also shown.   The agreement is good.

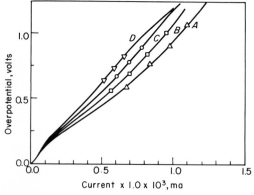

Figure 38   Overpotential vs. total current per pore relations at a porous gas-diffusion electrode using the finite-contact-angle meniscus model for the hydrogen-dissolution reaction showing the effect of variation of the contact angle of the meniscus.   Contact angles are 1, 2, 3, and 4° in curves *A*, *B*, *C*, and *D*, respectively.

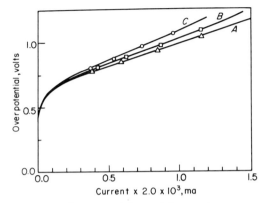

Figure 39 Overpotential vs. total current per pore relations at a porous gas-diffusion electrode using the finite-contact-angle meniscus model for the oxygen-dissolution reaction showing the effect of variation of the contact angle of the meniscus.[6] Contact angles are 1, 2, 3, and 4° in curves *A*, *B*, *C*, and *D*, respectively.

These reactions are typical examples of fast and slow electrode reactions, occurring within a pore.

The solutions show that in most cases the currents at higher overpotentials are produced within very short distances (10^{-4} to 10^{-5} cm) from the tip of the pore and they are relatively independent of pore size. One can qualitatively arrive at this conclusion since δ_z tends to 0 as z approaches 0. This means that

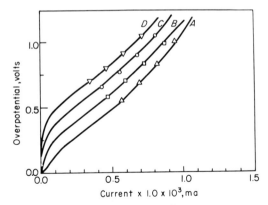

Figure 40 Overpotential vs. total current per pore relations at a porous gas-diffusion electrode using the finite-contact-angle meniscus model for the oxygen-dissolution reaction showing the effect of variation of pore size.[6] Pore sizes are 5×10^{-2}, 5×10^{-3}, 5×10^{-4}, and 5×10^{-5} cm in curves *A*, *B*, *C*, and *D*, respectively.

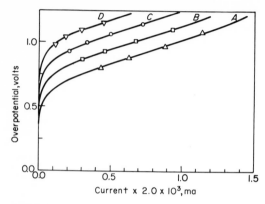

Figure 41 Overpotential vs. total current per pore relations at a porous gas-diffusion electrode using the finite-contact-angle meniscus model for the oxygen-dissolution reaction showing the effect of variation of pore size.[6] Pore sizes are 5×10^{-2}, 5×10^{-3}, 5×10^{-4}, and 5×10^{-5} cm in curves *A*, *B*, *C*, and *D*, respectively.

there is negligible concentration overpotential in this region. The result obtained here is valuable from the point of view of localization of expensive catalyst materials. It has been tested thuswise (Cahan[6]): Thin sheets of porous glass have received deposits of platinum sputtered onto tantalum subdeposits at only 10–20 μg of Pt cm^{-2} of electrode. The side of the porous glass which lacks catalyst is brought into contact with solution and this is sucked up through the glass by means of capillary action. It emerges on top of the glass, but as a very thin film, which makes a finite-angle meniscus contact with grains of Pt. Fuel (e.g., H$_2$) is blown against this thin layer. Now, all the Pt is used as catalyst. Debilitating diffusion of fuel through pores and IR drops in menisci

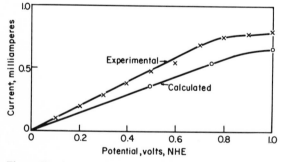

Figure 42 A comparison of the theoretical (see Table 10 for assumed kinetic parameters) and experimental overpotential vs. total current per pore relations for the hydrogen-dissolution reaction at a porous gas-diffusion electrode possessing a finite-contact-angle meniscus model.[6]

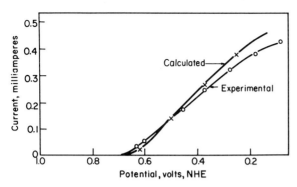

Figure 43 A comparison of the theoretical (see Table 10 for assumed kinetic parameters) and experimental overpotential vs. total current per pore relations for the oxygen-dissolution reaction at a porous gas-diffusion electrode possessing a finite-contact-angle meniscus model.[6]

which produce heat but lose useful electric energy are avoided. However, in its rudimentary form, the Cahan electrode still possesses excessive IR drop, that due to the passage through the pores of the glass. A satisfactory version might arise from the development of extremely thin vycor plates.

8 THEORETICAL ANALYSIS FOR POROUS GAS-DIFFUSION ELECTRODES USING THE INTERSECTING-PORE MODEL

A different emphasis has been placed upon the development of the theory of porous gas-diffusion electrodes by Russian workers.[9] These have tended to stress how much the capability of the electrode, in terms of its activity per external unit area, depends upon the distribution of pores—in particular the number of pores of a given radius—inside the electrode.

Conversely, Western electrochemists[4–6,12–15] have stressed particularly the distribution of current inside the pores, with the simplifying assumption that the pores are all of the same radius and straight.

Of course, both the pore-distribution-oriented and current-distribution-oriented theories have usefulness and should be combined. One considerable disadvantage of the pore-distribution-oriented theory[9] is that in order to achieve analytical equations, the influences of activation overpotential and concentration overpotential upon the distribution of current within the pore have been left out. Hence the *maximum* amount of current which could be expected from a certain distribution of pores is obtained, but, having cognizance of the enormous effect of hold-up due to diffusion in nonwetting situations and localization of current near the top of the menisci for wetting situations, the significance of the results is open to doubt. The expression for the maximum current density i_m according to the pore-distribution-oriented theory is

$$i_m = k \sqrt{\frac{\delta v_1{}^2 v_2}{\tau r_2}} \tag{8.1}$$

where δ is the length of the reaction zone; v_1 and v_2 are the porosities of the liquid-filled (micropores) and gas-filled (macropores) pores; τ is the tortuosity factor in the micropores; r_2 is the mean radius of the gas-filled pores; and k is a constant.

Suppose one makes the assumption that $v_2 = v_1 = v$, the maximum current density would be proportional to $v^{3/2}$. i_m also varies inversely with the square root of the radius of the macropores. Table 11 shows the values of i_m calculated by Burstein et al. as a function of r_2.

TABLE 11   Dependence of maximum Current Density, According to Intersecting-pore Model, on Pore Radius

Pore radius, μ	Maximum current density, amp cm^{-2}
10	0.119
1	0.375
0.1	1.190
0.01	3.750

9   SUMMARIZING CONCLUSIONS ON THE THEORETICAL ANALYSIS OF POROUS GAS-DIFFUSION ELECTRODES

The production of electrical energy from the reactions of chemical substances at interfaces has one difficulty in principle as compared with that from chemical reactions which occur in the bulk of a phase: namely, the interfacial reaction takes place in two dimensions and consequently has an intrinsic slowness when the rate is calculated in output per unit *volume* and compared with the rate of a chemical reaction which takes place in three dimensions. The way out of this fundamental disadvantage is in the direction of different electrode forms, particularly those which tend toward making the reaction three-dimensional. A leading form is that of a *porous* electrode.

In considering future researches on porous electrodes, it must be remembered that the present chapter describes an early stage in a developing situation. This is exemplified by the lack of experimental verification[15b] which exists for all models referred to above (Sec. 4), except for the finite-contact angle meniscus at wetted surfaces.

In particular, the present theories are lacking in that they are one-sided. The center of attention is the variation of the current and potential within the individual pore (Secs. 5 to 7). Alternatively, a playing down of this detailed consideration of electrode kinetics *in* pores may take place, together with a playing up of the distribution of the various types and sizes of pores and the entry into them of liquids (Sec. 8). Hitherto, the two aspects of the theory of porous electrodes have not been joined in mathematical equations. The difficulty is essentially one of complexity, so that analytical solutions cannot be derived without crippling approximations. More correct advances in porous electrode theory will have to be associated with numerical solutions.

A few of the principal questions in porous electrode theories at the present time may be mentioned:[15a]

(*i*) The present theories (Secs. 5 to 7) indicate that the current has a very limited penetration down a pore, so that the concept of attaining a three-dimensional scene for the reaction by the use of porous electrodes is partly negated. However, the predictions concerning penetration of the current are theoretical, and the degree of their realization is not yet known in a real porous electrode situation. Investigations of such a distribution would be experimentally simple. It is surprising that the first decade of detailed investigations of porous electrodes approaches its end without such investigations having been described.

(*ii*) A vital parameter is obviously the contact angle of menisci,[6] and these have seldom been measured in real porous electrodes. For the nonwetting case (Sec. 5), $\theta > 90°$, the mass transport of dissolved gaseous fuel from the boundary which it makes with the liquid down the pore may be of great importance. Even when the exchange current density is 10^{-9} amp cm^{-2}, so that activation overpotential should be several tenths of a volt for reasonable current outputs, there is still a large variation of concentration, and thus current, down a pore. Thus, 99 percent of the current may arise in the first 1 percent of the pore. Localization of catalyst would have a great effect here, or pumping the solution through the electrode would give rise to considerable improvement in current per unit external area. Essentially, this nonwetting case would tend to be that which obtains with Teflon-filled porous electrodes in use in many fuel cells at present.

(*iii*) In situations of partial wettability, there are two possibilities: Either a thin film extends out above the meniscus and maintains a constant thickness on the electrode,[18,19] or no such thin film exists past the end of the meniscus, and the latter has a finite, small, contact angle. Calculations from the thin-film situation (Sec. 6) indicate that the localization of the current to a small area of the pore is not great in this situation: even at high-current densities, as Fig. 23 shows, a relative uniformity may be obtained.

(*iv*) However, the difficulty is that one does not know whether there are any cases in which this thin film actually exists in fuel-cell electrodes. More probable is the existence of the finite-contact angle situation for wettable electrodes (Sec. 7) and thus for non-Teflon situations in real porous electrodes. At the present time this model has the advantage of being the only one for which there is some basis in reality, namely, the optical determinations of the contact angle for single-slit electrodes with platinum and in aqueous sulfuric acid (see Sec. 7). The finite-contact-angle-meniscus model does seem to provide good agreement between theory and experiment in this case, but the experiments have been on simulated slit systems, not real porous electrodes. If this model is verified in actual electrodes, there is a strong incentive for development of electrodes in which the catalyst is localized. For example, in a typical case with a finite-contact angle meniscus, 99 percent of the current is developed in 10^{-4} cm of the meniscus.

(*v*) Pore-distribution-oriented treatments (Sec. 8 and Iczkowski[15]) which have appeared hitherto seem to be too oversimplified in the diffusional and activational aspects of the current-potential relation to justify reliance upon calculated values. The principal lack is the absence of attempts to establish the applicability of the models of pores assumed, particularly the distribution of current within them, and the lack of mathematical combination of a theory of the size of pores with the distribution of current in individual pores.

(*vi*) The development of heat in the meniscus[6] should be examined because it is likely that it causes evaporation of the solution in the meniscus region; this would give rise to increase of diffusion and limitation of the extent of the meniscus, which would have important effects upon detailed theory of the meniscus region. Theoretical formulations connected with the meniscus heating effect have been attempted (Cahan[6]) but not completed.

(*vii*) It seems likely that, at least in cases of relatively high exchange-current-density reactions, the current distribution within pores *is* nonuniform (Secs. 5 to 7). Considerable downward revision of catalyst costs could be achieved by a device which gives rise to a localization of the catalyst in a region where the pore shows its electrochemical activity. A possible decrease of catalyst cost per unit of power would be one and perhaps two orders of magnitude. Achievement of such a possibility would revolutionize the applicability of fuel cells.

(*viii*) Remarkable predictions arise when one calculates the consequences of removing concentration hold-ups in the diffusion of fuel from the gas-liquid boundary (Sec. 5) in the nonwetting situation. The work of pumping has to be subtracted from the increase in the power produced from such an arrangement. The calculation[4] invites experimental test.

10   THE MECHANISM OF CHLORINE DISSOLUTION ON A POROUS GRAPHITE ELECTRODE IN MOLTEN LITHIUM CHLORIDE AT 650°C

10.1   General

Since molten lithium chloride does not wet the porous carbon electrode, the thin-film model does not apply for this case. The more probable model is the simple-pore model.

The basic steps in the overall reaction are: (1) flow of chlorine gas through the porous plug; (2) dissolution of chlorine at gas-liquid interface; (3) diffusion of dissolved chlorine to C-LiCl interface; (4) dissociation of chlorine and charge transfer; (5) migration of chloride ions into the bulk of the electrolyte.

Steps (2) and (5) may be assumed to be fast. With respect to step (4), a detailed examination of the chlorine-dissolution reaction under very low time transients,[16] where diffusion cannot play a role in the kinetics, shows that the magnitude of the activation overpotential reached before diffusion overpotential becomes important is relatively small (30–40 mv). Hence, if the chlorine-dissolution reaction occurs near the limiting current density, then activation overpotential may be neglected. Thus, the only possible rate-determining steps are steps (1) and (3). These predictions are confirmed by an analysis of the observed limiting current for the chlorine-dissolution reaction.

10.2   Expression for Limiting Current Density

In the preceding sections dealing with the theoretical analysis of porous gas-diffusion electrodes according to various types of models, it has been tacitly assumed that the process of diffusion of reactant gas through the electrolyte free part of the pore is fast compared with the other intermediate steps of the reaction. If the exchange current density is sufficiently high, this assumption may not be valid and step (1) may be rate-determining. For a single straight pore of length L and radius r_2, the total flow rate Q_1 (in cubic centimeters per second, measured at a pressure P and temperature T) due to viscous flow (Poiseuille) and molecular streaming (Knudsen) is given by[17]

$$Q_1 = \pi r_2^2 \left[\frac{\Delta P}{P} \frac{1.013 \times 10^6 r_2^2 (P_1 + P_2)}{16vL} + \frac{4\delta r_2}{3L} \sqrt{\frac{2RT}{M}} \right] \tag{10.1}$$

where P_1 and P_2 are the pressures of the gas at the entrance and exit of the pore: $\Delta P = P_1 - P_2$; $L = \tau t$ where t is the electrode thickness in centimeters and τ is the tortuosity factor of the pores; v is the viscosity of Cl_2 in poise; M is the molecular weight of Cl_2; $R = 8.317 \times 10^7$ erg mole^{-1}; and δ is a constant equal to 0.9.

If the porosity φ of the electrode is assumed to be uniform, the total flow rate Q_t through 1 cm² of the electrode is

$$Q_t = \frac{\varphi}{\pi r_2^2} Q_1 \tag{10.2}$$

The equivalent current density i_{fl} for a flow rate of Q_t cm³ sec^{-1} at a pressure of P and a temperature of T is

$$i_{fl} = nF \frac{0.273 \, Q_t P}{22.415 T} \tag{10.3}$$

assuming ideal gas behavior for Cl_2; n is 2 for the chlorine-dissolution reaction.

The limiting current density i_L due to the slow diffusion of Cl_2 to the electrode surface for a nonwetted porous electrode is given by (Sec. 5.3.1):

$$i_L = \frac{\pi DnFc^0\varphi}{r_2} \tag{10.4}$$

c^0 is the equilibrium solubility of Cl_2 in LiCl and is equal to KP_2 where K is Henry's constant and D is the diffusion coefficient of Cl_2 in the electrolyte.

It is interesting to examine the conditions under which either of the steps (1) or (3) is rate-determining. From Eqs. (10.1) to (10.4), it follows that if step (1) is rate-determining, the limiting current density should increase with the pore radius r_2, whereas if step (3) is rate-determining, the limiting current density should decrease with increase of pore radius r_2.

10.3   Conclusions

A plot of the experimental limiting current densities versus the pore radii for the chlorine-dissolution reaction on porous graphite electrodes (Fig. 44) shows that the limiting-current-density–pore-radius plot passes through

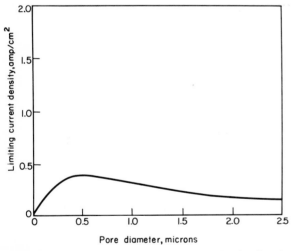

Figure 44   Dependence of limiting current density for the chlorine-dissolution reaction at a porous graphite electrode in molten lithium chloride on pore diameter at a temperature of 650°C.[10]

a maximum. It follows from the analysis in the preceding subsection that on the left of the maximum (i.e., for small-pore radii) the flow of gaseous chlorine through the pores controls the rate, whereas on the right of the maximum (i.e., for large-pore radii) the diffusion of dissolved chlorine to the electrode surface through the electrolyte controls the rate. There is good agreement between the theoretical prediction of the i_L-versus-r_2 relation, according to Eqs. (10.3) and (10.4) and the above experimental curve.

11　FUTURE RESEARCH ON FORMS OF ELECTRODES

It is intended here to list a few possibilities for future research on the form of electrodes for electrochemical-energy converters, as they appear in the late 1960s. It must be realized that the porous electrode is only one approach to the realization of power densities greater than those which may be available from planar electrodes. A few alternatives will also be mentioned.

(*i*) Advances with the porous electrode principle, for example, homoporous electrodes, as already developed,[7] together with the conical type of situation[8] and adjustable pore position (Sec. 4.5) are possible. Thus an ideal porous electrode would be thin and have the solution adjust itself in position so that the active area of its meniscus coincides with a small extent of catalyst. Such porous electrodes would be less than 1 mm in thickness. Alternatively, circulation of electrolyte through the pores of the electrode may be developed, particularly for the nonwetting case. Or, one may be able to form ideal homoporous electrodes by utilizing some device (for example, a laser beam) to punch ideal cylindrical pores in great numbers.

(*ii*) In the slurry electrode principle (Chap. 4, Sec. 11.4), several of the intermediate steps of the electrode reaction take place in the slurry (i.e., three-dimensionally) as it is being pumped around the circuit connected with the electrical collector. The contact with the fuel is in the bulk, and then the resultant electric charges on each particle transfer to the collector electrode. The adsorption and charge-transfer processes are spatially and temporarily separated.

(*iii*) Various means may be developed for reducing the diffusion-layer thickness independently of the use of pores (which, by virtue of their having radii much less than that of the normal diffusion-layer thickness, δ, introduce spherical diffusion and thus cause an increase of the limiting current density). One may consider the possibilities of jet electrodes (Chap. 4, Sec. 11.5), together with oppositely spinning wheel electrodes separated by a thin layer of electrolyte.

(*iv*) Local heating arrangements may be developed in which the surface of the electrode is only heated so long as the power is at a sufficiently high frequency. In this way the relevant part of the solution is heated, and one does not need heat for the bulk.

(*v*) Ultrasonics may reduce concentration gradients at planar surfaces.

(*vi*) Other concepts may be envisaged in a later stage of research [for example, programmed pulsing and activation of electrodes (Bockris et al.[20])], but are not yet at a practical level. Radiative and electromagnetic stimulation of the velocity of the electrode reaction can be envisaged, although this approaches the area of electrocatalysis.

The subject of this book is the direct production of electricity from the energy of chemical reactions. However, it is likely that many technologically developed countries will attain a situation in which, in order to provide electricity at minimum cost to the consumer, an excess electricity capacity must be developed. Consequently, a large amount of presently used chemical processes will tend to become electrochemical. A number of large-scale chemical processes may be more economically made to occur electrochemically. Hence, the development of electrochemical *reactors* (involving, for example, the analogs of the fluidized bed) may be of importance. Such developments would clearly feed back to new designs in fuel-cell electrodes, and vice versa.

REFERENCES

1. Westphal, German Patent 22393, 1880; L. Mond and C. Langer, *Proc. Roy. Soc.*, *Ser. A*, **46**, 296 (1889); A. H. Bucherer, German Patent 88327, 1895.
1a. Liebhafsky, H. A., and E. J. Cairns: "Fuel Cells and Fuel Cell Batteries," John Wiley & Sons, Inc., New York, 1968.
2. Newman, J. S., and C. W. Tobias: *J. Electrochem. Soc.*, **109**, 1183 (1962).
3. Micka, K.: *Advan. Chem. Ser.*, **47**, 73 (1965).
4. Srinivasan, S., H. D. Hurwitz, and J. O'M. Bockris: *J. Chem. Phys.*, **46**, 3108 (1967).
4a. Pratt and Whitney Aircraft, Division of United Aircraft Corporation, Fact Sheet, Powercel 3A-2, May, 1967.
5. Austin, L. G., M. Ariet, R. D. Walker, G. B. Wood, and R. H. Comyn: *Ind. Eng. Chem. Fundamentals*, **4**, 321 (1965) (earlier references found in this paper); L. G. Austin, chap. 1, in C. Berger (ed.), "Handbook of Fuel Cell Technology," Prentice-Hall, Inc., Englewood Cliffs, N.J., 1968.
6. Bockris, J. O'M., and B. D. Cahan: *J. Chem. Phys.*, **50**, 1307 (1969).
7. Adams, A. M., F. T. Bacon, and R. G. H. Watson: Chap. 4, in W. Mitchell (ed.), "Fuel Cells," Academic Press Inc., New York, 1963.
8. Justi, E., and A. W. Winsel: "Kalte-Verbrennung," Franz Steiner Verlag, Wiesbaden, Germany, 1962.
9. Burstein, R. Kh., V. S. Markin, A. G. Pshenichnikov, Yu A. Chismadzhev, and Yu G. Chirkov: *Electrochim. Acta*, **9**, 773 (1964).
10. Swinkels, D. A. J.: *J. Electrochem. Soc.*, **113**, 6 (1966).
11. Srinivasan, S., and H. D. Hurwitz: *Electrochim. Acta*, **12**, 495 (1967).
12. Will, F. G.: *J. Electrochem. Soc.*, **110**, 152 (1963).
13. Winsel, A. W.: *Advan. Energy Conv.*, **3**, 427 (1963).
14. Darby, R.: *Advan. Energy Conv.*, **5**, 43 (1965).
15. Iczkowski, R. P.: *J. Electrochem. Soc.*, **111**, 608, 1078 (1964).
15a. Bockris, J. O'M., B. D. Cahan, and S. Srinivasan: *Energy Conversion*, **8**, 111 (1969).
15b. Srinivasan, S., and E. Gileadi: Chap. 2, in C. Berger (ed.), "Handbook of Fuel Cell Technology," Prentice-Hall, Inc., Englewood Cliffs, N.J., 1968.
16. Triaca, W., C. Solomons, and J. O'M. Bockris: *Electrochim. Acta*, **13**, 1949 (1968).
17. Adzumi, H.: *Bull. Chem. Soc. Japan*, **12**, 292 (1938).
18. Will, F. G.: *J. Electrochem. Soc.*, **110**, 145 (1963).
19. Bennion, D. N.: Doctoral dissertation, University of California, Berkeley, Calif., 1964; D. N. Bennion and C. W. Tobias, Extended Abstracts of the Battery Division, *Electrochemical Society*, **9**, 15 (1964).
20. Bockris, J. O'M., B. J. Piersma, E. Gileadi, and B. D. Cahan: *J. Electroanal Chem.*, **7**, 487 (1965).

CHAPTER SIX

Electrocatalysis

1 INTRODUCTION

1.1 Definition of Electrocatalysis

Electrocatalysis may be defined as the acceleration of an electrodic reaction by a substance which is not consumed in the overall reaction. The substance is generally the electrode, though, to a lesser extent, the catalytic activities of the solvent may also be envisaged. Further, electrocatalysis is analogous to heterogeneous catalysis since at least one step of the electrochemical reaction occurs at the electrode-solution interface and at a given electrode-solution potential difference, it is specifically the property of the electrode surface that affects the overall reaction rates.

1.2 Some Examples of Electrocatalysis

Only a few reactions have been examined from an electrocatalytic viewpoint. The electrolytic hydrogen-evolution reaction has received most attention.[1] In Table 1 the exchange current densities for the hydrogen electrode reaction on a number of metals in acid solution are tabulated.[2] It may be seen that for this reaction the electrocatalytic activity of the metals varies by a factor of 10^9 from Hg to Pt. The noble metals have the highest catalytic activity for this reaction. The other transition metals have an intermediate catalytic power. In Table 2 are presented the exchange current densities for the oxygen-dissolution reaction on some metals.[3] In this case, the catalytic activity varies by some 10^7 times from Ru to Au.

A knowledge of electrocatalysis is particularly important in the case of electroorganic oxidation. For example, the electrochemical reactivity of ethylene in its oxidation to CO_2 is low[4] (Table 3) compared with that of hydrogen. Hence, the rate at which it can be converted with high efficiency, and the corresponding power, is relatively small. The products of the overall reaction here depend on the catalyst[5]: complete oxidation to CO_2 occurs on Pt, Rh, and Ir,

TABLE 1 Exchange Current Densities for the Hydrogen-electrode Reaction on Some Metals in H_2SO_4 at 25°C

Metal	Normality of H_2SO_4 electrolyte	i_0 amp cm^{-2}
Pt	0.5	1×10^{-3}
Rh	0.5	6×10^{-4}
Ir	1.0	2×10^{-4}
Pd	1.0	1×10^{-3}
Au	2.0	4×10^{-6}
Ni	0.5	6×10^{-6}
Nb	1.0	4×10^{-7}
W	0.5	3×10^{-7}
Cd	0.5	2×10^{-11}
Mn	0.1	1×10^{-11}
Pb	0.5	5×10^{-12}
Hg	0.25	8×10^{-13}
Ti	2.0	6×10^{-9}

TABLE 2 Exchange Current Densities for the Oxygen-electrode Reaction on Some Metals at 25°C

Metal	i_0 in 0.1 N HClO$_4$ (pH ∼ 1), amp cm^{-2}	i_0 in 0.1 N NaOH (pH ∼ 12), amp cm^{-2}
Pt	1×10^{-10}	1×10^{-10}
Pd	4×10^{-11}	1×10^{-11}
Rh	2×10^{-12}	3×10^{-13}
Ir	4×10^{-13}	3×10^{-14}
Au	2×10^{-12}	4×10^{-15}
Ag		4×10^{-10}
Ru		1×10^{-8}
Ni		5×10^{-10}
Fe		6×10^{-11}
Cu		1×10^{-8}
Re		4×10^{-10}

TABLE 3 Exchange Current Densities for the Oxidation of Ethylene on Some Metals in 1N H$_2$SO$_4$ at 80°C

Metal	i_0, amp cm^{-2}
Pt	10^{-10}
Pd	10^{-10}
Rh	5×10^{-11}
Ir	8×10^{-11}
Au	2×10^{-10}
Ru	5×10^{-11}

whereas partial oxidation to aldehydes occurs on Pd and Au. From free-energy considerations it is as important to oxidize a fuel completely as it is to reduce overpotential to obtain the maximum efficiency of electrochemical energy conversion.

In some cases, the electrocatalyst may also function as a chemical catalyst and may interfere with or aid the following electrocatalysis. An example is the electrooxidation of propane to CO_2 using platinum as a catalyst.[6] The metal also catalyzes the *chemical* cracking of propane to inert products, mainly methane at open circuit and low overpotentials. The efficiency of the electrochemical energy conversion is thereby reduced at low current densities.

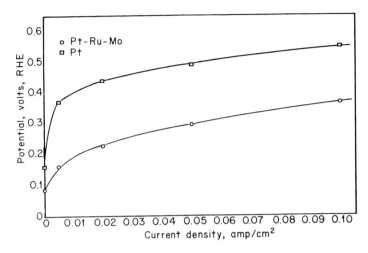

Figure 1 Overpotential–current-density relations for oxidation of methanol on Pt-Ru-Mo (70% Pt, 15% Ru, and 15% Mo) and on Pt in $1N$ H_2SO_4 at 25°C.[7]

Alloys often have considerably higher activity than the constituent metals. A good example is in the enhanced activity of platinum-ruthenium-molybdenum ternary alloys, which are better catalysts in the oxidation of methanol than are any of the constituent metals.[7] The overpotential at a Pt-Ru-Mo electrode (70 percent Pt, 15 percent Ru, 15 percent Mo) is less than that at a Pt electrode by about 0.2 volt at a current density of 100 ma cm^{-2} (Fig. 1).

1.3 Necessity for Study of Electrocatalysis†

1.3.1 Use of Smooth Electrodes

Electrocatalysis is mainly concerned with the search for materials which have high exchange current density for electrodic reactions. These studies are far more significant on smooth electrodes in the form of wires, foils, or spheres than on porous electrodes. This is because in the former case, one is able to study only under conditions of activation overpotential without interferences from concentration and ohmic overpotential. As seen from the preceding chapter, it is essential to have high exchange current density electrocatalysts even when using porous electrodes. With porous electrodes, the apparent current density generally varies linearly with the exchange current density or its square

† A section, The Necessity of Finding Nonnoble Metal Catalysts, may be found in Appendix A.

root (Chap. 5, Secs. 5 and 6). With smooth electrodes, the current densities vary linearly with exchange current densities for a given overpotential.

1.3.2   Increasing Efficiency and Power of Energy Conversion

The two important parameters to be considered in electrochemical energy conversion are voltage efficiency and the power density. The voltage efficiency of an electrochemical energy converter is given by (Chap. 3, Sec. 4):

$$\epsilon_e = \frac{E_R - \eta_a - \eta_c}{E_R} \tag{1.1}$$

where E_R is the reversible potential of the cell, and η_a and η_c are the numerical values of the total overpotentials at the anode and cathode, respectively, when a current density of i is drawn from the cell.

The maximum-power density P_M per square centimeter, for several fuel-cell reactions, is given by

$$P_M = i_L(E_R - \eta_a - \eta_c) \tag{1.2}$$

where i_L is the limiting current density (Chap. 4, Sec. 7).

Let it be assumed for simplicity that the overpotential at one of the electrodes is negligible ($\eta_a = 0$). Further, at a current density considerably less than i_L, the overpotential is mainly that of activation control and the Tafel relation is obeyed. Thus,

$$\eta_c = \frac{RT}{\alpha F} \ln \frac{i}{i_0} \tag{1.3}$$

Under these conditions, and with $\alpha = \frac{1}{2}$, the overpotential is reduced by 0.2 volt if the heat of activation of the overall reaction, at the reversible potential, is reduced by 2.3 kcal mole^{-1}. For example, such a change could be brought about by a change in the heat of adsorption of a reactant, intermediate or a product, depending on the mechanism of the reaction concerned, by about 5 kcal mole^{-1}. Such a consequent reduction of overpotential increases both the efficiency and maximum power density by about 25 percent.

Thus, electrocatalysis is essential in virtually all electrochemical energy conversion systems at low and intermediate temperatures. The hydrogen-oxygen fuel cell is at present the most-developed electrochemical energy-conversion system. Nevertheless, a principal problem in this energy converter is overpotential reduction at the oxygen cathode. For example, in the low temperature (67°C) hydrogen-oxygen system developed by Justi and coworkers,[8] the overpotential at a current density of 0.25 amp cm^{-2} is about 0.5 volt. This overpotential mainly exists at the oxygen electrode and causes a loss in voltage efficiency and also in power of about 40 percent.

There is, of course, the possibility of reducing the overpotential by working at higher temperatures. The efficacy of this approach may be examined in a simple hypothetical case. As an example, the oxidation of ethylene using platinum in acid solution will be considered.† Thus, in the case of the hydrocarbon-air fuel cell, overpotential losses are more severe at the hydrocarbon electrode than at the oxygen electrode. Let it be assumed for simplicity that the overpotential at the counter electrode (oxygen) is negligible. At 80°C, the exchange current density for ethylene oxidation on a Pt electrode in 1 N H_2SO_4[9] is 4×10^{-8} amp cm^{-2}. The activation energy of this reaction at the reversible potential is 20 kcal mole^{-1}. Thus, at a working current density of 0.1 amp cm^{-2} (and, say, a limiting current density of 1 amp cm^{-2}), the overpotential is 0.9 volt and therefore the voltage efficiency is only about 10 percent (for the reversible potential is in the region of 1 volt). The maximum power per unit area is thus only about 10 mw cm^{-2}.

For practical purposes, the highest temperature which can be used without involving extensive high-pressure equipment (i.e., by working only up to a few atmospheres in pressure) is about 200°C. At this temperature, the exchange current density is approximately 5×10^{-5} amp cm^{-2}. The limiting current density at this temperature is related to the limiting current density at 80° by the formula

$$(i_L)_{200} = (i_L)_{80} \frac{D_{200}}{D_{80}} \tag{1.4}$$

where D_{200}/D_{80} is the ratio of the diffusion coefficient of ethylene in solution at 200° to that at 80°C. Using an activation energy for diffusion of ethylene of 5 kcal mole^{-1}, the limiting current at 200°C is higher than at 80°C by some ten times. Since it was assumed that the limiting current density at 80°C is 1 amp cm^{-2}, i_L at 200°C is 10 amp cm^{-2}. The overpotential at a current density of 1 amp cm^{-2} is now about 0.8 volt. Assuming only a negligible change of E_R on increasing the temperature from 80°C to 200°C, the voltage efficiency increases only by 10 percent. The maximum power per unit area at 200°C becomes 200 mw cm^{-2}, which represents an increase by a factor of twenty but it is still necessary to increase the efficiency considerably to use the fuel more economically.

It would, of course, be possible to reduce the overpotential considerably by going to still higher temperatures, which would be feasible, were it possible to use molten instead of aqueous electrolytes. However, this approach involves increased cost of the necessary apparatus, and the use of materials capable of withstanding the high temperatures required which may not be available at the present time. Further, with increase of temperature, problems of temperature control and heat balance increase.

In summary, with the present knowledge of the temperature resistance of materials, it does not appear to be practical to enhance sufficiently the rates of reactions (e.g., hydrocarbon oxidation on the currently available electrocatalysts),

---

† The example is calculated in terms of planar electrodes because of the great increase in simplicity which this brings. A similar indication can be obtained from a porous-electrode calculation.

which have low exchange current densities (say, less than 10^{-6} amp cm^{-2}) at temperatures less than $100°C$, by the use of high temperatures alone.† Of course, in practice, both approaches, i.e., the use of temperatures above room temperature but below that which would give rise to corrosive difficulties, together with the development of electrocatalysts, will be used.

Any arrangement made only to increase the effective or true area is not sufficient to alleviate the need for electrocatalysts. The best possible manner to increase the effective area is by using suspended catalysts.[10] In this method, catalyst particles of colloidal dimensions, adsorb the reactant from the solution and then react electrochemically during intermittent contact with a collector electrode (Chap. 4, Sec. 11.4). The decrease in overpotential brought about by such a method depends on the size of the particle and also on the concentration of the catalyst particles in solution. It is not practical to reduce particle dimensions below those of a few microns. Even under such conditions, it is desirable to increase the exchange current densities by several orders of magnitude compared with that on a noncatalyst surface. This is not possible with the slurry arrangement because the current density only varies inversely with the radius of particles (r) [current density varies directly with area (that is, r^2) and directly with concentration (that is, inversely with volume r^3)].

If hydrocarbon-air fuel cells, in particular, are to be developed, it is unlikely that raising the temperature or development of new forms of electrodes will give rise to practical power densities. It is only the development of the infant field of electrocatalysis (leading even to new types of electrodes, such as semiconductor or insulator electrodes[12]) which could do this.

1.3.3 Maintenance of Constant Activity of Electrocatalyst

As in heterogeneous catalysis, impurities from the solution or in some cases intermediates or products of the reaction adsorb on the electrode and block the active sites. Thus, the activity of the electrocatalyst may decrease (and does so in a number of cases) with time. A solution to the problem of maintaining a constant activity of the catalyst appears more hopeful in electrochemical reactions than in chemical reactions. At the present time, at least one method is available for this purpose (Sec. 5.1). It is necessary to investigate further methods for maintenance of constant activity.

2 DISTINCTIVE FEATURES OF ELECTROCATALYSIS

2.1 General

Electrocatalysis may be considered as a special case of heterogeneous chemical catalysis, but with one major difference, namely that one or more of the intermediate steps in the overall reaction is a charge-transfer step. In heterogeneous

---

† But this statement is not true for fuel cells involving solid electrolytes, where the corrosive problems are greatly reduced.

catalysis, the reaction rate is measured by the number of moles of reactant consumed in unit time per unit area of the catalyst. By analogy, in electrocatalysis the current density at the electrode is a measure of the reaction rate. The relation between current density i and velocity v is given by

$$i = nFv \tag{2.1}$$

where i is expressed in amperes per square centimeter and v in moles per square centimeter per second. Electrocatalysis has several novel features which will be considered in the following subsections.

2.2 Dependence of Reaction Rate on Potential

The forms of equations relating reaction rate to temperature are the same in heterogeneous and electrocatalysis but with one fundamental difference. In heterogeneous catalysis, the velocity v is expressed by the well-known Arrhenius equation

$$v = A \exp\left(-\frac{E^{\ddagger}}{RT}\right) \tag{2.2}$$

where A is a product of certain constants and activities of the reactants and $E^{\ddagger}$ is the activation energy. In electrocatalysis, the current density is given by

$$i = C \exp\left(-\frac{E^{\ddagger}}{RT}\right) \exp\left(\frac{BV}{RT}\right) \tag{2.3}$$

In Eqs. (2.2) and (2.3), A, B, and C are either independent of temperature or depend on it little compared with the exponential term.

As was seen in Chap. 2, the potential V may be expressed by

$$V = V_R + \eta \tag{2.4}$$

where V_R is the reversible potential for the overall reaction and η is the overpotential. Introducing Eq. (2.4) into (2.3),

$$i = C \exp\left(-\frac{E^{\ddagger}}{RT}\right) \exp\left(\frac{BV_R}{RT}\right) \exp\left(\frac{B\eta}{RT}\right) \tag{2.5}$$

Equations (2.2) and (2.5) show the essential difference between electrocatalysis and catalysis, i.e., the electrocatalytic velocity depends exponentially upon the overpotential, the difference between the electrode potential at which the reaction takes place at the rate corresponding to a current density i and the reversible (or zero net rate) electrode potential. Thus, overpotential is a kind of variable component of the activation energy. In the case of electrocatalysis in driven cells, for example, cells in which ethylene is coupled with a hydrogen electrode, the applied potential increases the overpotential at each electrode and thus catalyzes the reactions, i.e., the oxidation of ethylene to CO_2 at the anode and the reduction of hydrogen ions to hydrogen at the cathode. In a fuel cell, the catalysis is likewise aided by the overpotential across the metal-solution interfaces, but these are then the causes of a decrease of its terminal cell potential. Thus, "electrocatalysis" is brought about at the expense of the loss of some energy from the energy conversion, and this is the fundamental reason why electrocatalysis must be improved, i.e., to lead to a situation where a minimum overpotential is needed to obtain maximum efficiency of conversion.

The energy of activation in heterogeneous catalysis $E^{\ddagger}$ is given by

$$E^{\ddagger} = -R \frac{\partial \ln v}{\partial (1/T)} \tag{2.6}$$

from Eq. (2.2).

By analogy, the energy of activation for the electrochemical reaction $E_{\eta}^{\ddagger}$ is given by

$$E_{\eta}^{\ddagger} = -R \frac{\partial \ln i}{\partial (1/T)} = E^{\ddagger} - BV$$

$$= E^{\ddagger} - BV_R - B\eta \tag{2.7}$$

as obtained from Eqs. (2.3) and (2.5).

Equation (2.7) shows that the energy of activation of the reaction at an overpotential η is linearly reduced by the overpotential. At a high enough overpotential (η_L) it should then be possible to reduce the activation energy to zero. Above an overpotential of η_L the current density should be independent of overpotential. In the case of most reactions, it is not possible to reach this value of η_L due to other factors, e.g., mass-transfer limitations, passing over into a region of potentials where another reaction sets in, etc. However, η_L has been reached in the case of silver-deposition reaction.[13]

2.3 The Possibility of Carrying Out Chemical Reactions Electrochemically

It is not widely realized that many chemical reactions can be formulated electrochemically. For example, the oxidation of propane to carbon dioxide may be represented as an overall process from a chemical point of view as:

$$C_3H_8 + 5O_2 \rightarrow 3CO_2 + 4H_2O \tag{2.8}$$

In the chemical path the important step occurs by collision between reactant particles either in gas phase or heterogeneously on a catalyst. In the electrochemical path, the reaction occurs in two quite distinct partial reactions:

$$C_3H_8 + 6H_2O \rightarrow 3CO_2 + 20H^+ + 20e_0^- \tag{2.9}$$

$$5O_2 + 20H^+ + 20e_0^- \rightarrow 10H_2O \tag{2.10}$$

which occurs on two spatially separated electrodes. The thermal aspects of these two fundamentally different methods of achieving the same reaction are discussed in Sec. 2.6.

In addition, some so-called heterogeneous chemical reactions are probably electrochemical in nature, i.e., they occur at two separated locations on the same catalyst. A heterogeneous chemical reaction would then be analogous to a corrosion reaction in which two partial electrochemical reactions occur in an overall reaction with no net electron transfer. This is without doubt the mechanism of some heterogeneous reactions—for example the chemical reaction producing titanium by the Kroll method (Chap. 2, Sec. 11). The importance of the conductivity of the substrate is clear. The electrochemical path for overall chemical reactions may be more generally present than has hitherto been realized.

2.4   Large Variations in Reaction Rates

A significant advantage of electrocatalysis is that the effective energy of activation, and hence the reaction rate, can be controlled by change of applied potential in the case of a driven cell [cf. Eq. (2.5)]. Thus, it is possible to change the reaction rate by many orders of magnitude (e.g., 10^{14} in the case of certain slow reactions). It is possible to bring about such changes easily; a much increased potency in range of reaction rate variation and also control, compared with those of chemical reactions, is possible.

By comparison, the maximum feasible variation in the rate of a chemical reaction may be calculated for an activation energy of 10 kcal mole^{-1}. In order to increase the reaction rate by only 10^5 times, it is necessary to raise the temperature from 25°C to 1000°C.

2.5   The Dependence of the Overall Reaction on the Region of Potential

The potential at which a reaction commences at an appreciable rate depends on the reversible potential for the overall reaction under the conditions of the experiment and also on the degree of irreversibility of the reaction.

Thus, depending on the region of the applied potential, it should be possible to study more than one reaction on an electrocatalyst. The simplest example is the case of a platinum electrode immersed in acid solution. If the potential of the electrode is maintained at potentials more cathodic than the reversible hydrogen electrode, the hydrogen evolution reaction takes place; on making the potential more anodic, no reaction occurs till a potential of about 1.0 volt, with respect to a reversible hydrogen electrode, is reached. Oxide formation then commences and on further increasing the potential oxygen evolution is visible at about 1.8 volt. The current-potential relation on such an electrode is shown in Fig. 2. Several other examples are available. In some cases a stepwise oxidation or reduction of a reactant occurs depending on the

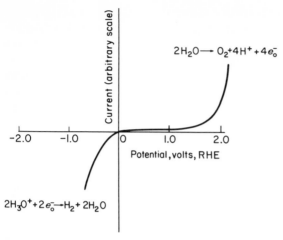

Figure 2   Current-potential relation on Pt electrode in acid solution showing dependence of overall reaction on region of potential.

potential.[14]   An example is the stepwise reduction of nitrobenzene as follows:

$$C_6H_5NO_2 \xrightarrow{2e_0^-} C_6H_5NO \xrightarrow{2e_0^-} C_6H_5NHOH \xrightarrow{2e_0^-} C_6H_5NH_2 \qquad (2.11)$$

Nitrobenzene   Nitrosobenzene   Hydroxylamine   Aniline

The desired product is obtained by a control of the potential of the electrode.

2.6   Use of Low Temperatures

A significant advantage of electrochemical reactions is that most of them can be carried out at low and intermediate temperatures.   For example, it is quite simple to carry out the electrochemical oxidation of hydrogen to water at room temperature.   The chemical oxidation of hydrogen to water over catalysts like platinum occurs at significant rates only at temperatures over 200°C.

Further, it is possible to oxidize many hydrocarbons to carbon dioxide at temperatures less than 100°C.   In the chemical oxidation of unsaturated hydrocarbons it is necessary to have temperatures of at least 200°C and in the case of saturated hydrocarbons of over 300°C.   It is also necessary to have higher temperatures with increasing number of carbon atoms in the organic compound for chemical oxidation, although this is not so in the electrochemical case.

2.7   Identification of Intermediates and Variation of their Concentrations with Potential

One of the major reasons why progress in heterogeneous catalysis has been hindered is because it has not been possible to identify intermediates in reactions.

With the recent advent of new techniques—infrared spectra of chemisorbed species, electron spin resonance—it may be possible in the future to identify intermediates in chemically catalyzed reactions. In electrochemical catalysis, however, it has been possible for a few years in the case of some reactions, e.g., hydrogen evolution,[15] oxygen evolution,[16] Kolbe reaction,[17] to identify intermediates, e.g., adsorbed hydrogen, chemisorbed oxygen, carboxylate radical, respectively, and to determine their concentrations as a function of potential. These are useful mechanism-determining criteria for the reactions. Transient methods, discussed in Chap. 9, are used for this purpose. Intermediates in more complex reactions, e.g., hydrocarbon oxidation, have not been identified as yet; but even for these reactions, which only recently have been investigated, it should be possible to obtain information on intermediates.

2.8 Maintenance of Constant Catalytic Activity

One of the difficulties in heterogenous catalysis is the maintenance of a constant activity of the catalytic surface. The loss in activity of the surface is generally caused by the adsorption of impurities. In some cases, the poisoning of the surface is caused by adsorption of intermediates or products of the reaction. The same type of loss of activity of the surface occurs in electrochemical reactions as well and should be considered as more probable. Thus, impurities may be present in larger concentrations in solution than are found in the gas phase where the reaction vessels are evacuable and then the purified reactants introduced. In solution, it is more difficult to reduce impurity concentrations to very low levels and in some cases impurity concentrations as low as 10^{-10} mole l^{-1} may block the surface.[18]

It is possible to renew the surface of an electrocatalyst by the application of suitable pulses. This method is discussed in greater detail in Secs. 5.1 and 5.2.

2.9 Change of Paths of Reactions Using Redox Systems

It is well known that the oxygen dissolution reaction is highly irreversible (i.e., slow or occurs at an appreciable rate only at high overpotential) on most electrodes and thus reduces the efficiency of electrochemical energy conversion (Chap. 8). A way out of the difficulty may be by the use of redox systems. In this method, there is a change in the path of reaction. The electrode reaction is the reduction of nitric acid to nitric oxide instead of the electrochemical reduction of oxygen. The oxygen then oxidizes the nitric oxide to nitric acid.[19] Thus, though the overall reaction is still the same, the path of the reaction is considerably altered. Further, the electrochemical reduction of nitric acid is fast. The chemical oxidation of the nitric oxide is also rapid. Thus problems of overpotential losses are considerably reduced.

2.10   Electrochemical Nature of Biological Reactions

As exemplified in the case of some heterogeneous chemical reactions (Chap. 2, Sec. 11), it is probable that many biological reactions also occur by an electrochemical path.[20] The investigation of the detailed nature of electrochemical path for biological reactions is a primary research problem of the immediate future. It may be that enzymes, which are catalysts for many biological reactions, serve as "polyelectrodes" (electrodes at which two or more electrochemical reactions occur as in a corrosion reaction). For example, many enzymes show high catalytic activity when they are wet[21] and conduct electronically only when wet, as required by such a model. Correspondingly, heats of activation of enzymatic reactions are sometimes very low, a fact most easily interpreted in terms of rate-determining electron tunneling as part of the enzymatic reaction path.

3   FACTORS AFFECTING ELECTROCATALYSIS

3.1   General

The three main processes in which the catalyst plays a role in electrochemical reactions are adsorption, charge transfer, and surface reactions. Two of these processes, adsorption and surface reactions, are common to chemical catalysis. By analogy with chemical catalysis, one may expect geometric and electronic factors also to be important in electrochemical catalysis. Since there is an additional process in electrocatalysis—charge transfer—the potential at the metal-solution interface is an additional important factor for electrochemical reactions. One may also expect electronic factors to influence the charge-transfer step besides their effect on the other processes.

Before dealing with the influence of the three main factors in electrocatalysis, it is worthwhile discussing the nature of the catalysts—both bulk and surface properties. From such a discussion, the factors affecting catalytic activity will be seen readily.

3.2   Nature of Catalysts

Since the catalysts usually employed are metals, alloys, and semiconductors (e.g., oxides, borides, carbides, etc.), it is best to deal with the nature of catalysts in this order.

3.2.1   Metals

3.2.1.1   Crystallography of the Ideal Bulk Structure.   Metals are characterized by the presence of free electrons and each ion in the bulk of a metallic

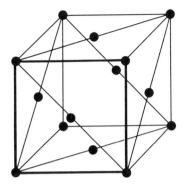

Figure 3   Unit cell of face-centered cubic lattice.

lattice is equally attracted to all its nearest neighbors.   In covalent crystals, directed bonds are present.   Due to the absence of directed valencies in metallic crystals, a close-packed structure is expected.   There are two possible types of close-packed structures—face-centered cubic (fcc) and close-packed hexagonal (cph) and most metals do exist in one of these structures.   Some metals also crystallize in the body-centered cubic (bcc) structure.   The unit cells corresponding to the three possible structures are depicted in Figs. 3 to 5.   The points in the diagrams denote the positions of the centers of atoms in the crystal.

In an ideal crystal, the entire structure is built up of unit cells, around the atoms, maintaining the structure of the unit cell.   For a close-packed structure, an atom in any layer can locate itself in any one of three positions relative to the atoms in the neighboring layer.   Looking down vertically on a close-packed structure, two types are possible: in one, the sequence of layers is *ABAB . . .* (Fig. 6) and in the other, it is *ABCABC . . .* (Fig. 7).   *A, B,* and *C* represent the

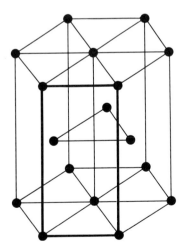

Figure 4   Unit cell of close-packed hexagonal lattice.

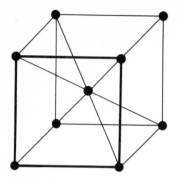

Figure 5   Unit cell of body-centered cubic lattice.

three possible types of arrangement of atoms in one layer relative to the next. The close-packed hexagonal structure is of the former type whereas the face-centered cubic structure is of the latter type.

The atoms in the face-centered cubic and close-packed hexagonal structures have a coordination number (number of nearest neighboring atoms at an equal distance from the atom in question) of 12, whereas the body-centered cubic structure has a coordination number of 8. However, in the body-centered cubic structure, any atom has 6 surrounding equidistant atoms, which are only slightly further away than the 8 atoms in the closest positions.

The important physical properties of the metals, relevant to catalysis,[28] are given in Table 4. In the long series of the periodic table, it is found that the Group IIIA, IVA, VIIA, and VIII$_1$ metals have a close-packed hexagonal structure, group VA and VIA metals have a body-centered cubic structure, and

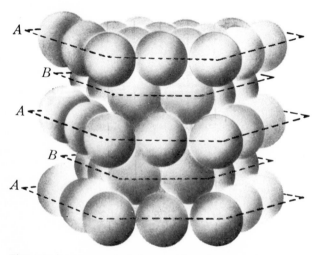

Figure 6   Arrangement of close-packing of atoms—close-packed hexagonal structure.[23b]

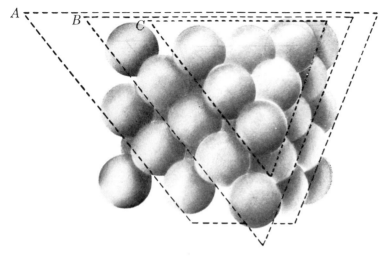

Figure 7 Arrangement of close-packing of atoms—face-centered cubic structure.[23b]

the Group IB and VIII₂ metals have a face-centered cubic structure. The exceptions are Mn, Hg, and Fe.

3.2.1.2 Nature of the Surface in an Ideal Crystal Structure. The surface of a metal is not homogeneous at temperatures above the absolute zero. The reason for this is due to the presence of steps, kinks, and edge vacancies. In order that these terms may be understood, it is necessary to realize what would be the appearance of a homogeneous surface. A homogeneous surface is close-packed with all its surface atoms at the same distance from a plane parallel to it (Fig. 8). Such a surface should be visualized only at the absolute zero of temperature. At higher temperatures, a non-close-packed or a stepped surface is formed. A step is the boundary line which divides two levels, one higher than the other by an interatomic distance on the surface (Fig. 9). However, in a stepped surface, the flat portion between the two steps is close-packed.

TABLE 4 Important Physical Properties of Metals Relevant to Catalysis[28]

Normal lattice structure	Metallic radius
Melting and boiling points	Latent heat of sublimation
Work function	Density and specific resistance
Standard electrode potential†	Magnetic susceptibility

† That is, the potential between the metal and a solution containing its charged uncomplexed ions (for example, Mo^{3+}, Mn^{3+}, Au^{3+}).

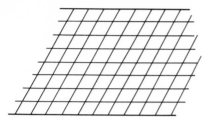

Figure 8   A homogeneous surface.

By common sense, a step is expected to be straight.   But in general, a step is incomplete because it has a kink, which is the region where two parallel steps, at an interatomic spacing apart, meet (Fig. 10).   An atom at a kink site is in a state of higher energy than that in the straight portion of a step which is in turn at a greater energy than that on a site in a homogeneous surface.   As seen in Fig. 11, this fact is easily understood since there are decreasing number of neighboring atoms for an atom at a plane (5), a step (4), and a kink (3).

At higher temperatures, more kinks are found.   Further, at these tempera-tures, some atoms leave their regular positions, causing a vacancy on the surface. These atoms may then remain adsorbed on another part of the surface (Fig. 11). A smaller number of paired vacancies may also be found.

3.2.1.3 Imperfections in Real Crystals.   Three types of imperfections, which depend on the number of dimensions that are involved, are commonly found in real crystals.   They are (1) point defects, (2) line defects, and (3) plane defects.

Each of the three types will be discussed in the following subsections.

(i) Point defects (vacancies)

This type of defect arises when foreign atoms take up normal positions in the crystal lattice or when foreign atoms are present in interstitial positions of a regular crystal lattice.   The latter are referred to as "Frenkel defects."   Lattice vacancies, which are a special case of the former type, are referred to as "Schottky defects," and are also "point defects."

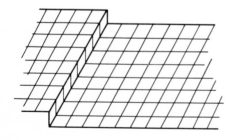

Figure 9   A stepped surface.

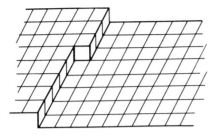

Figure 10   A kink on a surface.

(ii) Line defects (dislocations)

A line defect is the locus of points representing atoms, with a coordination number differing from that for any atom in a regular structure.   Line defects are also referred to as dislocations.   There are two types of dislocations—"edge dislocations" and "screw dislocations."   These types may easily be understood from Figs. 12 to 14.

An edge dislocation is a line discontinuity in the periodic arrangement of atoms.   The best illustration of an edge dislocation is given by considering a crystal in which a section of a plane of atoms is cut in the middle of the crystal as in Fig. 12.   To elucidate this illustration, the same effect is seen if, in a pack of cards, one of the cards is cut into halves and only one of them is inserted back into the middle of the pack.   On one side of the pack there will be one more card than on the other.[22]   Further, the cards would bend towards one another in the region of the "half-card."   The interruption in the periodicity of arrangement of atoms near the dislocation causes a region of high strain in the crystal.

Figure 13 represents an ideal crystal.   In Fig. 14, a cut is made along the plane *ABCD* and the crystal structure to the right of the plane is sloping downwards and the height at the edge perpendicular to *AB* at the end of the

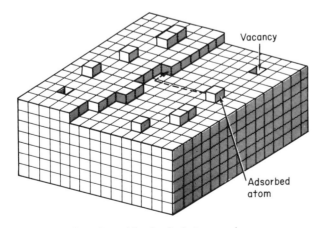

Figure 11   A surface with adsorbed atoms and a vacancy.

Figure 12 A single crystal with an edge dislocation.

crystal is one atomic layer lower on the right than on the left side of *AD*.   The step, created on the surface, extends only from *D* to *A* and not throughout the entire crystal.

Such a type of defect is referred to as a "screw dislocation."   A crystal containing a single screw dislocation consists of successive atomic planes coinciding with the surface of a helix with the dislocation line as its axis.

Line defects, unlike point defects, have an effect on the lattice structure at distances greater than a few interatomic spacings.

Screw dislocations play an important part in crystal growth and catalysis.[22a] Thus, atoms tend to be adsorbed for a longer time when in contact with an edge site, for here coordination forces are stronger than on a plane.

(iii) Plane defects (grain boundaries, etc.)

When a melt of a metal is solidified slowly under carefully controlled conditions, the freezing process occurs around a nucleus until all the atoms become part of a regular arrangement.   The whole mass of the metal then forms

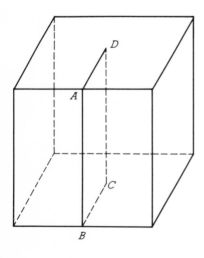

Figure 13 An ideal crystal.

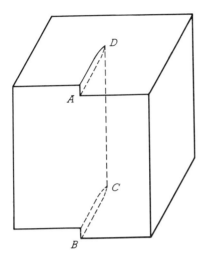

Figure 14   A screw dislocation.

a large single crystal.   Single crystals possess large areas of well-defined planes on the surface.   Because of this great degree of definition with respect to interatomic distance, such single crystals are of wide applicability in catalytic research.

If the cooling process of the melt is not carried out slowly and under carefully controlled conditions, many nuclei are formed which compete with each other to incorporate atoms from the melt.   Each nucleus forms a single crystal, which is also referred to as a "grain" or "crystallite" and the entire solid is now a polycrystal.   Most of the ordinary crystals consist of many small crystals called crystallites.   The orientation within a crystallite is a constant but there are slight variations in orientations from one crystallite to the next.

At the boundary of two grains in a polycrystal, there is a region of misfit where the regular arrangement within each grain is broken, since in general the periodic arrangements within each neighboring single crystals are not the same.   This irregular region, which is generally only one or two atomic layers thick, is referred to as a "grain boundary."   Atoms in the grain boundary are not in stable positions and hence they have a higher energy.   These atoms also have different properties from those in regular grains.   The existence of grain boundaries is an example of a plane defect.   A grain boundary in a regular crystal is illustrated in Fig. 15.

A second type of plane defect is due to "stacking faults."   If in a close-packed hexagonal structure which follows the sequence . . . *ABABAB* . . . the nth layer is one of the *C*-type, which is the third possible way of arranging a layer, as in cubic close-packing, . . . *ABABCB* . . . , a stacking fault is said to have occurred.   Similar stacking faults may arise in the case of the fcc structure if the ideal sequence of this structure *ABCABCABC* becomes . . . *ABCABC BCA* . . . .   A stacking fault may arise during the process of crystal growth when a layer starts incorrectly or by plastic deformation of the crystal.   A stacking

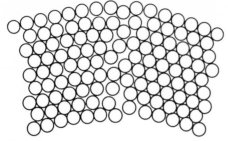

Figure 15 A grain boundary in a regular crystal.

fault does not alter the coordination number of any of the atoms though it does alter the energy of the atoms in the incorrect layer.

3.2.1.4 Nature of the Surface in Real Crystals. The surface of any polycrystalline metal generally contains grains, which exhibit, predominantly, planes of low index. The essential characteristic of such planes is the arrangement of atoms in them, e.g., the internuclear distances of the atoms are characteristic of that which would be expected for the plane concerned (Fig. 16). This assumption is not exactly correct for surface atoms but the deviation is quite small.

As mentioned in Sec. 3.2.1.2, surface defects are present even in ideal crystals above the absolute zero. Due to the existence of imperfections in the bulk structure of real crystals, similar types of imperfections (but in addition to the defects found even in ideal crystals above the absolute zero) may be expected on the surfaces in real crystals. Thus, the types of surface defects may be summarized as follows: (1) boundaries between grains, (2) edges on the surface arising from screw dislocations, (3) notches on the surface arising from edge dislocations, (4) vacancies or foreign atoms on the surface. All these types of imperfections are pictorially represented in Figs. 9 to 15.

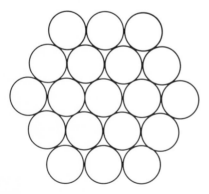

Figure 16 Arrangement of atoms on a layer in a crystal.

Surface heterogeneity has been assumed for many years because there was much evidence from gas-phase catalytic work that active sites—points at which either reaction occurs quickly or poisons are adsorbed—exist. Only during the last decade have these active sites been identified with the surface defects of the crystal.

The surface-to-volume (or mass) ratio increases with decrease in grain size. It follows that the ratio of the number of atoms on the surface to that in the bulk increases with decreasing particle size.

3.2.2 Alloys

3.2.2.1 Bulk Structure. An alloy is defined as a homogeneous substance which consists of two or more elements. The elements are generally metals though in some cases even nonmetals like hydrogen, boron, or nitrogen may be one of the constituents. There are two types of alloys: (1) substitutional alloys; (2) interstitial alloys.

Substitutional alloys are those in which atoms of one element replace those of another in a regular lattice. One of the necessary criteria for substitutional alloy formation over a wide range of concentration of each of the constituents is that their lattice structures and parameters must be similar. Otherwise, there is only a small concentration range of one of the components in which alloy formation occurs. The lattice spacing in substitutional alloys falls as expected between those of the constituent metals. In fact, most of these alloys deviate only slightly from Vegard's law according to which there should be a linear relationship between the lattice spacing and the composition of the alloy. As an example, the nickel-copper alloys may be considered (Fig. 17) where the deviations are quite small.[23] Substitutional alloys are easily prepared by melting together the constituent metals and allowing the solution to cool.

Interstitial alloys are those in which atoms of one of the components are so small that they occupy interstitial positions in a regular network of the other component without disturbing (or only slightly so) the order in the latter. Hydrides, nitrides, borides, and carbides of the transition metals are good examples of interstitial alloys. Compositions of such alloys may be as high as 70 percent in the nonmetal. When the ratio of radii of the nonmetal to metal atoms exceeds 0.59, the nonmetals become too big to occupy the interstitial position and distortion of the lattice structure occurs.

3.2.2.2 Nature of the Surface in Alloys. The defects in the surface structure of substitutional alloys are similar to that of metals. However, it is found that the surface and bulk compositions are not the same. (For example, new phases are formed on the surface, which are not the same in composition as that of the bulk.[23a]) Further, the compositions at grain boundaries and in crystallites are also not identical. These differences cause a difference in the

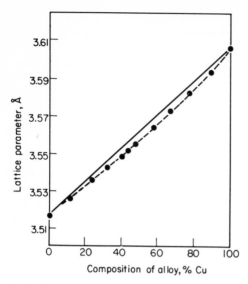

Figure 17 Lattice spacing as a function of composition of alloy for the Ni-Cu system (Broken line stands for experimental; solid line for theoretical).[23]

number of active sites on the surface of an alloy, compared with that which would exist were the surface and bulk concentrations the same.

3.2.3 Semiconductors

3.2.3.1 General. Semiconductors may broadly be divided into three types depending on whether they are composed of single elements, inter-metallic compounds, or inorganic compounds (e.g., oxides, sulfides). Further, they may also be classified under intrinsic semiconductors (in which the electronic conductivity is that characteristic of the pure element or compound) and extrinsic semiconductors (in which the electronic conductivity is caused or increased by the presence of foreign atoms in structure).

3.2.3.2 Semiconductors: Elements. The elements silicon, germanium, and tin (gray) which are intrinsic semiconductors have the diamond type of structure. In this structure, each atom is tetrahedrally surrounded by four other atoms. Unlike the case of metals, the bonding between the atoms in the diamond structure is of the covalent type, caused by sp^3 hybridization. The covalent character is strongest in diamond itself and weakest in tin. With increasing interatomic spacing, as in the series Si, Ge, and Sn, the semiconductivity increases. This is as expected since with increasing interatomic spacing, there is a weakening of the binding between the atoms as well as an increase in the sizes of the atoms. In turn, the forces binding the electrons to the metals become weaker with increase of interatomic distances, causing an increase of semi-conductivity with increase of atomic weight. It must be added that diamond itself (carbon in one of its forms) is an insulator, the interatomic spacing being less than that in Si (from Si to Sn there is a gradual variation in inter-atomic spacing), so that the bonding to the electron is small and the conductivity is low.

Carbon exists in a second form—graphite—which is a semiconductor. In the graphite structure, the atoms arrange themselves in parallel layers. The forces between the atoms in each layer are of the covalent type in which hybridized sp^2 electrons take part in bond formation. The interatomic distance in each layer is 1.42 Å. The interatomic distance in the perpendicular direction is considerably larger, being 3.50 Å. The fourth valency of carbon is satisfied by a resonating bond which is either part of a double bond between atoms in the same plane or a single bond between atoms in two adjacent planes. The bond between atoms in adjacent planes is hence much weaker than between those in the same plane. The conductivity of graphite is accounted for by the mobility of the fourth electron. It must be pointed out that graphite is aniso-tropic—conduction in a direction parallel to a layer is much greater than in the perpendicular direction.

A third form of carbon has a structure which is similar to the hexagonal close packing of metals. The layer sequence . . . *ABCABC* . . . is followed. This form is also conducting. The elements As, Sb, and Bi crystallize in this form and are also semiconductors.

3.2.3.3 Intermetallic Semiconductors. The intermetallic semiconductors are similar to alloys in that they are both composed of two or more elements. In the case of alloys, the elements are metals, whereas in the case of semi-conductors, they are metals or metalloids. The main difference between the two types is that in alloys, the bond formation is of the metallic type, but in intermetallic semiconductors, the bonding is predominantly covalent.

Most of the intermetallic semiconductors are of the binary type AB with A and B belonging to the Nth and $(N - 8)$th group, respectively, of the periodic table. Examples of this class are HgTe, AlSb, CuBr. These compounds crystallize in the sphalerite structure of ZnS. This structure is akin to the diamond structure except that the alternate atoms are different in these com-pounds. Intermetallic semiconductors constituted of the group III and group V elements have been most extensively studied, since they are quite similar to Si and Ge and possess higher electronic conductivity than a number of other types of semiconductors.

There are a few intermetallic semiconductors which crystallize in the halite (NaCl) structure. Examples of this type are SnTe, CaTe, and MgTe. Inter-metallic semiconductors may also be composed of more than two elements. An example is $AgTlTe_2$. The structures of this class are quite variant.

3.2.3.4 Semiconducting Compounds. The most common compounds, which are semiconductors, are oxides, sulfides, and sometimes these compounds modified by the presence of defects.   Mixtures of oxides or of sulfides are often better semiconductors than the component oxides or sulfides.

Generally, in oxides the oxygen atoms are arranged in the hexagonal or cubic close packing and the cations place themselves at octahedral or tetrahedral sites.   The bonding between the metal and oxygen atoms is mainly ionic in character and hence the electronic conductivity of oxides is low.   The introduction of very small quantities of a second compound causes the semiconductivity of oxides.   Two types of defects may be introduced: one of which (*n* type) gives electrons in excess of those available to the conductivity band in the original substance and electron-defect semiconductors (*p* type) where the added substance absorbs electrons and creates electron vacancies ("holes") in the lattice.   Zinc oxide belongs to the former class and nickel oxide to the latter. Zinc oxide is made a semiconductor by heating it to above 1000°C and annealing it at that temperature for a short time.   Electron *h* defect semiconductivity may be induced by the absorption of oxygen, e.g., absorption of oxygen increases the semiconductivity of NiO, Cu_2O.

Many complex oxides and sulfides, for example the spinels, are also semiconductors.   The structures of these compounds are quite variable.

3.3 Geometric Factors

3.3.1 General

As in heterogeneous catalysis, geometric factors will be expected to be important in electrocatalysis as well.   In heterogeneous catalysis, a reactant must be sufficiently strongly adsorbed to reach a finite concentration on the surface but must not be too strongly adsorbed to permit a high enough rate constant for the subsequent desorption reaction.

The reaction is initiated by adsorption of reactant atoms and completed by desorption of products.   According to an early model of catalysis, proposed by Balandin,[24] it is assumed that in the adsorption process, the bonds between atoms in the reactant molecules are weakened, distorted, and in the limiting case may undergo rupture.   As an example, the reaction:

$$A - B + C - D \rightarrow A - D + B - C \tag{3.1}$$

may be considered to take place as shown in Fig. 18.

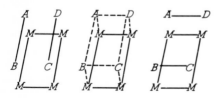

Figure 18 Reaction sequence for heterogeneously catalyzed reaction AB + CD → AD + BC. *M*'s represent metal atoms.

The four metal catalyst atoms may be supposed to be situated at the four corners of the square with bonding positions at right angles to the planar surface. The new bonds A-D and B-C begin to link up in the multiplet-activated complex even before the original bonds are completely broken. Thus, it was supposed that these forces are solely determined by the lattice parameters of the surface and reactant atoms. The catalytic activity of the surface then depends on its lattice structure and spacing. The first example to support the Balandin model is the hydrogenation of benzene and its reverse reaction. As expected the face-centered cubic and close-packed hexagonal structures are more active catalysts than the body-centered cubic structure. Adsorption of benzene on the catalyst takes place as represented in Fig. 19. As seen from the figure, it is clear that a hexagonal array of surface catalyst atoms is advantageous

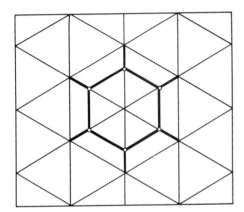

Figure 19 Adsorption of benzene on a face-centered cubic crystal.[24]

for the adsorption of benzene. Further, it is necessary to have some optimum interatomic distance between the catalyst atoms.

It has been confirmed that many body-centered cubic crystals (for example, W, Ge) are inactive in the hydrogenation of benzene. However, the fact that evaporated iron films, in which the crystal planes are randomized, are very active illustrates that geometric factors are by no means the only factors which are important in catalysis. Further confirmation of this view is the relative inactivity of Cu and Ag in the hydrogenation of benzene though these metals have a face-centered cubic structure and nearly the same interatomic spacing as in Ni, which is active in this reaction.

In the following subsections, several types of geometric factors besides lattice spacing will be considered which are or should be important in catalysis. Examples of their influence in either chemical or electrochemical catalysis will be given wherever they exist.

3.3.2   Lattice Spacing in Crystals

If there is more than one point of attachment of the reactant, the energy of activation for the adsorption process is affected by the internuclear distance. For dissociative adsorption, the activation energy is a minimum for an optimum spacing.   At larger spacings, the activation energy is higher because dissociation has to occur before adsorption, and at smaller distances, the same result arises because repulsive forces retard adsorption.   Sherman and Eyring[25] showed by a theoretical calculation that the optimum internuclear distance for the adsorption of hydrogen on carbon is 3.5 Å.   Similar calculations have been carried out to determine the energy of activation for adsorption of hydrogen[26, 27] and ethylene[28] on Ni for the various possible internuclear distances.   It was concluded that in the case of hydrogen adsorption on Ni, the activation energy was less when the 2 Ni atoms are separated by 3.52 Å rather than 2.49 Å.   This was confirmed experimentally.

A limited amount of work has been carried out using single crystal (of different crystal planes) metal electrodes.   Some exchange current densities on various crystal planes for Ni[29] are given in Table 5.   The (111) plane has the highest exchange current density.   This result is consistent with a slow electrochemical desorption mechanism since the (111) plane is the most densely packed plane which will hence have a higher coverage of atomic hydrogen and hence a higher activity.

TABLE 5   Exchange Current Densities for the Hydrogen-electrode Reaction on Various Crystal Planes of Ni in $HClO_4$ at 25°C[29]

Crystal plane	$\log i_0$, amp cm^{-2}
100	−5.20
110	−5.20
111	−4.85

3.3.3   Intersite Distance in Crystals

It is commonly assumed that the adsorption of reactant atoms occurs on the atoms of the catalyst.   This assumption may not always be correct since with small atoms a more probable adsorption site is an interstitial position on the surface.   Thus, if there is more than a one-point attachment the intersite (adsorption) distance is more critical than the interlattice spacing.   Some evidence for this prediction follows from the adsorption of hydrogen on W single crystals.[30]   The rate of adsorption on the (110) plane exceeds that on the other planes.   In the (110) plane a shorter intersite distance exists than on the other planes and hence may facilitate the adsorption process (Fig. 20).

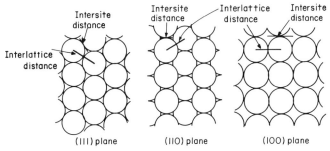

Figure 20   A comparison of interlattice and intersite distances on various low index planes of a face-centered cubic crystal.[28]

3.3.4   Grain Size

The rates of hydrogen evolution and of $Fe^{2+} \rightarrow Fe^{3+}$ oxidation reactions on platinum electrodes with grain size varying from 100 to 700 μ have been determined.[31]   It was thought that grain size would have an effect on reaction rates, because decreasing grain size for a given area should cause an increase in the number of plane defects.   No dependence of reaction velocity on grain size was observed.   It may be necessary to reduce the grain size further to observe appreciable effects.

The effect of grain size has also been studied using plantinized-platinum electrodes.   It was found that in the oxidation of formic acid on platinized-platinum electrodes, the only effect of platinization is to increase the roughness factor.[32]   Similar results were obtained in the oxidation of hydrocarbons on platinized-platinum electrodes.

3.3.5   Presence of Steps, Kinks, and Surface Vacancies

It was mentioned in a previous subsection that even in a perfect crystal the surface may contain edges, steps, and kinks.   It was also pointed out that an atom at a plane has the highest number of neighbors which is followed by the atoms at a step and then by atoms at a kink.   Thus, due to the variation in number of free valencies available at the different possible adsorption sites, one could expect that adsorption, the preliminary step of the reaction, is easiest at a kink, then at a step, and finally at a plane.

There are other considerations.   Adsorption at defects is not always easy. From potential-energy calculations for metal-deposition reactions, it was shown that transfer of the hydrated metal ion from the solution occurs more easily at a site on a crystal plane rather than on a kink site because of the energy necessary to distort the ionic hydration shell during transfer to a kink site[32] (Fig. 21).

3.3.6   Presence of Point Defects (Vacancies, Impurities)

Introduction of point defects increases the rates of some electrode reactions. For example, the exchange current density for hydrogen evolution on iron

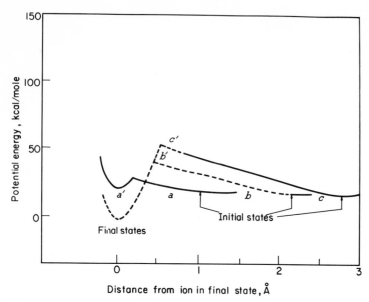

Figure 21   Potential-energy-profile diagrams for transfer of a hydrated Ag$^+$ ion from the solution to a planar site (curve *aa'*) to an edge (curve *bb'*) and to a kink site (curve *cc'*).[32]

containing 0.2 percent impurities (carbon) is higher than on zone refined iron containing 0.01 percent impurities by a factor of ten.[33]   One of the difficulties of investigating the effect of trace inclusions in a substrate is that its bulk concentration only is known and Gibbs adsorption will cause the concentration of the trace substance to be different on the surface than in the bulk.

It is also probable that the introduction of point defects may influence electronic factors as well—the work function is lowered in the region of the defect.[34]   This may be one cause of the effect of traces as exemplified here for hydrogen evolution on iron.

3.3.7   Presence of Line Defects (Dislocations)

The presence of dislocations in the substrate should affect the rate of an electrochemical reaction because atoms in the region of the dislocation have a higher energy than the atoms on a plane surface.   Thus, one can expect energies of adsorption of reactants at defects to be higher which in turn accelerates reaction rates.

At the present time, there are no examples among reactions of relevance to fuel cells for which the rates have been examined as a function of dislocation density.   However, equations relating current and dislocation density have been derived.[35]   They show that the number of steps on a surface, which could act as a center for crystal growth, varies with potential.

The rate constants for the surface diffusion step in metal deposition reaction have been shown to depend on the distance between growth steps which is related to dislocation density.[13] A detailed treatment on the dependence of current density on dislocation density resulted in an expression for the current density i_x in metal deposition as a function of the distance x between dislocations.[36] Thus:

$$i_x = i_0 \left\{ \exp\left(-\frac{\beta F\eta}{RT}\right) - \exp\left[(1-\beta)\left(\frac{F\eta}{RT}\right)\right] \right\} \frac{\cosh mx}{\cosh \sqrt{p/4ND}} \tag{3.2}$$

where η is the constant overpotential, $m \neq p/D$,

$$p = \frac{i_0}{zFc_0} \exp\left[(1-\beta)\frac{F\eta}{RT}\right] \tag{3.3}$$

c_0 = adion concentration, i_0 = exchange current density, N = number of dislocations per square centimeter, and D = diffusion coefficient. Such considerations may be applicable to electrocatalysis.

3.4 Electronic Factors

3.4.1 *General*

The transition metals are the most active catalysts for a variety of reactions. These metals are known to adsorb atomic hydrogen and oxygen as well as molecules and fragments of hydrocarbons. The question then arises as to what is the nature of the bond between the adsorbent and adsorbate. In most cases, bonds formed are as strong as chemical bonds. Thus, it would be necessary to consider the electronic structure of the adsorbent atoms. Electronic structures of surface atoms have not been studied directly. The alternate course is to understand the electronic structures of the bulk atoms and make the assumption that the surface atoms have similar electronic structures. There are two approaches to the electronic structure of transition metals which will be considered in the next two subsections. The factors important to catalysis will be dealt with in these sections. In the following subsection another important electronic factor will be dealt with and in the final subsection, some examples of the influence of electronic factors on electrocatalysis will be presented.

3.4.2 *Electron-band Theory of Metals and d-vacancies*

The transition metals have partly filled d shells and, in the gas phase, the number of electrons in these shells increase from one to nine in each of the long periods of the periodic table (Fig. 22). If the same electronic structure were maintained in the case of the solid metals (as opposed to the individual atoms), one would

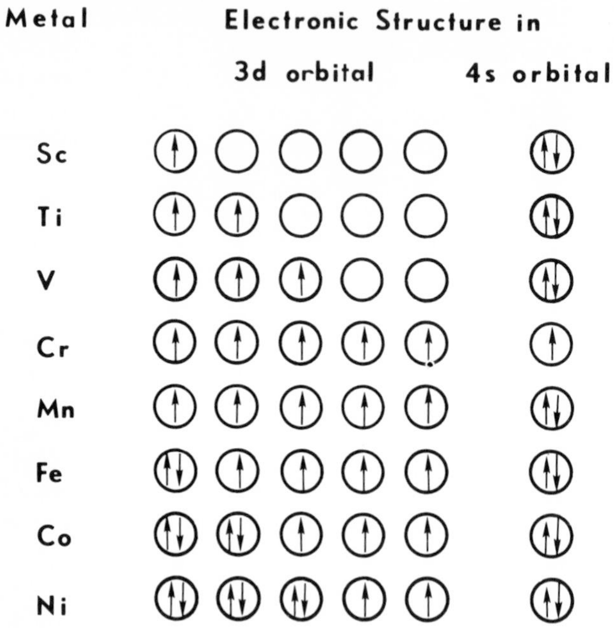

Metal	Electronic Structure in	
	3d orbital	4s orbital

Figure 22   Electronic structure of some transition metals.

have 6, 7, and 8 electrons in the d shells of the atoms Fe, Co, and Ni, respectively. Thus, since by the Pauli exclusion principle, the number of unpaired electrons are 4, 3, and 2 for Fe, Co, and Ni, the expected magnetic moments would be 4, 3, and 2 Bohr magnetons, respectively. However, the measured values or the magnetic moments are 2.22, 1.61, and 0.61 Bohr magnetons, respectively. The discrepancy is due to a difference in the electronic structure of these metals in the solid state, from that which would exist if the atoms maintained the same electronic structure as for individual atoms in the gas phase. Of the transition metals, only the electronic structures of Fe, Co, Ni, Pd, and Pt have received much attention.

In order that many of the properties of the transition metals may be explained, the electron-band theory[37] invokes the idea of electron overlap of d levels with the immediately higher s level. In the case of Cu, which has a completed d band, the Fermi energy is considerably higher than the energy level of the 3d electrons and thus there is no promotion of an electron from the 3d to the 4s band. The latter is the outer electronic level in the isolated state and possesses the conducting electrons in the metallic state. The bands are shown in Fig. 23. Since all the electrons in the 3d band are paired, Cu has a zero magnetic moment. In the case of Ni with 10 electrons available for distribution in the 3d and 4s bands but for which the separation in energy of the 3d and 4s levels is negligible (Fig. 23), 0.54 electrons enter the 4s level, leaving 9.46 electrons for the 3d band. Arranging these electrons in the 3d shells, it is

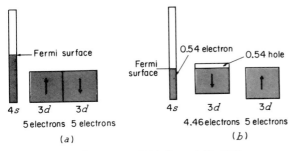

Figure 23 Band structure of (*a*) Cu and (*b*) Ni.[37]

found that 0.54 electrons are unpaired. The electrons in the 4*s* levels divide themselves equally with opposite spins. Thus, Ni should have a magnetic moment of 0.54 Bohr magnetons. [The deviation of this value from the saturation moment (0.61 Bohr magnetons) is due to orbital electronic interaction.] The reason is now apparent as to why metallic Ni does not have the same magnetic moment as would be expected from gas phase structure of individual atoms. Essentially, it is because the magnetic moment depends on the number of unpaired electrons, which is not the same in the metallic state as for individual Ni atoms in the gas phase, due to overlap of electron energy levels in the metal. When the metal is heated above the Curie temperature, the holes in the *d* shell divide themselves equally and the saturation moment becomes zero.

Addition of Cu to Ni introduces 4*s* electrons of Cu into the 3*d* holes. It is found that the magnetic moment decreases linearly with increasing Cu concentration and is zero at about 60% Cu (Fig. 24).

Pd in the second long period must be similar to Ni. It is found that with increasing concentration of dissolved hydrogen in Pd, the magnetic susceptibility

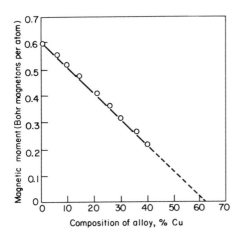

Figure 24 Magnetic moment of Ni-Cu alloys as a function of composition.[37]

decreases and becomes zero when 60% hydrogen is added.   It may be supposed that when hydrogen enters the metal it is ionized like metals and the free electrons enter the vacant d orbital.

3.4.3   Valence-bond Theory and Percentage d-band Character

The electron-band theory is quantitatively satisfactory only for the group VIII metals and not for the transition elements preceding it.   Pauling put forward an alternate theory—valence-bond theory[38]—which is of more general applicability than the electron-band theory and is thus more useful for an interpretation of the electronic structure of the transition metals.   In this theory, promotion of several electrons to higher orbitals (for example, $3d$ to $4s$) is suggested as playing a basic role in the bonding of metals.

For example, in the case of Cu, which has the outer electronic structure $3d^{10}4s^1$ for an atom in the gas phase, with the promotion of some of the electrons into the $4p$ states, the resulting configuration may be $3d^84s4p^2$ or $3d^74s4p^3$ corresponding to valencies of 5 and 7 in the metallic state, respectively; "dsp hybridization" (or "cross breeding") is said to have occurred.   From the bond length, it is found that the effective valency of a Cu atom in the metallic state is 5.56.

In the case of the group VIII metals, Fe, Co, and Ni, similar considerations show that the valency of these atoms in the metallic state is 5.8.   In Fe, since there is a total of 8 electrons in the $3d$ and $4s$ states, 2.2 electrons do not, therefore, take part in metal-metal bonding, i.e., cohesion.   These 2.2 electrons are thus "unpaired" and hence have the characteristics of electrons with parallel spins.   But only electrons with parallel spins contribute to the paramagnetism, and Fe, as expected, has the experimentally measured value of 2.2 Bohr magnetons for this property.   Thus, the number of electrons which do *not* take part in the "dsp hybridization" is equal to the numerical value of the paramagnetism in Bohr magnetons.   These are the electrons which contribute to the conduction in Pauling's theory.   Agreement between the predicted and measured paramagnetism has also been reached in the case of Co and Ni.

The percentage d-band character is defined as the extent to which the electrons participate in the dsp hybridization.   The wave function of a hybridized orbital (ψ_h) may be represented by

$$\psi_h = a\psi_d + b\psi_s + c\psi_p \tag{3.4}$$

where ψ_d, ψ_s, and ψ_p are the wave functions of the $3d$, $4s$, and $4p$ orbitals and

$$a^2 + b^2 + c^2 = 1$$

The constants a, b, and c represent the extent to which the three types of orbitals participate in forming the hybrid orbital.   Then, $100a^2/(a^2 + b^2 + c^2)$ represents the percentage d-band character.   But since $a^2 + b^2 + c^2 = 1$, the percentage d-band character is given by $100a^2$.

For the metals of the first-transition series, Pauling[38] proposed the empirical equation

$$R_1 = 1.825 - 0.043z - (1.600 - 0.1002)a^2 \tag{3.5}$$

from which a may be obtained, where R_1 is the single-bond radius of the atom and z is the number of electrons outside the argon core. Similar equations for the second and third transition series were also suggested by Pauling. The values of percentage d-band character for the transition metal are given in Table 6.

As may be seen from Table 6, the percentage d-band character ($d = 100a^2$) is a measure of the filling up of d shells. In the first long period, the group VIII

TABLE 6 Percentage d-band Character in the Metallic Bond of Transition Elements[28]

Sc	Ti	V	Cr	Mn	Fe	Co	Ni	Cu
20	27	35	39	40.1	39.5	39.7	40	36
Y	Zr	Nb	Mo	Tc	Ru	Rh	Pd	Ag
19	31	39	43	46	50	50	46	36
La	Hf	Ta	W	Rh	Os	Ir	Pt	Au
19	29	39	43	46	49	49	44	

metals, Cr and Mn, have about the same value of d. Similar relationships in values are seen in the second and third long series as well. The d values for the corresponding elements in the second and third long series are approximately the same as that for the first series.

Metals having more unpaired electrons in the d band have a lower percentage d-band character. Thus, metals having unpaired d electrons would pair with unpaired electrons from donating atoms or molecules. If adsorption is the slow process in a reaction, then the catalyst to be sought is one with, among its other properties, a comparatively lower percentage d-band character, i.e., many unpaired electrons in the d shell. The converse holds if a desorption step is rate-determining.

3.4.4 Work Function

The work function of a metal (Φ) is defined as the energy required to remove an electron from the bulk of the metal to a point well outside it. Though the work function is primarily a bulk property of the solid, it is strongly affected by the nature of the surface, since it includes the energy required to transfer the electrons across the surface. Even in the case of a pure metal, the work function depends on the crystal plane. It is also affected by the presence of impurities on the surface. Impurities on the surface create surface dipoles which affect the potential gradient through which the electron has to pass. If the surface dipole has the negative end away from the surface, the work function is increased, whereas, if the negative end is towards the surface, the work function is decreased. Due to the difficulty in obtaining clean metal surfaces, widely discrepant values have been recorded. A plot of the most reliable values of work function versus the group number in the periodic table is shown for the transition metals in the three long periods (Fig. 25). It is striking that the three lines for the three long periods are practically collinear. Further, the values remain approximately constant from group VI to group IB.

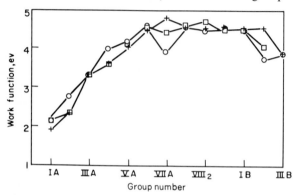

Figure 25 Work function vs. group number in periodic table of transition metal for each of the long periods. ○ stands for first long period; □ stands for second long period; + stands for third long period.[28]

An interesting relationship is the increase of work function with increasing percentage d-band character[39] (Fig. 26). This behavior is expected since with increasing d character, more electrons are paired and thus a higher energy is required to extract an electron from a metal. As the work function increases with the d character and the heat of adsorption of a species on the metal (ΔH) decreases with increase of percentage d character, it follows that ΔH decreases with increase of Φ.

A plot of the work function of the metal against the standard free energy of ionization of the metal to a singly charged ion, ΔG_1^0, bears a linear relationship[40]:

$$\Phi = 0.415\Delta G_1^0 \tag{3.6}$$

where ΔG_1^0 is expressed by

$$\Delta G_1^0 = \Delta G_s + I_1 \tag{3.7}$$

ΔG_s is the heat of sublimation of the metal and I_1 is the first ionization potential of the gaseous metal atom. The agreement is satisfactory for most metals (Fig. 27). Since mercury is the only metal where there has been good agreement in the values of work function obtained by different workers, the line was drawn through mercury in the Φ-ΔG_1^0 plot. A straight line was also

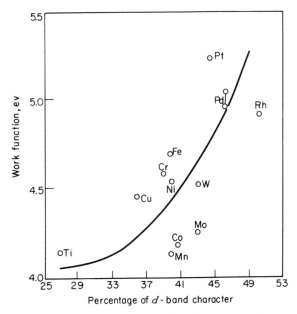

Figure 26   Relationship of work function to percentage-
d-band character for some transition metals.[39]

obtained when the corresponding standard heat of ionization (ΔH_1^0) was
plotted against the work function. It obeys the equation

$$\Phi = 0.40 \ \Delta H_1^0 \tag{3.8}$$

There is better agreement with a linear relationship, when the work
function is plotted against the standard free energy of ionization (ΔG_2^0) to

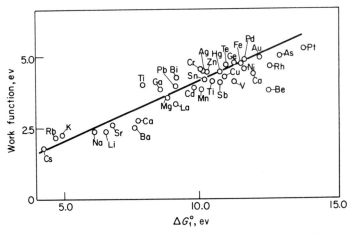

Figure 27   Work function vs. standard free energy of ionization of metal
to first ionization potential (ΔG_1°) for some metals.[40]

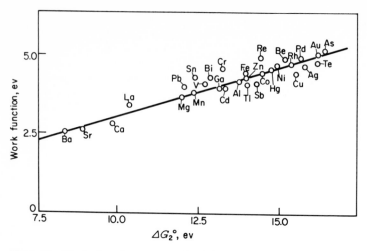

Figure 28 Work function vs. standard free energy of ionization to second ionization potential (ΔG_2^0) for some metals.[40]

the doubly charged ion[40] (Fig. 28). ΔG_2^0 is given by the equation

$$\Delta G_2^0 = \frac{\Delta G_1^0 + I_2}{2} \tag{3.9}$$

I_2 is the second ionization potential of the gaseous metal atom.   The ΔG_2^0-Φ relationship is represented by

$$\Phi = 0.305 \Delta G_2^0 \tag{3.10}$$

In this case too, the straight line was drawn through mercury, since the work function of Hg is known fairly accurately.   This relationship is useful in the case of metals for which work function cannot be measured easily.

3.4.5 Some Examples of the Influence of Electronic Factors on Electrocatalysis

3.4.5.1 *Redox Reactions Not Involving Chemisorbed Reactants, Inter-mediates, or Products.*   Electrode reactions may be broadly divided into two types: (1) those in which the reactants, intermediates, or products do not chemisorb, and (2) those in which reactants, intermediates, or products do chemisorb on the electrode.   Reactions of the first type are necessary in a study of electrocatalysis to separate effects which are caused directly by the electrode material from the indirect effect due to the formation of chemibonds.   A convenient reaction of the first type is

$$Fe^{3+} + e_o^- \rightarrow Fe^{2+} \tag{3.10a}$$

and it has been subjected to a detailed examination on some nonoxide-forming noble metals and their alloys by Bockris, Mannan, and Damjanovic.[41]

The exchange-current densities i_0 for the reaction on the various substrates were obtained from the slopes of the overpotential–current-density relation in the linear region (Chap. 2, Sec. 3.6.6). In all cases, the anodic and cathodic lines were collinear. The heats of activation ($\Delta H_0^{\ddagger}$) at the reversible potential were obtained from the slope of the log i_0 versus $1/T$ plots. A typical plot of log i_0 versus $1/T$ is shown for platinum in Fig. 29. The $\Delta H_0^{\ddagger}$ values were found

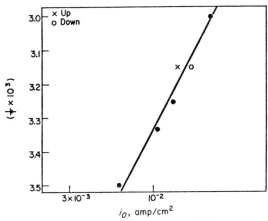

Figure 29 A typical plot of log i_0 versus $1/T$ for platinum in 0.1 M Fe^{2+}/Fe^{3+} ammonium-sulfate solution (x for measurements with increasing temperature, and ○ for measurements with decreasing temperature).[41]

to be essentially independent of the work functions of the metals (Fig. 30). However, a linear relation between the work function and the exchange-current density was obtained for the various metals (Fig. 31). Further, it was found that the exchange-current density varied linearly with the percentage composition of Au in Au-Pd and Au-Pt alloys (Fig. 32). From the absence of a dependence of $\Delta H_0^{\ddagger}$ on the work function, strong evidence for an electron-transfer, nonbonding mechanism for redox reactions[41a] was obtained. This work stresses the importance of determining $\Delta H_0^{\ddagger}$ on different catalysts and correlating its values with the electronic properties of the substrate. As seen in Sec. 3.4.5.5, the variation in exchange-current densities of the reaction with the nature of the substrate is due to secondary effects on the reactant concentrations caused by the double-layer structure.

The independence of the heat of activation for redox reaction on the work function of the electrocatalyst but the dependence of the exchange-current density on this factor stresses that electrocatalytic investigations should include a determination of the heats of activation of a reaction on various substrates. Simple measurements of rates (for example, exchange-current densities) are evidently fraught with secondary factors, such as those discussed in Sec. 3.4.5.5 below, which are not those connected with electronic bonding and the geometric effects of catalysts. The same conclusion may apply to classical chemical

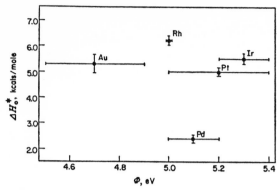

Figure 30   The standard heat of activation ($\Delta H_0{}^{\ddagger}$) for the Fe^{2+}/Fe^{3+} redox reaction on noble metals in 0.1 M Fe^{2+}/Fe^{3+} ammonium-sulfate solution vs. the work functions (Φ) of the metals.[41] The inconsistent result with Pd arises probably because of the effect of dissolved hydrogen in the metal.

catalysis, where changes in entropy factors may complicate the significance of correlations of electronic or geometric factors with velocities of reactions.

3.4.5.2 Hydrogen-electrode Reaction.   Since there is a relation between melting point of a metal and its position in the periodic table as well as to its hydrogen overpotential, the hydrogen overpotential at a constant current density might be expected to be a periodic function of atomic number.[42]   There is a relation of overpotential (at a constant current density) to atomic number (Fig. 33).[43]   A recent analysis[2] of the Φ-log i_0 relation (Fig. 34) showed that two straight lines with opposite slopes result for the high-overpotential metals

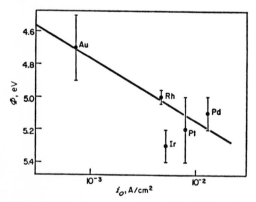

Figure 31   Exchange current densities (i_0) for the Fe^{2+}/Fe^{3+} redox reaction on noble metals in 0.1 M Fe^{2+}/Fe^{3+} ammonium-sulfate solution vs. the work function of the metals.[41]

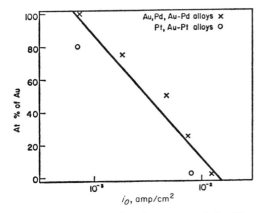

Figure 32 Variation of exchange current densities for the Fe^{2+}/Fe^{3+} redox reaction on Au-Pd and Au-Pt alloys in 0.1 M Fe^{2+}/Fe^{3+} ammonium-sulfate solution vs. the Au composition in these alloys.[41]

on the one hand and the medium overpotential metals on the other. These relations are consistent with the view that the slow discharge mechanism is operative on the high-overpotential metals and that the electrochemical desorption step controls the rate in the case of the medium-overpotential metals (Chap. 2, Sec. 10.1).

It was pointed out earlier that the work function increases with percentage d character (Fig. 26). Thus, since there is a linear relationship between the work function and log i_0, a similar relationship between percentage d character

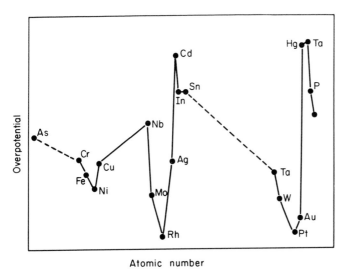

Figure 33 Plot of hydrogen overpotential at a constant current density versus atomic number for some metals.[43]

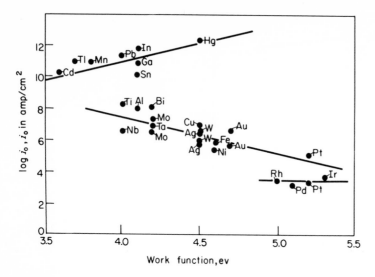

Figure 34   Relationships of log i_0 versus work function for hydrogen evolution on the high-overpotential, medium-overpotential, and low-overpotential metals.[2]

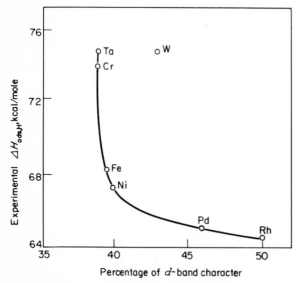

Figure 35   Plot of heat of adsorption of hydrogen on the metal ($\Delta H_{ads,H}$) versus percentage d-band character for several metals.[39]

and log i_0 should be expected for the transition metals and this was found by Conway and Bockris.[39]

The greater the percentage d-band character, the lesser is the number of unpaired electrons in the d band. The lesser the number of unpaired electrons, the lower should be the heat of adsorption of hydrogen on the metal, for there will be a lesser chance of finding electrons in the metal which can pair with electrons from the hydrogen atom. This prediction has been confirmed by plotting the experimental heats of adsorption of hydrogen on metal versus the percentage d-band character (Fig. 35). Further, a plot of log i_0 versus the experimental heat of adsorption for the transition metals indicates that as the heat of adsorption increases, log i_0 decreases (Fig. 36). A plot was also made of the overpotentials at a constant current density of 10^{-3} amp cm^{-2} versus the bond energy of M-H for a number of metals.[39] For this purpose, the bond energies D_{M-H} were calculated using Pauling's equation:[38]

$$D_{M\text{-}H} = \tfrac{1}{2}(D_{M\text{-}M} + D_{H\text{-}H}) + 23.06(\chi_M - \chi_H)^2 \tag{3.11}$$

where $D_{M\text{-}H}$ and $D_{H\text{-}H}$ are the bond dissociation energies of two adjacent metal atoms on the surface of a metal and of molecular hydrogen, respectively.† χ_M and χ_H are the electronegativities in electron volts of the metal and H atoms,

† In the calculation of bond energies according to Eq. (3.11), the contribution of the electronegativity term can be important. Due to its neglect, plots of log i_0 as a function $D_{M\text{-}H}$, obtained by Ruetschi and Delahay,[39a] differ in direction and significance from those of Conway and Bockris[39] who utilized the complete Eq. (3.11) to calculate $D_{M\text{-}H}$. The relation of the former workers has been reproduced in a book by Liebhafsky and Cairns,[36b] published in 1968.

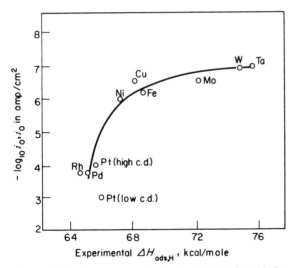

Figure 36 Exchange current density for the electrolytic hydrogen-evolution reaction on some metals vs. heat of adsorption of hydrogen on these metals.[39]

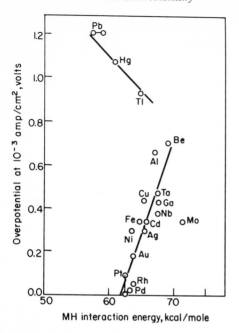

Figure 37 Plot of hydrogen overpotential at a constant current density vs. heat of adsorption of hydrogen for several metals.[39]

respectively.   In the $\eta D_{\text{M-H}}$ plots, two distinct groups were obtained (Fig. 37). In one group, which consists of the transition metals, as $D_{\text{M-H}}$ increases, η increases.   In the case of the other group, which consists of Hg, Pb, and Tl, η decreases with an increase of $D_{\text{M-H}}$.   In the slow discharge mechanism of hydrogen evolution, the rate-determining step involves an adsorption of atomic hydrogen in the metal.   Thus, an increase in the heat of adsorption of hydrogen on the metal should accelerate the reaction.   Conversely in the slow electrochemical desorption mechanism of hydrogen evolution, a hydrogen atom is desorbed from the surface in the rate-determining step.   Hence, a decrease in the heat of adsorption should accelerate the reaction.   These results, along with other evidence, confirm the view of a rate-determining discharge mechanism on Hg, Pb, and Tl and of a rate-determining electrochemical desorption mechanism on the transition metals.

A recent study of the hydrogen evolution reaction on Au, Pd, and their alloys[44] showed the interesting result that when log i_0 is plotted against % Au composition, there is a rapid decrease of i_0 with increase of gold composition in the alloy until a composition of 60% Au is reached (Fig. 38).   Thereafter, the decrease in i_0 with increase in percent of Au composition is much slower. With increase in Au composition of the alloy from 0 to 60% Au, there is a gradual filling up of the d band of the alloy and a consequent decrease in the rate of hydrogen evolution.   At 60% Au composition, the d band is completed in the alloy and thus between 60 and 100% Au in the alloy, there is hardly any change in the rate of hydrogen evolution in it.   The exchange-current density for the hydrogen-electrode reaction on sodium-tungsten bronzes, Na_xWO_3

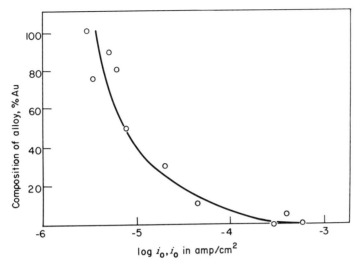

Figure 38 A plot of exchange current density for hydrogen evolution on Au, Pd, and their alloys vs. percentage of Au composition.[44]

with $x < 1$ (Sec. 5.2), passed through a minimum at $x = 0.65$, with increase in Na content.[44] At this composition, the work function of the bronze has a maximum value, corresponding to a minimum in the heat of hydrogen adsorption; thus, on the basis of a slow-discharge mechanism for the reaction, the minimum in the i_0 versus x relation could be rationalized. Incorporation of a small amount of polyvalent transition-metal atoms (for example, Mo, V) into a noble metal (Pt) caused a decrease in the rate of hydrogen evolution at low overpotentials but an increase in the rate at high overpotentials, as compared with the rates in the corresponding overpotential regions on the pure metal.[44] Alloying with these polyvalent metal atoms reduces the work function. Thus, the observed behavior may be explained on the basis of a slow-recombination mechanism in the low-overpotential region and a slow-discharge step in the high-overpotential region, which mechanisms are substantiated by other evidence.[44a]

The recent work of Bockris, Damjanovic, and Mannan[44] on the hydrogen-electrode reaction clearly signifies that electronic factors markedly influence the heat of activation in reactions involving chemisorbed species (reactants, intermediates, or products) unlike the case of reactions which do not proceed via chemisorbed species[41] (Sec. 3.4.5.1).

3.4.5.3 Oxygen-electrode Reaction.   A plot of the M-OH bond strength, $D_{\text{M-OH}}$, against the overpotential at a current density of 10^{-3} amp cm^{-2} showed that as the M-OH bond strength increases, the overpotential decreases[45] (Fig. 39).†   Since six out of the nine metals considered form fairly thick oxides

† The electronegativity term [cf. Eq. (3.11)] is taken into account in the calculation of $D_{\text{M-OH}}$ in Chap. 8. This results in a significantly different dependence of η on $D_{\text{M-OH}}$ (cf. Fig. 39 in this chapter).

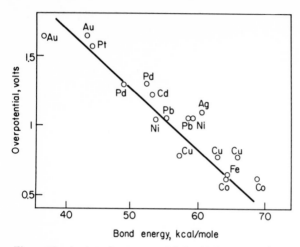

Figure 39 A plot of overpotential (at 10^{-3} amp cm^{-2}) vs. $D_{\text{M-OH}}$ for the oxygen-evolution reaction on some metals in NaOH at 25°C.[45]

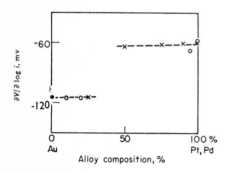

Figure 40 Tafel slopes vs. alloy composition for Pt-Au ($\bigcirc$) and for Pd-Au (x) alloys; $\bullet$ represents slope on Au.[46]

during oxygen evolution, it appears that the linear plot can only be explained on the basis of not yet rationalized indirect effects of $D_{\text{M-OH}}$ on the properties of oxide substrates.

In a study of the oxygen-dissolution reaction on Au and Pd or Pt as well as their alloys, it was found[46] that the Tafel slopes changed sharply at a composition greater than 50% Au. It is probable that this change actually occurs at 60% Au, 40% Pd or Pt, at which composition the d band is completed when adding increased amounts of Au to Pd or Pt (Fig. 40).

The uptake of oxygen by an oxide-free metal follows a dissociative adsorption.[47] In Table 7 are shown the observed-oxygen coverages on the noble metals, at 1-atm pressure, obtained by measuring the quantity of electricity necessary for the reduction of adsorbed oxygen. The table also shows the corresponding maximum coverages, assuming a monolayer of adsorbed oxygen on the surface; the fraction of surface covered by oxygen; and the number of unpaired d electrons per atom. As the number of unpaired d electrons increases,

TABLE 7 Relationship of Oxygen Coverages to Number of Unpaired *d* Electrons per Atom for the Noble Metals[47]

Metal	Observed oxygen coverage, $\mu C\ cm^{-2}$	Calculated oxygen coverage of a monolayer, $\mu C\ cm^{-2}$	Fraction of surface covered by oxygen (θ)	No. of unpaired d electrons per atom
Pd	110	510	0.22	0.55
Pt	110	500	0.22	0.55–0.6
Pt	135	500	0.27	0.55–0.6
Rh	480	530	0.90	1.7
Ir	440	525	0.84	1.7
Ru	500	530	0.95	2.2
Au	<15	500	<0.03	0

the oxygen coverage increases. Thus, unpaired *d* electrons directly participate in the bonding of oxygen atoms adsorbed on these metals, in oxygen saturated solutions. Gold, with no unpaired *d* electrons, shows the lowest coverage whereas ruthenium, with the highest number of unpaired electrons, has the highest coverage. Further confirmation of this view is obtained from a plot of the maximum degree of coverage with adsorbed oxygen (θ) on platinum-rhodium alloys versus the composition of the alloy.[47] It was found that θ increases linearly with increasing rhodium concentration in the alloy (Fig. 41) and thus with the number of unpaired *d* electrons in these alloys.

The influence of electronic factors on the rate of oxygen electroreduction has been recently examined on a number of metals and alloys.[3] From the Tafel lines obtained on the metals Pt, Pd, Ir, Rh, and Au (Fig. 42) in acid solutions, it appears that Au with no impaired *d* electrons has a significantly lower exchange current density than the other metals. Rh and Ir, with the

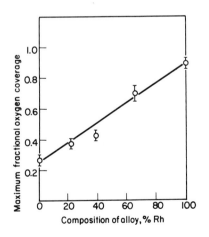

Figure 41 Plot of maximum degree of coverage of adsorbed oxygen θ on Pt, Rh, and their alloys vs. the composition of the alloy.[47]

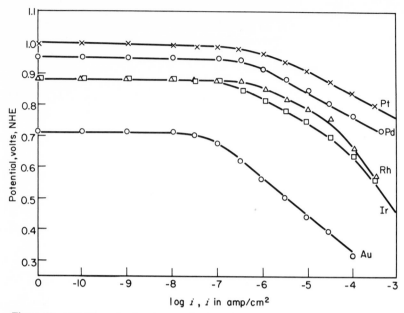

Figure 42   Tafel lines for the electroreduction of oxygen on Pt, Pd, Ir, Rh, and Au in 1 N H$_2$SO$_4$ at 25°C.[3]

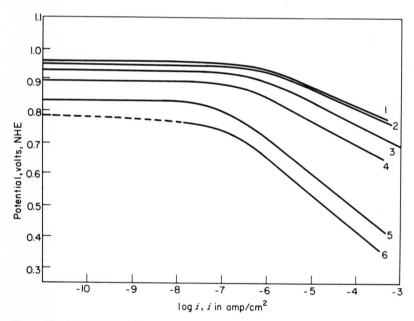

Figure 43   Tafel lines for the electroreduction of oxygen on Au, Pd, and a series of Au-Pd alloys in 1 N H$_2$SO$_4$ at 25°C: (1) 0%, (2) 10%; (3) 25%; (4) 50%; (5) 75%; (6) 100% Au.[3]

same number of unpaired electrons, show essentially an identical current-potential behavior: the regions of a constant plateau in the V–log i curve coincide; both show two Tafel slopes. Pd and Pt, which have approximately the same number of unpaired electrons, exhibit similar Tafel behavior. The rest potential observed on Pt is higher than on the other metals. On comparing the current-potential behavior obtained with Au, Pd, and a series of alloys of the two metals[46] (Fig. 43), it is found that (1) the rest potential decreased from the value for Pd to that for Au with increasing Au concentration of the alloy; (2) Au and the alloy containing 75% Au have considerably higher Tafel slopes than Pd or the other alloys which have nearly the same slope. Thus, a change in mechanism must occur between 50 and 75% Au. At 60% (or higher) Au, there are no d vacancies and a change in mechanism could be expected. There is no significant change in the behavior of the Au-Pd alloys in alkaline solution, probably because adsorption of oxygen atoms is easier in this medium.

3.4.5.4 Electroorganic Oxidation. The study of the catalysis of electrochemical oxidation of organic compounds commenced only recently with increasing interest in the potential application of cheap organic compounds in electrochemical energy generators. Dahms and Bockris[5] found in a study of the electrochemical oxidation of ethylene on the platinum metals, gold, and palladium that the noble metals fall into one group and Au, Pd into another. There was complete oxidation to CO_2 in the case of the former group but not so with the latter metals. Table 8 shows a comparative study of the various physical parameters which may affect the oxidizing power of these metals along with the currents extrapolated to the potentials of zero charge. The current-potential relations for these metals are shown in Fig. 44.

As seen from the table, the latent heats of sublimation are comparatively higher for the Pt group of metals than for Au or Pd. The latent heat of sublimation is about six times the strength of the M-M bond. Thus, assuming covalent bonding between the metal and an organic intermediate oxidation product, and using the Pauling equation,[38] the strength of this bond is given by:

$$D_{\text{M-C}} = \frac{1}{2}(D_{\text{M-M}} + D_{\text{org-org}}) + 23.06(\chi_{\text{M}} - \chi_{\text{org}})^2 \tag{3.12}$$

χ_{M} and χ_{org} are the electronegativities of the indicated species. The electronegativities of the metals concerned are constant to within 0.3 unit. Thus, for a given organic species, the bond strength $D_{\text{M-C}}$ is higher for the platinum group than for Au or Pd by 20 ± 5 kcal mole^{-1}. The incomplete oxidation of ethylene on Au or Pd is consequently probably due to the easier desorption of intermediate oxidation products on these metals.

The latent heat of sublimation of a metal is a measure of the M-M bond strength, which is in turn related to that between the metal and the adsorbed species. Recently, a parabolic relation was found between the current density for ethylene oxidation at 600 mv (NHE) and the latent heat of sublimation for a number of metals[48] (Fig. 45). Similar parabolic relations have been obtained

TABLE 8 Influence of Electrocatalytic Properties of Some Metals on the Rate of Electrooxidation of Ethylene

Metal	Reaction product	"Chemical" reaction rate at PZC amp cm^{-2}	pH dependence $\left(\dfrac{dV}{dpH}\right)_i$ mv	Tafel slope $\left(\dfrac{dV}{2.3d \log i}\right)_{pH}$, mv	Crystal structure and lattice spacing Å	Potential of zero charge (PZC) volts, NHE	Vacant d orbitals per atom	Latent heat of sublimation L_s, kcal $mole^{-1}$
Platinum	CO_2	1×10^{-7}	70	160	fcc 3.914	+0.30	0.55	135
Iridium	CO_2	1×10^{-11}	75	132	fcc 3.823	$+0.05 \pm 0.1$	1.5	165
Rhodium	CO_2	5×10^{-11}	70	155	fcc 3.794	0.05 ± 0.1	1.5	138
Gold	No CO_2; aldehydes	1×10^{-11}	0	72	fcc 4.070	+0.30	0	84
Palladium	No CO_2; aldehydes	7×10^{-10}	0	80–110	fcc 3.879	+0.25	0.55	91

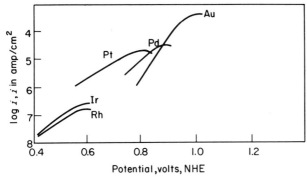

Figure 44 Tafel lines for ethylene oxidation on platinum metals Pd and Au in 1 N H_2SO_4 at 80°C.[5]

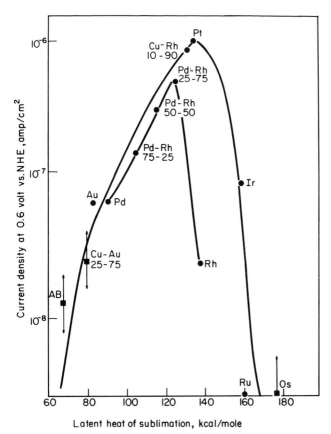

Figure 45 Current density for ethylene oxidation on some metals and on some alloys in 1 N H_2SO_4 (80°C) at a constant potential (600 mv, NHE) vs. latent heat of sublimation of these metals.[48]

for some chemical reactions—formic acid decomposition, hydrogenation of hydrocarbons, ammonia exchange, and acetone hydrogenation.[28]   It was also found that by using alloys of varying composition between metals, one on the left-hand side of the peak and the other on the right-hand side of the peak, similar relations were obtained but with peaks somewhat lower than that for the pure metals.[48]   The peak obtained in the case of pure metals is at Pt.   Thus, since it is not feasible to use Pt for large-scale electrochemical energy conversion, the alloys showing peak activities may be good substitutes.

The parabolic relations shown in Fig. 45 may be interpreted in the following manner: The rate-determining step in the ethylene oxidation reaction on all the metals and alloys studied except platinum where the rate is controlled by the water discharge step in sulfuric acid at 80° is:

$$C_2H_{4.ads} + OH_{ads} \rightarrow -CH_2-O-CH_3 \tag{3.13}$$

The rate i is given by:

$$i = A\theta_E \theta_{OH} \exp\left(-\frac{\Delta G_0^{\ddagger}}{RT}\right) \exp\left(\frac{\gamma r \theta_{OH}}{RT}\right) \tag{3.14}$$

where θ_E and θ_{OH} are the adsorbed ethylene and OH coverages, respectively; $\Delta G_0^{\ddagger}$ is that part of the free energy of activation independent of coverage of adsorbed species; the last exponential term takes into account variation of free energy of activation with coverage; and A, γ, and r are constants. $\Delta G^{\ddagger}$ is approximately given by

$$\Delta G^{\ddagger} = \Delta G_0^{\ddagger} + \gamma[D_{M-O} + D_{M-C} - D_{C-O} - D_{C-H} - D_{O-H}] \tag{3.15}$$

D's represent the dissociation energies of the indicated bonds.   The last three terms are independent of the substrate.   Equation (3.15) shows that $\Delta G^{\ddagger}$ increases with $(D_{M-O} + D_{M-C})$ and since the latter varies linearly with the latent heat of sublimation (L_s) of the metal, $\Delta G^{\ddagger}$ also increases with this parameter.   However, there is an increase of the product $\theta_E \theta_{OH}$ with the latent heat of sublimation.   One can now easily see why the plot of the rate at a constant overpotential versus the latent heat of sublimation passes through a maximum. On the left of the maximum, the increase of the product $\theta_E \theta_{OH}$ is higher than the decrease of $\exp(-\Delta G^{\ddagger}/RT)$.   Thus, there is an increase of i with L_s. On the right of the maximum, the converse holds and there is a decrease of i with L_s.

3.4.5.5   Double-layer Effects.   In Sec. 3.4.5.1, it was pointed out that the heat of activation of the redox reaction (3.10a), which does not involve any chemisorbed reactants, intermediates, or products, is independent of the work function of the metal (Fig. 30), whereas a linear relation exists between the exchange-current density of the reaction and work function (Fig. 31) for some noble metals.   This anomaly could be resolved only on the basis of a dependence of the exchange-current density on the entropy of activation $(\Delta S_0^{\ddagger})$, or on the reactant concentration in the double layer.[41]   A change in $\Delta S_0^{\ddagger}$ with the substrate may only be caused by different librational rearrangements in the formation of the activated complex; however, because of the absence of any chemibonding, one may expect $\Delta S_0^{\ddagger}$ to be small.   Thus, the dependence of i_0 on Φ is in all probability caused by changes in reactant concentration in the double layer.   The exchange-current density for reaction (3.10a) may be expressed by the relation

$$i_0 = k c_{Fe^{3+}} \exp \frac{-5 V_{2-b} F}{2RT} \exp \frac{-V_{rev} F}{2RT} \tag{3.16}$$

where $c_{Fe^{3+}}$ is the concentration of Fe^{3+} in the bulk of the solution.   The rate constant k contains a work-function term and a number of other terms which do not depend on the metal.   Also, V_{rev} is measured with respect to the case in which there is no potential difference across the electrode-solution interface. Taking both these factors into consideration, one may rewrite Eq. (3.16) in the form

$$i_0 = k' \exp \frac{-\Phi}{2kT} c_{Fe^{3+}} \exp \frac{-5 V_{2-b} F}{2RT} \exp \left[-(V'_{rev} - V_{PZC}) \frac{F}{2RT} \right] \exp \frac{-\Delta \chi F}{2RT} \tag{3.17}$$

V'_{rev} is a potential measured with respect to the potential of a reference electrode and is independent of the work function of the substrate.   There is an approximately linear relation between V_{PZC} and Φ.[49]   Under these conditions, Eq. (3.17) reduces to

$$i_0 = k' c_{Fe^{3+}} \exp \frac{-\Delta \chi F}{2RT} \exp \frac{-5 V_{2-b} F}{2RT} \exp \frac{-V'_{rev} F}{2RT} \tag{3.18}$$

Thus,

$$\frac{\partial \ln i_0}{\partial V_{PZC}} = -\frac{5F}{2RT} \frac{\partial V_{2-b}}{\partial V_{PZC}} \tag{3.19}$$

Further, experimentally[49a]

$$\Phi = 0.9 V_{PZC} \tag{3.20}$$

Using Eq. (3.20) in Eq. (3.19)

$$\frac{\partial \ln i_0}{\partial \Phi} = -0.9 \left(\frac{5F}{2RT} \frac{\partial V_{2-b}}{\partial V_{PZC}} \right) \tag{3.21}$$

No data is available for $(\partial V_{2-b} / \partial V_{PZC})$ on solid metals.   Making the not very satisfactory assumption that this differential is the same as on mercury for the same medium in the same potential region, it is equal to -0.12,[49b] whereupon

$$\frac{\partial \log i_0}{\partial \Phi} = 4.1 \tag{3.22}$$

The experimentally observed value of $\partial \log i_0 / \partial \Phi$ (Fig. 31) is 3.3 and is in quite good agreement with the calculated value [Eq. (3.22)], considering the assumptions made in the derivations and calculations.

A similar interpretation may be used to explain the dependence of i_0 on the percent composition of Au-Pd and Au-Pt alloys (Fig. 32).

3.5   Effect of Potential†

3.5.1   *General*

A change in the potential across the double layer at the electrode-solution interface has two effects. It affects (1) the rate constants of any of the intermediate steps involving a charge transfer (Chap. 2, Sec. 4) and (2) adsorption characteristics of most reactants, intermediates, and products (Chap. 2, Sec. 5).

The effect of potential on the rate constants of charge-transfer steps was dealt with in Chap. 2. In particular, it was pointed out that a considerably greater variation in reaction rate is obtained by changing the potential than by change of concentration or temperature. The latter factors are those usually varied in chemical reactions.

The rate of an electrochemical reaction (i.e., current density at any desired potential) is also affected by the adsorption characteristics of reactants, intermediates, or products which may be a function of potential. This subject was discussed in Chap. 2.

As stated, the rate of an electrochemical reaction may be expressed by the equation

$$i = k_0 e^{\alpha V F / RT} \tag{3.23}$$

when the activities of the reactants are taken as unity. In Eq. (3.23), k_0 is the rate of the reaction when the metal solution potential difference is zero. It is necessary to know in Eq. (3.23) the potential at which the rate of a reaction on different electrode materials must be compared in order to investigate the influence of the various factors (geometric, electronic, electric field) on the respective electrocatalytic activities of the various substrates.

3.5.2   *Elucidation of a Potential for the Comparison of Catalytic Activities*

The most general form of the relation between the rate (expressed in terms of current density) of an electrocatalytic reaction and potential is given by

$$i = k_0 \prod c_N{}^n \exp BV \tag{3.24}$$

where k_0 is the chemical rate constant (i.e., when $V = 0$); $\prod c_N{}^n$ is the product of concentrations of reactants raised to the appropriate power; n is the reaction order; V is the potential drop across the metal solution interface; and B is a

† A section, An Important Parameter in Adsorption: the Potential of Zero Charge, may be found in Appendix B.

constant. The rate i thus depends on three factors, the first two of which, k and $\prod c_N{}^n$, are essentially chemical, and the third is the potential, V.

Equation (3.24) needs a standardization in terms of the electric potential, when one has to compare the rates of the same reaction on several electrocatalysts. There are two reasons why it would be desirable to separate chemical and electrical influences in electrocatalysis. Such a separation, if it could be achieved, would solve the difficulty of having an unknown extent of effect of potential for the same electrode reaction on different catalysts. Further, it would permit application of reasoning from a catalytic point of view of the chemical rate constant.

One can approach the problem of choosing the potential of comparison for electrocatalytic activity independent of field effects in the following way. One makes the assumption that the transfer coefficients are the same for the various metals on which the rates are to be compared. From Eq. (3.23), it follows that the ratio of exchange current densities on two electrocatalysts A and B is given by

$$\frac{i_{0,1}}{i_{0,2}} = \frac{k_{0,1} \exp\left(\alpha V_{R,1} F / RT\right)}{k_{0,2} \exp\left(\alpha V_{R,2} F / RT\right)} \tag{3.25}$$

As seen in Chap. 2, Sec. 3.6.10, the k_0 terms involve the work function Φ and in the case of an anodic reaction, the higher the work function the higher is k_0. Φ appears directly in k_0 due to the transfer of an electron from a species in solution to the metal for an anodic reaction (or vice versa for a cathodic reaction). From the potential energy formulations in Chap. 2, Sec. 3.6.10, it follows that Eq. (3.25) may be written in the form

$$\frac{i_{0,1}}{i_{0,2}} = \frac{k'_{0,1}}{k'_{0,2}} \exp \frac{\alpha(\Phi_1 - \Phi_2)}{RT} \exp \frac{\alpha F(V_{R,1} - V_{R,2})}{RT} \tag{3.26}$$

where the k_0's are the chemical rate constant terms excluding that part directly due to work function. But $V_{R,1}$ and $V_{R,2}$ are referred to the potentials of zero charge of electrocatalysts A and B, respectively. Thus, Eq. (3.26) becomes

$$\frac{i_{0,1}}{i_{0,2}} = \frac{k'_{0,1}}{k'_{0,2}} \exp \frac{\alpha(\Phi_1 - \Phi_2)}{RT} \exp \left[\alpha F(V_{\mathrm{PZC},2} - V_{\mathrm{PZC},1})\right] \tag{3.27}$$

where the V_{PZC}'s represent the potentials of zero charge of the indicated metals. Making use of the empirical relation that the potential of zero charge varies linearly with the work function,[49] Eq. (3.27) reduces to

$$\frac{i_{0,1}}{i_{0,2}} = \frac{k'_{0,2}}{k'_{0,1}} \tag{3.28}$$

The above equation shows that the effects due to the field across the electrode-electrolyte interface and due to the work function of the electrode are eliminated by comparing rates of electrocatalytic reactions at a constant overpotential (assuming that the transfer coefficients are the same). The effect of work function may still exist but indirectly through its effect on the strength of adsorption bonds between the electrode and reactants, intermediates, or products of the reaction.

In summary, at the present time, it appears that, both from a theoretical and practical standpoint, the rates of electrocatalytic reactions having the same transfer coefficients may be meaningfully† compared *at the same overpotential*. The situation is more complex if the transfer coefficients of two electrocatalysts for the same reaction are different. The deduction given here—which shows that, in fundamental electrocatalysis, it is necessary to compare exchange current densities for the same reaction on different substrates—is better modified to the view that the heat of activation at the reversible potential be the arbiter (Sec. 3.4.5.1). This is because exchange current densities may be a function of secondary factors, for example, double layer effects (Sec. 3.4.5.5).

4   METHODS USED IN ELECTROCATALYSIS

4.1   Activation by Superimposition of an External Field

It is possible to activate certain electrode materials by the application of alternate anodic and cathodic pulses.[50]   Activation by this method may be due to one or more of the following reasons: (1) During the anodic pulse, a layer of chemisorbed oxygen covers the electrode and during the cathodic pulse (with pulse time of 10^{-3} sec), this layer is removed. During this process, the surface is cleaned and inhibiting impurity layers are not allowed to build up, thereby maintaining a surface of constant catalytic activity. In addition, reduction of the oxide by the cathodic pulse produces a fresh surface of increased area. (2) Impurities, adsorbed on the electrode, are removed by oxidation when the potential moves over into the anodic region. Thus, by the application of repeated pulse, a constant activity may be maintained. (3) Dissolution of the metal takes place during the anodic pulse, yielding a fresh surface. (4) During the activation procedure, the potential passes through the region of adsorption of a reactant. If this adsorption process is one of the steps of the overall reaction, pulsing may accelerate the reaction.

Activation by pulsing has been applied mainly in the case of platinum and the other noble metals. Thus, it is doubtful that sufficient dissolution of the metal takes place to cause activation of the electrode. The suggestion that during the activation procedure reactants are adsorbed also does not appear

---

† Of course, how meaningfully depends on the purpose in mind. The statement in the text is tainted with the slightly idealistic aspiration of a fundamental researcher who is trying to find out why a reaction goes faster on one metal than on another in molecular terms. The engineer is interested in amperes, volts, weight, and cost. As far as amperes and volts are concerned, he could use the data of the fundamentalist in terms of exchange current densities, were it not for the fact that the data sometimes vary with the same reaction on different metals. A few Tafel lines are needed, then, to check the current-potential relation on indicated catalysts, before i_0 data are directly indicative of the catalyst's performance in a given potential region.

feasible. First, activation occurs even in the cases of some reactions, where it is not necessary for the reactants to adsorb. Second, a wide range of potential is covered during the activation procedure, and it is likely that the reactants are desorbed sufficiently fast in regions far away from the adsorption maximum and before the reaction can occur. The hypothesis that an oxide is formed and subsequently reduced appears quite feasible. However, in the case of some metals cathodic reduction of the oxide takes a long time and the cathodic pulse time may not be sufficient to reduce the oxide. It would be of interest to examine ellipsometrically whether the oxide is reduced. Even if this mechanism were to be accepted, it must be pointed out that the activation is not merely due to an increase in roughness factor. For example, pulsing makes the current-potential relations in the case of the hydrogen evolution reaction on platinum in acid solution more reproducible and significantly different with a higher exchange current density and lower Tafel slope than on an untreated smooth electrode.[51]

Mechanism (2) suggested above may apply in the case of some reactions. An example will be given in the following subsection.

4.2 Change of Field by Self-activation

In the above method, significant power is lost during the activation process of the electrode. A more advantageous method of activation was introduced by Bockris et al.[52] which has possible applications in hydrocarbon-oxygen fuel cells. In this method, the potential of the electrode at which the anodic oxidation of ethylene or any other organic compound is taking place, is momentarily increased to a value near to that of oxide formation (e.g., 0.9 to 1.0 volt versus NHE for a platinum electrode), thereby increasing the activity of the electrode.

The activation process may be interpreted on the basis that an intermediate, formed by the partial oxidation of the hydrocarbon, tends to accumulate on the surface with time and retards the reaction but is rapidly removed from the surface by oxidation to carbon dioxide on momentarily increasing the potential, and thereafter the rate of hydrocarbon reaction is accelerated (Fig. 46). A similar suggestion was made independently by Giner[53] who studied the anodic oxidation of methanol.

It was suggested by Bockris et al. that in a fuel cell, a high activity may be maintained by the use of repeated self-activated pulsing at the fuel electrode. The percentage gain in power output was calculated as follows. The optimum operating conditions of a fuel cell, without activation of the fuel electrode, are at a current density 1 ma cm^{-2} and a cell voltage of 0.3 volt. Thus, the power output is 3×10^{-4} watt cm^{-2}. The fuel electrode may be activated using a current of 40 ma cm^{-2} at 0.15 volt for 0.1 sec every 20 sec. The power consumed in the activation of the electrode is 3×10^{-5} watt, i.e., 10 percent of the hypothetical fuel-cell power. By this activation procedure, the overpotential at the fuel electrode is reduced by 0.18 volt and the corresponding gain in power is 1.8×10^{-4} watt cm^{-2}, that is, 60 percent total increase in power. Since the

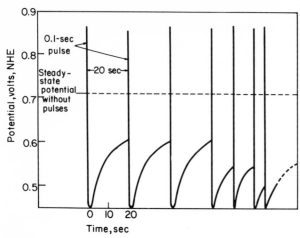

Figure 46 Activation of Pt electrode at which ethylene oxidation is occurring at a current density of 1 ma cm^{-2}, by pulsing for various times.[52]

fuel cell stops delivering power for only 0.1 sec every 20 sec, during activation, the net gain in power is reduced by only 0.3 percent.

Since the pulse current is in the same direction as the output current, the fuel cell may be activated by continuous momentary short circuiting.

4.3　Activation by Radiation

The activation of an electrode process can also be brought about by causing irradiation from a source, which is deposited on the electrode or is situated externally.

Schwabe[54] has investigated the influence of β and γ emitters, deposited on the substrate, on the activity of the oxygen electrode. In this case, one of the following radioactive elements, Ru[106], Ir[192], Tl[204], Po[210], was deposited electrolytically on a platinum or nickel electrode, in the form of sheets, sieves, or cylinders.

In the case of Tl[204] and Po[210], the electrodes were further coated with platinum, due to the risk that the radioactive material would participate in the electrode reaction. Radioactive Tl and Po were generally used due to their long half-life. In cases where isolation of the radioactive material on the electrode, in the way indicated, was not possible, the radiation source was placed in a platinum capsule which was then introduced into a cylindrical electrode of platinum wire mesh. The electrolyte used was generally 1 *N* KOH. The potentials of the electrode were measured against a saturated calomel electrode. In the absence of any radiation, the rest potential of an oxygen electrode reached a steady value, which was about 200 to 250 mv below the reversible value, in about 20 min. In the presence of radioactive Tl deposited on the electrode (activity 3 mc cm^{-2}), a stationary value within 150 to 180 my of the reversible potential was attained in 10 min. The current-potential relations on the activated and unactivated electrodes are shown in Fig. 47. The activated electrodes show less polarization than the unactivated ones. Further, even under load, the potential-time behavior, using varying galvanostatic currents, is uniform with activated electrodes, which is not so with unactivated ones. With ruthenium 106, similar behavior as with Tl^{204} was obtained, though it was less. In the experiments with ruthenium, better behavior was obtained, if the radioactive source was deposited on the electrode rather than being separated from it.

It is too early to make any mechanistic conclusions about this type of activation. Some of the possibilities are: (1) There is a local heating effect caused by the radiation. (2) The activity of the electrode surface is increased by the introduction of defects caused by the radiation. (3) Decomposition of particles takes place in solution and the decomposed particles act either in redox reactions or alter an important activity ratio—for example, in the oxygen electrode reaction in alkaline solution, the rest potential is influenced by the $a_{OH^-}/a_{HO_2^-}$ ratio and if this is changed, the potential is altered.

At the present time, it appears that the energy released is insufficient to cause any local heating effects or radiation damage to the electrode. The most likely explanation is the effect of radiation on the electrolytic solution. The study of the effect of radiation on the hydrogen-evolution reaction on platinum in sulfuric acid supports this view.[55]

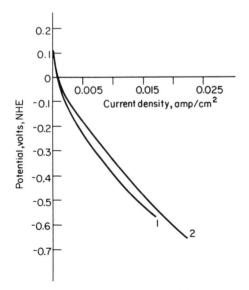

Figure 47 Current-density–potential relations for the electroreduction of oxygen (partial pressure 10 m on Hg) on Pt in 1 N KOH at 20°C. Curves 1: electrode without radiation; curve 2: electrode with 45 mc Ru 106 radiation.[54]

α and β radiation are found to catalyze hydrogen and oxygen dissolution reactions at porous electrodes as well.[56]   Radiation activation methods are in their preliminary state of development but show some promise, if arrangements can be made in which shielding is not a problem.

4.4   Use of Redox Systems to Change the Paths of Reactions

One possible way of improving the performance of the cathode in a fuel cell using oxygen as the oxidant is by use of redox systems (Chap. 4, Sec. 11.2).   The nitric acid–nitric oxide redox couple has been successfully used.[19]   The electrode reaction is the reduction of nitric acid to nitric oxide instead of the electrochemical reduction of oxygen.   Oxygen then oxidizes nitric oxide back again to nitric acid.   Thus, though the overall reaction is still the same, the path of the reaction is considerably altered.   Since the electrochemical reduction of nitric acid and the chemical oxidation of nitric oxide are considerably faster than the electroreduction of oxygen, problems of polarization losses are considerably reduced.

Molybdenum redox couples have been used in two ways for the oxidation of methanol[57,58]—use of a Pt-Mo alloy as the catalyst or the use of molybdates in the electrolyte.   The electrode reaction is the oxidation of the Mo^{5+} to Mo^{6+} ion and the chemical regeneration of Mo^{5+} ion is effected with methanol.

Although some cases of this method may show promise, difficulties occur from the fact that the efficiency of the regeneration reaction is not 100 percent, and hence new redox material may have to be added.   The area is one which has been little investigated.

5   NEW TYPES OF ELECTROCATALYSTS

5.1   Chelate Catalysts

Recently, chelates have been used as catalysts in the electrochemical oxidation of soluble (e.g., formic acid, hydrazine) and some insoluble (hydrogen, propane) fuels.[59]   Since electrocatalysis is markedly affected by the coordination characteristics of the substrate, surrounding a metal atom with electron donor groups of varying ligand strengths should change both the stereochemistry and the coordination characteristics of the metal and hence its electrocatalytic activity. In this work, square planar chelates of metals of the first three transition series, with ligands having field strengths varying from weak to strong, were selected. The chosen ligands, their structure and relative field strength, are found in Table 9.

Stable metal chelates, having square planar configurations, can react with molecules (e.g., fuels, catalyst support molecules) above and below the plane of the metal ion forming an octahedral configuration. Thus, square planar chelates may arrange themselves parallel to the plane of the catalyst support with an open-bonding position available above the plane of the complex to react

TABLE 9 Some Legends Used in Preparation of Chelate Electrocatalysts[59]

Ligand	Structure	Relative field strength
1. Hexafluoroacetylacetone (HFAA)		Weak
2. Acetylacetone (AA)		Weak
3. Bisacetylacetone-ethylenediimine (BAAEDI)		Moderate
4. Bissalicylaldehyde-ethylenediimine (BSAEDI)		Moderate
5. Tetraphenylporphin (TPP)		Strong
6. Tetrabenzodiazoporphin (TBDP)		Strong
7. Phthalocyanine (PC)		Strong

TABLE 10 Chelate Electrocatalysts Prepared from Ligands in Table 9 and Their Decomposition Temperature[59]

Chelate		Decomposition temperatures, °C
1. Bissalicylaldehydeethylenediamine	Ni(II)	283
2. Bissalicylaldehydeethylenediamine	Cu(II)	280
3. Bissalicylaldehydeethylenediamine	Pt(II)	300
4. Bissalicylaldehydeethylenediamine	Pd(II)	300
5. Bissalicylaldehydeethylenediamine	Co(II)	273
6. Bissalicylaldehydeethylenediamine	Zn(II)	300
7. Bisacetylacetonate	Co(II)	Material started to slowly sublime 140 decomposition 210
8. Bisacetylacetonate	Pd(II)	230
9. Bisacetylacetonate	Cu(II)	230
10. Bisacetylacetonate	Ni(II)	220
11. Bisacetylacetonate	Zn(II)	300
12. Bisacetylacetonate	Pt(II)	300
13. Tetraphenylporphine	Pd(II)	360
14. Tetraphenylporphine	Ni(II)	320
15. Tetraphenylporphine	Zn(II)	360
16. Tetraphenylporphine	Pt(II)	360
17. Tetraphenylporphine	Co(II)	360
18. Phthalocyanine (Monastral)	Cu(II)	360
19. Bisacetylacetoneethylenediimine	Ni(II)	mp 200
20. Bisacetylacetoneethylenediimine	Cu(II)	mp 141
21. Bis-hexafluoroacetylacetone	Ni(II)	mp 194
22. Bis-hexafluoroacetylacetone	Mn(II)	mp 140
23. Tetrabenzodiazoporphine	Cu(II)	360
24. Phthalocyanine	Ni(II)	300

TABLE 11 Electrocatalytic Activity of Some Chelates in the Oxidation of Hydrazine and of Formic Acid at 90°C (for Comparison, Electrocatalytic Activity of Pt in the Two Cases is Shown)[59]

Metal	Ligand	Fuel	Electrolyte	Open circuit potential vs. hydrogen electrode in same solution, volts	Polarization (volts) from open circuit at:	
					10 $ma\ cm^{-2}$	100 $ma\ cm^{-2}$
Pt	None	N_2H_4	IMKOH	0.15	0.01	0.08
Mn	HFAA	N_2H_4	IMKOH	0.28	0.17	0.48
Ni	HFAA	N_2H_4	IMKOH	0.03	0.03	0.23
Pd	Salicylaldehyde ethylenediimine	N_2H_4	IMKOH	0.20	0.13	0.17
Pt	None	HCOOH	pH6 phosphate buffer	0.16	0.11	0.34
Zn	Salicylaldehyde ethylenediimine	HCOOH	pH6 phosphate buffer	0.68	0.64	1.08
Pd	Acetylacetonate	HCOOH	pH6 phosphate buffer	0	0.02	0.37
Pt	Salicylaldehyde ethylenediimine	HCOOH	pH6 phosphate buffer	0	0.2	0.36

with the fuel and a bonding position below the plane of the complex to interact with the catalyst support, which favors electron transfer from the catalyst to the conducting support. By a suitable choice of metal ions and ligands, a series of chelates of varying coordinating tendency may be prepared for different types of fuels. The chelates, prepared from the seven tetradentate ligands in Table 9, are given in Table 10 along with their thermal stability (decomposition temperature). These chelates were found to be electrochemically stable. They are stable in most media except strong acids; chlorinated phthalocyanines are, however, inert to strong acids. The catalysts were impregnated on carbon cubes or disks. The catalytic activity of some chelates in the oxidation of hydrazine and of formic acid is given in Table 11. The results show that chelates are active catalysts for oxidation of these fuels. The field strength of the ligand in a metal chelate has a marked effect on the catalytic activity of the metal ion.

The use of metal chelates for the oxidation of insoluble fuels (hydrogen, hydrocarbons) requires careful design of the electrode assembly to maximize the three-phase contact of fuel-electrode-electrolyte. Chelates have been found to be active in oxidation of hydrocarbons using cesium carbonate as electrolyte at 150°C. In a few cases, concentrated phosphoric acid was used with phthalo-cyanines and chlorophthalocyanines as electrocatalysts.

5.2 Sodium Tungsten Bronzes

The desired region of potential in which a fuel cell oxygen cathode should operate is 0.8 to 1.2 volts (NHE) in acid solutions. Due to oxide formation or metal dissolution in this region in the case of most metals or alloys, it is only possible to use noble metal catalysts. In alkaline solutions, conditions are more favorable. However, in the case of organic compound–air fuel cells, it is necessary to develop acid electrolyte fuel cells since carbon dioxide re-jection is immediate in this medium.

Three basic requirements for an oxygen electrode material are that it must be highly conducting (electronic), be corrosion resistant, and have good catalytic properties for the electrode reaction. Recently, the sodium tungsten bronzes, of general formula Na_xWO_3 with x varying from 0.2 to 0.93, were found by Sepa, Damjanovic, and Bockris[60] to satisfy all these requirements.

Electrodes were prepared by allowing a molten mixture of sodium tungstate and tungsten trioxide to crystallize. They were found to be stable at high anodic potential—even after 9 days of oxygen evolution on the electrode, only 10^{-9} g l^{-1} of tungsten was found in solution. In Fig. 48, the potential-vs.-current-density relations for oxygen reduction on a sodium tungsten bronze ($Na_{0.6}WO_3$) on an oxide-covered platinum electrode and on an oxide-free platinum electrode in $0.5M H_2SO_4$ are shown. The sodium tungsten bronze is more active than the other two electrodes at potentials greater than 0.85 volt. Further, with the sodium tungsten bronze electrodes, open circuit potentials exceed those on bare platinum electrodes.

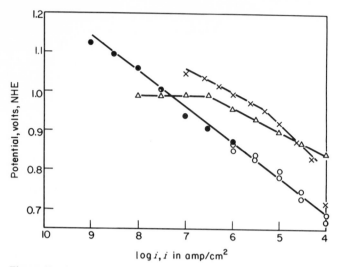

Figure 48 A comparison of the electrocatalytic activities of sodium tungsten bronze (x), oxide-covered platinum (○, ●), and oxide-free platinum (△) electrodes.[60]

A curious aspect of the bronzes is the presence of a type of promotor activity. Small traces of metals, for example, 1 ppm of nickel, promote the reduction of O_2 by 10^2–10^3 times in rate. A negative aspect arises from the fact that oxide films form at higher potentials on bronzes. If single crystals are used, these films have little importance for the resistance. However, for porous-electrode use, the oxide layers are in series through all the small crystal catalysts in contact, and hence there is considerable diminution in activity in porous electrodes. Investigation of the replacement of Pt by the cheap bronze as electrocatalysts is an important and worthwhile research objective.

6 SOME CONCLUDING REMARKS

The field of electrocatalysis was named explicitly for the first time only in 1963.[6] Correspondingly, the orientation of fundamental electrochemists to a way of thinking about their electrode surfaces in terms of catalysis is something which is only a few years old.[61,62] A remarkably small number of people are involved in the field, when one considers the considerable commercial, technological, and sociological† consequences of a change in the position of electrocatalysis.

The present chapter may be concluded with the following comments:

(*i*) A result of central importance[41] (Sec. 3.4.5.1) showed that there was no correlation between the Fermi level of the electrons and the heat of activation

---

† Successful progress in electrocatalysis for the air cathode alone would, for example, make fuel cell power (using natural gas) in homes and factories commercially feasible and thus change significantly the air pollution situation.

for a nonbonding reaction. Although theoretically predicted earlier,[39] the result offends common sense,† and implicit in much thinking in electrocatalytic work has been the assumption that an increase in Fermi level gives rise to a decrease in the heat of activation for a cathodic reaction. It is likely that the efficacy of electrocatalytic thinking will be increased by this result.

To some extent, a similar remark may be made concerning the separation (cf. Sec. 3.4.5.5) of the effects of changing of metal upon the concentration of reactant in the double layer, and other influences which affect the exchange current density of a reaction.

(*ii*) A consequence of the aforementioned basic result[41] is that in the type of reaction where electrocatalysis is practically interesting, there is a dependence upon the metal, at a given overpotential, *only* upon bonding. This expresses itself first as an influence on the equilibrium constants of the steps, if any, in equilibrium before the rate-determining step and mainly in the bond of the substrate to the reactant in the initial and final states of the rate-determining step. *If the rate-determining step is known*, something may be gained in the direction of developing improved substrates in terms of this conclusion.

(*iii*) One of the least good aspects of the present situation in electrocatalysis is that the rate-determining steps of only a few electrode reactions are known to a certain probability (those involved in hydrogen evolution, oxygen dissolution, and an outline of the situation for simple hydrocarbons is the extent of present knowledge). This is not essentially because of difficulties in research, but is because nearly all the work supported hitherto has been for direct empirical attempts to find catalysts before the electrochemical principles were understood.

(*iv*) The least stressed aspect of electrocatalysis is the importance of attempting to attain a low α value. Thus (Chap. 4, Sec. 7) for a given i_0 value (the first approximation arbiter of catalysis), the amount of loss of power in a fuel cell is simply proportional to α. Attempts to tamper with α have been in the past hampered by a lack of realization among most electrochemists of the relation of the transfer coefficient α to the symmetry factor β. This has often[64] been erroneously written:

$$\alpha = \beta n \tag{6.1}$$

where n is the number of electrons transferred in the overall reaction. However,

---

† The result is not generally a realized one. Thus, for example, physicists[63] who approach the theory of electrocatalysis without realizing how electrocatalysis is measured (i.e., the rate of the reaction at a certain potential *with respect to a reference electrode*) tend to step in with treatments in the area in which some[41,48] would fear to tread. The electrochemical treatment of the whole cell, with its metal-metal junction and the resultant cancellation of the work function and its direct effect upon the heat of activation, is not as yet part of the conventional wisdom.

the relation is[65]

$$\alpha = \frac{s}{v} + \beta r \tag{6.2}$$

where $r = 0$ or 1 and is the number of electrons taking part in the rate-determining step, s is the number of electrons which are transferred before the rate-determining step, and v is the stoichiometric number (Chap. 2, Sec. 3.6.7). Thus, $\alpha \neq \beta$ or βn. It may be greater than $\frac{1}{2}$.

(*v*) No research work in which the objective is the investigation of electrocatalysis should ever be done on porous electrodes. Inspection of equations such as found in Chap. 5, Sec. 5.7, indicates that an exchange current density is very difficult to pull out of a complex influence of catalytic, transport, and active area factors which determine the power output of an electrode.

(*vi*) Lack of realization of the great importance of the electrochemical stability of the substrate has lead to unproductive conclusions. Two reactions in which developments in electrocatalysis are most needed are oxygen reduction and hydrocarbon oxidation, which occur in the potential range from about 0.2 to about 1.0 volt on the reversible hydrogen scale. Of the pure metals, only silver and the platinum group have high enough standard electrode potentials such that they do not corrode under these conditions in acid solutions. Indeed, it is doubtful whether an exchange current density for the reduction of oxygen on platinum of about 10^{-10} amp cm^{-2} justifies the description of platinum as a good catalyst. But it has the advantage that it does not dissolve itself.

(*vii*) Study of the potential dependence of the adsorption of fuels has been a much neglected factor in electrocatalysis: it is pointless to aim at excellent rate constants if the potential is far away for the potential of zero charge, because then there would be a low coverage of the electrode with fuel.

(*viii*) Electrocatalysis at present has become one of the most exciting areas in electrochemical research. This is because, on the one hand, it touches on the basic aspects of the "New Electrochemistry"[66]—that of the relation of rates to solid state physics—and, on the other, it touches on such very large and attractive consequences for the community if it can succeed. It is still in an early stage. Areas which are in need of investigation are the following: (*a*) the effect of the adsorption of anions on electrodes—this is largely speculative because little is known about the adsorption of anions on solids; (*b*) the mode of adsorption of organic substances—to what extent and when they dissociate on adsorption; (*c*) effects of traces (1 ppm) of metals in oxides or carbon in metals which appear to be able to cause increases of rates much greater than promoters in catalysis; (*d*) organic semiconductors which exhibit a large range of possible variations of properties; (*e*) development of the quantum-mechanical approach to electrode processes in formulating new ideas concerning substrates which may give the lowest heat of activation for a reaction.

(*ix*) Finally, fundamental work on electrocatalysis would seem to have a much better chance of contributing to practical development than has similar work of greater extent in chemical catalysis. There are three reasons for this: (*a*) the work has been commenced some forty to fifty years after that on gas phase catalysis; (*b*) it is much easier to measure the rate of a reaction on a catalyst if it can be done by measuring a current than, say, a gas pressure change; and (*c*) the dependence of rate on potential gives an extra mechanism-indicating criterion compared with those available in the study of gas catalysis.

As with investigations of porous electrodes, those of electrocatalysis will contribute to progress in realizing favorable conditions in electrochemical electricity producers as well as in electrochemical substance producers.

REFERENCES

1. Bockris, J. O'M.: Chap. 4, in J. O'M. Bockris and B. E. Conway (eds.), "Modern Aspects of Electrochemistry," vol. 1, Butterworth & Co. (Publishers), Ltd., London, 1954.
2. Matthews, D. B.: Doctoral dissertation, University of Pennsylvania, Philadelphia, Pa., 1965.
3*a*. Damjanovic, A., and V. Brusic: *Electrochim. Acta*, **12**, 615 (1967).
3*b*. Damjanovic, A., A. Dey, and J. O'M. Bockris: *Electrochim. Acta*, **11**, 791 (1966); *J. Electrochem. Soc.*, **113**, 739 (1966).
3*c*. Damjanovic, A.: "Oxygen Electrode Reactions," chapter in J. O'M. Bockris and B. E. Conway (eds.), "Modern Aspects of Electrochemistry," vol. 5, Plenum Press, New York, 1969.
4. Piersma, B. J., and E. Gileadi: Chap. 2, in J. O'M. Bockris (ed.), "Modern Aspects of Electrochemistry," vol. 4, Plenum Press, New York, 1967.
5. Dahms, H., and J. O'M. Bockris: *J. Electrochem. Soc.*, **111**, 728 (1964).
6. Grubb, W. T.: *Nature*, **198**, 883 (1963).
7. Adlhart, O. J., and K. O. Hever: Engelhard report on Fuel Cell Catalysis, Contract No. Da 36-039 SC-90691, E.S.A.E.R.D.L., 1964.
8. Justi, E., and A. Winsel: *Naturwissenschaften*, **47**, 289 (1960); A. W. Kalberlah and A. Winsel, *Electrochim. Acta*, **13**, 1689 (1968); E. W. Justi and A. W. Kalberlah, *Energy Convn.*, **8**, 47 (1968).
9. Wroblowa, H., B. J. Piersma, and J. O'M. Bockris: *J. Electroanal. Chem.*, **6**, 401 (1963).
10. Gerischer, H.: *Ber. Bunsenges. Physik. Chem.*, **67**, 164 (1963).
11. Pourbaix, M.: "Atlas D'Equilibres Electrochimiques," Gauthier-Villars, Paris, 1963; English Translation: M. Pourbaix, "Atlas of Electrochemical Equilibria in Aqueous Solution," Pergamon Press, New York, 1966.
12. Mehl, W., J. M. Hale, and F. Lohmann: *J. Electrochem. Soc.*, **113**, 75C, Abstract No. 159 (1966); W. Mehl and J. M. Hale, Chap. 5, in P. Delahay and C. W. Tobias (eds.), "Advances in Electrochemistry and Electrochemical Engineering," vol. 6, Interscience Publishers, Inc., New York, 1967; J. M. Hale, *J. Electrochem. Soc.*, **115**, 208 (1968).

13. Despic, A. R., and J. O'M. Bockris: *J. Chem. Phys.*, **32**, 389 (1960).
14. Allen, M. J.: "Organic Electrode Reactions," Reinhold Publishing Corporation, New York, 1958.
15. Devanathan, M. A. V., J. O'M. Bockris, and W. Mehl: *J. Electroanal. Chem.*, **1**, 143 (1959–1960).
16. Visscher, W., and M. A. V. Devanathan: *J. Electroanal. Chem.*, **3**, 127 (1964).
17. Conway, B. E., and M. Dzieciuch: *Can. J. Chem.*, **41**, 21, 38, 55 (1963).
18. Conway, B. E., J. O'M. Bockris, and B. Lovrecek: *Compt. Rend. CITCE*, **6**, 207 (1955).
19. Shropshire, J. A., and B. L. Tarmy: *Advan. Chem. Ser.*, **47**, 153 (1965).
20. Bockris, J. O'M., and S. Srinivasan: *Nature*, **215**, 197 (1967).
21. Schwan, H. P.: *Advan. Biol. Med. Phys.*, **5**, 147 (1957).
22. Rajagopalan, S. R., and A. K. N. Reddy: *Accet. Mag.*, **17** (1960).
22*a*. Damjanovic, A., and J. O'M. Bockris: Chap. 4, in J. O'M. Bockris and B. E. Conway (eds.), "Modern Aspects of Electrochemistry," vol. 3, Butterworth & Co. (Publishers), Ltd., London, 1964.
23. Coles, B. R.: *J. Inst. Metals*, **84**, 346 (1956).
23*a*. Rubin, B. T.: Doctoral dissertation, University of Pennsylvania, Philadelphia, 1969; J. O'M. Bockris and B. T. Rubin, To be published.
23*b*. Azaroff, L. B.: "Introduction to Solids," McGraw-Hill Book Company, New York, 1960.
24. Balandin, A. A.: *Z. Physik. Chem.*, **B2**, 28 (1929); **B3**, 167 (1929).
25. Sherman, A., and H. Eyring: *J. Amer. Chem. Soc.*, **54**, 2661 (1932).
26. Okamoto, G., J. Horiuti, and K. Hirota: *Sci. Papers Inst. Phys. Chem. Res.* (*Tokyo*), **29**, 223 (1936).
27. Bockris, J. O'M., and S. Srinivasan: *J. Electrochem. Soc.*, **111**, 853 (1964).
28. Bond, G. C.: "Catalysis by Metals," Academic Press Inc., New York, 1962.
29. Piontelli, R., L. Peraldo Bicelli, and A. La Vecchia: *Rend. Accad. Naz. Lincei VIII*, **27**, 312 (1959).
30. Damjanovic, A.: Private communication, 1968.
31. Reddy, A. K. N., M. Paunovic, and J. O'M. Bockris: NASA Contract (No. NsG 325), report for half-year ending Sept. 30, 1964, submitted by University of Pennsylvania, Philadelphia.
32. Conway, B. E., and J. O'M. Bockris: *Electrochim. Acta*, **3**, 349 (1961).
33. Drazic, D., and J. O'M. Bockris: *Electrochim. Acta*, **7**, 293 (1962).
34. Herring, C.: Chap. 1, in R. Gomer and C. S. Smith (eds.), "Structures and Properties of Solid Surfaces", The University of Chicago Press, Chicago, 1953.
35. Kita, H., M. Enyo, and J. O'M. Bockris: *Can. J. Chem.*, **39**, 1670 (1961).
36. Damjanovic, A., and J. O'M. Bockris: *J. Electrochem. Soc.*, **110**, 1035 (1963).
37. Mott, N. F., and H. Jones: "The Theory of Metals and Alloys," Oxford University Press, Fair Lawn, N.J., 1940.
38. Pauling, L.: *Phys. Rev.*, **54**, 899 (1938); *Proc. Roy. Soc., Ser. A* **196**, 343 (1949); "Nature of the Chemical Bond," Cornell University Press, Ithaca, N.Y., 1961.
39. Conway, B. E., and J. O'M. Bockris: *J. Chem. Phys.*, **26**, 532 (1957).
39*a*. Ruetschi, P., and P. Delahay: *J. Chem. Phys.*, **23**, 195 (1954).
39*b*. Liebhafsky, H. A., and E. J. Cairns: "Fuel Cells and Fuel Cell Batteries," John Wiley & Sons, Inc., New York, 1968.

40. Khomutov, N. E.: *Russ. J. Phys. Chem.* (English translation) **36**, 1475 (1962).

41. Bockris, J. O'M., R. J. Mannan, and A. Damjanovic: *J. Chem. Phys.*, **48**, 1898 (1968).

41a. Hush, N. S.: *J. Chem. Phys.*, **28**, 962 (1958); R. A. Marcus, *J. Phys. Chem.*, **67**, 853 (1963), and *J. Chem. Phys.*, **43**, 679 (1965); H. Gerischer, *Z. Physik. Chem.*, **26**, 223 (1960); V. G. Levich, *Dokl. Akad. Nauk. USSR*, **67**, 309 (1949), and **124**, 809 (1959); R. R. Dogonadze and A. Chizmadzhev, *ibid.*, **144**, 1077 (1962), **145**, 849 (1962), and **150**, 333 (1963).

42. Ellingham, H. J. T., and A. J. Allmand: *Trans. Faraday Soc.*, **19**, 748 (1924).

43. Bockris, J. O'M.: *Trans. Faraday Soc.*, **43**, 417 (1947).

44. Bockris, J. O'M., A. Damjanovic, and R. Mannan: *J. Electroanal. Interf. Electrochem.*, **18**, 349 (1968).

44a. Schuldiner, S.: *J. Electrochem. Soc.*, **99**, 488 (1952).

45. Ruetschi, P., and P. Delahay: *J. Chem. Phys.*, **23**, 556 (1955).

46. Damjanovic, A., and V. Brusic: *Electrochim. Acta*, **12**, 1171 (1967).

47. Rao, M. L. B., A. Damjanovic, and J. O'M. Bockris: *J. Phys. Chem.*, **67**, 2508 (1963).

48. Kuhn, A. T., H. Wroblowa, and J. O'M. Bockris: *Trans. Faraday Soc.*, **63**, 1458 (1967).

49. Frumkin, A. N.: *J. Colloid Sci.*, **1**, 260 (1946); S. D. Argade: Ph.D. dissertation, University of Pennsylvania, Philadelphia, 1968.

49a. Bockris, J. O'M., and S. D. Argade: *J. Chem. Phys.*, **49**, 5133 (1968).

50. Schuldiner, S., and R. M. Roe: *J. Electrochem. Soc.*, **110**, 332 (1963); S. Schuldiner and T. B. Warner, *J. Phys. Chem.*, **68**, 1223 (1964); S. Schuldiner and T. B. Warner, *J. Electrochem. Soc.*, **112**, 212 (1965).

51. Bockris, J. O'M., I. A. Ammar, and A. K. M. S. Huq: *J. Phys. Chem.*, **61**, 879 (1957).

52. Bockris, J. O'M., B. J. Piersma, E. Gileadi, and B. D. Cahan: *J. Electroanal. Chem.*, **7**, 487 (1965).

53. Giner, J.: *Electrochim. Acta*, **9**, 63 (1964).

54. Schwabe, K.: Chap. 6, in G. J. Young (ed.), "Fuel Cells," Reinhold Publishing Corporation, New York, 1963.

55. Feates, F. S.: *Trans. Faraday Soc.*, **56**, 1671 (1960); F. S. Feates and B. Knight, *Trans. Faraday Soc.*, **56**, 1680 (1960).

56. Salcedo y Gumucio, R., and M. Lang: 120th Meeting of the Electrochemical Society, Detroit, Mich., Paper No. 30, 1961.

57. Heath, C. E.: *Proc. Ann. Power Sources Conf.*, **18**, 33, 1964.

58. Shropshire, J. A.: Paper delivered at Electrochemical Society Meeting, Washington, D.C., Oct. 12–15, 1964.

59. Smith, J. O., et al.: Monsanto Research Corporation Annual Technical Report for period 15 May—15 November, 1963, under USAERDL Contract No. DA-44-009-AMC 202 (T).

60. Sepa, D. B., A. Damjanovic, and J. O'M. Bockris: *Electrochim. Acta*, **12**, 746 (1967); A. Damjanovic, D. Sepa, and J. O'M. Bockris, *J. Res. Inst. Cat.*, **16**, 1 (1968).

61. Srinivasan, S., H. Wroblowa, and J. O'M. Bockris: Chap. 6, in D. D. Eley, H. Pines, and P. B. Weisz (eds.), "Advances in Catalysis," vol. 17, Academic Press Inc., New York, 1967.

62. Bockris, J. O'M., and H. Wroblowa: *J. Electroanal. Chem.*, **7**, 428 (1964).

63. Bocciarelli, C. V.: *Energy Conversion*, **8**, 57 (1968).

64. Delahay, P.: "New Instrumental Methods in Electrochemistry," Interscience Publishers, Inc., New York, 1954.

65. Matthews, D. B., and J. O'M. Bockris: Chap. 1, in J. O'M. Bockris and B. E. Conway (eds.), "Modern Aspects of Electrochemistry," vol. 5, Plenum Press, New York, 1969.

66. Bockris, J. O'M., and A. K. N. Reddy: "The Essentials of Modern Electrochemistry," Plenum Press, New York, 1969.

CHAPTER SEVEN

Electrochemical Combustion of Organic Substances

1 DESIRABILITY OF DEVELOPING ELECTROCHEMICAL ENERGY CONVERTERS USING ORGANIC FUELS

The most exploited path of energy conversion is the conversion of the energy released as heat during chemical oxidation of a fossil fuel into mechanical energy (e.g., in a steam turbine) followed by the conversion of mechanical energy into electrical energy, using a generator. The demand for power production is increasing throughout the world at a rapid rate. The exhaustion of the fossil fuels has often been predicted[1] and new discoveries then made. The present statement of geologists concerning this matter is in more realistic terms. There are large oil reserves in shale deposits, and it is possible that there are very large reserves under the sea bed. What can be predicted with a high degree of probability is that in 20 years (plus or minus 5 years), given a continuation of the present trend in respect to increase each year of the need for power, the oil which would then have to be used would be about double its present cost, and that its cost would continue to rise thereafter at an increasing rate.

In order that the lifetime of the presently available fossil fuels be extended, it is necessary to use them more efficiently than in conventional engines. In this respect, electrochemical energy conversion offers an advance because of the attainment of significant increases in efficiency of conversion up to doubling even at the present time.

Another important reason for the development of fossil-fuel electrochemical conversion is the presence in the United States of very large amounts of coal, sufficient for many hundreds of years of energy supply. Were it possible to convert this coal directly into electricity without production of pollutants, except CO_2, a considerable aid to the atomic power plants (which depend on exhaustible uranium) would be available. Such a development of coal to electricity converters has recently been achieved by the Westinghouse Corporation; however, the system works with attendant material difficulties.

2 BRIEF HISTORY OF ELECTROORGANIC OXIDATION

The first evidence of electroorganic oxidation was the oxidation of alcohol, dissolved in an aqueous solution.[2]   Progress in this field was slow thereafter, and most of the work was directed towards electroorganic synthesis.   Electrochemical oxidation of an aromatic compound, benzene, was first reported in 1880, but the products were not analyzed.[3]   It was observed soon after that aliphatic hydrocarbons were formed by the oxidation of benzene in alcoholic sulfuric acid at platinum anodes.[4]

The biggest contribution of the early work arises from the work of Haber,[5] who realized that for oxidation and reduction processes, the potential of the electrode and not the current density plays the major role.   Haber studied the reduction of nitrobenzene and found that the product could be either azoxy benzene or hydrazo benzene, depending on the potential.   The importance of the potential and not the current density was ignored by subsequent workers until the invention of the potentiostat by Hickling in 1942.[6]

The initial systematic work on mechanism investigations on electroorganic oxidation was carried out by Müller and coworkers[7-12] during the 1920s. These workers studied the oxidation of methanol, formaldehyde, and formic acid on the noble metals.   This work is perhaps the first published study of electrocatalysis (see Fig. 1), although not at that time presented in terms of electrocatalysis.

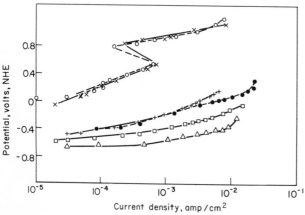

Figure 1   Anodic oxidation of formate ion from 1 *N* HCOONa showing effect of catalyst.   Δ, palladized Pd at 20°C;   □, platinized Pt at 20°C;   ●,   Pd at 75°C;   +, rhodenized Pt at 20°C;   ×, Pt at 75°C;   ○, Ir at 75°C.[7]

Oxidation of olefins to acids was first reported in 1948.[13]   The spontaneous electrochemical oxidation of a saturated hydrocarbon yielding electrical energy was first reported by Heath and Worsham[14] of the Esso Research and Engineering

Company. Complete oxidation to carbon dioxide, which is essential for the maximum recovery of electrical energy, was observed. This result greatly enhanced the interest in the field of electrochemical energy conversion using organic fuels. Since this work, complete oxidation to carbon dioxide has been observed with a variety of organic compounds, e.g., saturated and unsaturated hydrocarbons, alcohols, formaldehyde, and formic acid.

3 DIRECT AND INDIRECT USE OF ORGANIC FUELS IN ELECTROCHEMICAL ENERGY CONVERSION

Organic fuels may be used either directly or indirectly in fuel cells. In the direct method the fuel is the anodic reactant. In the indirect method, the organic compound is reformed chemically in a separate chamber into hydrogen or a mixture of hydrogen and carbon monoxide, which gas or gases are then led into the anode gas chamber of the fuel cell.

The advantage of the latter method is that the electrode reaction is the oxidation of hydrogen, which is a well known and easily attained process. In some cases, it is the reaction of a mixture of H_2 and CO at high temperatures, which is also fast. Further, relatively cheap electrocatalysts may be used here at working temperatures of about $70°C$, which are not excessive. On the other hand, the disadvantages are the weight and volume of the reformer and its deactivation with time. The chemical catalytic reaction is not a source of Carnot limitations and is only the source of fuel-cell reactants. The competition at the present time between the direct and indirect methods of utilization of hydrocarbons lies with the size, weight, cost, and efficiency of the chemical reformer for the indirect method on the one hand and the electrochemical activity and cost of electrode materials for direct oxidation on the other.

The only stable materials for the direct oxidation of organic fuels are at present the noble metals. The efficiencies, which are obtained using noble metals in the oxidation of hydrocarbons (e.g., butane) at practical current densities, are nearly 50 percent. This is considerably better than the 25 percent efficiencies obtained with conventional combustion engines using hydrocarbons.

A detailed comparison of the advantages and disadvantages of the direct and indirect utilization of organic fuels in electrochemical energy conversion is made in Sec. 5.2.

4 CONSIDERATION OF IMPORTANT CRITERIA IN THE PRODUCTION OF POWER AND ENERGY

A consideration of the important criteria in the production of power and energy depends on the application of the energy-conversion or storage device. It is possible to think of a wide variety of applications. They may, however, be broadly classified into three groups: (1) space; (2) ground—mobile; and (3) ground—stationary.

The necessary criteria in each of the three groups will be dealt with in the following sections.

(i) Space applications

In space applications, the most important criterion is the weight of the energy conversion and of the energy storage systems for a specified mission duration.   In Chap. 1, it was seen that fuel cells are the most advantageous in terms of weight for mission durations from a few hours to over one month (Chap. 1, Fig. 11).   To a lesser extent, the volume of the system is also important.   In order that a fuel in an electrochemical energy converter may be used economically, it is necessary to have a high voltage efficiency.   Thus, the criteria which are to be evaluated for space application of fuel cells are the efficiency of the system and the power/weight, power/volume, energy/weight, and energy/volume ratios.   The last two criteria depend on the duration of the mission.   For long missions, these two criteria may be approximated by the energy/weight and energy/volume ratio of only the fuel and oxidant (Chap. 4).

Apart from the above criteria, the reliability of the system is also equally, if not more, important.   The reliability of the system is ascertained from the life tests (see Chaps. 4 and 9).

(ii) Ground—mobile

A number of mobile applications, such as for automobiles, city delivery trucks, and industrial trucks, may be envisaged.   When it becomes possible to produce an electrochemical power source with a sufficiently attractive power/weight ratio, electric cars will probably displace automobiles powered by internal-combustion engines.   In the present chapter, the main factors to be taken into consideration are the efficiency, power/weight ratio, power/volume ratio, cost per kilowatt (initial investment), and cost per kilowatthour (essentially the fuel costs).   The criteria thus depend strongly on how fast the reactions at the electrode take place, i.e., upon the velocity (or current-density) potential relation.

(iii) Ground—stationary

The stationary applications include use of fuel cells for large-scale central-power generation, industrial on-the-site production of dc power for metallurgical and electrochemical processes, and individual home power plants.   For such applications, the most important factor is the cost per kilowatthour. Other factors are the initial costs, i.e., cost per kilowatt.   The efficiency of the system determines, of course, the cost per kilowatthour for a given fuel.   The rate of working, and hence the exchange current density and electrode kinetics of the system, are also of great importance—first, because they control the efficiency of conversion, and second, because they determine the area and volume of the generating station (Chap. 4, Secs. 2 to 7).

5 COMPARISON OF VARIOUS TYPES OF ELECTROCHEMICAL ENERGY CONVERTERS

5.1 Fuel Cells Using Organic Fuels Directly

An analysis of the various parameters is made of the performance of some fuel cells that use organic fuels directly. The assumptions made in the calculations of the various parameters are: (1) the weight of the fuel cell is twice the weight of the electrodes and that of the electrolyte; (2) the thickness of each cell is ¼ in., (3) the initial cost is calculated on the basis of electrode costs per square centimeter (which is essentially the cost of Pt per square centimeter where this metal is used as the catalyst) plus 25 percent of the electrode costs to cover accessories, labor, etc. (it is assumed that 90 percent of the platinum is recoverable and thus only 10 percent of the cost of the platinum is taken into account); (4) for the calculation of total cost[15] it is necessary to apportion the cost of capital (initial cost) per kilowatthour of operation. It is assumed that the cell life is 5 years and the fuel cell is run for 2,000 hr per year. Interest on capital is assumed to be 10 percent per annum. The ratio of energy per weight of fuel and fuel cost for each system is calculated from the data in Table 1, in which the ideal voltage efficiency of unity has been assumed as a basis for calculations in Tables 2 to 6.

TABLE 1 Theoretical Energy and Cost Parameters for Various Fuels

Fuel	E_F, kwh lb^{-1}	E_{F+0}, kwh lb^{-1}	Cost of fuel,† cents lb^{-1}	C_F, cents kwh^{-1}	C_{F+0}, cents kwh^{-1}‡
Methane	6.430	1.288	0.72	0.111	2.155
Ethane	6.155	1.302	1.40	0.227	2.858
Propane	6.030	1.302	1.02	0.170	2.154
Butane	5.959	1.301	2.85	0.478	2.464
Octane	5.858	1.301	3.41	0.582	2.525
Decane	5.837	1.301	1.09	0.186	2.127
Hydrogen	14.837	1.660	35	2.359	4.082
Ammonia	2.510	1.041	4.11	1.637	3.567
Hydrazine	2.492	1.246	100	40.128	41.43
Lithium	6.132	1.004	1,000	163.025	165.734
Methanol	2.764	1.106	4.23	1.530	3.293
Gasoline	5.852	1.300	2.44	0.401	1.806
Diesel oil	5.762	1.284	1.09	0.195	2.127

E_F, and E_{F+0} are the theoretical ratios (energy/weight of fuel) and (energy/weight of fuel and oxidant), respectively. C_F and C_{F+0} are the theoretical ratios of (cost/energy) for fuel and (cost/energy) for fuel and oxidant, respectively.

† Costs of fuels obtained either from Philadelphia Gas Works or from *Food and Drug Reporter*.

‡ Calculations were made assuming O_2 is oxidant for all systems except Li, where it is Cl_2; if air instead of O_2 is oxidant, $C_{F+0} = C_F$.

TABLE 2 Performance Characteristics of Fuel Cells Using Organic Fuels Directly

Fuel	Fuel-cell reaction	Temp., °C	E°, volts	Maximum power density, watts cm⁻²	Voltage efficiency	Power/ weight, watts lb⁻¹	Power/ volume, kw ft⁻³	Energy/ weight of fuel, kwh lb⁻¹	Initial cost, $ kw⁻¹	Fuel cost, cents kwh⁻¹	Total cost, cents Kwh⁻¹
Methane[16]	$CH_4 + 2O_2 \rightarrow CO_2 + 2H_2O$	150	1.05	0.02	0.29	3.30	0.87	1.82	385	0.39	5.46
Ethane[16]	$C_2H_6 + \frac{7}{2} O_2 \rightarrow 2CO_2 + 3H_2O$	150	1.07	0.022	0.28	3.81	1.00	1.70	333	0.81	5.20
Propane[16a]	$C_3H_8 + 5O_2 \rightarrow 3CO_2 + 4H_2O$	200	1.08	0.04	0.37	6.89	1.69	2.23	187	0.46	2.93
Butane[16]	$C_4H_{10} + \frac{13}{2} O_2 \rightarrow 4CO_2 + 5H_2O$	150	1.08	0.04	0.28	6.60	1.74	1.63	192	1.72	4.25
Octane[18]	$C_8H_{18} + \frac{25}{2} O_2 \rightarrow 8CO_2 + 9H_2O$	200	1.09	0.05	0.46	8.55	2.24	2.69	150	1.26	3.24
Decane[17]	$C_{10}H_{22} + \frac{31}{2} O_2 \rightarrow 10CO_2 + 11H_2O$	100	1.09	0.02	0.32	3.38	0.89	1.87	375	0.58	5.53
Methanol[18]	$CH_3OH + \frac{3}{2} O_2 \rightarrow CO_2 + 2H_2O$	68	1.21	0.05	0.42	9.15	2.22	1.13	150	3.73	5.71

A comparison of the power/weight and power/volume ratios among fuel cells using organic fuels (Table 2) shows that the methanol fuel cell is the best, although the performances of cells using propane, butane, and octane are comparable. The efficiencies of all the systems at the maximum power point are over 30 percent but well below that expected were catalysts with increased reaction velocity to be realizable. However, it must be realized that electro-oxidation of these fuels is a new field, compared with that of conventional indirect devices, and research carried out in electrocatalysis is in its infancy. With the assumption made in the cost calculations, the initial costs per kilowatt are quite reasonable. The methanol and octane fuel cells are the least expensive. The fuel costs for the hydrocarbons are considerably lower than those for methanol. Because of this, fuel cells using propane, butane, and octane are also less expensive than are those using methanol with respect to total cost.

Because of this early stage of practical development of organic fuel-cell systems, it is interesting to compare the *projected* performance characteristics, allowing reasonable assumptions of research progress (Table 3). For this

TABLE 3 Projected Performance Characteristics of Fuel Cells Using Organic Fuels

| Fuel | Voltage efficiency | Energy/weight of fuel, kwh lb^{-1} | Fuel cost, cents kwh^{-1} | Total cost, cents, kwh^{-1}, using | | |
				1 mg	100 μg	10 μg cm^{-2}
Methane	0.67	4.28	0.17	1.58	0.31	0.18
Propane	0.65	3.92	0.26	1.67	0.40	0.27
Decane	0.64	3.74	0.29	1.70	0.43	0.30
Methanol	0.58	1.60	2.64	4.05	2.78	2.65

Other characteristics which are the same for all fuels in table (see text) are:

$$\text{Current density} = 0.1 \text{ amp cm}^{-2}$$
$$\text{Cell potential} = 0.7 \text{ volt}$$
$$\text{Power/area} = 0.07 \text{ watt cm}^{-2}$$
$$\text{Power/weight} = 11.84 \text{ watts lb}^{-1}$$
$$\text{Power/volume} = 3.12 \text{ kw ft}^{-3}$$

Initial cost per kw (assuming use of
   1 mg cm^{-2} of Pt for each electrode) = $107
Initial cost per kw (assuming use of
   100 μg cm^{-2} of Pt for each electrode) = $10.70
Initial cost per kw (assuming the use of
   10 μg of Pt for each electrode) = $1.07

purpose, it was assumed: (1) The achievable current density is 0.1 amp cm^{-2} at a cell potential of 0.7 volt; this performance should be considered practicable with further work in electrocatalysis. (2) The quantity of Pt may be reduced to 1 mg cm^{-2} (present-day figures are about 10 mg cm^{-2}; with some hydrogen and oxygen electrodes, quantities as low as 2 to 3 mg cm^{-2} are being used). (3) Considerable improvement of nearly 100 times this value of 1 mg cm^{-2}

(i.e., reduction to 10 to 20 μg cm^{-2}) has been obtained in single-pore studies of the hydrogen and oxygen dissolution.[18a]   Thus, second and third projected estimates were made assuming that the platinum content of each electrode is 100 and 10 μg cm^{-2} respectively.   If it is thus assumed and the catalyst is spread uniformly, there will only be two to three monolayers of the catalyst on the electrode substrate.

With these assumptions, the voltage efficiencies are quite satisfactory, as seen in Table 3.   Fuel costs are also somewhat lowered compared with the present available data, but the significant reduction is seen in the initial costs, mainly because the amount of Pt needed per kilowatt has been assumed to be reduced.   Other ways of considering a reduction in initial cost are to recall that some potential new electrode material, e.g., an organic semiconductor, or one of the bronzes,[23a] something at least ten times cheaper than Pt, is used.   With these assumptions, the lighter hydrocarbons again become the most economical.

5.2   Direct versus Indirect Use of Organic Fuels in Electrochemical Energy Conversion

Until cheaper electrocatalysts are found for the direct utilization of electro-organic fuels, there are some advantages of using a reformer-fuel cell.   First, very pure hydrogen can be generated from (purified) organic compounds using cheap catalysts (e.g., nickel).   Second, hydrogen-air fuel cells are sufficiently advanced to use nonnoble metal catalysts (e.g., nickel or silver).   Further, there are no problems of CO_2 rejection as is found in the direct method.   The main problems about the indirect method are the cost and weight of the generator.   The performance characteristics for some of the reformer-fuel cells are given in Table 4.   There are two types of reformer-fuel cells—the reformer is either separated from or integrated with the fuel cell.   The overall efficiencies of both types of reformer-fuel cells are of the same order as those for the direct conversion of the organic fuels to electricity because the reformer efficiency is about 50 percent.   The estimated initial costs of separate reformer-fuel cells using hydrocarbons are considerably lower than that of the integrated system— the main reason being that the former uses cheap catalysts for both reforming and fuel-cell reactions, whereas the latter uses a silver-palladium alloy for separation of hydrogen from the other products of reforming and also for the fuel-cell reaction.   The separate reformer-fuel cell uses only small quantities of silver-palladium alloy to separate hydrogen from other products and impurities of the reformer reaction.   At the present time, the fuels which have been used for the indirect method are more costly than the lighter hydrocarbons used in the direct method in all cases except the natural gas reformer-fuel cell, where the low fuel cost is offset by the somewhat lower overall efficiency of the system.

Thus, as it stands at the present time, from economic (initial cost) considerations the indirect method appears more feasible than the direct method. The projected performances of the direct method are better than those of

TABLE 4 Performance Characteristics of Reformer-fuel Cells Using Organic Fuels

Method	Fuel	Reformer reaction	E_0, volts	Maximum power density, watts cm^{-2}	Overall efficiency	Power/weight, watts lb^{-1}	Power/volume $kw\,ft^{-3}$	Energy/weight of fuel, $kwh\,lb^{-1}$	Initial cost, $\$\,kw^{-1}$	Fuel cost, cents kwh^{-1}	Total cost, cents kwh^{-1}
Separate[19,20] reformer-fuel cell	Decane	$C_{10}H_{22} + 20H_2O \rightarrow 10CO_2 + 31H_2$	1.2	0.11	0.34	25	3.3	1.98	130	0.55	2.26
Separate[21] reformer-fuel cell	Methanol	$CH_3OH + H_2O \rightarrow CO_2 + 3H_2$	1.2	0.10	0.25	35	2.5	0.69	150	6.12	7.77
Separate[22] reformer-fuel cell	Natural gas	$CH_4 + 2H_2O \rightarrow CO_2 + 4H_2$	1.2	0.05	0.21	25	2.0	1.35	300	0.53	4.48
Integrated[23] reformer-fuel cell	Octane	$C_8H_{18} + 16H_2O \rightarrow 8CO_2 + 25H_2$	1.2	0.06	0.42	40	4.5	2.45	200	1.39	4.03
Internal[23b] reformer-fuel cell	Natural gas	$CH_9 + 2H_2O \rightarrow CO_2 + 4H_2$	1.2	0.15	0.25	10	1.0	1.61	200	0.44	3.08

the indirect method.   Of the indirect methods, the integrated reformer-fuel cell should help in reducing the size of the system.   These considerations would, of course, be radically altered if it were possible to develop new nonnoble metal catalysts for the direct electrochemical oxidation of organic compounds.   Research here is inadequate.   It seems that investigation of catalytic electrodes having chelating organic films, together with the use of organic semiconductors, give the best possibility (Chap. 6, Sec. 5).

5.3 Energy Conversion by Conventional and Electrochemical Methods Using Organic Fuels

Considerations of power/weight and power/volume ratios show that the conventional methods have better performances (Table 5) than the electrochemical methods (Tables 2 and 4) in their present state of development (which corresponds to less than 10 years extensive research).   The efficiencies of the electrochemical methods are, however, higher (Tables 2 and 4).   The total costs per kilowatthour of the electrochemical methods, though higher, are comparable with those of the conventional methods.   A careful comparison of Tables 3 and 5 shows that conservatively projected fuel-cell performances are considerably better than the older conventional methods in respect to efficiency, energy per weight of fuel, fuel cost per kilowatthour, and total cost per kilowatthour.

Electrochemical engines are today what conventional engines were 50 years ago.   An increase in electrocatalysis of only to two three times in terms of exchange current density is needed, whereupon the fuel cell would easily surpass the conventional engines in all comparison parameters except for power per unit weight.   On the other hand, since conventional engines have been subject to extensive research, indeed, for more than 50 years, the percentage improvements to be expected are relatively small.   The other advantages of fuel cells over conventional systems are given in Chap. 1.

5.4 Organic versus Inorganic Fuels in Electrochemical Energy Conversion

At the present time, the power densities of electrochemical energy converters using inorganic fuels (Table 6) are about an order of magnitude better than those using organic fuels directly (Table 2).   The separate reformer-fuel-cell combination has a performance (Table 4) comparable with converters using inorganic fuels.   Power/weight and power/volume ratios of cells using inorganic fuels are also superior to those of organic fuel-cell systems.   Efficiencies of reformer-fuel cells are comparable with those of inorganic systems.   The advantages of organic systems are mainly connected with the cost of the fuel. The lower cost of fuel reduces both the fuel cost per kilowatthour as well as the total cost per kilowatthour.   In spite of the better performances of the inorganic systems (e.g., hydrogen-oxygen) and the low initial cost for these systems, total costs per kilowatthour of these inorganic systems (with the exception of the

TABLE 5 Performance Characteristics of Conventional Engines Using Organic Fuels

Type of engine	Efficiency	Power/weight, kw lb⁻¹	Power/volume, kw ft⁻³	Energy/weight of fuel, kwh lb⁻¹	Initial cost, $ kw⁻¹	Fuel cost, cents kwh⁻¹	Total cost, cents kwh⁻¹
Internal combustion[24]	0.27	0.224	5.22	1.641	4	1.485	1.538
Gas turbine[24]	0.28	0.746	52.19	1.702	34	1.432	1.880
Diesel engine[24]	0.42	0.075	5.22	2.338	4	0.464	0.517
Engine generator[25]	0.35			1.948	146	0.557	2.484

TABLE 6 Performance Characteristics of Fuel Cells Using Inorganic Fuels

Fuel	Fuel-cell reaction	Temp., °C	$E°$, volts	Maximum power density, watts cm⁻²	Voltage efficiency	Power/weight, watts lb⁻¹	Power/volume, kw ft⁻³	Energy/weight of fuel, kwh lb⁻¹	Initial cost, $ kw⁻¹	Fuel cost, cents kwh⁻¹	Total cost, cents kwh⁻¹
Hydrogen[26]	$H_2 + \tfrac{1}{2}O_2 \rightarrow H_2O$	60	1.23	0.10	0.62	45	7.5	9.27	75	3.78	4.78
Hydrogen[27]	$H_2 + \tfrac{1}{2}O_2 \rightarrow H_2O$	60	1.23	0.17	0.69	50	8.2	10.26	44	3.41	3.99
Hydrogen[28]	$H_2 + \tfrac{1}{2}O_2 \rightarrow H_2O$	67	1.23	0.15	0.368	17	6.89	5.44	72	6.43	7.38
Hydrogen[29]	$H_2 + \tfrac{1}{2}O_2 \rightarrow H_2O$	250	1.23	0.39	0.75	55	17.23	10.86	35	3.14	3.61
Hydrogen[29a]	$H_2 + \tfrac{1}{2}O_2 \rightarrow H_2O$	25	1.23	0.06	0.52	15	4	7.71	120	4.54	6.12
Ammonia[30]	$4NH_3 + 3O_2 \rightarrow 2N_2 + 6H_2O$	300	1.14	0.05	0.44	9	2.2	1.43	150	3.73	5.71
Hydrazine[31]	$N_2H_4 + O_2 \rightarrow N_2 + 2H_2O$	70	1.56	0.25	0.38	35	11.2	0.89	30	104.23	104.63
Lithium[32]	$Li + \tfrac{1}{2}Cl_2 \rightarrow LiCl$	625	3.5	15.5	0.51	2,350	691	3.16			

hydrazine-air system) are of the same order as those for fuel cells using organic systems directly or reformer-fuel cells.

With respect to the position of hydrogen, this gas is produced on a large scale by reforming or partial combustion of natural gas. Thus, hydrogen-air fuel cells must more appropriately be classified under fuel cells using organic fuels indirectly. Conversely, the production of hydrogen from seawater on a very large scale at atomic power stations and its piping to factories and houses would introduce "true" hydrogen-air fuel cells. The economic possibilities here depend on whether tungsten bronzes or other cheap catalysts can be used satisfactorily.

6 BASIC STEPS IN THE MECHANISM OF DIRECT ELECTROCHEMICAL OXIDATION OF ORGANIC COMPOUNDS

6.1 General

The basic steps in the electrochemical oxidation of organic compounds are: (1) dissolution of the fuel (either gas or liquid) in the electrolyte; (2) diffusion of dissolved fuel to (and into) the electrode; (3) adsorption of fuel on the electrode; (4) electrochemical oxidation of adsorbed fuel; and (5) diffusion of products of reaction away from the electrode.

A number of potential electroorganic fuels (e.g., hydrocarbons) have low solubilities (solubility less than 10^{-4} mole l^{-1}) in the electrolyte. A knowledge of their solubilities is required for an understanding of the transport processes occurring at the fuel-cell anodes. For example, the limiting current density for the oxidation of a hydrocarbon on a planar electrode is given by

$$i_L = \frac{DnFc_0}{\delta}. \tag{6.1}$$

where c_0 is the concentration of the organic compound in the electrolyte, D is its diffusion coefficient, n is the number of electrons transferred in the overall reaction, and δ is the diffusion-layer thickness (Chap. 2, Sec. 3.7). Since the solubilities of hydrocarbons are fairly low, the limiting currents for their oxidations would also be low ($<10^{-4}$ amp cm^{-2}) if planar electrodes are used. However, by altering the structure of the electrode, e.g., by introducing into its pores, the diffusion-layer thickness may be decreased and, in addition, the area of the reaction zone per unit area of external surface may be considerably increased. Due to the importance of mass transport in porous electrodes used in electrochemical energy conversion, this subject was dealt with in detail in Chap. 5. The other steps, characteristic of electroorganic oxidation, will be dealt with in the following subsections. Study of step (4) involves knowledge of the rate-determining step in the overall reaction. This aspect is dealt with in Sec. 7.

6.2 Solubilities of Organic Compounds

There is little data on the solubilities of organic compounds in aqueous acid and alkaline media, the electrolytes normally used in low- and intermediate-temperature fuel cells. The solubility of organic compounds in molten electrolytes (e.g., carbonates) is even less known. Generally, gases are less soluble in aqueous solutions of electrolytes than in pure water owing to the phenomenon of the "salting out" effect.[33] The variation of the gas solubility s with concentration of the electrolyte c_e is given by the Setschenow equation[34]

$$\log \frac{s}{s_0} = k_s c_e \tag{6.2}$$

where s_0 is the solubility of the gas in pure water and k_s is the salting out parameter. Equation (6.2) holds if the solubility is low as it is for gases in the electrolyte or water. For high and moderate solubilities of gases in the electrolyte, the equation[33]

$$\log \frac{s}{s_0} = k_s c_e + k_g (s - s_0) \tag{6.3}$$

is found to give better agreement than Eq. (6.2). In Eq. (6.3), k_g is the non-electrolyte self-interaction parameter.

The decrease of solubility of an organic compound in water upon addition of electrolyte may be comprehended in the following manner. Before the addition of the electrolyte, all the water molecules in solution are available for interaction with the organic compound and hence its dissolution. But after the addition of the electrolyte, a number of water molecules are bound in the hydration sheaths of ions of the electrolyte. Hence, there are a lesser number of water molecules for interaction with molecules of the organic compounds and its solubility is thus decreased.

There is sometimes a converse phenomenon of salting in, whereby the solubility of an organic compound increases with addition of electrolyte. From the above discussion of the salting-out effect, it follows that salting in occurs when the interaction of molecules of the organic compound with ions of the electrolyte is greater than that of water molecules with the ions.[35]

Some generalizations concerning the solubilities of organic compounds in water arise from the work of Hildebrand.[36] These should also apply in aqueous solutions for slightly polar or nonpolar solutes, since there is hardly any interaction between the solute and ions of the electrolyte. The solubilities of compounds depend on solvent-solvent, solvent-solute, and solute-solute interactions. Thus, the organic compounds that are soluble in water, at least to an appreciable extent (say greater than 1 percent), are those that have a polar group and can form hydrogen bonds with water. Examples are alcohols, aldehydes, ketones, acids, ethers, esters, amines, and nitriles. The extent of solubility depends on the number of polar groups as well as the length of the hydrocarbon chain present in the molecule of the organic compound.   The foregoing statement may be exemplified by the fact that methanol is quite soluble, whereas butanol is only sparingly soluble in water.   Compounds that cannot form hydrogen bonds, e.g., hydrocarbons and halogenated hydrocarbons, are only sparingly soluble in water (less than 10^{-4} mole l^{-1}).   The solubilities of some of these compounds, e.g., ethylene, are of the order of solubilities of gases like hydrogen, oxygen, nitrogen, etc.   The solubilities of compounds in a homologous series decrease with increase in molecular weight.

For two compounds with the same heat of fusion, the one with the higher melting point would be expected from the theory of ideal solutions to have the lower solubility; and if two compounds have the same melting point, the one with the higher heat of fusion is less soluble.

With increasing interest in electrochemical energy conversion using organic fuels, some work has been carried out to determine the solubilities of hydrocarbons in various electrolytes.[37,38]   The solubilities of ethane and propane in aqueous solutions of sulfuric and of phosphoric acid (2N and 4N) are shown in Figs. 2 and 3 at temperatures from 25 to 70° at gas partial pressures of 1 and

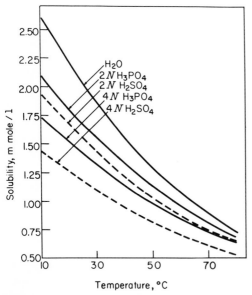

Figure 2   Solubility of ethane in water and in aqueous H_2SO_4 and H_3PO_4 as a function of temperature.[37]

2 atm.[37]   For comparison, the solubilities of these gases in water are also plotted in each diagram.   It is seen that at higher temperatures, the solubilities of these gases in each of the acids approach those for pure water.   Further, the

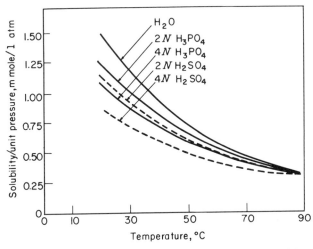

Figure 3 Solubility of propane in water and in aqueous H_2SO_4 and H_3PO_4 as a function of temperature.[37]

solubilities are higher in phosphoric acid than in sulfuric acid. Solubilities of propane in higher concentrations of phosphoric acid (90 to 100 percent) and over a wider range of temperatures (25 to 170°C) have been determined[38] (Table 7). It was found that the solubility of propane in these high concentrations of phosphoric acid at 25°C is about one-eighth that in pure water.

TABLE 7 Solubility of Propane in the Phosphoric Acid–Water Systems at Various Temperatures[38]

Temperature, °C	Weight, % H_3PO_4	Solubility, millimoles l^{-1}, 8 atm propane
25	85.8	0.229
66	96.6	0.164
100	89.1	0.192
100	93.2	0.179
100	96.2	0.173
130	97.3	0.168
130	97.6	0.154
150	96.8	0.180
150	96.7	0.189
170	99.3	0.165

Further, the solubilities in these high concentrations are relatively insensitive to temperature. The solubility of octane in phosphoric acid is about one-tenth that of propane at elevated temperatures (Table 8).[38]

Diffusion coefficients of organic fuels in an electrolyte vary little with the

TABLE 8   Solubility of Octane in the Phosphoric Acid–Water Systems at Various Temperatures[38]

Temperature, °C	Weight, % H_3PO_4	Partial pressure octane, mm Hg	Solubility, millimoles l^{-1}
130	85.2	100	0.000557
130	85.2	200	0.000978
130	85.2	300	0.00175
130	85.2	400	0.00182
150	93.1	435	0.0163
150	93.4	250	0.00706
150	93.4	357	0.00755
150	94.2	564	0.00679
170	94.6	400	0.00308

fuel.   Viscosity changes of the solution affect the diffusion-layer thickness δ only slightly.   Thus, for the same type of electrode construction, the order of limiting currents per electron transferred in the overall reaction for a series of organic compounds in the same fluid state should roughly follow the same order as their solubilities.   Deviations from this rule may be caused by differences of mass-transfer phenomena for the fuels in question.

6.3   Electroadsorption of Organic Compounds on Metals from Solution

6.3.1   General

Most of the work on the adsorption of organic compounds from solution has been carried out on mercury.   Frumkin[39] was the first to point out a similarity between adsorption of organic compounds at the metal-solution interface and at the air-water interface, i.e., adsorption of an organic compound containing a polar group occurs in such a way that the polar group is oriented toward the solution and the hydrocarbon end is toward the air or metal.   There are some differences between the two types, e.g., thiourea is inactive at the air-water interface but is adsorbed at the metal-solution interface.   Investigations on the adsorption of organic compounds on solid electrodes have been undertaken only recently.   The methods used to determine the extent of adsorption of organic compounds on solid electrodes are discussed in Chap. 9.

The vital role played by adsorption of organic solutes on solid electrodes was not realized by workers in the field of electrochemical energy conversion using organic fuels until the early sixties.   Thermodynamic conditions may thus be well satisfied for the electrooxidation of an organic compound in a fuel cell, and even relatively rapid rate constants may be indicated for the oxidation process; but if the substance is not adsorbed on the electrode, there can be no reaction.   The knowledge of the region of adsorption of the organic fuel on the catalyst is essential to its characterization.   Because the adsorption of organic compounds is generally related in degree to the determination of the potential of zero charge (Chap. 6, Sec. 3.5.2), there is a considerable need for the extension of data in this little-studied area.

In the following summary of present knowledge concerning adsorption of organic compounds, the assumption is that the adsorption is nondissociative. There seems to be much evidence of this for adsorption of organic materials on mercury. On solid electrodes, the situation is less ascertained. Without any doubt, the mechanism of all organic oxidation reactions involves the dissociation of the organic molecules into a number of fragments which are immediately adsorbed on the electrode surface. These are intermediates in the series of consecutive reactions, which lead from the organic molecule and water molecules to CO_2 and electrons. The question is: Do these radical reactions begin with

an adsorbed *radical* (for example, $-\overset{\displaystyle\diagdown}{\underset{\displaystyle\diagup}{C}}-OH$, formed from a discharge *reaction*,

$CH_3OH \rightarrow -\overset{\displaystyle\diagdown}{\underset{\displaystyle\diagup}{C}}-OH + 3H^+ + 3e_0^-$), or do they originate from *molecules*

adsorbed on the surface, which then react to give radicals and finally CO_2? (This topic is discussed in Sec. 6.3.5.)

6.3.2 Special Features of Adsorption of Organic Compounds from Solution

Unlike the comparatively new field of organic adsorption from solution, adsorption of organic compounds on metals from the gas phase has been extensively studied. It is worthwhile comparing distinctive features of adsorption of organic compound from solution and from the gas phase.

(*i*) Adsorption of organic compounds from the gas phase takes place on the free surface of metals. Adsorption from solution takes place by displacement of water molecules on the electrode by molecules of the organic compound and is essentially a replacement reaction of the type

$$R_{soln} + nH_2O_{ads} \rightleftarrows R_{ads} + nH_2O_{soln} \qquad (6.4)$$

R represents the organic and n is the number of molecules of water adsorbed on the electrode which one molecule of R replaces. The observed thermodynamic properties (free energy, entropy, and enthalpy of adsorption) are thus those for the above displacement reaction. The apparent values of these thermodynamic properties should thus be less than the corresponding values for adsorption of organic compounds from the gas phase essentially because the desorption of the water molecule tends to compensate for the adsorption of the organic molecule.

(*ii*) An important physical property determining the adsorption of organic compounds from solution is the solubility of the compound. In general, the less soluble compound is more adsorbable, as was first observed in the work of Blomgren et al.,[40] who found a linear relationship between the standard free energy of adsorption and the free energy of solvation within each class of several organic compounds (Fig. 4). Furthermore, in more recent work,[41] it was found that the extent of adsorption of butanol and phenol was higher from aqueous than from methanolic solutions, which is clearly because of the higher solubility of these compounds in the methanolic solvent.

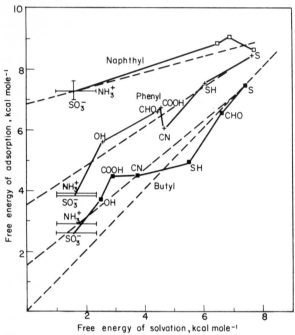

Figure 4   Dependence of standard free energy of adsorption on free energy of solvation for some organic compounds.[40]

(*iii*) The most significant distinctive feature of adsorption of organic compounds from solution is its potential dependence. A plot of the extent of adsorption as a function of the potential is generally parabolic (Fig. 5), and the adsorption maximum is often situated at potentials cathodic to the point of zero charge. The region of potential over which adsorption of the organic compound takes place is important from the point of view of the usefulness of the compound in electrochemical energy conversion. The region of adsorption of $0.1 < \theta < 0.9$, say, should be largely anodic to the reversible potential for the oxidation and by an amount, with respect to the maximum, which corresponds to the overpotential at the current density concerned. [The variation of potential due to *IR* drop in a porous electrode (Chap. 5, Secs. 5–7) is of importance here.]

6.3.3   Experimental Data on Electrosorption of Organic Fuels

A detailed work on the electrosorption of an organic compound of interest to fuel cells is that of ethylene on platinum.[42] A radiotracer method was used to determine the coverage-potential relationship at a series of temperatures. The

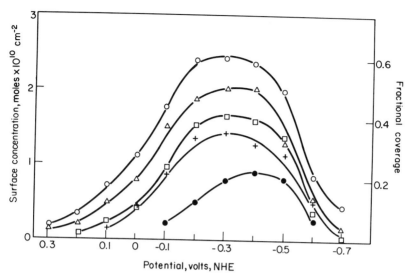

Figure 5 Adsorption of naphthalene on platinum from 0.9 N NaClO$_4$ + 0.1 N NaOH as a function of potential and concentration at 25°C. ○, 10^{-4}; △, 5 × 10^{-5}; □, 10^{-5}; +, 5 × 10^{-6}; ●, 2.5 × 10^{-6} mole/l naphthalene.[44]

roughness factors were determined by the capacitance method. Adsorption measurements at any one temperature were carried out with increasing and decreasing anodic potentials to test the reversibility of adsorption. Adsorption isotherms were obtained at each potential by adding varying amounts of ethylene after adsorption equilibrium at any one concentration was reached. The time-dependence of the adsorption was also measured.

The variations of surface concentration of ethylene with potential for five values of its bulk concentration are given in Fig. 6. Measurements at more cathodic potentials are not possible because of hydrogen evolution, and at more anodic potentials they are prevented by oxidation of the hydrocarbon. It is assumed that ethylene requires a four-site adsorption, and hence the maximum coverage is 6 × 10^{-10} mole cm^{-2} of real surface area. At higher concentrations of ethylene, the adsorption maximum occurs at 0.40 volt (NHE), and the value of this potential extrapolated to zero coverage is 0.46 volt.

Figure 7 shows the adsorption isotherms (potential 0.4 volt) at various temperatures. The adsorption isotherms at various potentials (temperature 30°C) are shown in Fig. 8. The shapes of the isotherms are not substantially affected by the potential. There is a rapid change of θ from zero to a saturation value (0.35 to 0.45) over a small concentration range of ethylene in solution.

The extrapolated value of the potential of zero charge (Chap. 2, Sec. 2) at a pH of 0.5 (1 N H$_2$SO$_4$) is 0.63 volt (NHE). The position of the potential of maximum adsorption with respect to the potential of zero charge is consistent with results of electrosorption of other organic compounds.

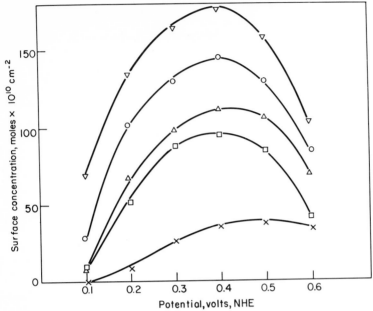

Figure 6   Adsorption of ethylene on platinum from 1 N H_2SO_4 as a function of potential for various bulk concentrations of ethylene at 30°C. $\triangledown$, 1.7 × 10^{-5}; $\bigcirc$, 9.1 × 10^{-6}; $\triangle$, 4.6 × 10^{-6}; $\square$, 4.0 × 10^{-6};   ×, 2.1 × 10^{-6} mole/l ethylene.[42]

The maximum degree of coverage is between 0.35 and 0.45.   Probable reasons for the departure of this value from unity are the presence of inactive sites or the large size of the ethylene molecule, which require the presence of four adjacent free sites on the metal.

A comparative study of the coverages of various saturated and unsaturated hydrocarbons on platinized platinum (Fig. 9) was made by Niedrach[43] using

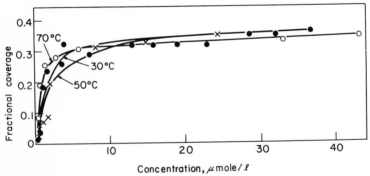

Figure 7   Ethylene adsorption isotherms on platinum from 1 N H_2SO_4 at a potential of 0.4 volt (NHE) for various temperatures.[42]

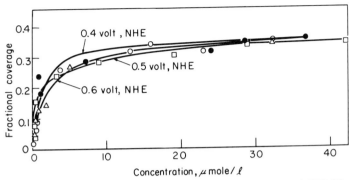

Figure 8 Ethylene adsorption isotherms on platinum from $1\,N\,H_2SO_4$ at 30°C for various potentials.[42]

galvanostatic techniques (Chap. 9, Sec. 4). It was found that (1) methane adsorbs to a very small extent; (2) ethane and propane are adsorbed to a considerably greater extent than methane in acid medium; (3) the adsorption of ethylene exceeds that of any other hydrocarbon; (4) cyclopropane adsorbs to a slightly lesser extent than ethylene; (5) in alkaline solutions the adsorption of all the compounds except the unsaturated hydrocarbons occurs to a considerably lesser extent; (6) in the galvanostatic charging curves observed on the

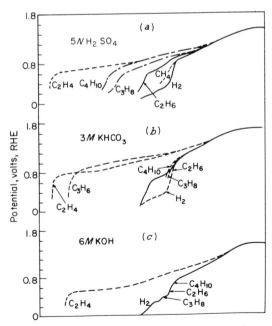

Figure 9 Galvanostatic oxidation curves for hydrocarbons adsorbed on platinum black electrodes at 25°C in (a) $5\,N\,H_2SO_4$, (b) $3\,M\,KHCO_3$, and (c) $6\,M\,KOH$.[43]

saturated hydrocarbons, an initial break is observed in the range of 0.2 to 0.3 volt (NHE).

Volumetric measurements of gas adsorbed were found to be consistent with the galvanostatic measurements[43] (Fig. 10).

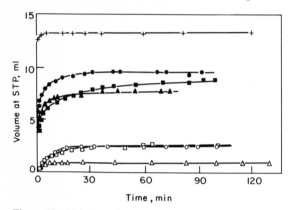

Figure 10 Volumes of gases adsorbed on platinum black electrodes during equilibration from 5 N H_2SO_4 at 25°C. +, H_2; $\triangle$, CH_4; $\bigcirc$, C_2H_6; $\square$, C_3H_8; ●, C_2H_4; ▲, C_3H_8; ■, C_3H_6 (cyclopropane).[43]

6.3.4 The Dependence of Organic Adsorption on Potential

6.3.4.1 Free Energy of Adsorption of Organic Compound. Since adsorption of an organic compound at the metal-solution interface can be considered as a replacement reaction, it may be represented by Eq. (6.4) (page 373). The standard free energy of adsorption (ΔG_a^0) for this reaction may be represented by

$$\Delta G_a^0 = -RT \ln \frac{X_{org,ads} X_{w,soln}^n}{X_{org,soln} X_{w,ads}^n} \tag{6.5}$$

where X represents the mole fractions of the indicated species.

For dilute solutions, $X_{w,soln} = 1$ and $X_{org,soln} = c_{org}/55.4$ (55.4 is the molar concentration of water in a liter of solution). Also

$$X_{org,ads} = \frac{\theta}{\theta + n(1 - \theta)} \quad \text{and} \quad X_{w,ads} = \frac{n(1 - \theta)}{\theta + n(1 - \theta)} \tag{6.6}$$

therefore

$$\Delta G_a^0 = -2.303RT \log \frac{55.4\theta}{c_{org}} \frac{[\theta + n(1 - \theta)]^{n-1}}{(1 - \theta)^n n^n} \tag{6.7}$$

Transforming the above equation results in the following adsorption isotherm:[44]

$$\frac{\theta}{(1 - \theta)^n} \frac{[\theta + n(1 - \theta)]^{n-1}}{n^n} = \frac{c_{org}}{55.4} \exp\left(-\frac{\Delta G_a^0}{RT}\right) \tag{6.8}$$

If $n = 1$ in this equation, the familiar Langmuir isotherm results.

It follows that the standard free energy of adsorption of an organic compound from solution should be less than that from the gas phase, since in the former case, the measured free energy of adsorption represents the difference in free energies of adsorption of the organic and n water molecules. The same holds true for the enthalpy and entropy of adsorption.

The theoretical analysis becomes more difficult if adsorption occurs under Temkin conditions (Chap. 2, Sec. 5.2), but in most cases Langmuir conditions apply for organic adsorption.[44a]

6.3.4.2 Relation of Standard Free Energy of Adsorption to Solubility of Organic Compound.

By using the Born-Haber cycles for the adsorption of water and of the organic, it can be easily shown[44] that

$$\Delta G_a^0 = RT \ln \frac{c_s}{55.4} - RT \ln \frac{P_{org}}{P_w^{\ n}} + \Delta G_{v,org}^0 - n \Delta G_{v,w}^0 \tag{6.9}$$

where c_s is the saturation concentration of the organic, P_{org} and P_w are the vapor pressures of pure organic and of pure water at temperature T, and $\Delta G_{v,w}^0$ and $\Delta G_{v,org}$ are the standard free energies of adsorption from the gas phase.

Equations (6.7) and (6.9) show that for a given concentration of the organic compound, the amount of adsorption increases with decrease of solubility of the compound—a result which is in agreement with experiment.[40]

6.3.4.3 Effect of Electric Field on Adsorption of Undissociated Organic Compounds.

Any theory of the dependence of organic adsorption on the electric variable has to be consistent with the following facts: (1) The coverage-charge relations are parabolic, and (2) the potential of maximum adsorption is usually somewhat negative to the potential of zero charge for organic compounds which do not themselves interact with the electrode's field.

It was pointed out in Chap. 2, Sec. 2, that the charge on the metal is a more fundamental variable than the potential difference across the metal-solution interface. An example of this advantage is seen if the coverage of an electrode with an organic substance is plotted against potential and charge[45] (Fig. 11).

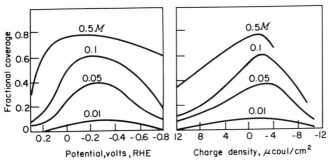

Figure 11 Coverage vs. potential and charge density on the electrode[45] for adsorption of *n*-butyl alcohol, at different concentrations, on mercury in 0.1 *M* hydrochloric acid at 25°C.

The θ-q plots have a symmetrical shape, and the maximum coverage occurs at the same charge and is independent of the concentration of the organic species in solution as well as the organic compound in a number of cases, whereas the θ-V plots are more complex in shape.

The first theory of the dependence of organic adsorption on the electric variable was proposed by Frumkin.[46]   This theory is concerned with the energy change arising as a result of the change in capacity consequent upon adsorption. It deals in essence with changes in the thickness and dielectric constant of the double layer.   It does not deal with the situation at a molecular level nor does it account for the influence of the solvent and its electrical properties on the shape of the θ-q curves.   No calculations of an absolute kind can be made from it.   It is, of course, absolutely correct, but it is relatively unhelpful in understanding nondissociative adsorption.

Butler[47] considered the adsorption reaction as a replacement of the adsorbed water by the organic compound.   It was assumed in this theory that the work of inducing a dipole moment on the adsorbing organic compound ($\Delta\alpha X^2/2$) is of the same order as the energy change required to transfer the polar molecule of dipole moment μ from the solution where the field $X = 0$ to the compact layer where there is a field X. For this assumption to be correct, $\frac{1}{2}(\Delta\alpha)X^2$ should be of the same order as $(\Delta\mu)X$, where $\Delta\alpha$ and $\Delta\mu$ are the differences of polarizabilities and of dipole moments of the organic and water molecules and X is the electric field strength at the interface.   To obtain α, a value of ϵ corresponding to the *bulk* value was used in the equation

$$\alpha = \frac{\epsilon - 1}{4\pi} \tag{6.10}$$

This value of ϵ is inapplicable because the water structure at the surface differs from that in the bulk and the appropriate dielectric constant is approximately an order of magnitude less than this value.   Further, even if the correct values of ϵ are used, values of α obtained from Eq. (6.10) are in sharp disagreement with those obtained experimentally.

In fact, exact calculations of the term $\Delta\alpha X^2/2$ show that for values of field strengths corresponding to those of practical range, the term has a very small or negligible effect on the energy of adsorption of organic compounds so long as real values of α [not those from Eq. (6.10)] are used.   This necessitates a *radical revision* of the theory of the potential dependence of adsorption of organic compounds, because the principal feature which any theory has to explain is that there is an approximately *symmetrical parabolic relation* between the extent of adsorption and the corresponding potential.   In earlier theories, the parabolic shape of the coverage-potential plot was interpreted on the basis of the term $\Delta\alpha X^2/2$, which does not change sign with field and would lead to an increase in the attraction of water to the electrode surface and hence a decrease in the occupancy by organic species on *both* sides of the maximum of the adsorption-potential relation.   But this term is found to be far too small, so long as correct values of α are used, and theories based on it therefore cannot be accepted.

This dilemma was avoided in the theory of Bockris, Devanathan, and Müller.[45] In this theory, attention was focused on the dipolar characteristics of water molecules at the electrode-solution interfaces. Properties of water on electrodes have previously been considered[48,49] in electrode kinetic and double-layer studies. More recently, attention was drawn to the probable importance of the dipole nature of water on the double-layer-capacitance-vs.-potential relation[50] (Chap. 2, Sec. 2). The theory of Bockris, Devanathan, and Müller is based on the fact that on the positive side of the potential of zero charge, water molecules are adsorbed on the electrode with their oxygen atoms oriented preferentially towards the metal, whereas on the negative side of the potential of zero charge, the hydrogen atoms are directed towards the metal. Due to electrostatic forces, the attraction of water molecules by the electrode increases with electrode charge (either positive or negative) and hence with departure of potential from the potential of zero charge, *both in the positive and negative directions.* With increasing attraction of water molecules towards the electrodes, molecules of the organic compound are rejected from the surface. Hence, one could expect maximum adsorption of organic compounds at the potential of zero charge, with the extent of adsorption steadily decreasing symmetrically on either side of this potential. Chemibonding of water or of the organic compound causes a dissymmetry in its coverage-potential relation and also a slight shift in the adsorption maximum from the potential of zero charge.

Expressions for the dependence of coverage of the organic on the electric variable may be derived for the cases of absence and presence of lateral interactions, as shown below.

(i) Absence of lateral interaction

The standard electrochemical free energy of water on an electrode is

$$\Delta \bar{G}_w{}^0 = \Delta G_w{}^0 + \frac{N_\downarrow}{N_T} \mu X - \frac{N_\downarrow}{N_T} \mu X \tag{6.11}$$

where $N_\uparrow$ and $N_\downarrow$ are the numbers of water molecules oriented in the two possible orientations of the dipoles parallel to the field; $N_T = N_\uparrow + N_\downarrow$; X is the field at the center of the water dipole; and $\Delta G_w{}^0$ is the chemical part of the free energy.

Let the adsorption of one molecule of organic displace n adsorbed water molecules. Thus

$$\Delta \bar{G}^0_{ads} = \Delta G^0_{ads} - \frac{n\mu X(N_\uparrow - N_\downarrow)}{N_T} \tag{6.12}$$

Hence, the isotherm is given by

$$\frac{\theta_{org}}{1 - \theta_{org}} = \frac{c_{org}}{c_w} \exp\left(-\frac{\Delta G^0_{ads}}{RT}\right) \exp\left[-\frac{n\mu X}{RT}\frac{(N_\uparrow - N_\downarrow)}{N_T}\right] \tag{6.13}$$

The variation of θ with charge q_m ($X = 4\pi q_m/\epsilon$) according to Eq. (6.13) is of the right shape as observed.

(ii)   Presence of lateral interaction

Under these conditions:

$$\Delta \bar{G}^0_{\text{ads}} = \frac{N_\uparrow}{N_T}\left[\mu X - \left(\frac{N_\uparrow}{N_T} - \frac{N_\downarrow}{N_T}\right)Ec\right] + \frac{N_\downarrow}{N_T}\left[-\mu X + \left(\frac{N_\uparrow}{N_T} - \frac{N_\downarrow}{N_T}\right)Ec\right] + \Delta G^0_{\text{ads}}$$

$$= \frac{N_\uparrow - N_\downarrow}{N_T}\left\{\mu X\left[1 - \left(\frac{N_\uparrow - N_\downarrow}{N_T}\right)X\right]Ec\right\} + \Delta G^0 \tag{6.14}$$

Hence

$$\frac{\theta_{\text{org}}}{1 - \theta_{\text{org}}} = \frac{c_{\text{org}}}{c_w}\exp\left(-\frac{\Delta G^0_{\text{ads}}}{RT}\right)\exp\left[-nR\left(\mu X - \frac{RE}{kT}c\right)\right] \tag{6.15}$$

where $R = (N_\uparrow - N_\downarrow)/N_T$; E is the interaction energy between two adsorbed parallel water molecules; and c is the coordination number of an adsorbed water molecule.

A plot of θ versus q_m ($X = 4\pi q_m/\epsilon$) according to Eq. (6.15) is in good agreement with experiment. The theoretical curve shows a maximum at $q_m = 0$, whereas the experimental curves show a maximum at slightly negative charges on the metal (i.e., around $q_m = -2\mu\text{coul cm}^{-2}$).[45] The reason for this discrepancy is probably the greater image force interaction of the water with the metal surface when the oxygen atom is nearer to the metal.

The maximum adsorption should occur when $N_\uparrow = N_\downarrow$ (thus, $R = 0$) and when the energies of the water molecules in the *two* possible orientations are equal,[44] that is,

$$\bar{E}_\uparrow = E_\uparrow + \mu X - RcE \tag{6.16}$$
$$\bar{E}_\downarrow = E_\downarrow - \mu X + RcE \tag{6.17}$$

that is,

$$\bar{E}_\uparrow = \bar{E}_\downarrow \tag{6.18}$$
$$E_\uparrow + \mu X = E_\downarrow - \mu X \tag{6.19}$$

therefore

$$E_\uparrow - E_\downarrow = -2\mu X = -\frac{8\pi q_m}{\epsilon} \tag{6.20}$$

Thus, the energy difference between two water molecules oriented in opposite directions can be calculated from the charge at which the coverage of an organic compound, which has negligible interaction with the field, is a maximum. Equation (6.20) also shows that the maximum adsorption should occur at a constant charge, independent of the compound, concentration, or type of isotherm.

According to the theory, in the absence of chemisorption of water, the difference in the non-field-dependent energy of the water molecule in the two possible orientations arises because of the image interaction energy differences in these two orientations. This difference is due to the center of the water dipole not coinciding with the center of the molecule, but it is not sufficient to account for the observed values of displacement of the potential of the adsorption maximum from that of the potential of zero charge for solid metals (ΔV^0). The observed variation of ΔV^0 with the metal, not expected on image interactions alone, was explained by the contribution of the dispersion interaction energy differences of the water molecules in the two different orientations and by an additional asymmetry of the water molecule resulting from the surface dipole of the metal.[52] It is difficult to estimate the latter quantitatively.

The model is quite satisfactory in the case of adsorption of an organic compound which itself interacts only to a negligible extent with the electric field. However, in the case of adsorption of organic compounds which interact strongly with the field—e.g., thiourea adsorption on mercury—the presence of the adsorbent causes a change in the potential distribution in the double layer. This effect was considered in later theories,[41,51] but it is unimportant in the case of adsorption of aliphatic molecules.

6.3.4.4 Contributions to Standard Free Energy of Adsorption.

One of the more surprising facts about the adsorption of *n*-decylamine and of naphthalene on the metals Pt, Ni, Fe, Cu, and Pb is that the standard free energy of adsorption is hardly dependent on the metal or on the organic compound[44] ($-\Delta G^0_{\text{ads}} =$ 6 to 8 kcal mole^{-1}). This result appears unexpected because according to the proposed model, a naphthalene molecule replaces six water molecules whereas a *n*-decylamine molecule displaces only one water molecule.[52] These facts favor physical adsorption of the molecules concerned, and the free energy of adsorption is thus due to a difference in image and dispersion interactions of the organic compound and of water. For the calculation of the dispersion interactions, the expression

$$U_{\text{disp}} = \frac{\pi N_m C}{6R^3} \tag{6.21}$$

where

$$C = 6mc^2 \frac{\alpha_1 \alpha_2}{\alpha_1/\chi_1 + \alpha_2/\chi_2} \tag{6.22}$$

was used. N_m is the number of metal atoms per cubic centimeter; R is the distance between the center of the molecule (organic compound or water) and the surface of the metal; m is the mass of the electron; c is the velocity of light; and χ_1 and χ_2 are the diamagnetic susceptibilities of the water and the metal, respectively.

The calculation of the image interaction was carried out using the equation

$$U_{\text{image}} = -\frac{\mu^2}{8r^3} \tag{6.23}$$

where r is the distance from the center of the dipole to the surface of the metal.

The conclusion that physical adsorption prevails in the case of naphthalene and of *n*-decylamine on several solid electrodes is based largely on the fact that apart from dispersion and image interactions, the interaction energy between the metal and organic compound in the case of the five metals is low. This conclusion cannot be considered to be of a general nature in the case of electrosorption of other organic compounds on metals.   An example where this does not hold is in the electrosorption of benzene on platinum,[53] where a chemisorption mechanism is applicable in the more anodic part of the coverage-potential plot. It is necessary to carry out experimental work on the electrosorption of a variety of organic compounds on solid electrodes before some general theory can be evolved (see Sec. 6.3.5).

6.3.5   *The Solution-Catalyst Transition: Molecules in Equilibrium with the Solution or with the Charge-transfer Adsorption*

A degree of misunderstanding sometimes is present in the discussion of whether, in electroorganic reactions, there is adsorption of molecules which are in equilibrium with those solutions, or discharge of the organic molecules to form radicals on the surface of the catalyst. The misunderstanding arises because of the necessary presence on the electrode of radicals and/or intermediates in the oxidation sequences.   This is thought, sometimes wrongly, to favor a model of charge-transfer adsorption.   Radicals must, of course, be present.   The question is: Does the transfer of the molecule in solution to a position on the catalyst take place with or without dissociation?   A consequent question is: Are the adsorbed species undissociated fuel molecules or are they dissociation products of its adsorption in equilibrium with the fuel molecule in solution?

The nondissociative view is often assumed illogically, because it is true for adsorption on mercury.   Conversely, it seems equally illogical to assert that adsorption of an organic molecule on Pt must be dissociative.

(*i*) Thus there is no doubt that for Pt in contact with a propane containing H_3PO_4 solution at 120°C, an amount of electricity is transferred when the electrode is brought into contact with the solution which is consistent with the occurrence of the reaction (Fig. 12)[71]

$$C_3H_8 \rightleftharpoons C_3H_{7ads} + H^+ + e_0^- \tag{6.24}$$

Here *no* bell-shaped curve of coverage of organic species vs. potential is observed, although the fact is not quite as clear as one would like because the course of the θ-V relation is interrupted by phosphate-ion adsorption (Fig. 13).

(*ii*) However, if the radiotracer plots for benzene adsorption as a function of potential (Fig. 14) are compared with those obtained by coulometric electrochemical transient methods,[53a] assuming that the desorptive reaction of the adsorbed species C_6H_5 is

$$C_6H_5 + 12H_2O \rightarrow 6CO_2 + 29H^+ + 29e_0^- \tag{6.25}$$

then agreement is obtained up to a potential of about 0.50 volt.   Hence, in this less anodic region at least, benzene adsorbs undissociatively.   (The same conclusion has now been reached by Frumkin et al.[53b])

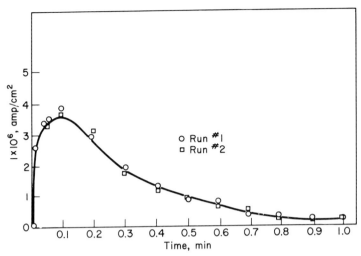

Figure 12 Initial current-time transients for the oxidation of propane on platinized-platinum electrodes[71] in H_3PO_4 at 120°C.

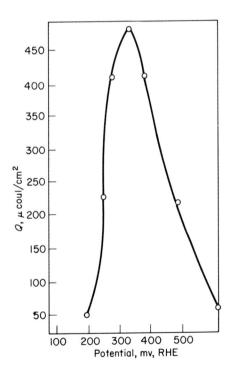

Figure 13 Dependence of adsorption of propane on a platinized-platinum electrode from a solution of H_3PO_4 containing propane on potential.[71]

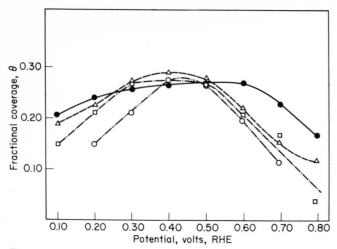

Figure 14 Potential dependence of electrosorption of benzene on Pt at 50°C.[53a] Comparaison of results by four techniques: ●, radiotracer, 1.1 μM; △, linear potential sweep, 1.4 μM; ○, potentiostatic, 1.1 μM; □, galvanostatic, 1.3 μM C_6H_6.

It seems that the *predominant* presence of molecules in equilibrium with solution as the adsorbed entity is indicated when there is an agreement of radiotracer measurements (which measure, of course, "carbon") and the transient electrochemical methods which measure the coulombs needed to burn off (as is usually assumed) the undissociated molecule.   When these two methods do not agree, the indication is that the substance principally adsorbed is a radical.   By determining the number of electrons n used in the overall reaction which have to be used to account for the coulombs needed to remove the adsorbed material from the surface, one can get information which (knowing the overall reaction) often brackets the number of possibilities for the predominant radical.†

It is relevant to inquire whether the bell-shaped dependence of coverage on potential (Fig. 15) has significance in the determination of the mode of adsorption.   This shape is very much the one expected [Sec. 6.3.4.3 (*ii*)] from the model of the variation of θ with V in terms of the change of the electrostatic-attraction energy of the electrode for the water dipoles which, in different positions of orientation, are always more attracted as the charge on the electrode increases or decreases with change of electrode potential.[41]   That such a shape

† Extensive use of this kind of approach had been earlier made by Brummer.[70]   Instead of using the radiotracer approach to indicate free surface, Brummer determined the cathodic charge needed to introduce sufficient H to fill the empty spaces when the adsorbents were present.   One may have to be cautious here concerning errors arising from diffusion into the metal, interaction of H_{ads} and the adsorbent, and the possibility of direct discharge of H^+ onto the adsorbed organic radicals, when present at higher concentrations.

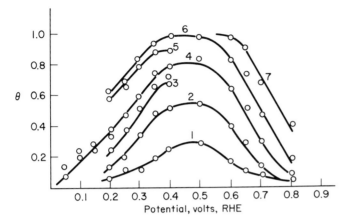

Figure 15 Dependence of coverage by methanol upon potential of a smooth Pt electrode in 1 N H_2SO_4 solution containing different concentrations of methanol.[75] (1) 10^{-3}; (2) 10^{-2}; (3) 5×10^{-2}; (4) 10^{-1}; (5) 5×10^{-1}; (6) 1; and (7) 5 mole l^{-1}.

is not consistent with a charge-transfer adsorption (even if in equilibrium) can easily be seen from elementary considerations,[53a] which give (Langmuir assumptions)

$$\theta = \frac{A \exp \{f(V)\}}{1 + B \exp \{(V)\}} \tag{6.26}$$

and hence an asymptotic value at V values much cathodic to the potential at which Pt forms an oxide in acid solutions.[53c]

Bell-shaped adsorption curves seem to indicate a predominant *molecular* adsorption (cf. conclusion for methanol on Pt[53b]). A corresponding conclusion, in the presence of such bell-shaped adsorption curves, is that the rate-determining step for the oxidation sequence following will be a reaction following the one in which a radical-forming dissociation from the adsorbed molecule occurs.

7 MECHANISMS OF SOME ELECTROORGANIC OXIDATION REACTIONS

7.1 General

7.1.1 Problems Involved in Mechanism Determination

Mechanism evaluations in the electrooxidation of organic compounds are, as expected, more complex than those of corresponding studies of inorganic reactions (e.g., hydrogen and oxygen evolution). The simple two-electron-transfer hydrogen-evolution reaction has taken thirty years of research by several groups (though before present knowledge was available) to be brought to the reasonably resolved position that now exists (Chap. 2, Sec. 10.1). There are some other difficulties as well in the case of electroorganic oxidation. For instance, parallel reactions may occur, which make the kinetic studies complex;[54] and because of the probability of a greater number of intermediate steps, the identification (both qualitative and quantitative) of intermediate species is not yet feasible in many cases, particularly for species that are involved after the rate-determining step.[55]

Conversely, there is a likelihood that elucidation of the mechanism of an electrochemical reaction involving an organic reactant may be easier than that of a chemical reaction involving the same reactant in the gas phase. Thus, as indicated earlier, there is a greater ease in experimental work and in information concerning surface coverage available from various pulse treatments, which has no parallel in the gas-phase measurements. There is, similarly, no parallel to the rate-potential relation, to which an electrochemical organic oxidation reaction gives rise.

In spite of these extra, powerful weapons, there is no doubt that the complete determination of the mechanism of an organic electrochemical reaction, even one as relatively simple as the oxidation of methanol to carbon dioxide, is very difficult.[55a] Two easements arise, which encourage one to contribute to the field. The first is an arbitrary limitation on what is called "mechanism determination." "Complete determination" would mean that one would attempt to elucidate the nature of each sequential step, from the adsorption from solution onto the electrode, to the desorption as CO_2. In the absence of better methods than are now available for the identification of intermediate radicals and the concentration of each, *this* is rather difficult. However, from the viewpoint of the needs of electrochemical energy conversion, there is much less need for knowledge of how the reaction proceeds *after* the rate-determining step. It is knowledge of *this* which influences the possibility of reducing the amount of costly empiricism involved in the search for new, cheap catalysts. If it is only the identity of the rate-determining step and those steps which precede it which are meant by "mechanism determination," then the situation is greatly eased!

Lastly, there is at present no correspondingly general interpretation for the fact that the rate-determining step takes place generally rather early in the sequence of the organic reaction. This itself greatly facilitates its determination. However, it also implies a relatively low value of α, namely, perhaps $\frac{1}{2}$, and from the Tafel equation [Chap. 2, Eq. (3.85)], one can see that a lower value of α inclines the situation towards a higher value of η for a given current density. This implies, of course, a loss of efficiency and therefore of energy.

7.1.2 Basic Steps in Mechanism Determination

In a mechanism determination, three steps are involved. The first is the determination of the overall reaction, which is generally carried out by a product analysis at various potentials. In electrochemical energy conversion, conditions are sought so that CO_2 is the principal product. Second, it is necessary to determine the extent of adsorption of species on the surface of the electrode as a function of potential (Blomgren and Bockris[56]). It is necessary to determine the coverage both under equilibrium and nonequilibrium conditions. Many studies of nonequilibrium radical concentrations have been made by Breiter[56a] and also by Brummer.[70] By application of a combination of types of transient pulses to the surface, it is possible (see Sec. 6.3.5) to obtain some information concerning the radicals present in larger concentrations. If one species (perhaps the reactant in its original molecular form) is in equilibrium with the surface, a determination of the isotherm (is it Temkin- or Langmuir-like in form?) is important because it affects the details of the kinetic reasoning.

Finally, one attempts to determine the useful electrode kinetic parameters, e.g., the transfer coefficient, reaction orders, exchange current densities, etc., to gain information on the reaction path and rate-determining step. Some of the parameters, for example, stoichiometric numbers, are more difficult to determine, mainly because of competing reactions in the lower current density region where it is necessary to make measurements to obtain these parameters.

The determination of mechanisms of electrochemical oxidation of organic compounds is a young field.[44a,56a] Interest in this field has arisen mainly because of the potentialities of electrochemical energy conversion. A knowledge of mechanisms of electrooxidation should be of help in the development of electrocatalysts. Mechanism studies which have been carried out on electrochemical oxidation of organic compounds and which are concerned with electrochemical energy conversion will be dealt with in the following sections.

7.2 Electrochemical Oxidation of Carbon Monoxide

7.2.1 Overall Reaction

This reaction should be considered as the basic one in the field, since it involves the transfer of only two electrons. The overall reaction in an acid medium is

$$CO + H_2O \rightarrow CO_2 + 2H^+ + 2e_0^- \tag{7.1}$$

7.2.2 Rest Potentials

The thermodynamic reversible potential for reaction (7.1) is -0.04 volt. However, the observed rest potential on a Pt electrode in 1 N H_2SO_4 is 0.36 volt and is independent of the pressure of carbon monoxide.

7.2.3 Current-potential Behavior

The current-potential curve is a strange one.[58] There is no appreciable current until 0.91 volt and then the current begins suddenly and at a slightly more anodic potential, falls off again, and becomes stirring-dependent (Fig. 16). The fact that hardly any current is observed at potentials below 0.91 volt may be due to the strength of the adsorption of CO on the electrode. At a potential of 0.91 volt, the coverage of CO rapidly drops to zero probably because of oxide formation,[57] and the current becomes diffusion-controlled. The fall in current

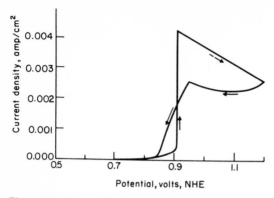

Figure 16   Current-density–potential relation for the anodic oxidation of CO on platinum[58] in 1 N H$_2$SO$_4$ at 25°C.

above 0.91 volt is probably due to steric factors caused by the simultaneous formation of oxide at these potentials.

7.2.4   Probable Mechanisms

The mechanism proposed by Gilman[58] is, in simple and essential aspects,

$$CO_{sol} \rightleftarrows CO_{ads} \tag{7.2}$$

$$CO_{ads} + H_2O_{ads} \xrightarrow{\text{rds}} CO - OH_{ads} + H^+ + e_0^- \tag{7.3}$$

$$CO - OH_{ads} \rightleftarrows CO_2 + H^+ + e_0^- \tag{7.4}$$

rds denotes the rate-determining step in the overall reaction.

There are some sophistications in the suggested mechanism depending on the fact that there is evidence for the attachment of CO to the electrode both by a one-site and a two-site mechanism (supported by *IR* investigations of the corresponding solid-gas system).

An alternative mechanism, due to Warner and Schuldiner,[59] is

$$CO_{sol} \rightleftarrows CO_{ads} \tag{7.2}$$

$$Pt + H_2O \xrightarrow{\text{rds}} PtOH_{ads} + H^+ + e_0^- \tag{7.5}$$

$$PtOH \rightleftarrows PtO + H^+ + e_0^- \tag{7.6}$$

$$PtO + CO_{ads} \rightleftarrows CO_2 \tag{7.7}$$

In the Warner and Schuldiner mechanism, water discharge is rate-determining. The first mechanism of Gilman is analogous to the slow electrochemical desorption mechanism in the electrolytic hydrogen-evolution reaction (Chap. 2, Sec. 10.1). No attempt seems to have been made to distinguish these mechanisms.

There is no reason to believe that any mechanism substantially different from the two proposed exists. A number of other pieces of evidence would help the picture: for example, there is a lack of evidence on reaction orders and the adsorption of CO has not been studied directly.

7.3 The Oxidation of Unsaturated Hydrocarbons on Platinum

7.3.1 *Overall Reaction*

The overall reactions in the oxidation of unsaturated hydrocarbons have been established from determinations of faradaic efficiency.[60,61] For ethylene, the efficiency of oxidation of ethylene to CO_2 was 100 percent. Thus, the overall reaction is:

$$C_2H_4 + 4H_2O \rightarrow 2CO_2 + 12H^+ + 12e_0^- \tag{7.8}$$

For higher hydrocarbons, the efficiency is not 100 percent but is high in every case such that the main product is CO_2 (Table 9, page 394). The faradaic efficiency for benzene increases with increasing anodic potential, going from about 60 percent in the lower portion of the Tafel line to 90 percent in the upper region of the Tafel line. For butadiene the opposite behavior was observed, i.e., the faradaic efficiency decreased with increasing anodic potential.

7.3.2 *Methods Used to Determine the Mechanism*

Studies have been carried out using potentiostatic and galvanostatic steady-state experimental measurements in solutions of varying pH from 1 N H_2SO_4 to 1 N NaOH, at 80°C, on platinum anodes.[60,61] Since a characteristic time-dependence, i.e., decrease of current with time at constant potential, is associated with these reactions, the quasi-steady state can be defined as that condition when the current changes less than 10 percent per hour at constant potential, or when the potential changes less than 10 mv hr^{-1} at constant current. This is not an arbitrary definition; it is a result of experimental observations on the behavior of the current-potential relations determined at various times of approach to the steady state. Before each experiment, the platinum anodes were "activated" using a series of anodic and cathodic galvanostatic pulses. The kinetic parameters, i.e., Tafel slope, exchange current density, faradaic efficiency, and reaction orders, are available in the anodic oxidation of a number of unsaturated hydrocarbons.[60,61]

A current-potential curve obtained potentiostatically for the anodic oxidation of an unsaturated hydrocarbon is seen in Fig. 17. There are four regions of current potential behavior. In region A, at low potentials near the rest potential, the line deviates from linearity. In region B, the linear Tafel region has a slope of about 140 mv ($2RT/F$ at 80°C). In region C, the current reaches an apparent limiting current. Region D, above about 0.9 volt (RHE), shows a rapid decrease of the current with potential owing to "passivation" of the electrode. Acetylene shows a behavior somewhat different from the unsaturated hydrocarbons containing double bonds, having a Tafel slope of about 70 mv, or RT/F. Benzene gave a higher Tafel slope than ethylene, being in the

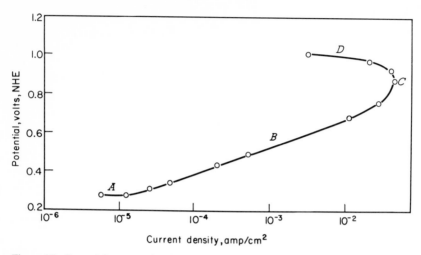

Figure 17 Potential–current-density curve for electrooxidation of ethylene on Pt[60] in 1 N H$_2$SO$_4$ at 80°C.

order of 160 to 190 mv.   This can be explained when one remembers that the faradaic efficiency for benzene changes with potential.   If the total current times the faradaic efficiency is plotted against potential, the Tafel slope becomes about 140 mv.   The same procedure for butadiene gives a Tafel slope of about 150 mv.

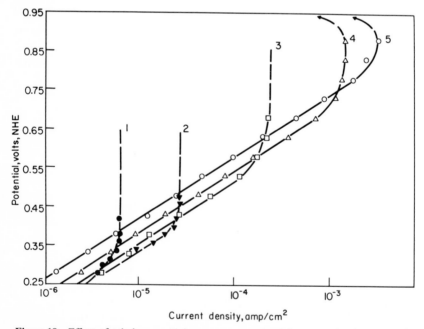

Figure 18 Effect of ethylene partial pressure on potential–current-density curves for electrooxidation of ethylene on Pt at 80°C.   (1) 10^{-4}, (2) 10^{-3}, (3) 10^{-2}, (4) 10^{-1}, (5) 1 atm partial pressure of ethylene.[60]

A plot of the dependence of the rate of oxidation on partial pressure of the organic reactant led to the interesting observations shown in Fig. 18.   The rate increases with decrease of pressure.   This result was common to all the unsaturated hydrocarbons examined *on platinized platinum*.

The effect of change of pH was determined in a similar way.   Here, one observed that at constant current density the potential is shifted in the cathodic direction by 70 mv (RT/F) per unit increase of pH.   If one extrapolates the Tafel lines to a constant potential, a plot of the current density versus pH gives approximately $(d \log i/dpH)_V \approx 0.5$ (Fig. 19).   The ionic strength of the

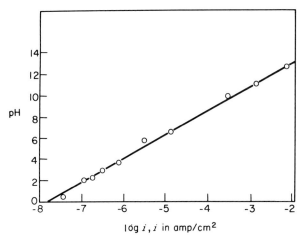

Figure 19   Effect of pH on rate of oxidation at 0.1 volt (NHE) of ethylene on Pt at 80°C.

solution was maintained approximately constant by addition of Na_2SO_4 to the solutions.

The influence of temperature showed the usual Arrhenius-type behavior (Fig. 20), and an apparent activation energy of about 22 kcal mole^{-1} was calculated for potentials in the Tafel region.

7.3.3   Mechanistic Conclusions

A comparison of the various parameters determined for the anodic oxidation of several hydrocarbons is given in Table 9.   From these results, it is possible to write an empirical relation for the anodic oxidation reactions of all hydrocarbons except acetylene, in the following form:

$$i = kc_{org}^{-\gamma} c_{H^+}^{-0.5} e^{FV/2RT} \tag{7.9}$$

where γ varies between 0.1 and 0.3 depending on the organic species.   To interpret this equation in terms of a mechanism for the reaction, it is important to know whether one must use Temkin or Langmuir kinetics.

From studies of adsorption of ethylene on various metal catalysts from the gas phase, there is no agreement as to whether associative or dissociative

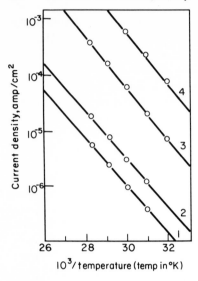

Figure 20 Current density as a function of temperature for ethylene oxidation on a Pt electrode in 1 N H_2SO_4. (1) 0.38; (2) 0.48; (3) 0.68; (4) 0.88 volt.[60]

adsorption is involved,[62] though it was recently pointed out[42,60] that energetically associative adsorption is favored by about 25 kcal mole^{-1}. Associative and dissociative adsorption of ethylene on metals are represented by the equations

$$CH_2 = CH_2 + 2M \rightarrow \underset{\underset{M}{|}}{CH_2} - \underset{\underset{M}{|}}{CH_2} \tag{7.10}$$

and

$$CH_2 = CH_2 + 4M \rightarrow \underset{\underset{M}{|}}{CH} = \underset{\underset{M}{|}}{CH} + 2M - H \tag{7.11}$$

respectively, where M's represent metal atoms. Associative adsorption is

TABLE 9   Diagnostic Parameters for Oxidation of Unsaturated Hydrocarbons at Pt Anodes at 80°C

Hydrocarbon	E_{rev}, volts (NHE)	$i_0 \times 10^{-8}$, amp cm^{-2}	ϵ_{CO_2}, %	$\left(\dfrac{d \log i}{d \log p}\right)_V$	$\left(\dfrac{d \log i}{d \text{ pH}}\right)_V$	$\left(\dfrac{dV}{d \text{ pH}}\right)_i$ mv	b, mv
C_2H_2	−0.05	1	100		0.8	−60	RT/F
C_2H_4	0.04	4	100	−0.2	0.45	−65	$2RT/F$
C_3H_4	0.00	2.5	93	−0.17	0.41	−68	$2RT/F$
C_3H_6	0.08	2.9	97	−0.14	0.35	−52	$2RT/F$
C_4H_6	0.06	0.7	88–62	−0.13	0.39	−65	$2RT/F$
C_4H_8-1†	0.09	1.8	71	−0.16	0.47	−67	$2RT/F$
C_4H_8-2‡	0.09	1.8	83	−0.20	0.45	−66	$2RT/F$
C_6H_6	0.10	0.3	90–60	−0.11	0.40	−51	$2RT/F$

† But-1-ene.
‡ But-2-ene.

favored energetically (by 70 kcal mole^{-1}) for adsorption from aqueous solutions, i.e., ethylene is adsorbed without breaking any carbon-hydrogen bonds but with probable breakage of the carbon-carbon double bond at low anodic potentials. At high anodic potentials, hydrogen ionization is favored and the two modes of adsorption have approximately the same heat of adsorption. From evidence in gas-phase catalysis for the relation of the *d*-band character of the substrate to adsorption, one assumes that since each Pt atom has about 0.5 *d*-vacancies, 2 Pt atoms will be required for each electron from the organic. Thus, 4 Pt atoms will be required for the adsorption of one ethylene molecule. A compound with two double bonds, like butadiene, would then be expected to require eight Pt atoms for adsorption.

Studies of adsorption of ethylene[42] and of benzene[53,53a] on platinum, using radiotracer techniques, reveal limiting high coverages of the hydrocarbons. The adsorption isotherm is indicated to be of the Langmuir type rather than the Temkin form. One may thus conclude that Langmuir conditions prevail in these cases under conditions of high coverage of the electrode by the organic species.

The kinetic parameters, which lead to the suggestion of the empirical equation (7.9), indicate that the rate-determining step does not involve the organic species. The observed reaction order of the organic species supports the idea that some species other than the organic reactant is involved in the rate-limiting step. Since the only other stable species present which participates in the reaction is H_2O or OH^-, it was concluded that either H_2O or OH^- was involved. From the uniformity of behavior throughout the pH range, the OH^- species is not likely to be involved, since in acid solutions its concentration would be too small to support the observed reaction rates. Thus, discharge of the water molecule was postulated as the rate-determining step for these reactions (except acetylene, which has a different Tafel slope). The scheme may be written as

$$H_2O \xrightarrow{\text{rds}} OH_{ads} + H^+ + e_0^- \tag{7.12}$$

$$C_2H_4 \rightleftarrows C_2H_{4\,ads} \tag{7.13}$$

$$OH_{ads} + C_2H_{4\,ads} \rightleftarrows \text{intermediate} \tag{7.14}$$

$$\text{Intermediate} \xrightarrow{-11e_0^-} CO_2 \tag{7.15}$$

One is not able, on present data, to discuss what happens to the first intermediate except that through a series of reactions, which include eleven electron transfers, it goes to CO_2.

The precise path after the rate-determining step is of less interest in fundamental considerations of electrochemical energy conversion than is the rate-determining step, which should be the preferred objective of a mechanism investigation. Knowledge of the rate-determining step gives rise to possibilities of applying fundamental considerations to the creation of new catalytic substrates.

For Langmuir kinetics applied to the sequence (7.12) to (7.15), one can write

$$i = k(1 - \theta_T)e^{\alpha FV/RT} \tag{7.16}$$

When α, the transfer coefficient, is 0.5, then

$$(dV/d \ln i) = \frac{RT}{\alpha F} = \frac{2RT}{F} \tag{7.17}$$

as observed.   To examine the reaction order of the organic species, one must obtain an expression for the $(1 - \theta_T)$ term.   For the generalized Langmuir isotherm [Eq. (6.9)], one can write

$$\frac{\theta}{(1 - \theta_T)^n} = Kp \tag{7.18}$$

where n is the number of metal sites required for the adsorption of one molecule of the organic species (for ethylene adsorption $n = 4$).

From Eq. (7.18), one may write

$$(1 - \theta_T) = \frac{p^{-1/n}}{K^{1/n}} \tag{7.19}$$

for $\theta \to 1$.   Using Eq. (7.19) in Eq. (7.16),

$$i = \frac{kp^{-1/n}}{K^{1/n}} e^{\alpha FV/RT} \tag{7.20}$$

and

$$\left(\frac{d \ln i}{d \ln p}\right)_V = -\frac{1}{n} \tag{7.21}$$

which agrees well with the observed result for the unexpected negative-pressure coefficient (Table 9).

The pH dependence is not so easy to derive.   The simple kinetic relation predicts a reaction order of zero with respect to the H^+ ion, whereas the observed reaction order is -0.5.   One can explain this if the potential is expressed in terms of the rational potential scale, i.e., with respect to the potential of zero charge (**PZC**).   Experimental observations[63,64] have shown that the PZC changes with pH by RT/F per pH unit as expressed by the equation[63]

$$V_{PZC} = V_{PZC}^0 + \frac{RT}{F} \ln a_{H^+} \tag{7.22}$$

If one then rewrites Eq. (7.16) to take this factor into account, one obtains

$$i = k(1 - \theta_T) \exp\left\{\left[V - \left(V_{PZC}^0 + \frac{RT}{F} \ln a_{H^+}\right)\right]\left(\frac{\alpha F}{RT}\right)\right\}$$

$$= k(1 - \theta_T)a_{H^+}^{-\alpha} \exp\left[(V - V_{PZC}^0)\left(\frac{\alpha F}{RT}\right)\right] \tag{7.23}$$

Thus

$$\left(\frac{d \ln i}{d \, \mathrm{pH}}\right)_V = \alpha \tag{7.24}$$

which is the experimentally observed dependence of the current density on pH at a constant metal-solution potential difference.

Thus, the water-discharge mechanism can account for the experimental observations in the anodic oxidation of various unsaturated hydrocarbons on platinum. For acetylene, a mechanism consistent with the experimental data is obtained if one assumes that the chemical combination of adsorbed hydroxyl radical and adsorbed acetylene is the rate-determining step,[65] the oxygen adsorption being under Temkin kinetics.

One problem which remains with this mechanism is that if water discharge is rate-determining on platinum in the oxidation of ethylenic hydrocarbons, one might expect the same rate in all cases, whereas one notes a difference of up to a factor of 10 in the exchange current densities for the unsaturated hydrocarbons referred to in Table 9. One factor that could give rise to this difference is the $(1 - \theta_T)$ term, which is itself small and could vary considerably for small changes in coverages among the various organic species. This variation is not known at the present time. Another possibility is that the dipole potential, or χ term, depends on the dipole moment of the organic molecule and thereby influences the potential difference across the interface for the electrode reaction.

7.4 Oxidation of Ethylene on Other Metals and Alloys

The electrooxidation of ethylene on a number of metals other than Pt and on alloys has been studied.[66,66a] The electrode kinetic parameters obtained in these cases are summarized in Table 10. An important mechanism-indicating criterion determined in this study is the kinetic isotope effect of the reaction rate.[66] This was obtained by comparing the rates of the reaction at the same overpotential in pure H_2O and D_2O solution.

From the experimental data tabulated in Table 10, the following empirical equations were proposed for the kinetics of ethylene oxidation on the various substrates:

$$i_{Pt} = k_{Pt} c_e^{-1/n} c_{H^+}^{-0.5} \exp\left(\frac{VF}{2RT}\right) \tag{7.25}$$

$$i_M = k_M c_e^{1/m} c_{H^+}^{-0.5} \exp\left(\frac{VF}{2RT}\right) \tag{7.26}$$

$$i_{Pd,Au} = k_{Pd,Au} c_e^{1/m'} c_{H^+}^{-0.5} \exp\left(\frac{VF}{3RT}\right) \tag{7.27}$$

Equation (7.25) expresses the rate on Pt; Eq. (7.26) on metals and alloys other than Pt, Pd, and Au; and Eq. (7.27) on Au and Pd.

TABLE 10   Diagnostic Parameters for the Anodic Oxidation of Ethylene on Some Metals and Alloys at $80°C$[66]

Metal or alloy	Tafel slope, mv	$\dfrac{d \log i}{d \log P_{Et}}$	$\left(\dfrac{d \log i}{d\,pH}\right)_V$	Reaction products	Coverage with ethylene	$\left(\dfrac{i\,H_2O}{i\,D_2O}\right)_V$	i (600 mv) $A\ cm^{-2}$
Platinum	~140	~−0.2	0.45	CO_2	~1	1.5–2.5	5×10^{-6}
Palladium	~190	~+0.5	~0.5	50% CO_2 balance aldehydic			2×10^{-7}
Rhodium	~160	~+0.5	~0.5	CO_2	~0.02	4–5	1×10^{-7}
Iridium	~160	~+0.5	~0.5	CO_2			3×10^{-7}
Gold	~200	~+0.5	~0.5	As Pd	~0.3	4–6	2×10^{-7}
Osmium							$<1 \times 10^{-8}$
Ruthenium	~165	+ve					1×10^{-7}
Silver		+ve					5×10^{-8}
Mercury							$<1 \times 10^{-8}$
Pd–Au							
20–80 at. %							6×10^{-7}
46–54 at. %	~160	~+0.5					3×10^{-7}
78–22 at. %							4×10^{-7}
Rh–Pd							
25–75 at. %							7.0×10^{-7}
50–50 at. %	~170	+ve					1.5×10^{-6}
75–25 at. %							3.0×10^{-8}
Cu–Rh							
10–90 at. %	~160	~+0.5					4.0×10^{-6}
Cu–Au							
25–75 at. %							1×10^{-7}
Pt–Rh							
80–20 at. %	~160	+ve					8×10^{-7}
50–50 at. %	160						5×10^{-7}
Pt–Ni							
85–15 at. %	170						4.0×10^{-7}

A scheme consistent with Eq. (7.25) was given in the last section. The mechanism associated with a rate expression given by Eq. (7.27) is

$$C_2H_4 \rightleftharpoons C_2H_{4\,ads} \tag{7.13}$$

$$H_2O \rightleftharpoons OH_{ads} + H^+ + e_0^- \tag{7.28}$$

$$C_2H_{4\,ads} + OH_{ads} \xrightarrow{\text{rds}} CH_2\!-\!O\!-\!CH_{3\,ads} \tag{7.29}$$

The potential dependence follows if one makes the assumption of adsorption of ethylene and of intermediates under *Temkin* conditions.

On Au and Pd, the unusual Tafel slope of $3RT/F$ arises because of incomplete oxidation to CO_2.[66] Aldehydic products have also been obtained. The same scheme (7.13, 7.28, and 7.29) was proposed for Au and Pd except that the parallel reactions

$$
\begin{array}{c}
\\
\text{M--CH}_2\text{--OCH}_3
\end{array}
\underset{\text{oxidation}}{\overset{\text{desorption}}{\Bigg\langle}}
\begin{array}{l}
\quad\ \ \text{H} \\
\quad\ \ / \\
\text{CH}_3\text{C} + \text{H}^+ + e_0^- \\
\quad\ \ \backslash\!\!\backslash \\
\quad\ \ \text{O} \\[8pt]
\text{H--CH}_2\text{--CH}_{2\,\text{ads}} + \text{H}_2\text{O} \rightarrow \text{CO}_2
\end{array}
\tag{7.30}
$$

occur after the rate-determining step in several intermediate steps.

The predicted kinetic isotope effect[66a] is between 1 and 2.7 for the scheme represented by Eqs. (7.12) to (7.15) and is 4.8 for the scheme given by Eqs. (7.13), (7.28), and (7.29), and these predictions are in excellent agreement with experiment (Table 10).

7.5   The Oxidation of Saturated Hydrocarbons

7.5.1   *General*

The subject of the anodic oxidation of saturated hydrocarbons has been approached by interested scientists who may be divided into two groups.   The first group has studied actual fuel cells under either operating or simulated operating conditions.   The engineering and construction problems as well as electrocatalysts, electrolytes, and membranes were worked on.[67-69]   All measurements made were aimed at optimizing the performance of certain hydrocarbon fuel cells.   However, it is also limited by the fact that two electrode processes are being studied at the same time without controlling the driving force (i.e., the potential) of one independently of the other.   Thus, the anodic process still remains generally unknown from a mechanistic point of view, and this gives rise to the need of a second group of researchers who study the velocity and mechanism of the individual anodic reaction.

7.5.2   *Approach from a Study of Intermediates*

The fundamental work group is further divided into two distinct groups according to the method of approach.   The first and the larger group consists of researchers who study anodic hydrocarbon oxidation on the basis of studies of intermediates only.[70]   The findings of this group are that saturated hydrocarbons will react in concentrated phosphoric acids (at platinum electrocatalysts) with the formation of various intermediates.   Each of these species is assumed to be formed in one of several possible parallel reactions, each going to CO_2, that is,

$$
\text{Hydrocarbon} \rightarrow \text{adsorption} \rightarrow
\begin{array}{c}
\nearrow \text{intermediate A} \searrow \\
\text{intermediate B} \rightarrow CO_2 \\
\searrow \text{intermediate C} \nearrow
\end{array}
\tag{7.31}
$$

The path involving the intermediate which oxidizes most rapidly is that which controls the rate. The kinetics of adsorption are also measured in this procedure, and the results are that the hydrocarbons adsorb maximally at about 0.2 volt and desorb almost completely below 0.55 volt. The rate-determining step is not elucidated.

7.5.3   *Approach from a Study of Electrode Kinetic Parameters*

A great deal of work has been done on this subject,[69] although most of it has been with porous electrodes; thus (because of the difficulty of unscrambling the overpotentials then involved) little progress has been made with the evaluation of mechanisms, at least in the region where the reaction is most likely to occur, namely, in the potential range at less than 1.0 volt on the hydrogen scale (at more anodic potentials, there is an oxide-film formation on platinum).

A study of the oxidation of propane, *n*-hexane, cyclohexane, and 2,2-dimethyl butane in concentrated phosphoric acid solution at 80 to 150°C has been made.[71] The study was carried out in two parts.

First, the electrode was held at a fixed potential and the reactant bubbled into the solution. Current was found to pass across the electrode and to last for the order of 1 min (Fig. 12). It rises for about 0.1 min and then decays for about 1.0 min. This current is consistent with the ionization reaction by the following mechanism, given in terms of propane:

$$
C_3H_{8\,\text{soln}} \rightarrow C_3H_{7\,\text{ads}} + H^+ + e
\tag{7.32}
$$

From such current-time lines, it is possible to make a calculation of the coverage of the electrode with the radicals concerned, and this comes out to values in the region of 0.1 of the electrode surface; i.e., the values are relatively small. This result is fairly independent of the hydrocarbons used.

Correspondingly, the rate of oxidation in the steady state was studied. It was found that the steady state was easily obtained, and that it was possible, while holding the potential constant, to examine the rate of the oxidation to CO_2 as a function of the propane pressure, the activity of water, and, of course, the potential difference across the double layer (Fig. 21).

The parameters which were found are:

$$
\frac{d \log i}{dV} = \frac{F}{RT}
\tag{7.33}
$$

$$
\frac{d \log i}{d \log c_{C_3H_8}} = 1
\tag{7.34}
$$

$$
\frac{d \log i}{d \log c_{H_2O}} = 0
\tag{7.35}
$$

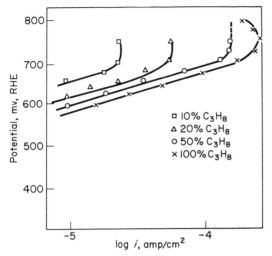

Figure 21 Current-density–potential behavior for the oxidation of propane on Pt electrodes[71] in H_3PO_4 at 120°C.

Correspondingly, when the potential across the double layer is constant, the rate of oxidation to CO_2 is in the order propane > 2,2-dimethyl butane > *n*-hexane > cyclohexane.

There is a remarkable inhibition effect when the potential is greater than 0.70 volt on the reversible hydrogen scale; the rate of oxidation (measured at 80 to 130°C in phosphoric acid) decreases anomalously with the increase in the field for propane (Fig. 21).

It is possible to make a large number of mechanism hypotheses with regard to this reaction. If the rate is in the noninhibited region (to which the above mechanism criteria refer), one has the possibilities indicated in Table 11.

A large number of alternative sequences are excluded by the value of the observed Tafel coefficient.

It turns out that two partial mechanisms are consistent with the observations. Energy considerations show that one of these is the more likely. It is, in terms of the saturated hydrocarbon RH,

$$RH \rightleftharpoons R_{ads} + H^+ + e_0^- \tag{7.36}$$

$$R_{ads} \xrightarrow{rds} \text{organic radicals} \tag{7.37}$$

It is hence the *chemical* decomposition of the radical, produced in the dissociative adsorption with charge transfer, which is the rate-determining step for the saturated hydrocarbons. The rate-determining step for the alternative possibility is also a *chemical* reaction.

A very interesting effect which has been shown by the same authors[71] is that the inhibition effect (Fig. 21) is due to the adsorption of an ion from

TABLE 11   Derived Kinetic Parameters for Propane Oxidation[71]

Mechanism†	$dV/d \ln i$			$(d \ln i/d \ln p_{C_3H_8})_{H_2O}$			$(d \ln i/d \ln c_{H_2O})_{RH}$		
	Low θ	Int. θ	High θ	Low θ	Int. θ	High θ	Low θ	Int. θ	High θ
Scheme *i*	$2RT/F$			+1			0		
Scheme *ii*	$2RT/3F$	0	$2RT/F$	+1	$-\frac{1}{2}$	0	0	0	0
Scheme *iii*	RT/F	$-2RT/F$	0	+1	$-\frac{1}{2}$	0	0	0	0
Scheme *iv*	RT/F	$-2RT/F$	0	+1	$-\frac{1}{2}$	0	0	0	0
Scheme *v*	RT/F	RT/F	RT/F	+1	$-\beta$	≈ 0	1	1	$1/n$
Scheme *vi*	$2RT/F$	$2RT/F$	$2RT/F$	0	$-\frac{1}{2}$	$-1/n$	1	1	$1/n$
Scheme *vii*	$2RT/F$	$2RT/F$	$2RT/F$	+1	$-\frac{1}{2}$	0	0	0	0
Scheme *viii*	$2RT/3F$	$2RT/3F$	$2RT/3F$	+1	$-\frac{1}{2}$	≈ 0	+1	+1	$1/n$
Scheme *ix*	RT/F	$2RT/3F$	RT/F	+1	$\frac{1}{2}$	≈ 0	+1	+1	1
Scheme *x*	RT/F			+1			+1		
Scheme *xi*	$2RT/F$			+1			+1		
Scheme *xii*	$2RT/3F$	0	$2RT/F$	+1	$-\frac{1}{2}$	≈ 0	+1	+1	1
Scheme *xiii*	RT/F	$-2RT/F$	0	+1	$-\frac{1}{2}$	≈ 0	+1	+1	≈ 1
Scheme *xiv*	$2RT/3F$		$2RT/3F$	+1		≈ 0	+1		$1/n$
Scheme *xv*	$RT/2F$	RT/F	0	+1	$\frac{1}{2}$	≈ 0	+1	+1	≈ 1
Experimental, 280–500 mv		RT/F			+1			0	

† Reaction schemes

i $C_3H_8 \text{ soln} \xrightarrow{\text{rds}} C_3H_{7\,ads} + H^+ + e^-$

ii $C_3H_8 \rightleftarrows C_3H_{7\,ads} + H^+ + e^-$
$C_3H_{7\,ads} \xrightarrow{\text{rds}} C_3H_{6\,ads} + H^+ + e^-$

iii $C_3H_8 \rightleftarrows C_3H_{7\,ads} + H^+ + e^-$
$C_3H_{7\,ads} \xrightarrow{\text{rds}} C_3H_{6\,ads} + H$

iv $C_3H_8 \rightleftarrows C_3H_{7\,ads} + H^+ + e^-$
$C_3H_7 \xrightarrow{\text{rds}} C_2H_{4\,ads} + CH_{3\,ads}$

v $C_3H_8 \rightleftarrows C_2H_{5\,ads} + CH_{3\,ads}$
$H_2O \rightleftarrows OH_{ads} + H^+ + e^-$
$C_2H_{5\,ads} \xrightarrow{\text{rds}} CH_2OH_{ads} + CH_{3\,ads}$

vi $C_3H_8 \rightleftarrows C_3H_{8\,ads}$
$H_2O \xrightarrow{\text{rds}} OH_{ads} + H^+ + e$

vii $C_3H_8 \rightleftarrows C_3H_{8\,ads}$
$C_3H_{8\,ads} \xrightarrow{\text{rds}} C_3H_{7\,ads} + H^+ + e^-$

viii $C_3H_8 \rightleftarrows C_3H_{8\,ads}$
$H_2O \rightleftarrows OH_{ads} + H^+ + e^-$ C_3H_7
$OH_{ads} + C_3H_{8\,ads} \xrightarrow{\text{rds}} C_3H_7OH_{ads} + H^+ + e^-$

ix $C_3H_8 \rightleftarrows C_3H_{7\,ads} + H^+ + e^-$
$H_2O \rightleftarrows OH_{ads} + H^+ + e^-$
$C_3H_{7\,ads} + OH_{ads} \xrightarrow{\text{rds}} C_3H_7OH_{ads}$

x $H_2O \rightleftarrows OH_{ads} + H^+ + e^-$
$C_3H_8 \text{ soln} + OH_{ads} \xrightarrow{\text{rds}} C_3H_7OH_{ads} + H^+ + e^-$

xi $H_2O \rightleftarrows OH_{ads} + H^+ + e^-$
$C_3H_8 \text{ soln} + OH_{ads} \xrightarrow{\text{rds}} C_2H_5OH_{ads} + CH_{3\,ads}$

xii $C_3H_8 \rightleftarrows C_3H_7 + H^+ + e^-$
$C_3H_7 + H_2O_{soln} \xrightarrow{\text{rds}} C_2H_4OH_{ads} + CH_{3\,ads} + H^+ + e^-$

xiii $C_3H_8 \rightleftarrows C_3H_{7\,ads} + H^+ + e^-$
$C_3H_{7\,ads} + H_2O_{soln} \xrightarrow{\text{rds}} C_2H_5OH_{ads} + CH_{3\,ads}$

xiv $C_3H_8 \rightleftarrows C_2H_{5\,ads} + CH_{3\,ads}$
$H_2O \rightleftarrows OH_{ads} + H^+ + e^-$
$C_2H_{5\,ads} + OH_{ads} \xrightarrow{\text{rds}} C_2H_5OH + H^+ + e^-$

xv $C_3H_8 \rightleftarrows C_3H_{7\,ads} + H^+ + e^-$
$C_3H_{7\,ads} \rightleftarrows C_3H_{6\,ads} + H^+ + e^-$
$C_3H_{6\,ads} + H_2O_{soln} \xrightarrow{\text{rds}} C_3H_7OH_{ads}$

phosphoric acid, possibly $H_2PO_4^{-1}$. It is difficult to examine the adsorption of entities from phosphoric acid on platinum from aqueous solution because the phosphoric acid is so concentrated. (This makes it difficult to apply either the radiotracer or electrochemical, transient methods of obtaining surface coverage.) Bockris, Stoner, and Cahan[71b] introduced a new method for the examination of this adsorption. They found that if a very thin film is evaporated upon a metal, the surface conductance of the film changes with adsorption of the phosphate because the phosphate uses up some bonds in the surface, which in turn immobilizes electrons conducting within the thin film (the film thickness is of the order of 100 Å). These workers obtained a rough idea of when the entity from phosphoric acid was adsorbing and the point at which adsorption switched or coincided with the point at which the inhibition of the propane oxidation to CO_2—shown by an inflection in the Tafel line (Fig. 21)—begins.

Although it is possible that the mechanism of the oxidation of saturated hydrocarbons changes with temperature and acid content, there is a certain similarity in its mechanism with that of the oxidation of unsaturated hydrocarbons on electrocatalysts other than platinized platinum, and the rate-determining step is a *chemical* reaction and comes a step or two after initial adsorption.

7.6 Oxidation of Methanol

7.6.1 General

Early work on this reaction was carried out by Müller.[7-12] Pavela[72] carried out a comprehensive investigation in 1954. Cyclic voltammetry has been used rather extensively in recent times[73-75] to gain information on the adsorption characteristics of methanol and of the intermediates formed during its oxidation. Buck and Griffith[74] determined the steady-state electrode-kinetic parameter and proposed a reaction scheme in which the second electron-transfer step in the reaction sequence is rate determining. More recently, the mechanism of electrooxidation of methanol on platinum electrodes in acid and in alkaline solutions has been investigated in great detail by Bagotzky and Vassilyev.[76] Information concerning the species adsorbed on electrodes in solutions containing methanol has been obtained using transient methods by Breiter[77] and by others.[78]

7.6.2 Overall Reaction

The overall reaction is

$$CH_3OH + H_2O \rightarrow CO_2 + 6H^+ + 6e_0^- \qquad (7.38)$$

in acid solution. In alkaline solution, there is partial oxidation to formate. Formaldehyde is an intermediate and has been detected.

7.6.3   *Adsorption Behavior*

Extensive work has been carried out to determine the nature of the species adsorbed on platinum electrodes from methanolic solutions. Potential sweep and anodic (also cathodic) changing-transient techniques were used. Temkin behavior was observed. Breiter showed that the adsorbed species differ from that formed during adsorption of CO or of reduced CO_2. Kamath and Lal,[78] however, showed that the adsorbed species from solution containing HCOOH, HCHO, and CH_3OH are similar. From an analysis of the non-steady-state–current-time plots at constant potentials, Bagotzky and Vassilyev showed that C-OH is probably the adsorbed species and is formed according to the step

$$CH_3OH \rightarrow C\text{-}OH_{ads} + 3H_{ads} \tag{7.39}$$

which is followed by

$$3H_{ads} \rightarrow 3H^+ + 3e_0^- \tag{7.40}$$

The non-steady-state current was attributed to the reaction (7.40). A measure of the adsorption of $C\text{-}OH_{ads}$ was obtained as a function of time from the non-steady-state current–versus time plot, and was found to be in good agreement with the values obtained by anodic or cathodic transient techniques.

7.6.4   *Kinetic Parameters*

Bagotzky and Vassilyev have carried out the most extensive work which is summarized below. Figure 22 shows the current density–potential relation for the oxidation of methanol on platinum electrodes in acid solution. The figure also contains the plot of the maximum non-steady-state current density (which corresponds to the case when $\theta_{org} = 0$ versus potential. Each of these lines shows a two-section Tafel plot followed by a decrease of current with potential. In the steady state, the lower slope is about $2.3\ RT/F$, while the higher slope is $2 \times 2.3\ RT/F$. Similar behavior was found in alkaline solution.

At low and medium concentrations of methanol, the reaction order with respect to methanol is $\frac{1}{2}$. At higher concentrations ($>10^{-1}$ M l^{-1}), the reaction rate decreased with increase in methanol concentration.

The current density at a constant overpotential decreases with pH initially, is nearly a constant from a pH of 5 to 9, and then increases again.

7.6.5   *Probable Mechanism*

Bagotzky and Vassilyev arrived at the conclusion that the initial adsorption step is fast by a comparison of the current-density vs. potential relation in Fig. 22. Taking into consideration the other experimentally determined

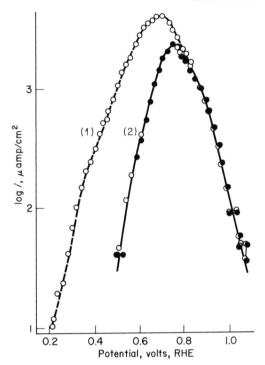

Figure 22   Dependence of the values of (1) the maximal nonsteady current, corresponding to $\theta_{org} = 0$, and (2) the steady current of electrooxidation of methanol on Pt upon potential in $1\,M\,CH_3OH$ and $1\,N\,H_2SO_4$.

parameters as well, the following reaction sequence was proposed:

$$M + H_2O \rightleftharpoons MOH_{ads} + H^+ + e_0^- \tag{7.41}$$

$$4M + CH_3OH \rightleftharpoons MCOH_{ads} + 3MH \tag{7.42}$$

$$3MH \rightleftharpoons 3M + 3H^+ + 3e_0 \tag{7.43}$$

$$MCOH_{ads} + MOH_{ads} \rightarrow MCO + M + H_2O \tag{7.44}$$

At low anodic potentials (i.e., at low θ_{OH}) and at medium electrode surface coverages with organic (i.e., Temkin condition for the organic) the expression for the reaction rate is of the form

$$i = k\theta_{OH}\exp\left(\gamma_1 r_1 \theta_{org}\right) \tag{7.45}$$

Substituting for θ_{OH} from equilibrium reaction (7.41)

$$i = ka_{OH^-}\exp(\gamma_1 r_1\,\theta_{org})\exp\left(\frac{VF}{RT}\right) \tag{7.46}$$

This equation is valid in the range $0.3 < V < 0.7$ volt (RHE).

At medium surface coverages of both θ_{OH} and θ_{org} (under Temkin conditions for both), the current density is expressed by

$$i = k \exp (\gamma_1 r_1 \theta_{org}) \exp (\gamma_2 r_2 \theta_{OH})$$

$$= k \exp (\gamma_1 r_1 \theta_{org}) \exp \left(\gamma_2 \frac{VF}{RT} \right) \tag{7.47}$$

This relation holds in the higher potential region but below that at which the current starts to decrease with potential. Thus one can expect a change of Tafel slope in passing over from the low- to medium-potential range.

7.7 Oxidation of Carboxylic Acids

7.7.1 General

Detailed mechanism-determination studies have been carried out on the oxidation of formic[75,79] and oxalic acids.[80] Since the latter reaction has been investigated more thoroughly as well as conclusively, this reaction is dealt with in the following sections.

7.7.2 Electrooxidation of Oxalic Acid

7.7.2.1 Overall Reaction. Oxidation of oxalic acid to carbon dioxide is quantitative in acid solution according to:

$$\begin{array}{l} COOH \\ | \\ COOH \end{array} \rightarrow 2CO_2 + 2H^+ + 2e_0^- \tag{7.48}$$

There is no reaction in alkaline solution. Similar phenomena have been observed with formic acid.

7.7.2.2 Kinetic Parameters. There are two slopes $2RT/F$ and RT/F. In the high-temperature region, at $80°C$, the slope is RT/F:

$$i_0 \approx 10^{-20} \qquad \frac{\partial \ln i}{\partial \text{pH}} \approx 0.5 \qquad \Delta H° \approx 22 \text{ kcal mole}^{-1} \text{ (at reversible potential)}$$

7.7.2.3 Mechanism Discussion. Several possible mechanisms have been suggested for the anodic oxidation of oxalic acid, including purely chemical oxidation of the acid by platinum oxide, partial oxidation by the oxide with one electron transfer from the acid, and both electron transfers from the acid molecule. Johnson et al.[80] have discussed a number of possible mechanisms with the derived kinetic parameters, and those leading to the proper parameters are discussed below for the high-temperature condition ($b = RT/F$). A mechanism involving both the charge-transfer steps from the organic species may be written:

$$H_2C_2O_4 \rightleftarrows HC_2O_{4\,ads} + H^+ + e_0^- \tag{7.49}$$

$$HC_2O_{4\,ads} \xrightarrow{\text{rds}} 2CO_2 + H^+ + e_0^- \tag{7.50}$$

For Temkin conditions, the rate expression for (7.50) rate-determining is

$$i = k\,\theta\,e^{\alpha FV/RT}\,e^{\alpha r\theta/RT} \tag{7.51}$$

For step (7.49) in quasi-equilibrium (i.e., the assumption that steps preceding the rate-determining step are virtually in equilibrium; Chap. 2, Sec. 3), $\alpha = 0.5$, and neglecting the preexponential coverage terms, one obtains

$$f\theta = RT \ln K + RT \ln c_{\text{ox}} - RT \ln c_{H^+} + FV \tag{7.52}$$

Substituting and neglecting the preexponential coverage term in Eq. (7.50) it follows that

$$i = k'c_{\text{oc}}c_{H^+}^{-1}e^{FV/RT} \tag{7.53}$$

and for $\alpha = 0.5$ the observed Tafel slope, pH dependence, and concentration dependence are obtained.

A second mechanism involving water discharge, which also satisfies the observed kinetic parameters, is the following:

$$H_2O \rightleftharpoons H^+ + OH_{ads} + e_0^- \tag{7.54}$$

$$H_2C_2O_4 + OH_{ads} \rightleftharpoons H_2O + HC_2O_{4\,ads} \tag{7.55}$$

$$HC_2O_{4\,ads} \to CO_2 + H^+ + e_0^- \tag{7.56}$$

For Temkin conditions with step (7.56) rate-determining one has

$$i = k\theta_{HC_2O_4}e^{\alpha FV/RT}e^{r\theta/RT} \tag{7.57}$$

Assuming quasi equilibrium in step (7.54) and that $\theta_{HC_2O_4} \approx \theta_T$, one finds

$$\theta_{OH} = \frac{K}{c_{H^+}}(1 - \theta_{HC_2O_4})e^{FV/RT}e^{-\alpha r\theta/RT} \tag{7.58}$$

where r is the interaction energy parameter. With step (7.55) in quasi equilibrium, $\theta_{HC_2O_4} = K'c_{H_2C_2O_4}\theta_{OH}$, and with substitution from the previous equation and neglecting the preexponential coverage terms, one obtains

$$r\theta = RT \ln K' + RT \ln c_{H_2C_2O_4} - RT \ln c_{H^+} + FV \tag{7.59}$$

Introducing this into the rate equation and neglecting preexponential terms in coverage, one finds

$$i = k'c_{H_2C_2O_4}c_{H^+}^{-1}e^{FV/RT} \tag{7.60}$$

and the observed parameters are derived. A large number of other mechanisms have been considered, but they do not give rise to the observed kinetic parameters. Mechanisms involving a rate-determining water-discharge step are not considered, since passivation phenomena observed at about 0.9 volt (NHE) for the anodic oxidation of other organic compounds (presumably due to discharge of water and oxide formation) were not observed for oxalic acid.

The similarity of the behavior of formic acid and of oxalic acid oxidations tends to indicate a common mechanism. The proper mechanism should be able to account for the change in Tafel slope with temperature (cf. above) while the pH and concentration dependence remain unchanged.

8 SOME CONCLUDING REMARKS

The following are outstanding conclusions from the present stage of fuel-cell-oriented organic oxidation reactions.

(*i*) Independently of the development of atomic power sources, the obtaining of electricity directly from fossil fuel oxidations seems to be a technology which will be needed. For example, it would effectively double the energy which could be obtained from the still remaining easily available oil. It would give us the energy from vast coal reserves otherwise relatively useless, except for possible textile manufacture. Technologically satisfactory conversion depends on developments in porous electrode technology (Can the necessary Pt be reduced to some 1 percent of that now used?) and electrocatalysis (Can chelate and organic semiconductor catalysts be found?).

(*ii*) Worth recording is the apparent relative simplicity of many electrochemical oxidations of hydrocarbons to CO_2. Although occurring in many steps, a 100 percent one-path oxidation with simple parameters is often observed.

(*iii*) Approaches to the study of the mechanism and some conclusions are nevertheless still fraught with controversy. In adsorption from the solution, is the fuel often in molecular form and in equilibrium with the solution? Or does it usually involve a discharge mechanism? Is the most fruitful method of study an exclusive concentration on the use of various kinds of transient pulses on the electrode? Or should such methods of determining coverage and obtaining information on radicals be used as powerful and necessary auxiliaries to the argument of rate-determining step "deduction" by determination of parameters from the steady-state kinetics which fit, or do not fit, various sets of parameters predicted on the basis of alternative hypotheses concerning the mechanism? Is it a task of value to attempt to proceed to elucidate all the steps? Or is the rate-determining step that upon which concentration should be made?

(*iv*) Cyclic voltammetry has often been used indiscriminately and without understanding of the limits of its applicability to complex reactions. Conversely an experimental approach which has much in favor of it is that of isotopic rate measurements and the comparison of these with values predicted for alternate paths and rate-determining steps.

(*v*) An increase in methods (optical?) for the measurement of surface intermediates is a primary requirement in mechanism research.

(*vi*) Knowledge of the rate-determining step is in the "strongly indicated" category for the oxidation of acetylenic, ethylenic and saturated hydrocarbons, methanol, and simple carboxylic acids. Determination of the complete mechanism, with knowledge of past-rate-determining steps, is closest for methanol.

(*vii*) A generalization seems justified: the most frequently occurring rate-determining step is the *chemical* reaction of an organic radical near (two or three steps from) the beginning of the series of partial reactions with an adsorbed OH radical.

REFERENCES

1. Chang, S. S. L.: "Energy Conversion," Prentice-Hall, Inc., Englewood Cliffs, N.J., 1963; B. Fall, private communication, 1969.

2. "Gmelins Handbook," vol. 1 (1848); vol. 8 (1853).

3. Renard, A.: *Compt. Rend.*, **91**, 125 (1880).

4. Gattermann, E., and F. Friedrichs: *Bër.*, **2**, 1942 (1897).

5. Haber, F.: *Z. Elektrochem.*, **4**, 506 (1898).

6. Hickling, A.: *Trans. Faraday Soc.*, **38**, 27 (1942).

7. Müller, E.: *Z. Elektrochem.*, **28**, 101 (1922); **29**, 264 (1923).

8. Müller, E., and G. H. Hindemith: *Z. Electrochem.*, **33**, 561 (1927).

9. Müller, E., and H. Schwabe: *Z. Electrochem.*, **33**, 568 (1927).

10. Müller, E., and S. Tanaka: *Z. Electrochem.*, **34**, 256 (1928); **35**, 38 (1929).

11. Müller, E., and K. Schwabe: *Z. Electrochem.*, **34**, 170 (1928).

12. Müller, E., and S. Takegume: *Z. Electrochem.*, **34**, 704 (1928).

13. British Celanese Ltd., Brit. 609,594, Oct. 4, 1948.

14. Heath, C. E., and C. H. Worsham: Chap. 14, in G. J. Young (ed.), "Fuel Cells," vol. 2, Reinhold Publishing Corporation, New York, 1963.

15. Adams, D. R. et al., "Power for the Future," Fuel Cell Associates, Cambridge, Mass., 1960; A. M. Moos, paper delivered at Electrochem. Society, National Meeting, Indianapolis, Ind., 1961.

16. Grubb, W. T., and C. J. Michalske: *Proc. Ann. Power Sources Conf.*, **18**, 17 (1964).

16a. Cairns, E. J., and E. J. McInerney: *J. Electrochem. Soc.*, **114**, 980 (1967).

17. Okrent, E. H., and C. E. Heath: Preprints of Papers at 154th Meeting of American Chemical Society, Division of Fuel Chemistry, Biennial Fuel Cell Symposium, 1967, pp. 265–275.

18. Heath, C. E., E. H. Okrent, M. Beltzer, and G. Ciprios: "Symposium on Power Sources for Electric Vehicles," Columbia University, 1967, pp. 307–312; C. E. Heath, G. Ciprios, and B. L. Tarmy, Extended Abstracts, 19th CITCE Meeting, Detroit, 1968, pp. 321–323.

18a. Bockris, J. O'M., and B. D. Cahan: *J. Chem. Phys.*, **50**, 1307 (1969).

19. Lodzinski, R. J.: Paper delivered at Third Biennial Aerospace Power Systems Conference, Philadelphia, September, 1964.

20. Geissler, H. H., and L. E. Goodman: *Proc. Ann. Power Sources Conf.*, **18**, 28 (1964).

21. Williams, K. R.: In S. Collins (ed.), "Power Sources 1968," Pergamon Press, New York, 1969.

22. Ng, D. Y. C., and D. K. Fleming: In Ref. 17, pp. 281–292; B. S. Baker and D. K. Fleming, private communication, 1969.

23. Gregory, D. P., and H. Heilbronner: In B. S. Baker (ed.), "Hydrocarbon Fuel Cell Technology," Academic Press Inc., New York, 1965, pp. 509–523.

23a. Damjanovic, A., D. Sepa, and J. O'M. Bockris, *J. Res. Inst. Cat.*, **16**, 1 (1968).

23b. Broers, G. H. J.: Private communication, 1969.

24. Kern, J. P.: Private communication, Allison Division, General Motors Corp., 1969.

25. Henwood, J. P.: Private communication, Philadelphia Gas Works, 1967.

26. Maget, H. J. R.: Chap. 4, in C. Berger (ed.), "Handbook of Fuel Cell Technology," Prentice-Hall, Inc., Englewood Cliffs, N.J., 1968.

27. Kordesch, K. V.: *Ibid.*, Chap. 3; K. V. Kordesch, private communication, 1969.

28. Justi, E., and A. Winsel: "Kalte Verbrennung," Franz Steiner Verlag, Wiesbaden, Germany, 1962; E. W. Justi and A. W. Kalberlah, *Energy Conversion*, **8**, 47 (1968).

29. Morrill, C. C., *Proc. Ann. Power Sources Conf.*, **19**, 38 (1965).

29a. Landi, H. P., J. D. Voorhies, and W. A. Barber, in Ref. 17, pp. 12–21; J. D. Voorhies, private communication, 1969.

30. Eisenberg, M.: *Proc. Ann. Power Sources Conf.*, **18**, 20 (1964).

31. Jasinski, R. J., and T. G. Kirkland: *Mech. Eng.*, **51** (1964).

32. Werth, J., J. Kennedy, and R. Weaver: Paper presented at third Biennial Aerospace Power Systems Conference, Philadelphia, September, 1964; D. A. J. Swinkels, *J. Electrochem. Soc.*, **113**, 6 (1966).

33. Long, F. A., and W. F. McDevit: *Chem. Rev.*, **51**, 119 (1952).

34. Setschenow, J.: *Z. Physik Chem.*, **4**, 117 (1889); *Ann. Chim. Phys.*, **25**, 226 (1891).

35. Bockris, J. O'M., J. Bowler-Reed, and J. A. Kitchener: *Trans. Faraday Soc.*, **47**, 184 (1951).

36. Hildebrand, J. H.: "Solubility," Reinhold Publishing Corporation, New York, 1936.

37. Schlatter, M. J.: Adsorption of Hydrocarbons, California Research Corp., Annual Rept., 1963.

38. Grubb, W. T., and L. W. Niedrach: Direct Hydrocarbon-Oxygen Fuel Cells, California Research Corp., Annual Rept., 1965.

39. Frumkin, A. N.: *Coll. Symp. Ann.*, **7**, 89 (1930).

40. Blomgren, E., J. O'M. Bockris, and C. Jesch: *J. Phys. Chem.*, **65**, 2000 (1961).

41. Bockris, J. O'M., E. Gileadi, and K. Müller: *Electrochim. Acta*, **12**, 1301 (1967).

42. Gileadi, E., B. T. Rubin, and J. O'M. Bockris: *J. Phys. Chem.*, **69**, 3335 (1965).

43. Niedrach, L. W.: *J. Electrochem. Soc.*, **111**, 1309 (1964).

44. Bockris, J. O'M., M. Green, and D. A. J. Swinkels: *J. Electrochem. Soc.*, **111**, 743 (1964).

44a. Piersma, B. J., and E. Gileadi: Chap. 2, in J. O'M. Bockris (ed.), "Modern Aspects of Electrochemistry," vol. 4, Plenum Press, New York, 1966.

45. Bockris, J. O'M., M. A. V. Devanathan, and K. Müller: *Proc. Roy. Soc.*, **A274**, 55 (1963).

46. Frumkin, A. N.: *Z. Physik.*, **35**, 792 (1926).

47. Butler, J. A. V.: *Proc. Roy. Soc.*, **A122**, 339 (1929).

48. Bockris, J. O'M., and E. C. Potter: *J. Chem. Phys.*, **20**, 614 (1952).

49. Bockris, J. O'M., and B. E. Conway: *J. Chem. Phys.*, **28**, 707 (1958).

50. Mott, N. F., and R. J. Watts-Tobin: *Electrochim. Acta*, **4**, 79 (1961).

51. Wroblowa, H., and M. Green: *Electrochim. Acta*, **8**, 679 (1963).

52. Bockris, J. O'M. and D. A. J. Swinkels: *J. Electrochem. Soc.*, **111**, 736 (1964).

53. Gileadi, E., W. Heiland, and J. O'M. Bockris: *J. Phys. Chem.*, **70**, 1207 (1966).

53a. Gileadi, E., L. Duic, and J. O'M Bockris: *Electrochim. Acta*, **13**, 1915 (1968).

53b. Petry, O. A., B. I. Podlovchenko, A. N. Frumkin, and H. Lal: *J. Electroanal. Chem.*, **10**, 253 (1965); **11**, 12 (1966).

53c. Reddy, A. K. N., M. A. Genshaw, and J. O'M. Bockris: *J. Chem. Phys.*, **48**, 671 (1968).

54. Gileadi, E., and S. Srinivasan: *J. Electroanal. Chem.*, **7**, 452 (1964).

55. Gileadi, E., and B. E. Conway: Chap. 5, in J. O'M. Bockris (ed.), "Modern Aspects of Electrochemistry," vol. 3, Butterworth & Co. (Publishers), Ltd., London, 1964.

55a. Breiter, M. W.: Private communication.

56. Blomgren, E., and J. O'M. Bockris: *J. Phys. Chem.*, **63**, 1475 (1959).

56a. Vijk, A., and B. E. Conway: *Chem. Rev.*, **67**, 623 (1967).

57. Reddy, A. K. N., M. A. Genshaw, and J. O'M. Bockris: *J. Electroanal. Chem.*, **8**, 406 (1964).

58. Gilman, S.: *J. Phys. Chem.*, **67**, 78, 1898 (1963); **68**, 70 (1964).

59. Warner, T. B., and S. Schuldiner: *J. Electrochem. Soc.*, **111**, 992 (1964).

60. Wroblowa, H., B. J. Piersma, and J. O'M. Bockris: *J. Electroanal. Chem.*, **6**, 401 (1963).

61. Wroblowa, H., E. Gileadi, J. O'M. Bockris, and B. J. Piersma: *Trans. Faraday Soc.*, **61**, 2531 (1965).

62. Hayward, C. O., and B. M. W. Trapnell: "Chemisorption," Butterworth & Co. (Publishers), Ltd., 1964.

63. Bockris, J. O'M., S. D. Argade, and E. Gileadi: *J. Phys. Chem.*, **70**, 2044 (1966).

64. Kheifets, V. L., and B. S. Krasikov: *Zh. Fiz. Khim.*, **31**, 1992 (1957).

65. Johnson, J. W., H. Wroblowa, and J. O'M. Bockris: *J. Electrochem. Soc.*, **111**, 863 (1964).

66. Kuhn, A. T., H. Wroblowa, and J. O'M. Bockris: *Trans. Faraday Soc.*, **63**, 1458 (1967).

66a. Dahms, H., and J. O'M. Bockris: *J. Electrochem. Soc.*, **111**, 728 (1964).

67. General Electric Corp.: Semiannual technical progress report 5, January–June, 1964, Direct Energy Conversion Operation, Lynn, Mass.

68. Grubb, W. T.: *Nature*, **201**, 699 (1964).

69. Cairns, E. J., and D. I. MacDonald: *Electrochem. Tech.*, **2**, 65 (1964).

70. Brummer, S. B., J. I. Ford, and M. J. Turner: *J. Phys. Chem.*, **69**, 3424 (1965).

71. Stoner, G. E., and J. O'M. Bockris: "Electro-oxidation of Saturated Hydrocarbons on Platinized Platinum in Phosphoric Acid," interim technical report 4, October, 1966, Contract No. DA44-009-AMC-469(T); J. O'M. Bockris, E. Gileadi, and G. Stoner, *J. Phys. Chem.*, **73**, 427 (1969).

72. Pavela, T. O.: *Ann. Acad. Sci. Fennicae*, Ser. *AII*, **59**, 1 (1954).

73. Gilman, S., and M. W. Breiter: *J. Electrochem. Soc.*, **109**, 622 (1962).

74. Buck, R. P., and L. R. Griffith: *J. Electrochem. Soc.*, **109**, 1005 (1962).

75. Bagotsky, V. S., and Yu. B. Vasilyev: *Electrochim. Acta*, **9**, 869 (1964).

76. Bagotzky, V. S., and Yu. B. Vassilyev: *Electrochim. Acta*, **12**, 1323 (1967).

77. Breiter, M. W.: *J. Electroanal. Chem.*, **14**, 407 (1967); **15**, 221 (1967); **19**, 131 (1968).

78. Kamath, V. N., and H. Lal: *J. Electroanal. Chem.*, **19**, 137 (1968).

79. Brummer, S. B., and A. C. Makrides: *J. Phys. Chem.*, **68**, 1448 (1964).

80. Johnson, H., H. Wroblowa, and J. O'M. Bockris: *Electrochim. Acta*, **9**, 637 (1964).

CHAPTER EIGHT

Electrodic Reactions of Oxygen

1 THE CENTRAL IMPORTANCE OF THE CATHODIC REDUCTION OF OXYGEN IN ELECTROCHEMICAL ENERGY CONVERSION

Oxygen, either pure or in air, is as important to electrochemical energy conversion as it is to chemical combustion and to life. Thus, practically all earth-based fuel cells use O_2 as the cathodic reactant. It is reduced at the cathode in acid solution to water according to

$$O_2 + 4H^+ + 4e_0^- \rightarrow 2H_2O \tag{1.1}$$

The advantage of using oxygen available in the surrounding atmosphere rather than this or other oxidants stored in a tank is that the tank and oxidant weights, in the latter case, decrease the energy weight ratio by about two to four times. It follows, therefore, that the oxygen-reduction reaction is the most important single reaction in electrochemical energy conversion. Investigation of its mechanism dates only from the mid-fifties.[1,2] The practical importance of understanding it and thus also the problem of being able to control it and reduce the associated overpotential is illustrated in Fig. 1, which shows the breakdown of the cell-potential–current-density relation for a typical H_2-O_2 cell into the half-cell-potential–current-density relations for the individual electrodes. In fact, the overpotential losses in most electrochemical energy converters, except those directly burning hydrocarbons, arise predominantly due to the slowness of the oxygen-reduction reaction (Chap. 10). Were it possible, therefore, to make it increasingly reversible, many electrochemical converters could approach the ideal efficiency, given by Eq. (4.1) in Chap. 3.

2 SPECIAL CHARACTERISTICS OF THE OXYGEN-DISSOLUTION REACTION

The phenomenology of the oxygen-dissolution reaction (odr) in the steady state, under conditions in which meaningful parameters may be determined, is

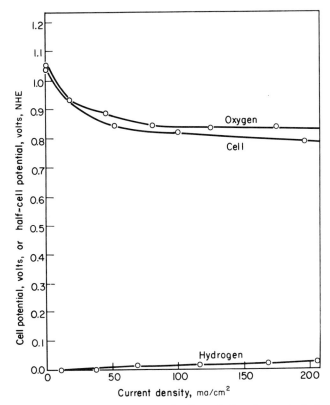

Figure 1 Cell-potential–current-density relation for a typical hydrogen-oxygen fuel-cell- and half-cell-potential–current-density relations for the individual electrodes.[2a]

still fairly sparse. Table 1 contains the principal parameters determined for the oxygen electrode reaction on some catalysts.

These quantitative data do not indicate, however, the special characteristics of oxygen-reduction reaction which make it so basic to electrochemical energy conversion. It is an electrode reaction of considerable difficulty with respect to mechanism evaluation and catalysis. These difficulties may be summarized as follows:

(*i*) The range of potential in which the reaction occurs in acid solution with respect to the potential of the normal hydrogen electrode (NHE) is about 1.0 to 0.5 volt. Reference to tables of standard potentials shows that this range is in a relatively anodic region. In particular, in this potential range, either most metals dissolve or form passivating (catalytically inactive) oxides. The number of electrocatalysts that can be used for the oxygen reduction in acid solution is limited effectively to the noble metals and the tungsten bronzes. Several others, e.g., lithiated nickel oxide and silver, can be used in alkaline

TABLE 1 Electrode Kinetic Parameters for the Oxygen-dissolution Reaction on Some Electrocatalysts in Acid and in Alkaline Electrolytes and the Most Probable rds

Electrocatalyst	pH	Rest potential, volts (RHE)	Tafel parameters i_0, amp cm^{-2}	Tafel parameters b, volts	$\partial V/\partial pH$, volts	$(\partial \log i/\partial \log p_{O_2})_v$, $(\partial V/\partial \log p_{O_2})_i$	v	Formation of H$_2$O$_2$	Probable rds	Reference no.
Pt	1.0	1.0	3×10^{-10}	0.060	-0.1	-1		Not detected	$O_2 + H^+ + e_0^- \rightarrow O_2H_{ads}$	5
Pt	13.0	1.0	1×10^{-11}	0.065	-0.03	0.24		Detected	$O_2 + H_2O + e_0^- \rightarrow O_2H_{ads} + OH^-$	3, 5
Rh	0.2		1×10^{-11}	0.065			2.1		$MO \cdots H \cdots OH^- + H^+ \rightarrow MOH + H_2O$	4
Rh	13.0	0.92	1.2×10^{-12}	0.055			1.9		Same as Pt in alkaline solution	4
Ir	0.2		1.0×10^{-11}	0.105			1.9		$MO + M \cdot H_2O + H^+ + e_0^- \rightarrow MOH + M + H_2O$	4
Ir	13.0	0.91	1.0×10^{-11}	0.100			1.9	Not detected	Same as Pt in alkaline solution	4
Au	1.0	0.80	1.5×10^{-11}	0.120			1.9		$O_2 + e_0^- \rightarrow O_2^-$	61
Pd	1.0	0.96	3.0×10^{-11}	0.060						61
Pd	13.0	1.0	1.2×10^{-11}	0.055					Same as Pt in alkaline solution	80
Ag	13.0	0.92	1.5×10^{-9}	0.110						80
Fe	13.0	0.77	4.3×10^{-10}	0.120						80
Ni	13.0	0.81	4.3×10^{-10}	0.120						80
Na$_{0.78}$WO$_3$	0.2–4.3		2×10^{-9}	0.120	0.06	0.120				7
Na$_{0.37}$WO$_3$	−0.7–2.4		5×10^{-9}	0.120	0.06	0.120				7
Na$_{0.37}$WO$_3$	0.3–9.0		5×10^{-10}	0.120	0.030	0.120				7
Sr$_{0.8}$NbO$_3$	0.3–12.5		3×10^{-7}	0.120	0.030	0.120				7
Ba$_{0.5}$TaO$_3$	0.3–12.5		1.5×10^{-6}	0.120	0.030	0.120				7

solution. This situation should be contrasted with that for the hydrogen-evolution reaction, which takes place in a region negative to the potential of the normal hydrogen electrode in acid solution, in which many substrates are stable in acid and alkaline solution.

(*ii*) The odr is relatively slow compared with other electrodic reactions, as seen in Table 2 which shows the exchange current densities for a number of

TABLE 2 **A Comparison of Exchange Current Densities for Several Reactions with That of the Oxygen-dissolution Reaction at 25°C (Values Quoted Are the Highest Area for Each Reaction as Found in the Literature)**

Reaction†	Electrode material	Exchange current density $-\log i_0$ (i_0, amp cm^{-2})	Reference no.
$2H^+ + 2e_0^- \to H_2$	Pt	3.0	8
$Cl_2 + 2e_0^- \to 2Cl^-$	Pt	3.0	9
$Ag^+ + e_0^- \to Ag$	Ag	1.0	10
$Fe^{3+} + e_0^- \to Fe^{2+}$	Pt	2.1	11
$Hg_2Cl_2 + 2e_0^- \to 2Hg + 2Cl^-$	Hg	0	12
$O_2 + 4H^+ + 4e_0^- \to 2H_2O$	$Ba_{0.5}TaO_3$	6.0	7

† Ionic activities approximately unity.

common electrode reactions. Therefore, when the odr carries a practical density of current, a large overpotential tends to be observed with corresponding decrease in energy-conversion efficiency [see Eq. (6.3) in Chap. 4]. Hence, the odr is the reaction which particularly needs catalytic research in electrochemical energy conversion.

(*iii*) The anodic potential range in which the reaction occurs causes substrate changes to occur within it. For example, on Pt there is a change in the nature of the surface at about 1.0 volt. Such a change greatly complexes a theoretical analysis of data intended to indicate the mechanism of the reaction.

(*iv*) The reversible potential of the oxygen electrode reaction (oer) is close to those of several other related reactions. For example, the standard reversible potential of the oer is 1.23 volts (NHE), but that for the reduction of PtO_2 is 1.11 volts and that for the reduction of PtO is 0.98 volt. Further, the odr tends to compete with another oxygen-reduction reaction in which H_2O_2 is formed:

$$O_2 + 2H^+ + 2e_0^- \to H_2O_2 \qquad (2.1)$$

The occurrence of this latter reaction may make ambiguous current measurements intended to register only the oxygen dissolution to water.

(*v*) The odr itself sometimes produces H_2O_2 as an intermediate. This may cause confusion in the mechanism analysis, particularly because of the possible presence of H_2O_2 as a consequence of reaction (2.1). It is only recently that a method was found to distinguish between these two cases,[13] which enabled one to clarify the mechanism of the reaction.

In summary, the odr is slow in rate and complicated in mechanism. Its use is essential to electrochemical energy conversion and hence the reaction represents a marked challenge in fundamental research. This is all the more so because the electrochemical reduction of oxygen may occur as an essential part of biological energy conversion.

3   ELECTRODIC REACTIONS WHICH COMPETE WITH THE OXYGEN-DISSOLUTION REACTION

There are three reactions in which oxygen and hydrogen peroxide are involved in electrochemistry (Table 3).

TABLE 3   Thermodynamic Reversible Potentials for the Reactions of Oxygen and Hydrogen Peroxide in Acid and Alkaline Solutions at 25°C

Reaction in acid solution	V_{rev}, volts (NHE)	Reaction in alkaline solution	V_{rev}, volts (NHE)	Eq. no.
$H_2O_2 + 2H^+ + 2e_0^- \rightarrow 2H_2O$	1.77	$HO_2^- + H_2O + 2e_0^- \rightarrow 3OH^-$	0.87	(3.1)
$O_2 + 4H^+ + 4e_0^- \rightarrow 2H_2O$	1.23	$O_2 + 2H_2O + 4e_0^- \rightarrow 4OH^-$	0.40	(3.2)
$O_2 + 2H^+ + 2e_0^- \rightarrow H_2O_2$	0.68	$O_2 + H_2O + 2e_0^- \rightarrow HO_2^- + OH^-$	−0.07	(3.3)

Hypothetical anodic and cathodic current-potential relations for these reactions are schematically represented in Fig. 2.

4   THE COMPLEX SITUATION NEAR THE REVERSIBLE POTENTIAL FOR THE ELECTRODIC REDUCTION OF OXYGEN TO WATER

4.1   Importance of Understanding Phenomena near the Reversible Potential

The limiting, not yet attained, ideal electrochemical energy converter should function at high power densities (greater than 1.0 watt cm^{-2}) very near to the reversible potential of the reaction, the chemical energy of which is being converted to electricity. It follows that the behavior of the electrode reactions in electrochemical energy converters near to the reversible potential is of great importance. It happens that the behavior of the odr is anomalous in the region of its reversible potential and this anomalous behavior tends to cause a loss in working voltage of electrochemical energy converters and hence a reduction in their efficiencies and power. For this reason, a detailed discussion of the anomalous behavior of the odr in the vicinity of its reversible potential and reasons for this behavior follows.

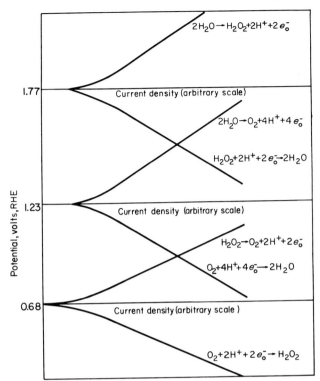

Figure 2 Hypothetical anodic and cathodic current-potential relations for the electrodic reactions of oxygen and of hydrogen peroxide.

4.2 Experimental Observations

4.2.1 Comparison of the Observed Rest Potential on Platinum with the Reversible Potential

When one determines a potential-log–current-density relation for the odr on a platinum electrode, the result is not as expected but rather as shown in Fig. 3. The Tafel equation breaks down at a potential of about 0.95 volt and the potential–current-density line, instead of passing through the reversible potential, turns over and passes through a potential in the region of 0.95 to 1.04 volt.[5,6,14] Thus, even at the lowest current density—in fact, even at the resting potential when the current density is zero—there is a loss in potential of the oxygen electrode from the reversible electrode potential by 0.2 to 0.3 volt. The maximum energy-conversion efficiency of a converter is hence decreased by some 25 percent.

One of the more pregnant questions of oxygen-electrode-reaction theory, therefore, is: Why is there a kind of "autopolarization" of over 0.2 volt?[14]

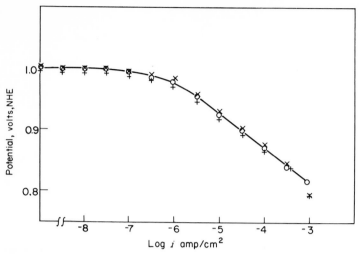

Figure 3   Current-density–potential relation for the electroreduction of oxygen on Pt in 1 N H$_2$SO$_4$ showing a leveling off of the potential at 1.0 volt at low current densities.[4]   Reversible potential is 1.23 volts (NHE). Measurements on electrodes pretreated are as follows: ○, thermally treated; ×, foil cold rolled to 50% reduction; and +, foil cold rolled and annealed, at 900°C for 2 hr.

4.2.2   Phenomenological Aspects of the Observed Rest Potential on Platinum

Some of the phenomenological aspects of the observed rest potential on platinum may now be mentioned:[15] (1) A linear dependence of the rest potential on log p_{O_2} was observed (Fig. 4).   The slope of the line is 60 mv.   (2) The plots of oxygen coverages as obtained by galvanostatic reduction vs. pressure are shown

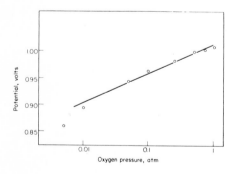

Figure 4   Dependence of rest potential at platinum electrode in 1 N H$_2$SO$_4$ on pressure of oxygen.[15]

for four temperatures in Fig. 5.   The coverages are nearly independent of p_{O_2} above 0.5 atm.   (3) The rest potential varies approximately linearly with oxygen coverage (Fig. 6).   In the same figure are shown the values of the oxygen

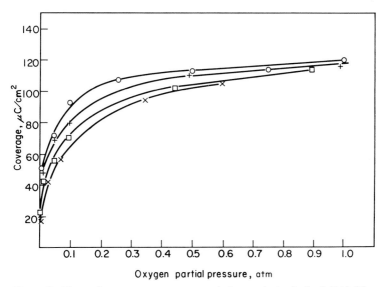

Figure 5 Plots of oxygen coverages on platinum electrode in 1 N H$_2$SO$_4$ versus pressure of oxygen at temperatures of 0 ($\bigcirc$), 20 (+), 50 ($\square$), and 80 ($\times$)$^\circ$C.[15]

coverages on the electrode as a function of its potential in nitrogen saturated solution. These values practically fall on the same line as that for the oxygen coverage vs. the rest potential. The relation is approximately linear in the coverage range 25 to 110 μcoul cm^{-2}. (4) The rest potential varies linearly with pH having a slope of $-2.3\ RT/F$. (5) The potential of the electrode was found to be independent of cathodic current densities up to 10^{-7} amp cm^{-2}. (6) An anodic limiting current density of about 10^{-7} amp cm^{-2} was observed. This limiting current gradually disappeared with *increasing purification* of the solution by preelectrolysis (Fig. 7).

4.3 Interpretations of Departure of Observed Rest Potential from Reversible Potential

Several models have been proposed as interpretations of the 1.0 potential.[15-18] Of these, one of the most stressed has been that in which the potential is ascribed to the formation of some form of peroxide which then enters into an electrode reaction.[16] For example,

$$O_2 + H^+ + e_0^- \rightarrow HO_2 \tag{4.1}$$

$$O_2 + 2H^+ + 2e_0^- \rightarrow H_2O_2 \tag{4.2}$$

However, when one calculates the amount of peroxide from these theories which should be present according to thermodynamics, it is very small, for example, 10^{-20} mole l^{-1} of HO$_2$ for reaction (4.1) and 10^{-13} mole l^{-1} of H$_2$O$_2$ for reaction

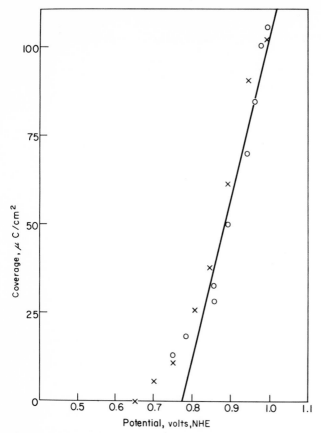

Figure 6   Plot of oxygen coverage (circles) on platinum electrode in $1\,N\,H_2SO_4$ at $25°C$ versus rest potential.   Crosses represent oxygen coverage on electrode as a function of potential of electrode in nitrogen-saturated solutions.[15]

(4.2).   These concentrations are far too small to support the observed anodic limiting current densities of the order of 10^{-7} amp cm^{-3}.   Thus (Table 4) theories involving reactions expressed by Eqs. (4.1) and (4.2) cannot be accepted.

Alternatively, the presence of two oxide potentials, namely, the Pt/PtO and PtO/PtO_2 near to the oxygen potential, has led to the suggestion[17] that either of them represents the origin of the observed rest potentials, i.e., one of them has an exchange current density greater than that of the four-electron reduction and hence would predominate in determination of the potential.   This model, in the absence of the reactions partaking in any mixed potential, must also be rejected because it does not allow interpretation of the effect of changing oxygen pressure, stated above.

A third suggestion[18] concerns a model in which the Pt/solution interface is regarded as polarizable (cf. Chap. 2, Sec. 2) in the potential region of 1.0 volt or

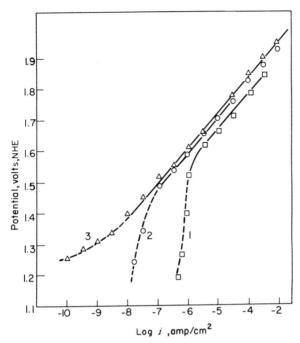

Figure 7 Gradual disappearance of anodic limiting current density with purification of electrolyte: (1) Unpreelectrolyzed solution; (2) after 40 hr preelectrolysis; (3) after 60 hr preelectrolysis. Upper portion of curves represent potential–current-density relations for oxygen evolution.[3]

TABLE 4 **Thermodynamic Reversible Potentials for the Platinum/Platinum Oxide Couples and for the Various Reactions Involving Oxygen and Hydrogen Peroxide**

Overall reaction	Standard electrode potential, volts
1. $H_2O_2 + 2H^+ + 2e_0^- = 2H_2O$	1.77
2. $PtO_3 + 2H^+ + 2e_0^- = PtO_2 + H_2O$	1.48
3. $O_2 + 4H^+ + 4e_0^- = 2H_2O$	1.23
4. $PtO_2 + 2H^+ + 2e_0^- = Pt(OH)_2$	1.11
5. $Pt(OH)_2 + 2H^+ + 2e_0^- = Pt + 2H_2O$	0.98
6. $PtO + 2H^+ + 2e_0^- = Pt + 2H_2O$	0.88
7. $O_2 + 2H^+ + 2e^- = H_2O_2$	0.68
8. $2H^+ + 2e_0^- = H_2$	0.0
9. $O_2 + H^+ + e_0^- = HO_2$	0.13
10. Impurities $+ 2nH_2O = nCO_2$ $+ 4ne_0^- + 4nH^+$	?

below. According to this theory, the variation of the rest potential with oxygen pressure originates from replacement of water dipoles in the surface with oxygen atoms. The difference in dipole moments of the M-O bond and adsorbed water dipoles would account for the change in potential with pressure. This type of theory fails to interpret the relatively large currents which may, in fact, flow across the surface in the vicinity of 0.9 potential, i.e., the surface is not sufficiently polarizable.

These and other models do not seem to give a qualitative understanding of the 1.0 potential, and for this reason a quite different type of suggestion has been made and worked out in detail by Wroblowa et al.[15] It is that the cathodic current for the oxygen-reduction reaction is compromised by another current due to some anodic process. In this way, a mixed potential is obtained. An attempt must, of course, be made to choose some appropriate second reaction with which the odr is to be coupled. A number of possibilities are shown in Table 4. Reaction 3 in this table cannot play a part because were its anodic reaction to occur at a mixed potential of about 1 volt, the concentration of H_2O_2 should be lower than about 10^{-20} mole l^{-1} and this will not maintain a limiting current of the order mentioned (cf. Sec. 4.2.2). Corresponding arguments eliminate all other reactions in the table, except a general reaction of the type 10, involving some substance such as an organic impurity present at low concentrations in solution and having a reversible potential of 0.2 to 0.3 volt.† It is then the anodic reaction to be coupled with the odr. This hypothesis has the disadvantage that the substance or substances in question remain unidentified. It has the advantage, however, of being consistent with the fundamental result that when the solution is well purified the 1.23 potential rather than the 1.0 potential is observed. Moreover, even some reasonably large variation of reversible potential of the anodic reaction of hypothetical impurity and its concentration should not make a large change in the observed rest potential, as seen in Fig. 8. In fact, the so-called 1.0 potential is, of course, by no means constant in various systems and varies by 0.1 volt. (In Fig. 8, *A* and *C* show effect of change of concentration of impurity on the limiting current density for the impurity oxidation reaction and hence on the mixed potential; *A* and *B* represent the current-density-potential relations for the oxidation of two impurities with different reversible potentials but with approximately the same limiting current densities.

Apart from these qualitative matters, Wroblowa et al. showed that the mixed potential model can give rise to correct functional dependences. pH and p_{O_2} dependencies can be quantitatively predicted. Correspondingly, the anodic limiting density decreases with increasing purification of solution (Fig. 7). An impurity concentration of 10^{-7} to 10^{-6} mole l^{-1} is indicated in many insufficiently purified solutions by the rotating-disk method.[13] This is in agreement with Tafel lines for oxygen reduction which deviates from linearity at about 10^{-7} amp cm^{-2} (Fig. 3).

---

† This is the observed rest potential on platinum electrodes in 1 N H_2SO_4 in the presence of any one of a large number of hydrocarbons (Chap. 7, Sec. 7.3).

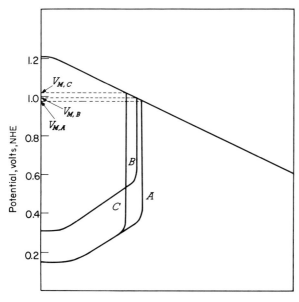

Figure 8 Current-density–potential relations for the oxygen-reduction reaction and some hypothetical anodic reactions (e.g., oxidation of organic impurity) showing the existence of a mixed potential at 1.0 volt. Two anodic reactions with reasonably different reversible potentials yield approximately same mixed potential (lines *A* and *B*). Effect of change of concentration of same impurity is also small (lines *A* and *C*).

The linear relation between oxygen coverage and the rest potential (Fig. 6) can be rationalized, in this mixed potential model, on the basis of adsorption of oxygen under Temkin conditions. Since the same coverage-potential relation is obtained in a nitrogen atmosphere, the process of oxygen adsorption occurs on the electrode due to the water-discharge reaction and not due to the dissociative adsorption of oxygen, which is again consistent with the mixed potential model.

In summary, the 1.0-volt potential is due to a mixed potential which is a result of the four-electron transfer reduction of oxygen and the anodic oxidation of an impurity in solution occurring at its limiting current density. Purification of the electrolyte reduces this impurity concentration and makes the rest potential tend toward the reversible potential for the four-electron oxygen-reduction reaction.

4.4 Mixed Potentials on Platinum and Gold Electrodes in the Presence of Hydrogen Peroxide

The complexity of oxygen-electrode reactions may be illustrated by phenomena that occur in the presence of hydrogen peroxide. When this is added to a

solution in which a platinum or gold electrode saturated with oxygen is dipped, a
potential is established which is dependent upon pH (Fig. 9) but *independent of*

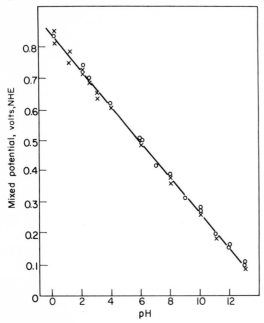

Figure 9 Dependence of mixed potentials set up at
Pt ($\bigcirc$) and Au ($\times$) electrodes in the presence of H_2O_2
in solution on pH.[20]

the hydrogen peroxide concentration,[20] though it is the origin of this potential, in
the range 10^{-6} to 10 moles l^{-1}.

This situation may be rationalized[21] as a result of a mixed potential between
reactions 1 and 7 in Table 4.   The concentration of hydrogen peroxide has no
effect upon the mixed potential of the electrode, because it is consumed in both
the anodic and cathodic reactions and the reaction order for each of these reactions is unity.[21]   Current-density–potential relations for the electrooxidation
and for the electroreduction of hydrogen peroxide on platinum for two concentrations[22] of H_2O_2 are shown in Fig. 10 using 1 N H_2SO_4 as electrolyte.   Independence of the mixed potential on the H_2O_2 concentration can be seen.

4.5   Experimental Attainment of the
Reversible Oxygen-electrode Potential

4.5.1   *Method of Electrolytic Purification*
by Anodic and Cathodic Preelectrolysis

As has been stressed above, attainment of the reversible oxygen potential is
extremely difficult because of interference by impurities at very low concentration.
This matter may be examined generally, as seen in Chap. 2, Sec. 12.   Thus, if

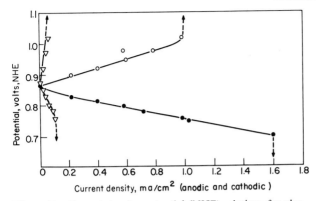

Figure 10   Current-density–potential (NHE) relations for electrochemical oxidation and reduction of H_2O_2 on Pt in 1 N H_2SO_4 for two concentrations of H_2O_2.[22] Intersection of anodic and cathodic lines is at 0.84 volt—the mixed potential for both concentrations of H_2O_2.

one is to attain a reversible potential in the case of the four-electron transfer oer [Eq. (1.1)], since its exchange current density on platinum is of the order of 10^{-10} amp cm^{-2}, it is necessary to reduce the amount of electroactive impurities present in the solution to some 10^{-10} mole l^{-1}.

These considerations were applied by Bockris and Huq[1] in 1956 using cathodic followed by anodic preelectrolytic purification of the solution. The effect of cathodic preelectrolysis may be to produce hydrogen peroxide which subsequently aids the oxidation of impurities in the system. Anodic preelectrolysis further oxidizes impurities, but in addition, it removes any H_2O_2 formed during cathodic preelectrolysis and still remaining in solution.

The potential obtained was 1.24 $\pm$ 0.03 volts after a cathodic preelectrolysis at 10^{-2} amp cm^{-2} for 24 hr, followed by anodic preelectrolysis at the same current density for twice this time.

Bockris and Huq verified that the potential they had observed was indeed that corresponding to Eq. (3.3) in a way which is illustrated in Fig. 11, that is,

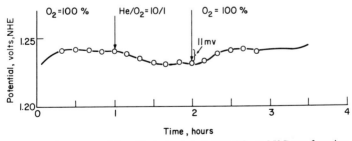

Figure 11   Rest potential on Pt electrode in 1 N H_2SO_4 at 25°C as a function of time, after 24 hr cathodic preelectrolysis and 48 hr anodic preelectrolysis at a current density of 10^{-2} amp cm^{-2}, showing effect of change in partial pressure of oxygen.[1]

this shows that the potential changes with partial pressure of oxygen in pre-electrolyzed solutions.   The theoretical pressure coefficient is given by

$$\frac{dV_{rev}}{d\log p_{O_2}} = \frac{2.3RT}{4F} = 15 \text{ mv at } 25°C \tag{4.3}$$

The experimentally observed coefficient was 11 mv.   It was also found that the potential remained steady for a long time if preelectrolysis was continued on an auxiliary electrode in the solution, but if preelectrolysis was interrupted the potential decreased from the value corresponding to the reversible potential (Fig. 12).   The reversible potential for the oxygen electrode reaction was indeed easily

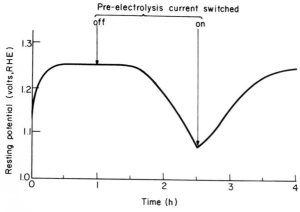

Figure 12   Effect of interruption of preelectrolysis, at an auxiliary electrode, on the rest potential at a Pt electrode in 1 N H$_2$SO$_4$ as a function of time.[1]

disturbed by the presence of impurities (e.g., hydrogen which diffuses through closed stopcocks between reference and test electrode compartments).

4.5.2 Other Methods

The first experimental observation of the reversible potential for the oxygen-electrode reaction was by Haber and Fleischmann in molten carbonate solution.[23] The cell used for this measurement is shown in Fig. 13.   Thereafter, Hoar (1933) made an indirect determination by showing that the anodic and cathodic Tafel lines of the oxygen-electrode reaction on a platinum electrode in sulfuric acid intersected at 1.20 $\pm$ 0.03 volts (Fig. 14).[14]   This was the first confirmation made in aqueous solutions that the reversible potential of oxygen reduction is indeed 1.23 volts, as indicated by thermodynamic calculations.   The reversible potential may also be observed by a somewhat different procedure (Watanabe and Devanathan).[24]   An oxide layer is formed on the electrode by prior anodic polarization and subsequent exposure to an oxygen atmosphere.   The theoretical pressure-dependence was also observed on this electrode.   It was shown

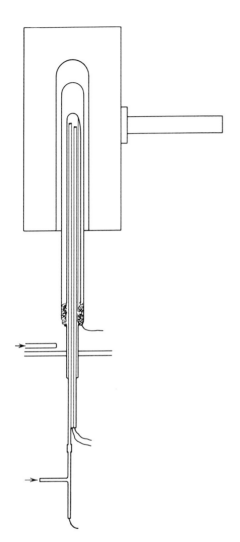

Figure 13 Cell of Haber and Fleischmann[23] in which the reversible potential for the oxygen-electrode reaction in molten carbonate electrolyte was realized.

that the reversible potential could be obtained in a manner much the same as that of Bockris and Huq except that the method of electrolytic purification was modified,[17] e.g., hydrogen peroxide was directly added to the electrolyte for oxidation of impurities, excess hydrogen peroxide was removed by heating the electrolyte to 70°C, and thereafter anodic preelectrolysis was applied.

A further establishment of the reversible potential for the evolution and dissolution of oxygen was made by Hoare.[25] Electrodes heated to 500°C, passivated by quenching in nitric acid, and subsequently washed with conductivity water repeatedly yielded the reversible potential, which was particularly stable for 72 hr. The possibility that this potential is for the NO_2/NO couple,[26] which reaction has a reversible potential in this region, was excluded on the grounds that when the electrodes were repeatedly washed with conductivity water between the passivation treatment and measurement of potential the

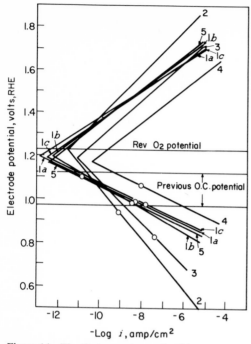

Figure 14   The first experimental evidence for the thermodynamic reversible potential of the oxygen-electrode reaction in aqueous solutions; intersection of the anodic and cathodic Tafel lines at the reversible potential.[14]

electrodes showed the same potential.   This method lends support to the view[24] that the reversible potential for the oxygen-electrode reaction is observed only on oxide-covered electrodes and indicates the necessity of investigating more closely the nature of the electrode substrate.

5   NATURE OF THE SURFACE OF OXYGEN ELECTRODES

5.1   Necessity of Examination

In the archetype of electrodic reactions, the hydrogen-evolution reaction, changes in the nature of the substrate during the reaction over a wide range of potential are unusual.   In reactions involving the dissolution of oxygen, however, such changes (due to the formation of oxides on many metals in the region of potential over which the reaction may be studied) are expected.   The nature and range of existence of these changes must be determined with respect to the study of mechanisms and electrocatalysis.   Many methods that are available to the classical catalyst chemist for investigation of the nature of surface of catalysts are not effective for electrodes in solution, e.g., electron microscopy is restricted to specimens in vacuum.

Three main methods have been used to determine the nature of the substrate. All have been applied to platinum.

5.2 Methods of Determination

5.2.1 Coulometry

The method of galvanostatic charging curves for the formation and reduction of oxygen layers on the surfaces of metals (Chap. 9, Sec. 4) has been extensively used.[17,27-39] Figure 15 gives the results of some recent work[39] on oxygen

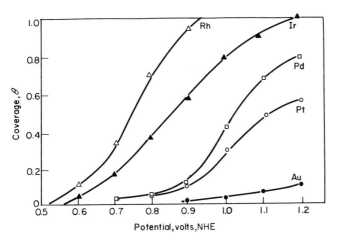

Figure 15 Oxygen coverage vs. potential relations on noble metals in 1 N H_2SO_4 at 20°C.[39]

coverages on the metals Pt, Rh, Ir, Pd, and Au as a function of potential in a relatively cathodic range. At more positive potentials, the relations are linear.

Basically, coulometric studies provide the electric charge per unit area Q necessary for the reduction of the oxide. To convert this charge into a thickness t, one uses the relation

$$t = \frac{QE}{nF\rho} \tag{5.1}$$

where E and ρ are the equivalent weight and density of the oxide, and n is the number of electrons required to form one molecule of the Pt oxide. Thus, unless some independent methods for thickness and density determinations are possible, the value of n and the chemical nature of film are not determined by coulometry. This method provides a rough estimate of thickness assuming an arbitrary value of n and, correspondingly, a rough estimate of ρ. It is also necessary not only to distinguish between chemical formulas of various oxides but also to create criteria by which an oxide may be distinguished from an "adsorbed" oxygen layer.   Distinctions between adsorbed oxygen layers and very thin layers of oxide have hitherto been somewhat misty.   Recently, definitive distinction between the two has been obtained (Sec. 5.2.3).   The term "adsorbed" is used when oxygen is bound only to surface metal atoms and the metal atoms have not entered into bonding with oxygen in the plane of adsorption. The extent of adsorption is such that it usually will not cover the electrode surface to monolayer proportions.   "Oxide films" are defined as those in which there is at least a monolayer of oxygen in which the oxygen is bound by several bonds to surrounding metal atoms and the coordination number is such that the oxygen must be regarded as "surrounded" by metal atoms on all but one side. When there are two or more oxygen layers, it seems justified to refer to the body as an oxide.   Methods other than these are necessary to distinguish between adsorbed oxygen and a lattice of oxide on the surface of a metal.

5.2.2   Chemical Methods

The first direct chemical evidence that oxides of platinum exist on an anodically polarized surface was obtained by Anson and Lingane.[40]   In this method, the film on the electrode was stripped by boiling the electrode in a solution of 0.2 M HCl and 0.1 M NaCl in an inert atmosphere.   The solution was then analyzed spectrophotometrically for a quantitative determination of $PtCl_4^{2-}$ and $PtCl_6^{2-}$. These two ions have sufficiently different absorption spectra to allow a distinction between them and thus separate estimations.   Standard solutions of K_2PtCl_4 and $(NH_4)_2PtCl_6$ were used for calibration.   Traces of oxide that were not removed by the stripping solution were cathodically *stripped*.   The total number of equivalents of $PtCl_4^{2-}$, $PtCl_6^{2-}$, and traces of oxide removed by cathodic stripping agreed well with the number of equivalents obtained by cathodic stripping alone, which directly followed anodization, thus showing that $PtCl_4^{2-}$ and $PtCl_6^{2-}$ are formed by the dissolution of the oxide only and not of the metal. Blank experiments were also carried out by dipping a Pt electrode in a solution containing known quantities of $PtCl_4^{2-}$ and $PtCl_6^{2-}$ ions.   Further, oxides were formed on the surface by chemical methods—treatment of the electrode with 0.1 M ceric sulfate in 1 M sulfuric acid (for stronger oxidizing conditions either 0.3 M ceric perchlorate in 6 M perchloric acid or Ag^{2+} solution in 8 M nitric acid were used).   These were all subjected to the same treatment as with preanodized electrodes, viz., cathodic stripping alone or chemical stripping followed by cathodic stripping of traces of oxide not removed by chemical stripping.   In this case, it was found that there was good agreement in both methods.   It was also found that if the films were formed with either strong anodic treatment or strong oxidizing agents, longer stripping times were necessary.   Table 5 gives the results obtained under various conditions.   It was found that the ratio of Pt^{2+} to Pt^{4+} remained constant (nearly 6:1) for the various treatments, but, as expected, the total quantity of oxide increased with stronger oxidizing conditions.   That any homogeneous phase reduction of Pt^{4+} or disproportionation

TABLE 5 A Comparison of Amounts of Oxides Formed on Platinum for Various Methods of Their Preparation, as Determined by Coulometric and Chemical Means[40]

Oxidation process	τ, sec†	*Equiv.* $PtCl_4^{2-}$ stripped, sec, at 2.00 ma	*Equiv.* $PtCl_6^{2-}$ stripped, sec, at 2.00 ma	τ‡ residual, sec	*Equiv.* $PtCl_4^{2-}$ + *equiv.* $PtCl_6^{2-}$ + τ residual, sec§
a	21.0	11.0	3.5	3.8	18.3
b	33.5	10.1	3.7	20.8	34.6
c	37.2	9.3	3.5	24.5	37.3
d	33.7	20.2	7.0	8.1	35.3
e	25.1	14.8	5.4	4.7	24.9

a Electrode oxidized just until its potential reached the inflection potential, 1.23 volts versus SCE, in the anodic chronopotentiogram
b Anodization for 5 min at 2.00 ma in 1 *M* sulfuric acid
c Standing for 5 min in 0.01 *M* + 2 silver solutions in 8 *M* nitric acid
d Standing for 5 min in 0.3 *M* ceric perchlorate solution in 6 *M* perchloric acid
e Standing for 5 min in 0.1 *M* ceric sulfate solution in 1 *M* sulfuric acid
  † Galvanostatic stripping time of oxide on surface with current of 2 ma.
  ‡ Galvanostatic stripping time of residue of oxide on surface after chemical stripping procedure.
  § There is excellent agreement between the electrochemical stripping on the one hand (results in the second column) and the chemical stripping followed by the electrochemical stripping of the residue on the other (sum of results in the third, fourth, and fifth columns which are found in the sixth column).

of Pt^{2+} occurred after chemical stripping was rejected by carrying out a blank experiment in which an unoxidized platinum electrode was subjected to the stripping treatment in a solution containing known quantities of $PtCl_4^{2-}$ and $PtCl_6^{2-}$ in 0.2 *M* HCl and 0.1 *M* NaCl. The $PtCl_6^{2-}$ concentration reduced by 30 percent and the $PtCl_4^{2-}$ increased accordingly, but only after the long time of 2 hr boiling of the stripping solution. The stripping treatment was carried out for only 20 to 60 min in the experiments with oxidized electrodes. In the blank experiments, hardly any change in the Pt^{2+}/Pt^{4+} ratio was observed for these times.

There appears, however, to be a disadvantage of this method. It is necessary to remove the electrode from solution for subsequent chemical analysis and air oxidation may be considered as a possible error. But if the results of the present chemical method are converted into equivalent coulombs, good agreement between this figure and that measured directly, electrochemically, is obtained.

5.2.3 *Ellipsometry*

The method of ellipsometry provides a unique tool for optical examination of electrode surfaces because it enables one to detect and investigate films of a fraction of a monolayer upwards.[41-43]

In the ellipsometric method, a beam of light is introduced into the system concerned, and it is so arranged that it strikes the surface, which must be highly reflective.   The incident light must be polarized.   Its state of polarization is described by two parameters—Δ, the phase difference between the two components of light in the plane of incidence and the one perpendicular to it; and ψ, the ratio of the amplitudes of the two components.   The system is arranged so that the beam strikes the reflecting metal for the first time at a potential sufficiently negative, at which no film forms on the electrode.   Thereafter, the parameters Δ and ψ in the reflected light are measured.   The potential of the metal substrate is then changed so that one approaches a region in which a film may form or the substrate may undergo some other change.   Parameters Δ and ψ for the reflected polarized light are again measured.   A relation exists that connects Δ and ψ to the three physical properties of film—its thickness t, refractive index n_∞, and coefficient in respect to absorption of light κ.   The last of these is closely connected to the electronic conductivity of the substrate.

    The remarkable and positive aspects of the ellipsometric method are that it (1) is sensitive to an average thickness of the order of 1 Å and (2) can be used to examine an electrode in solution (contrast the classical optical method, e.g., electron microscopy and infrared spectroscopy).   It provides connections to three properties of film, two of which relate to film constitution.

    On the other hand, the ellipsometric method has certain disadvantages.   In particular, there is a fundamental one in that two parameters Δ and ψ are related to three unknowns, t, n_∞, and κ.   Hence, in principle, it is only if a second method can be used to provide parallel information on one of three unknowns that the ellipsometric method can be used to give information on the other two. In certain special cases, it is possible to make estimates of maximum and minimum values of all three parameters without resource to a second method.

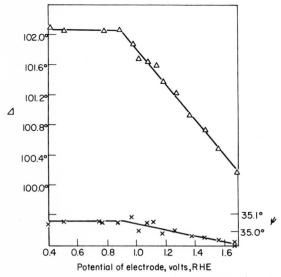

Figure 16   Plots of the ellipsometric parameters, Δ and ψ, as a function of the potential of a platinum electrode in 1 N H_2SO_4 at 25°C.[43]

The results of Reddy, Genshaw, and Bockris[43] on the ellipsometric examination of the surfaces of Pt electrodes in solution are shown in Fig. 16, where the experimentally determined parameters Δ and ψ are plotted as a function of the potential of the platinum electrode. It shows that there is a "switch-on" of a new property, to which the ellipsometric results are sensitive, at a potential of 0.95 volt.

A way out of the difficulty of having two ellipsometric parameters related to three unknowns is in a method developed by Hoogland and Visscher.[44] They made coulometric examinations of platinum oxide and plotted thickness-potential relations with the arbitrary assumption that the film was either PtO or PtO_2. The refractive indices of these two oxides in bulk form were measured in parallel. The ellipsometric measurements were made and equations were solved for the thickness and absorption coefficient using the refractive index for either PtO or PtO_2. The two thickness-potential relations thus arising ellipsometrically can then be compared with those obtained coulometrically with the two assumptions concerning the refractive index. It was found that the agreement between coulometric and ellipsometric thickness-potential relations was better if the refractive index for PtO were used. It was concluded therefore, that this was the predominant oxide, a result that is consistent with that from the chemical methods (Sec. 5.2.2). In this way, thickness and the nature of the oxide were determined. The possibility that the oxide is PtO_3 was not considered.

Figure 17 shows a comparison of the ellipsometric work on platinum with that of coulometry. There is excellent agreement between the thickness measurements in both methods in all regions of potential of the platinum electrode more positive than about 0.95, but at potentials below this value, coulometry

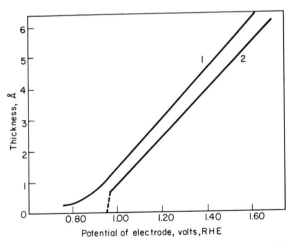

Figure 17 A comparison of the oxygen-coverage–potential relations on a platinum electrode in 1 $N\,H_2SO_4$ at 25°C, as obtained by ellipsometry (curve 2) and by coulometry (curve 1).[43]

continues to indicate oxygen on the surface, whether they be in the form of adsorbed species, such as oxygen atoms or hydroxyl radicals, or of oxides.

The interpretation given by Reddy, Genshaw, and Bockris to the sudden switch-on of the ellipsometric intensity on the surface is as follows: Below 0.95 volt, the film is due to chemisorbed O atoms or OH radicals and is less than a monolayer in extent.   Ellipsometric methods cannot detect this film because it probably resembles water in its optical properties.   Above 0.95 volt, an oxide film is present.   In consistency with this, it is at this potential that organic oxidation reactions on Pt diminish in rate.[19]   The absorption coefficient of the film is significantly different from that of water and is in the range characteristic of metals and semiconductors.

5.2.4   Summarizing Remarks on the Nature of the Platinum Surface in the Neighborhood of the Reversible Potential for the Oxygen-electrode Reaction

In summary, it appears that the substrates of platinum at sufficiently anodic potentials above about 0.95 volt, with respect to the normal hydrogen electrode, form a lattice of oxide.   At potentials less anodic than this potential, the optical properties are those of the metal surface, but this is not a free surface.   It is partly covered—apart from water molecules—with an adsorbed oxygen-containing radical, either oxygen atoms or OH radicals.   The coverage-potential relation for the oxide film on the electrode is linear over a considerable range of potential.   The oxide film is electronically conducting.

The kinetics of the oxygen-reduction reaction can be expected to differ radically depending upon whether it is carried out on the oxide substrate (more positive than 0.95 volt) or on the "metal" substrate (more negative than 0.95 volt).†   Qualitatively similar remarks probably apply to other substrates on which the oxygen-reduction reaction takes place.   The necessary ellipsometric results for other metals are not yet available.

6   REACTION MECHANISMS IN THE FOUR-ELECTRON TRANSFER CATHODIC REDUCTION (AND ANODIC EVOLUTION) OF OXYGEN

6.1   Relevance of Studies on the Electroevolution of Oxygen in an Understanding of the Mechanisms of the Cathodic Reaction

As pointed out in Sec. 1, the oxygen-reduction reaction is the most important reaction in electrochemical energy conversion.   At the same time, it is also one of the most difficult and complicated electrode reactions from the point of view of mechanism investigations.   The study of the oxygen-evolution reaction (oer) is less subject to the difficulties one is beset with in that for the odr.   Thus, it

† 0.95 is to be taken with a limit of +0.05volt.   The precise potential of film formation depends on the pretreatment of the Pt surface.

takes place in a potential range more positive than 1.23 volts (NHE) and is thus far from the potential range in which some of the complicated alternate reactions, including that of change of substrate, occur. The cathodic and anodic behavior of the same electrode reaction are, of course, related, and some of the relevant equations are given in Chap. 2, Sec. 3. It is always desirable to study both reactions, because information on the mechanism of the anodic reaction is instructive about the mechanism of the corresponding cathodic one. This is so in two ways. First, it is sometimes not possible to evaluate fundamental mechanistic criteria, e.g., stoichiometric numbers, unless the phenomenology in both directions of the reaction is known. Second, in a more fundamental way, in the application of the principle of microscopic reversibility, i.e., in the neighborhood of equilibrium, the mechanisms of the forward and backward reactions of a given reaction must be the same. This principle can be cautiously extended away from equilibrium if suitable evidence exists of the continuity of the mechanism of electrode reactions, at significant overpotentials, with that at the respective reversible potentials. Because of the difficulties of studying the cathodic reaction of oxygen (cf. Secs. 2 to 4), one tends to stress the study of the four-electron transfer evolution of oxygen and make conclusions on the cathodic side. A characteristic danger is found in this procedure for the oxygen-electrode reaction. There is a change in the substrate in the cathodic region. Consequently, the steady-state cathodic reduction of oxygen at potentials more negative than about 1.0 volt occurs on a surface which differs from that at both the reversible potential and at positive potentials at which the anodic measurements are made. Correspondingly, this restricts the relevance of the information from studies on the anodic reaction with respect to the mechanism of the cathodic reaction. The mechanism of the cathodic reaction at potentials more negative than about 0.95 volt on Pt thus needs separate examination.

6.2 Anodic Evolution of Oxygen

6.2.1 General

The oxygen-evolution reaction is one of the more fundamental anodic reactions and is the analog, in this respect, of the hydrogen-evolution reaction for cathodic reactions. In acid solution, the study of the oer is restricted to the noble metals and certain special substrates (e.g., the tungsten bronzes and some oxides such as PbO_2).[45] In alkaline solution, owing to the fact that the potential range is about 0.84 volt more cathodic than in acid solutions, there is less tendency for the substrate to dissolve, and hence it is possible to carry out the reaction on more metals. The overall reactions in acid and alkaline solutions are represented by Eqs. (3.2). This reaction is highly irreversible (low i_0) on most electrocatalysts. Hence, owing to competing reactions of impurities with higher exchange current densities (Chap. 2, Sec. 12), there has been great difficulty in observing the reversible potentials.

6.2.2   Probable Paths and Rate-determining Steps

There are two broad views concerning the type of path undergone by the re-actants in oxygen evolution.   One view is that hydrogen peroxide or a peroxide ion is an intermediate in the overall reaction and the reaction sequence may be represented by (3.1) followed by (3.3), both running anodically.   The other view is that the intermediates are principally oxides, hydroxides, or oxyhydrates and no peroxide intermediate forms.   It is known that oxides of platinum, as distinct from adsorbed oxygen, form in the whole region of oxygen evolution in acid solution.[43]   An example of a possible path involving only oxide inter-mediates may be represented by

$$M + H_2O \rightarrow MOH + H^+ + e_0^- \tag{6.1}$$

$$2MOH \rightleftarrows MO + M + H_2O \tag{6.2}$$

$$2MO \rightleftarrows 2M + O_2 \tag{6.3}$$

The origin of the concept that H_2O_2 is an intermediate in oxygen evolution arises from the frequent discussion of the formation of this entity in the cathodic reduction.   However, as pointed out in the previous subsection, the transfer of mechanistic implications from anodic to cathodic mechanisms, or vice versa, for the oxygen electrode reaction is only valuable when data for the cathodic re-action is obtained on oxide-covered platinum surfaces, i.e., in the condition in which the anodic reaction was studied.   This means they are measured rapidly in the cathodic region after anodic polarization, or that measurements of the cathodic reaction are restricted to the difficult region between 1.23 and 1.00 volts in which an oxide exists exactly on Pt.   Data from steady-state long-time cathodic measurements in which H_2O_2 may be produced cannot have direct implication for the mechanism of the anodic reaction.   All paths involve an oxygen-containing radical, whether they pass through H_2O_2 or not.   These models are consistent with the work of Rozenthaal and Veselovskii,[46] who by means of tracer experiments showed that oxygen evolved electrolytically on Pt-O^{18} surfaces contained the heavy oxygen isotope.

Bockris[47] has carried out a detailed analysis of the current-potential re-lations, stoichiometric numbers, and pH and salt effects for several possible paths and rate-determining steps for this reaction.   The anodic and cathodic Tafel slopes and stoichiometric numbers for various possible mechanisms treated in this as well as in another[3] work are given in Table 6.   There are a number of criteria useful in elucidating the mechanism which thus provides the basis for electrocatalytic studies of the odr in energy conversion.   They will now be examined in the light of available experimental data.

6.2.3   Mechanism Studies on Platinum in Acid Solution

6.2.3.1   Experimental Observations

(*i*)   *Tafel slopes*

A number of workers[1,3,14,17] have observed that the Tafel slope on platinum

TABLE 6 Tafel Slopes and Stoichiometric Numbers for the Most Probable Mechanism in the Oxygen-electrode Reaction[3]

| | Tafel slope | | | |
| | Anodic | | | |
Reaction path	low η	high η	Cathodic	v
1. The "oxide" path:				
$4M + 4H_2O \rightarrow 4MOH + 4H^+ + 4e_0^-$	$2RT/F$		$2RT/F$	4
$2MOH \rightarrow MO + MH_2O$	$RT/2F$		∞	2
$2MO \rightarrow O_2 + 2M$	$RT/4F$		∞	1
2. The "electrochemical oxide" path:				
$2M + 2H_2O \rightarrow 2MOH + 2H^+ + 2e_0^-$	$2RT/F$		$2RT/3F$	2
$2MOH + 2M + 2H_2O \rightarrow 2MO + 2MH_2O$	$2RT/3F$	$2RT/F$	$2RT/F$	2
$+ 2H^+ + 2e_0^-$				
$2MO \rightarrow O_2 + 2M$	$RT/4F$		∞	1
3. The "hydrogen peroxide" path:				
$4M + 4H_2O \rightarrow 4MOH + 4H^+ + 4e_0^-$	$2RT/F$		$2RT/F$	4
$2MOH \rightarrow MH_2O_2 + M$	$RT/2F$		$RT/2F$	1
$MH_2O_2 + MOH \rightarrow MOH_2 + MO_2H$	$RT/3F$		RT/F	1
$MO_2H + MOH \rightarrow MH_2O + M + O_2$	$RT/3F$		∞	1
4. The "metal peroxide" path:				
$4M + 4H_2O \rightarrow 4MOH + 4H^+ + 4e_0^-$	$2RT/F$		$2RT/F$	4
$2MOH \rightarrow 2MO + 2MH_2O$	$RT/2F$		$RT/2F$	1
$MO + MOH \rightarrow M + MHO_2$	$RT/3F$		RT/F	1
$MHO_2 + MOH \rightarrow O_2 + M + MH_2O$	$RT/4F$		∞	1
5. The "electrochemical metal peroxide" path:				
$3M + 3H_2O \rightarrow 3MOH + 3H^+ + 3e_0^-$	$2RT/F$		$6RT/5F$	3
$2MOH \rightarrow MO + MH_2O$	$RT/2F$	RT/F	$RT/2F$	1
$MO + H_2O \rightarrow MHO_2 + H^+ + e_0^-$	$2RT/5F$	$2RT/F$	$2RT/3F$	1
$MHO_2 + MOH \rightarrow M + O_2 + MH_2O$	$RT/4F$		∞	1
6. The "alkaline" path of Hoar:				
$2M + 2H_2O \rightarrow 2MOH + 2H^+ + 2e_0^-$	$2RT/F$		$2RT/3F$	2
$2MOH + 2H_2O \rightarrow 2MH_2O_2^- + 2H^+$	RT/F		RT/F	2
$2MH_2O_2^- \rightarrow M + MO_2^{2-} + 2H_2O$	$RT/2F$	RT/F	$RT/2F$	1
$MO_2^{2-} \rightarrow M + O_2 + 2e_0^-$	$RT/3F$		RT/F	1
7. Path suggested by Conway and Bourgault:				
$3M + 3H_2O \rightarrow 3MOH + 3H + 3e_0^-$	$2RT/F$		$6RT/5F$	3
$MOH \rightarrow MO + H^+ + e_0^-$	$2RT/3F$	$2RT/F$	$2RT/5F$	1
$MO + MOH \rightarrow MHO_2$	$RT/3F$	RT/F	RT/F	1
$MHO_2 + MOH \rightarrow M + MH_2O + O_2$	$RT/4F$		∞	1
8. Alternative path suggested by				
Conway and Bourgault:				
$2M + 2H_2O \rightarrow 2MOH + 2H^+ + 2e_0^-$	$2RT/F$		$2RT/3F$	2
$MOH \rightarrow MO + H^+ + e_0^-$	$2RT/3F$		$2RT/5F$	1
$MO + H_2O \rightarrow MHO_2 + H^+ + e_0^-$	$2RT/5F$		$2RT/3F$	1
$MHO_2 + MOH \rightarrow M + MH_2O + O_2$	$RT/4F$		∞	1
9. Path suggested by Riddiford:				
$2M + 2H_2O \rightarrow 2MOH + 2H^+ + 2e_0^-$	$2RT/F$		$2RT/3F$	2
$2MOH \rightarrow MO + MH_2O$	$RT/2F$		$RT/2F$	1
$MO + H_2O \rightarrow MHO_2 + H^+ + e_0^-$	$2RT/5F$	$2RT/F$	$2RT/3F$	1
$MHO_2 + H_2O \rightarrow O_2 + MH_2O + H^+ + e_0^-$	$2RT/7F$		$2RT/F$	1

TABLE 6   Tafel Slopes and Stoichiometric Numbers for the Most Probable Mechanism in the Oxygen-electrode Reaction[3] (*continued*)

Reaction path	Anodic low η	high η	Cathodic	ν
10. Path suggested by Krasilshchikow:				
$2M + 2H_2O \rightarrow 2MOH + 2H^+ + 2e_0^-$	$2RT/F$		$2RT/3F$	2
$2MOH \rightarrow 2MO^- + 2H^+$	RT/F		RT/F	2
$2MO^- \rightarrow 2MO + 2e_0^-$	$2RT/3F$	$2RT/F$	$2RT/F$	2
$2MO \rightarrow O_2 + 2M$	$RT/4F$		∞	1
11. Path suggested by Wade and Hackerman:				
$2M + 2H_2O \rightarrow MO + MH_2O + 2H^+ + 2e_0^-$	RT/F		$RT/3F$	1
$MO + 2MOH^- \rightarrow 2M + MH_2O$	$RT/3F$		RT/F	1
$\quad + O_2 + 2e_0^-$				
12. $M + H_2O \rightarrow MOH + H^+ + e_0^-$	$2RT/F$		$2RT/7F$	1
$MOH \rightarrow MO + H^+ + e_0^-$	$2RT/3F$	RT/F	$2RT/3F$	1
$MO + H_2O \rightarrow MO_2H + H^+ + e_0^-$	$2RT/5F$	$2RT/F$	$2RT/3F$	1
$MO_2H \rightarrow M + O_2 + H^+ + e_0^-$	$2RT/7F$		$2RT/F$	1
13. $2M + 2H_2O \rightarrow 2MOH + 2H^+ + 2e_0^-$	$2RT/F$		$2RT/3F$	2
$2MOH + 2H_2O \rightarrow 2MO—H—OH^- + 2H^+$	RT/F		RT/F	2
$2MO—H—OH^- \rightarrow 2MO—H—OH + 2e_0^-$	$2RT/3F$	$2RT/F$	$2RT/F$	2
$2MO—H—OH \rightarrow 2MO + 2H_2O$	$RT/2F$	RT/F	∞	2
$2MO \rightarrow M + O_2$	$RT/4F$		∞	1
14. $M + H_2O \rightarrow MOH + H^+ + e_0^-$	$2RT/F$		$2RT/7F$	1
$MOH + H_2O \rightarrow MO—H—OH^- + H^+$	RT/F		$2RT/3F$	1
$MO—H—OH^- \rightarrow MO—H—OH + e_0^-$	$2RT/3F$	$2RT/F$	$2RT/5F$	1
$MO—H—OH \rightarrow MO + H_2O$	$RT/2F$	RT/F	$RT/2F$	1
$MO + H_2O \rightarrow MHO_2 + e_0^-$	$2RT/5F$	$2RT/3F$	$2RT/3F$	1
$MHO_2 \rightarrow M + O_2 + H^+ + e_0^-$	$2RT/7F$		$2RT/F$	1

is $2RT/F$ (Fig. 18).   As pointed out earlier, because of the low exchange current density for the reaction, stringent purification of the system is necessary before it is possible to obtain results in low overpotential regions that are free from the effects of competing reactions due to impurities (Fig. 7).

(*ii*)   *Reaction orders*

The reaction order with respect to oxygen is 0.14 at a potential of 1.5 volts. The pH coefficient of the overpotential is -115 mv in the range of pH from 1.5 to 2.2.

(*iii*)   *Stoichiometric number*

The stoichiometric number for the oxygen-evolution reaction on Pt in dilute H_2SO_4 has been found to be 4 by two methods (Chap. 2, Sec. 3).

(*iv*)   *Temperature dependence*

The temperature dependence of the rate of the reaction for $0 < T < 80°C$ has been determined.[48]   The heat of activation at the reversible potential is 18 kcal mole^{-1}.

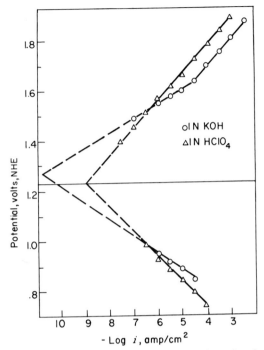

Figure 18 Potential–current-density relations for the anodic and cathodic oxygen-electrode reactions on Pt in acid (1 N HClO$_4$) and in alkaline (1 N KOH) media at 25°C.[3]

(v) *Time variation of overpotential*

The variation of overpotential with time on freshly prepared electrodes at a given current density in sulfuric acid solution, anodically preelectrolyzed for times varying from 1 to 3 days, has been determined.[1] The overpotential-log-time relations at a given intermediate current density are independent of the degree of preelectrolysis. Further, the η–log t relation shows two sections, one with a slope of 0.05 and the other with a slope of 0.095 (Fig. 19).

(vi) *Effect of anions and cations*

Anions of the acid play a role in the oxygen-evolution reaction, particularly at high current densities. Useful evidence results from some work in oxygen-labeled perchloric acid.[49] The water contained no labeled oxygen. Two linear sections of the Tafel line with about the same slope, separated by a steep region in which the potential changes markedly with current density, were observed in perchloric acid (Fig. 20). In the lower region, the overpotential increases with acid concentration, whereas in the upper region, there is the opposite effect (Fig. 20). The evolved gas contains heavy oxygen at the higher current densities but not at the lower current densities. Ozone is formed above the break point in HClO$_4$; chloric acid and chlorine dioxide have also been

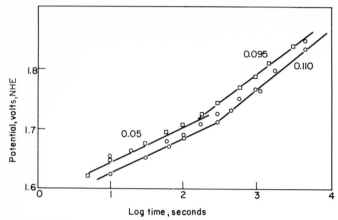

Figure 19 Overpotential for oxygen evolution on platinum in 1 N H$_2$SO$_4$ at 25°C as a function of time at constant current density (10^{-4} amp cm^{-2}).[1]

obtained in the higher current density regions.[50]   The η-versus-log i relation in concentrated sulfuric acid also shows similar behavior, although the transition to the Tafel line with different parameters occurs at higher current densities. In the case of sulfuric acid, ozone, permono, and perdisulfuric acid have also been isolated in the higher current density regions.

Cations strongly influence the overpotential.[51]   The overpotential and Tafel slope increase with addition of cations to sulfate solutions in the order K$^+$ > Al^{3+} > Zn^{2+} > Na$^+$ > Mg^{2+} > Li$^+$.

6.2.3.2 Mechanistic Conclusions.   The evaluation of the above phenomenology for the oer has been carried out by Damjanovic, Dey, and Bockris.[4]

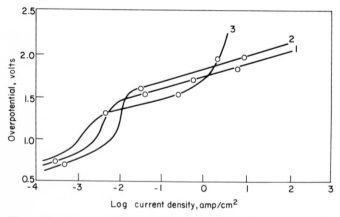

Figure 20 Overpotential–current-density relations for oxygen evolution on a smooth platinum electrode in varying concentrations of HClO$_4$ exhibiting a two-section Tafel behavior. (1) 5.8; (2) 7.6; (3) 10 N HClO$_4$.[49]

The first consideration pertains to whether the adsorbed intermediate radicals involved in the mechanism behave according to a Langmuir or Temkin isotherm. There is hitherto no direct evidence on this central point. However, there is some evidence that strongly supports adsorption under Langmuir conditions. A constant slope could hardly be expected for the Tafel line for oxygen evolution over 300 mv under Temkin conditions. However, constant slopes are observed at least over 600 mv. Temkin conditions for oxygen-evolution kinetics are thus improbable. (The fact that O adsorbs on the bare metal in a Temkin way is not, of course, relevant to the oxide-covered case.)

On this basis, the electrode kinetic parameters in Table 6 may be considered. This table shows that the experimental observations for oer on Pt in acid solution are consistant with three (paths 1, 3, and 4) of the suggested paths. The data appears to be unambiguous in indicating that the rate-determining step is the charge-transfer reaction from water to form OH radicals. According to the available data, a distinction between the three paths indicated above is not yet possible. For example, the predicted reaction order with respect to oxygen and hydrogen ion is the same for all mechanisms. Hypothetically, either one of two types of experimental data could be used to distinguish between these paths. For example, if the dependence of adsorption of intermediate radicals on potential could be measured (as is possible in principle), one would be able to compare this with the different predicted changes of coverages of the various radicals with potential. A choice between path 1 on the one hand and paths 3 and 4 on the other could be made from experiments with rotating disk with ring electrodes (Sec. 6.3.6). Such an investigation would give rise to the detection of peroxides.

Finally, it may be noted that the pH and salt effects are not apparently consistent with the above mechanistic suggestions but that they can be reconciled with them if the change of potential of zero charge with pH[51a] is taken into account, as done in the case of explanation of pH effect on the ethylene oxidation reaction on Pt (Chap. 7, Sec. 6).

6.2.4 *Mechanism Studies on Other Metals*

Mechanism studies similar to the one for platinum have been made on the other noble metals in acid solution.[4] In alkaline solution the range of metals covered is greater than that in acid.[4] The results of work on other metals in both acid and alkaline solutions are summarized in Table 7. The last column of the table shows the most probable rds, as inferred from the measured electrode kinetic parameters. For the sake of comparison, the results on platinum are also shown in the table for both electrolyte media.

6.3 Cathodic Reduction of Oxygen

6.3.1 *Probable Paths*

The elucidation of the mechanism of this reaction is one of the most important steps in fundamental work on electrochemical energy conversion.

The special difficulty of elucidating the paths for the odr on Pt (as well as

TABLE 7 Electrode Kinetic Parameters for the Oxygen-evolution Reaction on a Number of Electrocatalysts in Acid and in Alkaline Electrolytes and the Most Probable rds

Electro-catalyst	pH	i_0, amp cm⁻²	b, volts	Activation energy, kcal mole⁻¹	$\partial V/\partial$ pH, volts	$\dfrac{\partial \log il}{\partial \log P_{O_2}}$	v	θ, μc cm⁻²	Probable rds	Reference no.
Pt	0	4×10^{-10}	0.110 ($\pm$001)	11.4 at 1.5 volts (RHE)	0.030	0.14	3.6	1,000	$M + H_2O \rightarrow MOH + H^+ + e^-$	3
Pt	14	1×10^{-11}	low η: 0.055 $\pm$ 0.01	15.5 at 1.5 volts (RHE)	−0.065		1.8	1,200	$MOH + H_2O \rightarrow MH_2O_2^- + H^+$	3
Rh	0	3×10^{-11}	high η: 0.110 $\pm$ 0.01 low η: 0.060 high η: 0.125		−0.110		2.1 2.5		$M + H_2O \rightarrow MOH + H^+ + e_0^-$ $M + H_2O \rightarrow MOH + H^+ + e_0^-$ (high η) $MOH + H_2O \rightarrow MO \cdots H \cdots OH^-$ $+ H^+$ (low η)	4
Rh	14	6×10^{-12} 6×10^{-6}	low η: 0.042 high η: 0.115				1.9		$M + H_2O \rightarrow MOH + H^+ + e_0^-$ (high η)	4
Ir	0	1×10^{-11} 10^{-6}	low η: 0.040 high η: 0.120				1.9	At 0.9 volt, 800	Same as Rh in acid	4
Ir	14	1×10^{-11} 10^{-6}	low η: ca. 0.040 high η: −0.120				1.9		Same as Rh in alkali	4
Pt-Rh	0	3×10^{-11}	low η: 0.065–0.070 high η: 0.120				2.7		Same as Rh in acid	4
Pt-Rh	14	1×10^{-12} ca. -10^{-6}	low η: ca. 0.040 high η: 0.120				1.5		Same as Rh in alkali	4
Au	0	1.6×10^{-22}	0.0451 $\pm$ 0.003						$MOH \rightarrow MO + H^+ + e_0^-$	78
Au	14	1.1×10^{-8}	high η: 0.244 $\pm$ 0.007 low η: 0.045 $\pm$ 0.006						$MOH \rightarrow MO + H^+ + e_0^-$ (low η)	78
Pd	0	4×10^{-24}	0.100						$M + H_2O \rightarrow MOH + H^+ + e_0^-$	78
Pd	14	4×10^{-11}	0.113		−0.120				Same as in acid	78
Ni	14	3.1×10^{-11}	high η: 0.120[a] low η: 0.030[b]		0.060				$MOH^- \rightarrow MOH + e_0^-$ (high η) $MOH + MOH^- \rightarrow MO^- + H_2O$ (low η)	79

many other metals) is the presence of two radically different surfaces—the oxide-covered one at potentials more positive than 1.0 volt and the oxygen-adsorbed one at potentials more negative than this value. For a discussion of electrochemical energy converters, a knowledge of the mechanism of odr on both surfaces is of importance. In so far as the electrocatalytic activity is high and the overpotential at steady state tends to be less than 0.2 volt, the relevant substrate is the oxide. If the overpotential is greater than about 0.3 volt, the odr is expected to occur on the bare platinum surface.†

Applying the principle of microscopic reversibility, the mechanism of the odr on an oxide surface can be inferred largely from work done on the corresponding anodic reaction. The rds is thus probably charge transfer from adsorbed-oxygen (or hydroxyl) radicals to water after initial chemical reactions of O_2 that involve adsorption on the oxide substrate. Two broad views exist concerning the mechanism of reduction of oxygen on surfaces: the presence or absence of peroxide intermediates. The overall four-electron reduction might be regarded as occurring through successive mechanisms similar to those involved in reduction of O_2 to H_2O_2 and then the reduction of H_2O_2 to water. A general point in favor of this kind of mechanism is the fact that for many years the presence of H_2O_2 in solution during the reduction of oxygen has been reported.

However, it has recently been pointed out that such evidence may be of diminished value (Sec. 6.3.6). The standard potential of the two-electron transfer reduction of O_2 to H_2O_2 is 0.68 at 25°C. Thus, for the reduction of O_2 in a region negative to this value, the possibility exists that separate parallel reductions of oxygen to hydrogen peroxide by the two-electron transfer reaction and to water by the four-electron transfer reaction occur. This, of course, would then account for presence of H_2O_2 and would not have mechanistic implications concerning the four-electron transfer-reduction reaction. A recently developed method for distinguishing the source of H_2O_2 is described in Sec. 6.3.6.

It is noteworthy that the realization of the critical difference in the substrate of potentials above and below this potential is of recent origin,[43] so that many of the older discussions in the literature is subject to criticism for not taking this point into account.

Evidence on surface properties of other metals is hitherto lacking, and ellipsometric studies are desirable. Some very rough predictions may be made by comparing the coverage-potential relations, as obtained by coulometry, on other metals[39] (Fig. 15) with that on Pt. The figure shows that on Pd the onset of oxide formation is at about the same potential as for Pt. On Rh and Ir, it appears that the oxide forms at about 0.7 volt. On gold, it appears that there is hardly any oxygen coverage below 0.9 volt.

---

† Oxygen reduction may occur on an oxide surface even below 1 volt. This is possible when an electrode is first anodized and then the current is rapidly reversed. Oxides at potentials cathodic to 1 volt persist for some time, and this enables measurements to be made of the odr on oxide surfaces.

6.3.2   Qualitative Evidence in Favor of Reduction Mechanisms with H_2O_2 as an Intermediate

(i)   Half-wave potentials for oxygen reduction

The reduction of oxygen on "mercury"† proceeds in two stages (see Fig. 21). There are, consequently, two half-wave potentials,[52] one corresponding

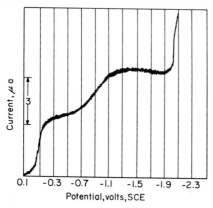

Figure 21 Current-potential relations for oxygen reduction at a dropping mercury electrode, obtained polarographically in 1 N H_2SO_4 at 25°C, shows two half-wave potentials. The first is for oxygen reduction to hydrogen peroxide, and the second is for hydrogen peroxide reduction to water.[52]

to the reduction to hydrogen peroxide and the other the hydrogen peroxide reduction to water.   Such a path is possible on other metals.

(ii)   Rest potentials

On "carbon," in the absence of peroxide decomposing catalysts, the rest potentials follow the variation with HO_2^-, OH^- concentrations, and partial pressure of oxygen, as expected from the Nernst equation for the reaction[53] expressed by Eq. (3.1).

(iii)   Detection of hydrogen peroxide using tracer techniques

In the tracer experiments of Davies and coworkers,[54] labeled oxygen was used with no labeled species initially in solution.   After cathodic reduction of oxygen to water on carbon, the solution was degassed to remove any dissolved molecular oxygen.   Subsequently, the hydrogen peroxide was decomposed with ceric sulfate to oxygen for mass spectrometric analysis.   The mass 32, 34, and 36 peaks obtained confirm the presence of oxygen and hence peroxide in solution.   The possibility that the H_2O_2 is formed in a parallel reaction exists.

6.3.3   Method for Detection and Quantitative Estimation of Hydrogen Peroxide Formed during Oxygen Reduction—Use of Rotating-disk Electrode with a Ring Electrode

6.3.3.1   Theory of Method.   A rotating disk with a ring-electrode arrangement[55] was used by Müller and Nekrassow[56] to detect hydrogen peroxide formed during the reduction of oxygen.   Reduction of the oxygen takes place at the

† The applicability of this evidence to reactions on more frequently used electrocatalysts for reduction of oxygen may, of course, be limited.

disk electrode.   Any hydrogen peroxide formed at the disk migrates to the concentric ring, maintained at a potential of about 1.4 volts, where it is oxidized at its limiting current density (Chap. 9, Sec. 2.4.1.3).   However, these workers did not consider the possibility of a parallel two-electron reduction as a source of hydrogen peroxide.   The distinction between H_2O_2 from this source and that from its existence as an intermediate in the four-electron reduction was made by Damjanovic, Genshaw, and Bockris,[57-60] for the same electrode arrangement, from the dependence of currents at the disk and at the ring electrode on the rate of rotation of the electrode.   The theory of their method is summarized below.[57]

The possible reactions at the disk electrode are

$$O_2 \xrightarrow{I_1} H_2O \tag{6.4}$$

$$O_2 \xrightarrow{I_2} H_2O_2 \tag{6.5}$$

Diffusion away from disk

I_1, I_2, and I_3 are the respective currents at the disk.   Thus, the total current at the disk I_d is

$$I_d = I_1 + I_2 + I_3 \tag{6.6}$$

The rate of diffusion of H_2O_2 away from the disk is expressed by the equivalent of a current (I_4).   The current at the *ring* (I_r) is proportional to I_4 and may be expressed by

$$I_r = NI_4 \tag{6.7}$$

where N is a constant obtainable from hydrodynamical considerations.

Under steady-state conditions at the disk electrode, the rate of formation of H_2O_2 (I_2) must be equal to the total rate of removal $(I_3 + I_4)$.   Thus

$$I_2 = I_3 + I_4 \tag{6.8}$$

One may also write

$$I_1 = xI_2 \tag{6.9}$$

where x, being positive or zero, depends on the kinetics of reactions (6.4) and (6.5) and should be a function of potential under the condition that the rates of these reactions do not have the same potential dependence.   Using Eqs. (6.7) to (6.9) in (6.6),

$$I_d = I_2(x + 2) - \left(\frac{I_r}{N}\right) \tag{6.10}$$

Rearranging the above equation,

$$I_2 = \frac{I_d + (I_r/N)}{x + 2} \tag{6.11}$$

The ring current I_r may be expressed by an equation of the form[55]

$$I_r = \frac{NI_2}{1 + k'\omega^{-\frac{1}{2}}} \tag{6.12}$$

where k' is a measure of the rate constant for the reduction of H_2O_2 at the disk and ω is the speed of rotation. Using Eq. (6.12) in Eq. (6.10) and rearranging,

$$\frac{I_d}{I_r} = \frac{x + 1}{N} + \frac{x + 2}{N}\frac{k'}{\omega^{\frac{1}{2}}} \tag{6.13}$$

Thus, a plot of I_d/I_r versus $\omega^{-\frac{1}{2}}$ should yield a straight line with a slope of $k'(x + 2)/N$ and an intercept of $(x + 1)/N$. From these parameters, one may determine whether H_2O_2 is formed as an intermediate or in a parallel reaction.

Several cases may be distinguished:[57]

(*i*) Only reaction (6.4) occurs: Under these conditions there is no ring current and hence no plot of I_d/I_r versus $\omega^{-\frac{1}{2}}$ exists.

(*ii*) Only reaction (6.5) occurs and the intermediate does not react further. Thus x and k' are zero and

$$\frac{I_d}{I_r} = \frac{1}{N} \tag{6.14}$$

A plot of I_d/I_r versus $\omega^{-\frac{1}{2}}$ is a straight line parallel to the $\omega^{-\frac{1}{2}}$ axis.

(*iii*) Only reaction (6.5) occurs and the intermediate is reduced at the disk. Thus, x is zero and k' is finite. Equation (6.7) becomes

$$\frac{I_d}{I_r} = \frac{1}{N} + \frac{2k'}{N\omega^{\frac{1}{2}}} \tag{6.15}$$

This case is the one usually considered in the literature. The slope of the line, I_d/I_r versus $\omega^{-\frac{1}{2}}$ depends on potential.

(*iv*) O_2 is reduced to H_2O and H_2O_2 in parallel reactions but H_2O_2 is not reduced further. Here k' is zero and

$$\frac{I_d}{I_r} = \frac{x + 1}{N} \tag{6.16}$$

There is no dependence of I_d/I_r on ω. But the position of the lines depends on potential.

(*v*) All reactions occur. No simplification is possible. The I_d/I_r versus $\omega^{-\frac{1}{2}}$ lines have finite slopes that are potential-dependent.

6.3.3.2 *Experimental Observations and Conclusions.*   Using a rotating-disk apparatus, the oxygen-reduction reaction was studied on Pt electrodes.[58,59]

In *purified sulfuric acid* solutions,[58] the disk I_d and ring I_r currents are shown as a function of the disk potential in Fig. 22 for a certain rotational velocity

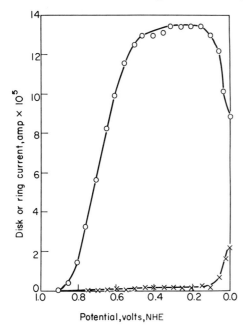

Figure 22 The currents at platinum disk ($\bigcirc$) and ring (x) electrodes as a function of disk potential in a study of the oxygen reduction in purified 1 N H₂SO₄ at 25°C, using rotating disk with ring electrode technique ($\omega = 60$ sec⁻¹).[58]

($\omega = 60$ sec⁻¹). This plot shows that I_r is practically zero (i.e., no hydrogen peroxide formed at the disk) till a potential of about 0.1 volt (NHE) is reached. Below this potential, the disk current falls but the ring current increases: their sum is practically constant (equal to that observed in the plateau region), which shows that oxygen is now reduced to water and hydrogen peroxide in parallel reactions at the limiting current density for oxygen diffusion to the electrode. Till the potential of 0.1 volt is reached, starting from about 1.0 volt, H_2O_2 *is hardly formed at all*, and thus in this region, O_2 is directly reduced to H_2O in a four-electron transfer reaction with no H_2O_2 intermediate (Fig. 22).

In sulfuric acid solutions, *which have not been rigorously purified*,[58] the ring current is appreciable in magnitude as compared with the disk current throughout the entire potential range (Fig. 23 shows the disk and ring currents as a function of potential for $\omega = 60$ sec⁻¹ in insufficiently purified sulfuric acid solution). Plots of I_d/I_r versus $\omega^{-\frac{1}{2}}$ yield parallel straight lines, for the different potentials, having a zero slope (Fig. 24). Thus, from the analysis in the preceding section, it follows that oxygen is reduced to H_2O_2 and H_2O *in parallel reactions* and H_2O_2 is not further reduced at the disk. The disk current has a minimum at about 0.3 volt. This potential corresponds to the region in which there is a maximum in the adsorption of some organic materials on Pt, and it is therefore reasonable to suppose that the minimum of the current corresponds to a maximum in the absorption. Progressive purification of the solutions makes the shapes of these curves tend towards that shown in Fig. 22.

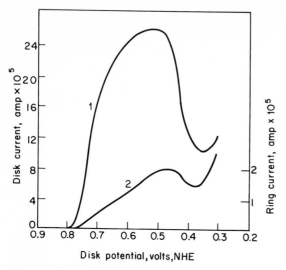

Figure 23   The currents at platinum disk (1) and ring (2) electrodes as a function of disk potential in a study of the oxygen reduction on Pt in unpurified 1 N H$_2$SO$_4$ at 25°C, using rotating disk electrode with ring electrode technique ($\omega = 60$ sec^{-1}).[9]   (Upper curve is for disk and lower is for ring currents.)

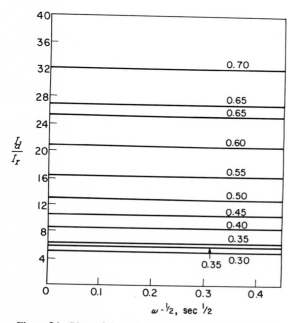

Figure 24   Plots of the ratio of the currents at disk and ring electrodes (I_d/I_r) in unpurified sulfuric acid solution versus $\omega^{-1/2}$ at various potentials of the disk electrode.[58]

In alkaline solutions,[59] the parallel reactions (6.4) and (6.5) occur on platinum electrodes, i.e., the peroxide ion is formed as a true intermediate even in purified solutions.   The peroxide ion formed according to Eq. (6.5) is further reduced at the disk electrode, as may be seen from Fig. 25 and from the theory in the preceding section.

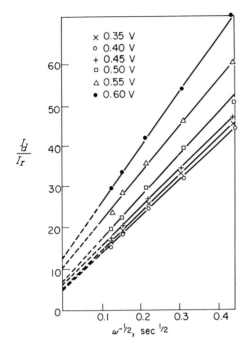

Figure 25 Plots of the ratio of the currents at disk and ring electrodes (I_d/I_r) in 1 N KOH versus $\omega^{-1/2}$ at various potentials of the disk electrode.[59]

Rhodium behaves in the same manner as platinum both in acid and in alkaline (i.e., peroxide intermediate) media.[60] With gold in acid solution, hydrogen peroxide is initially formed as an intermediate in the reduction of oxygen to water.[60]   However, the progressive oxidation of the electrode leads to an increasing number of sites at which the four-electron transfer reduction occurs without the intermediate formation of H_2O_2. With Au in alkaline solution, as in the case of Pt and Rh, HO_2^- ion is an intermediate in the reduction process.[60]

In summary, the rotating-disk electrode with a ring arrangement provides a unique method of determining whether hydrogen peroxide is formed as an intermediate, in a parallel reaction, or not at all.

6.3.4 Electrode Kinetic Studies on Platinum in Acid Solution

6.3.4.1 Experimental Observations

(i) *Tafel parameters*

(a) On oxide-free platinum electrodes, the substrate on which the reaction occurs in most electrochemical energy converters using Pt catalysts, the Tafel slope is $-RT/F$ (Fig. 26).[5] Figure 26 also shows the effect of pre-treatment on the current-potential relation.

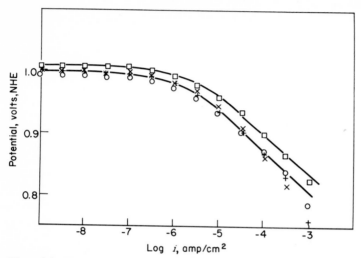

Figure 26 Potential as a function of current density for the electro-reduction of oxygen on Pt in 0.1 N HClO$_4$ at 25°C. × represents electrode degreased, cleaned with HCl and by cathodic pulse; + represents electrode degreased and heated at 850°C, 5 min in H$_2$ and 10 min in N$_2$; ○ represents electrode degreased and heated at 300°C, 5 min in H$_2$ and 10 min in N$_2$; □ represents electrode degreased and treated by an anodic and cathodic pulse.[5]

(*b*) On oxide-covered electrodes, the anodic and cathodic Tafel lines for the oxygen-electrode reaction intersect at 1.23 volts[1,3,14] (Figs. 14 and 18). The Tafel slope is $-2RT/F$. Exchange current densities are of the order of 10^{-10} amp cm^{-2} on oxide-covered electrodes.

(*ii*) *Reaction orders*

(*a*) On oxide-free electrodes,[5] the potential-current density plots, for various pressures of oxygen bubbling through the solution, for oxygen reduction in 0.1 N HClO$_4$ are shown in Fig. 27. The Tafel lines are approximately parallel in all cases, being about $-RT/F$. The reaction order with respect to oxygen is unity.

The change of potential with pH at constant current density is -100 mv per unit of pH change in the acid range on the bare metal.[5]

(*b*) The change in current density with oxygen pressure on oxide-covered electrodes at a constant overpotential ($\partial \log i / \partial \log p_{O_2})_\eta$ is 0.30.

There is no variation of overpotential with pH at constant current density.[3]

(*iii*) *Stoichiometric numbers*

(*a*) It is not possible to determine the stoichiometric numbers on bare metals by any of the known methods (Chap. 2, Sec. 3) because (1) the

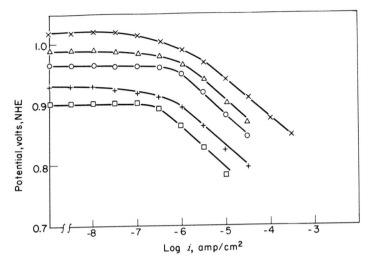

Figure 27 Dependence of Tafel lines for oxygen reduction at Pt in 0.1 N HClO$_4$ on partial pressure of oxygen bubbled through solution. ×, 1; Δ, 0.3; ○, 0.1; +, 0.3; □, 0.01 atm.[5]

overpotential is too high (at least 0.3 volt) and (2) the anodic Tafel slope cannot be determined.

(b)   The stoichiometric number is nearly 4 on oxide-covered electrodes.[1,3]

(iv)   *Dependence of coverage of oxygen-containing species on potential*

(a)   Oxygen-coverage–potential relations have been obtained both in oxygen-saturated and in nitrogen-saturated solutions.   The relations are approximately linear and practically identical (Fig. 6).

(b)   There is no data available concerning the oxygen-coverage–versus-potential relation on oxide-covered electrodes.

6.3.4.2   Mechanistic Conclusions

(i)   *Oxide-free metal*

Several mechanisms have been considered by Damjanovic and Brusic[5] for this reaction.   It is not possible to interpret the experimental data on the basis of any mechanism involving Langmuir adsorption.   The oxygen-coverage–potential relation is linear (Fig. 6) suggesting adsorption of intermediates under Temkin conditions.

The general expression for the velocity v of an electrochemical reaction, with the first electron-transfer step being rate-determining, is given by

$$v = k' \Pi a_k \exp\left(-\frac{\beta VF}{RT}\right) \exp\left(-\frac{\Delta G^{\ddagger} + \gamma \Delta \Delta H}{RT}\right) \tag{6.17}$$

where k' is a constant; Πa_k is the product of the activities of all the reactants in the rate-determining step; $\Delta G^{\ddagger}$ is the free energy of activation at low coverages; $\Delta\Delta H$ is the difference in heats of adsorption of reactants and products of the rate-determining step; and γ gives the fractional contribution of $\Delta\Delta H$ to the free energy of activation. Assuming that $\Delta\Delta H$ changes linearly with total oxygen coverage (Temkin conditions),

$$\Delta\Delta H = \Delta\Delta H^{\circ} - r\theta \tag{6.18}$$

where $\Delta\Delta H^{\circ}$ is the value of $\Delta\Delta H$ at zero coverage and r is the interaction energy parameter. It was shown experimentally that the coverage varies linearly with potential. Writing

$$\theta = KV \tag{6.19}$$

where V is the potential drop across the electrode-electrolyte interface and K is a constant, and combining (6.17) to (6.19),

$$v = k\Pi a_k \exp\left(-\frac{\beta VF}{RT}\right)\exp\left(-\frac{\gamma rKV}{RT}\right) \tag{6.20}$$

Assuming $\beta = \gamma = \frac{1}{2}$ and $rK = F$ gives the correct Tafel slope.

The oxygen pressure-dependence may be accounted for if one assumes that in sequence 14 of Table 6 the first electron-transfer step for the reverse reaction

$$M + O_2 + H^+ + e_0^- \rightarrow MHO_2 \tag{6.21}$$

is rate-determining. Such a mechanism does not apparently explain the pH effect. $\partial V/\partial pH$ is approximately $-3RT/2F$. This anomaly may be resolved, however, by assuming that the coverage is not only dependent on potential, as given by Eq. (6.19), but also dependent on pH.[5] The corrected equation becomes[5]

$$\theta = KV + \left(\frac{KRT}{F}\right)pH \tag{6.22}$$

It is not possible at this stage to present the entire reaction sequence. The last step is probably

$$OH + H^+ + e_0^- \rightleftharpoons H_2O \tag{6.23}$$

(ii) Oxide-covered metal

On oxide-covered electrodes, since the Tafel lines for the anodic and cathodic reactions for the oxygen-electrode reaction intersect at 1.23 volts (RHE), one can expect the mechanism to be the same as for the anodic reaction. This was discussed in Sec. 6.2.3.

6.3.5   Electrode-kinetic Studies on Other Metals

The electrode-kinetic studies on other metals[61] are summarized in Table 1. As stated earlier, these investigations are limited to the noble metals in acid solution. However, many more metals have been investigated in the alkaline range. The most probable mechanisms on these substrates are also shown in the table.

6.3.6 Summarizing Remarks

Considerable progress concerning the elucidation of the mechanism of the oxygen-electrode reaction was made in the later sixties. One of the best tools in mechanism studies is the technique using a rotating-disk electrode with a ring[55-60] (Sec. 6.3.3). This technique has clearly shown whether hydrogen peroxide is formed as an intermediate in a parallel reaction or is not formed at all. However, this knowledge is a central piece of information in the determination of the mechanisms of oxygen reduction.

The steady-state electrode-kinetic analysis can be applied particularly well here because of the low exchange current density, although a counterinfluence is the difficulty of obtaining some electrode-kinetic parameters, e.g., stoichiometric numbers, because of the great effect of small traces of impurities at very low current density situations. Another study which has been extremely valuable apart from the normal electrode-kinetic parameter determinations is the ellipsometric method to determine the nature of the surface of oxygen electrodes.[43] It has clearly led to the conclusion regarding the conditions of the surface and the critical potentials at which phase oxides are formed. It is now necessary to extend these techniques to many more metals, particularly in alkaline media.

7 THE TWO-ELECTRON TRANSFER REACTIONS INVOLVING HYDROGEN PEROXIDE

7.1 Hydrogen Peroxide/Oxygen Reaction

7.1.1 Anodic Oxidation of Hydrogen Peroxide to Oxygen

In acid and neutral solution, the potential on a Pt electrode satisfies the relation[62]

$$V = \text{const} + \frac{3}{2}\frac{RT}{F} \ln i - \frac{3}{2}\frac{RT}{F} \ln [H_2O_2] + \frac{3}{2}\frac{RT}{F} \ln [H^+] \tag{7.1}$$

and in alkaline solutions, the relevant equation is[62]

$$V = \text{const} + \frac{2}{3}\frac{RT}{F} \ln i - \frac{RT}{F} \ln [OH^-] \tag{7.2}$$

By using labeled oxygen in the HO_2^- ion but not in alkaline solution (that is, H_2O or OH^- ions are not labeled), it was shown by Davies et al. that the evolved oxygen on a carbon electrode arises only from the HO_2^- ion.[54] This experiment proves conclusively that the O-O bond is not ruptured.

Several reaction paths have been suggested, but in view of the experimental evidence stated above, particularly the nonrupture of the O-O bond in the peroxide, the following path[62] appears most probable:

$$H_2O_2 \rightleftarrows H^+ + HO_2^- \tag{7.3}$$

$$HO_2^- \rightarrow HO_2 + e_0^- \tag{7.4}$$

$$HO_2 \rightleftarrows H^+ + O_2^- \tag{7.5}$$

$$O_2^- \rightleftarrows O_2 + e_0^- \tag{7.6}$$

7.1.2   Cathodic Reduction of Oxygen to Hydrogen Peroxide

A knowledge of the mechanism of this reaction is of direct importance for fuel-cell development.   There is evidence in some cases that the desirable complete reduction of oxygen to water proceeds through hydrogen peroxide as an intermediate.   Hydrogen peroxide, formed by the two-electron reduction of oxygen, is on some metals chemically decomposed on the electrode and the rate of this reaction depends on the catalyst.   Thus, in these cases, the rate of the overall four-electron-transfer oxygen reduction depends on the rate of the reduction of oxygen to hydrogen peroxide.

Extensive work has been done in alkaline solution.[53,63–66]   It was found that the rest potential on a carbon electrode satisfies the Nernst equation

$$E = E^0 - \frac{RT}{2F} \ln \frac{a_{HO_2^-} a_{OH^-}}{p_{O_2} a_{H_2O}} \tag{7.7}$$

for the reaction (3.3), i.e., with regard to dependences on activity of HO_2^- ion ($a_{HO_2^-}$) and hydroxyl ion (a_{OH^-}) as well as oxygen pressure.

Use of O^{18} in the gas stream and unenriched electrolyte by Davies et al.,[54] or vice versa, showed that all of the oxygen in the perhydroxyl ion formed by cathodic reduction on a carbon electrode is from the oxygen gas and that the constituent oxygen atoms arise from the same oxygen molecule.[54]   This experiment confirms that any paths which involve breaking of the O-O bond may be excluded.

The following relations[66] hold in acid or neutral solutions:

$$E = \text{const} + \frac{2RT}{F} \ln p_{O_2} - \frac{2RT}{F} \ln i \tag{7.8}$$

and in alkaline solutions:

$$E = \text{const} + \frac{2}{3} \frac{RT}{F} \ln p_{O_2} - \frac{2}{3} \frac{RT}{F} \ln i + \frac{2}{3} \frac{RT}{F} \ln [H^+] \tag{7.9}$$

for Ag, Pt, and Hg electrodes.

The most probable path is

$$O_2 + e_0^- \rightarrow O_2^- \tag{7.10}$$

$$O_2^- + H^+ \rightarrow HO_2 \tag{7.11}$$

$$HO_2 + e_0^- \rightarrow HO_2^- \tag{7.12}$$

$$HO_2^- + H^+ \rightarrow H_2O_2 \tag{7.13}$$

The Tafel slopes and pH effects on Pt, Ag, and Hg are consistent with the view that the first discharge step is rate-determining in acid or neutral solutions and that the second discharge step is rate-determining in alkaline solutions.

7.2 Water/Hydrogen Peroxide Reaction

7.2.1 *Anodic Oxidation of Water to Hydrogen Peroxide*

This reaction cannot be studied because the reversible potential for the complete oxidation of water to oxygen is more cathodic than that for the oxidation of water to H_2O_2. Thus, water is more easily oxidized to oxygen than to hydrogen peroxide.

7.2.2 *Cathodic Reduction of Hydrogen Peroxide to Water*

The second polarographic wave for the reduction of oxygen on mercury[52] corresponds to the reduction of H_2O_2 to water (Fig. 21). Evidence for the high degree of irreversibility of this reaction on Hg is apparent in the polarographic wave corresponding to this reduction and also from the fact that the mixed potential set up at an inert Pt or Au electrode in the presence of H_2O_2 (which is that governed by both the reactions $O_2 + 2H^+ + 2e_0^- \rightarrow H_2O_2$ and $H_2O_2 + 2H^+ + 2e_0^- \rightarrow H_2O$) is much closer to the reversible potential of the H_2O_2/O_2 reaction[20-22] than it is to that of the H_2O_2/H_2O reaction (Figs. 9 and 10).

This reaction was studied in detail on mercury[67] and on platinum.[21,68] On platinum, H_2O_2 decomposes *initially* catalytically instead of electrochemically.

Since there is evidence that hydrogen peroxide may sometimes be an intermediate in the reduction of oxygen to water, the main problems of irreversibility of the overall reduction of O_2 to H_2O in these cases may be due to the reduction of H_2O_2 to water. It is thus necessary to overcome the irreversibility phenomena of the latter reaction to improve the performance of fuel cells.

The current-potential relation on a dropping mercury electrode may be represented by[67]

$$i = k[H_2O_2] \exp\left[-(1-\alpha)\frac{VF}{RT}\right] \tag{7.14}$$

where $[H_2O_2]$ is the undissociated H_2O_2 concentration which is given by

$$[H_2O_2] = \frac{c_{H_2O_2}[H^+]}{[H^+] + K} \tag{7.15}$$

where $c_{H_2O_2}$ is total peroxide concentration ($[H_2O_2] + [HO_2^-]$). K is the dissociation constant for H_2O_2 according to

$$H_2O_2 \rightleftharpoons H^+ + HO_2^- \tag{7.16}$$

The Tafel slope obtained on Pt[21] was extremely high, yielding $(1 - \alpha) = 0.2$.

The order of the reaction on Hg and Pt with respect to the undissociated $[H_2O_2]$ concentration is unity and it is zero with respect to $[H^+]$ ions.

The limiting current observed on Hg,[52] Pt,[21,70], and Au[69] was found to be proportional to the concentration of H_2O_2.

The experimental evidence is consistent with the following mechanism:[7]

$$H_2O_2 + e_0^- \xrightarrow{\text{rds}} OH_{ads} + OH^- \tag{7.17}$$

$$OH_{ads} + e_0^- \rightarrow OH^- \tag{7.18}$$

in alkaline solution.

8 ELECTROCATALYTIC ASPECTS OF THE OXYGEN-ELECTRODE REACTION

8.1 General

One of the main difficulties in making a systematic electrocatalytic study of the oxygen-electrode reaction in acid solution is that it has been possible to carry out the reactions only on the noble metals or their alloys because of the instability of the catalyst substrate itself in most other cases. The sodium-tungsten bronzes are highly effective oxygen electrodes so long as they are doped with 10 to 100 ppm of Pt or Ni.[7] In alkaline solutions, the range of metals on which the reaction has been carried out is wider. Electrocatalytic aspects of the oxygen-electrode reaction were briefly treated along with other reactions in Chap. 6. Due to the importance of this reaction in electrochemical energy conversion, its catalysis is treated in some detail in the present section.

8.2 Exchange Current Densities for the Oxygen-electrode Reaction

Table 1 shows the most recent data available for the exchange current densities of the oxygen-electrode reaction on a variety of electrocatalysts in both acid and alkaline aqueous electrolytes. In general, the reaction is faster at the same overpotential in alkaline media by 10 to 100 times. This aspect will be contrasted with that for the hydrogen-electrode reaction, which though highly reversible is faster in acid than in alkaline electrolytes. Of the metals, platinum is the most effective electrocatalyst. The doped sodium-tungsten bronzes as compared with platinum show superior performances in some potential ranges.

8.3 Comparison of Rates of Cathodic Reduction of Oxygen on Bare and Oxide-covered Metal Surfaces

The intersection of the anodic and cathodic Tafel lines for the oxygen-electrode reaction on Pt in 1 N H_2SO_4 at 1.23 volts (the reversible potential for the reaction) stimulated an important question: Do the anodic and cathodic reactions occur on bare or oxide-covered electrodes? Ellipsometry has clearly shown that an oxide film exists above 1.0 volt. Thus, the anodic reaction definitely occurs on oxide-covered substrates.   To obtain conclusive evidence on the nature of the substrate for the cathodic reaction the anodic and cathodic Tafel lines have recently been redetermined in solutions of high purity.[70]   The anodic Tafel plots were obtained in the usual way.   The cathodic Tafel lines were determined by three methods.   In the first, electrodes were subject to an anodic current density for a short time, the galvanostatic current was reversed, and the steady-state potential was measured.   This was done for a series of current densities, and the cathodic Tafel line is shown by line 1 in Fig. 28.

SHORT COMMUNICATIONS

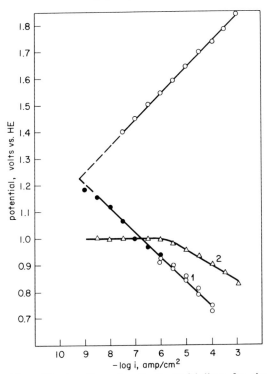

Figure 28   Anodic and cathodic Tafel lines for the oxygen-electrode reaction.   Cathodic Tafel lines are for different electrode treatments.[70]

In the second method, the cathodic measurements were made with gradual increase in current density on oxide-covered electrodes.   All points fall on line 1 in Fig. 28.   In the third method, the oxide surface on the metal was completely reduced and the cathodic-potential–current-density relation was obtained (line 2 in Fig. 28).   This experiment showed conclusively that at about 0.9 volt the rate of the reaction on the bare metal is about 100 times greater than that on the oxide-covered surface and that the ratio of rates is even greater at lower potentials.   Measurement on the oxide-free electrode reached a plateau value at about 1.0 volt.   It may be further concluded that the intersections of anodic and cathodic Tafel lines on platinum electrodes at 1.23 volts occur only on oxide-covered surfaces.

8.4   Dependence of Oxygen Coverage on Noble Metal Electrodes on Unpaired *d* Electrons

In Chap. 6, Table 7, a direct correlation was found between the oxygen coverages on noble metal electrodes and the number of unpaired *d* electrons per atom. Gold with no unpaired electrons has hardly any oxygen coverage.   From the information concerning coverage and reaction rate in Sec. 8.3, one may then expect gold to be a good electrocatalyst for oxygen reduction.   However, the oxygen-reduction reaction involves some oxygen intermediates that are chemisorbed on the electrode.   For this binding process, it is necessary to have some unpaired *d* electrons in the electrocatalyst.   Au does not meet this requirement and is therefore not an effective electrocatalyst.

In the case of Rh, Ir, and Ru, the oxygen coverages are extremely high, which means that they are practically covered with a layer of oxygen atoms.   As was seen in the last section, the presence of an oxide layer on the surface again lowers the activity of the metal for the electroreduction of oxygen.   Further, oxide formation occurs only at a potential of 1.0 volt on platinum.   This occurs at a lower potential for the metals Rh, Ir, and Ru, as may be inferred from the observation that oxygen coverages at the rest potentials are higher than on Pt. The strong binding of oxygen may account for the lower activity of these metals than of Pt in the electroreduction of oxygen.

Thus, the qualitative rule that the chemisorbed bond must not be too strong or too weak in catalysis is confirmed in these results.

8.5   Influence of Metal-Oxygen Bond Strength

A linear relation was found[71] between the overpotential for oxygen evolution at a current density of 1 amp cm^{-2} and the metal-oxygen bond strength (Chap. 6, Fig. 39): the overpotential decreases as the bond strength increases.   However, in the calculation of the metal-oxygen bond strength, the Pauling equation

$$D_{M-O} = \tfrac{1}{2}(D_{M-M} + D_{O-O}) + 23.06(\chi_M - \chi_O)^2 \tag{8.1}$$

was used neglecting the second term on the right-hand side of Eq. (8.1), in which equation D's with the appropriate suffixes represent the bond strengths. M and O stand for metal and oxygen, and χ_M and χ_O are the electronegativities of the metal and oxygen atoms, respectively.   The neglect of the term due to difference in electronegativities made an important difference in the predicted trend of the dependence of hydrogen overpotential on the D_{M-H} bond strength. Inclusion of the term made the predicted trend consistent with the accepted views on the mechanism of the hydrogen-evolution reaction on various metals (Chap. 2, Sec. 11).

Figure 29 is constructed after making corrections[72] to the M-O bond

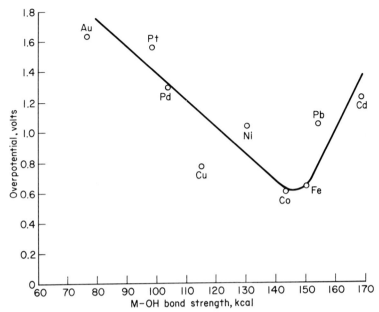

Figure 29 Overpotential at a current density of 1 amp cm^{-2} vs. strength of M-OH bond for the electroevolution of oxygen on some metals.

strength by including the second term of Pauling's equation [Eq. (8.1)].   This figure may be compared with the one (Chap. 6, Fig. 39) in which the electronegativity difference term was omitted.   Significant differences are seen when the electronegativity term is taken into account—the overpotential goes through a minimum as the $D_{M\text{-OH}}$ bond strength is increased; whereas when this term is omitted, the overpotential varies nearly linearly with bond strength over the entire range.

8.6   Conclusions Regarding the Directions of the Development of Suitable Catalysts for the Oxygen-reduction Reaction

8.6.1.   General

The present situation in the catalysis of the oxygen-reduction reaction is that hitherto only the tungsten bronzes have provided radically new catalysts with which to work.   They open a field of interest, particularly because of the remarkable effect of small traces of dopants in the 10-ppm range upon the catalysis.

In spite of the large extent of empirical work during the intensive support of fuel-cell research in connection with the space, military, and civilian programs by government and other agencies, remarkably little work has been done upon the catalytic-reaction aspects of oxygen reduction from a fundamental point of view.   The basic constants have not been measured on even some of the important metals, e.g., some noble metals; also, virtually no development of theories of mechanism and catalysis specific to the oxygen-reduction reaction has taken place.   Hence, no guidance in the direction of possible exploration has been available from newer areas in solid-state physics, for example, electron-energy levels in semiconductors and the relation to electron-energy levels in solution.

There is difficulty in the region in which the oxygen-reduction reaction takes place, essentially 0.5 to 1.0 volt on the hydrogen scale.   It is not at once clear to those who come to the area from catalysis and not from electrochemistry that such a potential range wipes out most of the possible metals because it makes the substrates electrochemically unstable.

This brings into focus a point not widely emphasized: the chief criterion of an oxygen cathode, at least at first, is its *stability*, rather than its catalysis.   For example, the order of magnitude of i_0 of 10^{-10} amp cm^{-2} for the oxygen reduction on platinum and other noble metals is poor indeed, when viewed as a catalytic rate in the context of other redox reactions known in electrochemistry.   The often-made statement, "platinum is the best catalyst," is superficial in respect to oxygen reduction.   In fact, platinum and the noble metals are poor catalysts of this reaction compared with the sort of rates which one expects from good catalysts in electrochemical reactions (cf. 10^{-3} amp cm^{-2} for the exchange-current density of hydrogen on Pt).   The point about the noble metals is that they are *stable* and do not themselves anodically dissolve in the potential range concerned.

These remarks refer essentially to acid solutions.   When one goes to alkaline solutions, the situation is better because the oxygen-dissolution reaction is now taking place at potentials of 0.83 volt in a more negative direction, with respect to the normal hydrogen electrode.   Thus, for example, silver can now be used as a catalyst and is significantly better than the noble metals.

A final general point, before attempting conclusions from those fundamental results which do exist, is that the most used catalyst, platinum, certainly does exhibit (as clearly indicated in Secs. 5 and 6) an unusually complicated situation.   Its surface changes with potentials, its oxides are potential dependent, and it catalyzes three closely related oxygen reactions (see Fig. 2) and several other oxide-forming reactions (Table 4) simultaneously with its catalysis of oxygen reduction to water.   An improved catalyst would aim not only at the stability shown by platinum and a higher exchange current density, but also at a substrate on which a lesser number of competing reactions occur.

8.6.2   *Possible Indications from Rate-determining-step Measurements*

Considerations of Table 1 suggest that the following are the more important rate-determining steps:

$$O_2 + e_0^- \rightarrow O_2^- \tag{8.2}$$

$$O_2 + H^+ + e_0^- \rightarrow HO_{2_{ads}} \tag{8.3}$$

$$O_2 + H_2O + e_0^- \rightarrow O_2H_{ads} + OH^- \tag{8.4}$$

$$2M + O_2 \rightarrow 2MO \tag{8.5}$$

It seems, then, that one possibility is that the rate-determining step upon catalysts involved in oxygen-reduction reactions on bare platinum is largely the electron transfer to oxygen molecules to form oxygen-molecule ions, and that no adsorbed species is formed in the rate-determining step. If this is so, there is fundamentally no way of changing the heat of activation at the reversible potential for the reaction (see Chap. 6, Sec. 3.4.5.1), and therefore no better catalyst can be expected.

There is a possibility of affecting the i_0 for the reaction, and this depends upon the relationships established by Bockris, Damjanovic, and Mannan[11] between the exchange-current density and the potential of zero charge upon a metal for redox reactions. Thus, it is seen that there is a linear relation of log i_0 to the work function (Chap. 6, Fig. 31), and that the more negative the work function, the less the exchange-current density.

The origin of this relation lies in the relationship between the so-called "zeta potential" and the actual potential at the metal-solution interface which changes with the work function of the metal. Thus the theoretical conclusion from this is that for oxygen reduction if the reaction

$$O_2 + e_0^- \rightarrow O_2^- \tag{8.2}$$

is important, the only possibility of improving the catalysis compared with that of oxygen is to work with a metal, the potential of zero charge of which is more negative than that of platinum. Further, the orders of magnitude of the change which might be expected of such a procedure would be that if one could shift the potential of zero charge by 1.0 volt, the expected increase in i_0 would be a factor of 10^4.

The fact that the exchange-current densities for the oxygen-reduction reaction on noble metals will fall near to each other (they vary by about one decade around 10^{-11}) does indeed suggest that a direct electron transfer without bonding may be frequently rate-determining for oxygen reduction.

The other rate-determining steps which may be considered (cf. above list) involve among themselves the same aspects insofar as catalytic considerations go, namely, that they would (as long as they remain rate-determining steps) become faster as the bond strength of the substrate of the changing catalyst with oxygen became greater. The conclusion—one must seek catalysts with the highest bond strength for oxygen—is not to be taken simply, mainly for two reasons. First, there will always be a point at which (with increasing M-O bond strength) the rate-determining step changes over. Reactions will occur further down the sequence of steps leading to the reduction of water which will become more difficult (rather than less difficult) as the bond strength increases: one of these will become eventually rate-determining as the bond strength increases, so that a reduction of the trend to increase bond strength would then be indicated (which would then make the previous reaction again rate-determining). Thus, an optimum bond strength would be reached around the point at which there is a changeover of rate-determining step on increasing the bond strength. In addition, of course, many aspects have to be taken into account when one increases the apparent bond strength (the bond strength of M-O should parallel the heat of sublimation of the metal). For example, increasing the bond strength does not necessarily bring about an improvement in actual catalysis with respect to platinum, because increase of bond strength does not necessarily give rise to a more stable metal. This is clear from comparing the properties of tungsten with those of platinum (melting point of platinum 2037°C, melting point of tungsten 3443°C). The tungsten forms complex ions in solution which make it dissolve more readily than the platinum. Thus, it has a standard potential of its own ions in solution of -0.1 volt, whereas that of platinum is 1.2 volts. At potentials anodic to 1.2 volts, platinum dissolves according to the reaction $Pt^{2+} + 2e_0^- \rightarrow Pt$. Although, of course, platinum does indeed dissolve as an anode in an acid solution, oxygen can be evolved for a long time on platinum without the dissolution of the substrate being appreciable.

On the basis of the bond-strength argument, the most hopeful catalysts for the oxygen-reduction reaction would be iridium and osmium, among the noble metals; also it would be of interest to investigate molybdenum, tungsten, and tantalum, although these would not remain as pure metals in solution but would form films which might or might not be conducting enough (perhaps with doping, conductivity may be induced in the latter case) to form suitable electrodes. Niobium probably falls into the same category. Graphite, of course, has the highest melting point of all, but its properties as a fuel-cell electrode appear to be distinctly less good than those of platinum. Pyrolytic graphite has received almost no attention in respect to its properties as an oxygen cathode.

Thus at the present time these considerations lead to a search for oxygen cathodes along the following lines:

(*i*) Noble metals, which are more refractory than platinum (thin films and the use of the active surface area only of the fuel cell may reduce cost sufficiently).

(*ii*) Refractory metals, which form conducting oxides.

(*iii*) Compounds of metals (typified by the tungsten bronzes[72a]), which are refractory and conduct electronically. A surprisingly large number of these exist. Examples of them are molybdenum silicide, tungsten carbide, etc., and some of these do not appear to dissolve significantly when made cathodes in acid solutions.

(*iv*) Semiconductors. A number of interesting possibilities appear to exist here. Thus, for example, the oxygen-reduction reaction needs a high concentration of electrons; i.e., an *n*-type semiconductor is needed. However, the dissolution of a semiconductor would be inhibited by lack of transport of sufficient holes from the surface during the functioning of the semiconductor as an oxygen cathode. Hence, the semiconductor might be electrochemically stable. Corresponding to this, organic semiconductors would seem to be of considerable interest.

Perhaps the brightest aspect of the future for good oxygen catalysts is the new research which seems to give ample possibility of introduction of high electronic conductivity into a number of refractory compounds.

While awaiting the results of research in some of the above areas, it may be that indirect methods of catalyzing the oxygen reduction may give rise to interesting results. The principles of these have already been mentioned in Chap. 6, Sec. 4. They consist of indirect catalysis by use of potential mediators, for example, redox substances which promote rapid electron transfer and then undergo a rapid homogeneous reaction with oxygen. The oxygen is reduced, and the reducing agent is returned to its oxidized form, which then becomes reduced at the cathode, and so on. The criteria for success in such a situation are not only the high i_0 of the redox couple, but it must have its own redox potential in the vicinity of the redox potential of the oxygen-reduction reaction. Otherwise, the ratio of the concentration of the reduced and oxidized forms of the redox couple will be too great, and one of them will be at a concentration too low to be able to supply itself at sufficient rate to the electrode. The rate of the homogeneous redox reaction may be too small to make a suitable situation; i.e., one may end up with an electrode which has to be too large in the sense of the number of cubic centimeters needed for a reduction of the oxygen by homogeneous means. In this area, little research has been done.

Other means suggested elsewhere include: acceleration by pulse, and local heating by superimposed ac, or irradiation by isotopes dissolved in the catalyst substrate (cf. Chap. 6, Sec. 4).

9 OXYGEN-ELECTRODE REACTIONS IN MOLTEN SALTS

9.1 General

Little work has been done in mechanism studies of the oxygen-electrode reaction in molten salts. Most of the work involving the oxygen electrode in molten salts has been in the direction of measurement of the cell-potential–current-density relations for fuel cells in molten alkali hydroxides or mixed carbonates.

9.2 Overall Reaction

The overall reaction in molten salts may in general be represented by two reactions. The first is a reduction of oxygen to the oxide ion:

$$O_2 + 4e_0^- = 2O^{2-} \tag{9.1}$$

This is followed by an equilibrium reaction in, for example, carbonates, of the type:

$$O^{2-} + CO_2 = CO_3^{2-} \tag{9.2}$$

The use of oxygen electrodes in molten salts as reference electrodes has been treated fairly extensively.[73]   Platinum, carbon, silver, gold, copper, and nickel electrodes have been used.

9.3   Mechanism Studies

Hardly any work has been carried out on mechanism studies of the cathodic reaction.   There is, however, some work on the mechanism of oxygen evolution from molten alkali (Li, Na, and K) carbonate mixtures on platinum, gold, and silver electrodes.[74]   Tafel lines with slopes approximating to $2\ RT/3F$ at temperatures of 600 and 700°C were observed.   Exchange current densities are of the order of 10^{-4} amp cm^{-2} on Pt at 600°C.   On silver no clear Tafel line was found and this was explained as being due to interference caused by the silver-dissolution reaction.   The mechanism of the evolution reaction on platinum and gold was interpreted on the basis of the following reaction sequence:

$$2CO_3^{2-} \rightleftarrows 2CO_2 + 2O^{2-} \tag{9.3}$$

$$M + O^{2-} \rightleftarrows MO + 2e_0^- \tag{9.4}$$

$$MO + O^{2-} \rightarrow M + O_2 + 2e_0^- \tag{9.5}$$

with the last step being rate-determining.

There is no evidence against the assumption that the step represented by the reverse of (9.5) is the rate-determining step for the cathodic reduction of oxygen.   Mechanism studies on the cathodic reactions are desirable because there is an interest for developing electrochemical energy converters using cheap fuels (e.g., natural gas) in molten electrolytes.   For example, one may oxidize CO at the anode and reduce O_2 at the cathode, the CO_3^{2-} ions acting as regenerated carriers:

$$2CO + 2CO_3^{2-} = 4CO_2 + 4e_0^- \tag{9.6}$$

$$O_2 + 2CO_2 + 4e_0^- = 2CO_3^2 \tag{9.7}$$

10   BEHAVIOR OF THE OXYGEN ELECTRODE AT HIGH PRESSURES

Mechanism studies of the oxygen-electrode reaction at high pressures are sparse. There is an advantage in using high pressures in electrochemical energy converters, for example, the Bacon hydrogen-oxygen fuel cell;[75] at a given cell voltage, the current doubles itself for a tenfold increase in pressure.   Important applications arise in energy supply for deep-sea exploration.   Oxygen pressures as high as 60 to 70 atm have been used in the Bacon fuel cell.   Recently, the oxygen-peroxide redox couple has been examined at platinum electrodes by Urbach et al.[76,77]   It was previously shown that this couple is quite reversible at carbon electrodes.[53]   The same was found to be true on platinum electrodes at peroxide concentrations less than 10^{-4} mole l^{-1} with no net current flow; the potential of a Pt electrode versus a reversible hydrogen electrode in the same solution was found to obey the equation

$$V = 0.762 + 0.030 \log [O_2] - 0.030 \log [HO_2^-] \tag{10.1}$$

Oxygen pressures were varied from 1 to 100 atm. The effects of oxygen pressure on the current-density–potential relations for oxygen reduction at a platinum electrode in the presence of peroxide ions in solution are shown in Fig. 30. It

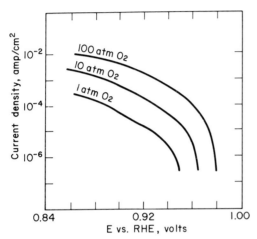

Figure 30 Effect of oxygen pressure on the current-potential relations for the reduction of oxygen on Pt electrodes in alkaline solution containing peroxide ion.

was found that

$$\left(\frac{\partial V}{\partial \log p_{O_2}} \right)_{i,T,C_{HO_2^-}} = 2.3 \times \frac{2RT}{F} \tag{10.2}$$

$$\left(\frac{\partial \log i}{\partial \log p_{O_2}} \right)_{V,T,C_{HO_2^-}} = 1 \tag{10.3}$$

The reaction order with respect to the peroxide concentration was found to be zero. On the basis of these electrode-kinetic parameters, the following mechanism was proposed:

$$O_2 + PtH_2O + e_0^- = PtO_2H + OH^- \tag{10.4}$$

$$PtO_2H + e_0^- = Pt + HO_2^- \tag{10.5}$$

with the second step being rate-determining.

For hydrogen peroxide concentrations greater than 10^{-4} mole l^{-1}, a mixed potential is established which is determined by the reactions

$$OH^- + HO_2^- = O_2 + H_2O + 2e_0^- \tag{10.6}$$

$$H_2O + HO_2^- + 2e_0^- = 3OH^- \tag{10.7}$$

It would be desirable to carry out studies on the effect of pressure on the four-electron transfer reaction of oxygen, which must obviously be done in the absence of peroxide ions in solution.

REFERENCES

1. Bockris, J. O'M., and A. K. M. S. Huq: *Proc. Roy. Soc., Ser.* A **237**, 277 (1956).
2. Bockris, J. O'M.: Chap. 4, in J. O'M. Bockris and B. E. Conway (eds.), "Modern Aspects of Electrochemistry," vol. 1, Butterworth & Co. (Publishers), Ltd., London, 1954.
2a. American Cyanamid Company, Stamford Research Laboratories, Stamford, Conn., 1967.
3. Damjanovic, A., A. Dey, and J. O'M. Bockris: *Electrochim. Acta*, **11**, 791 (1966).
4. Damjanovic, A., A. Dey, and J. O'M. Bockris: *J. Electrochem. Soc.*, **113**, 739 (1966).
5. Damjanovic, A., and V. Brusic: *Electrochim. Acta*, **12**, 615 (1967).
6. Damjanovic, A., M. A. Genshaw, and J. O'M. Bockris: *J. Phys. Chem.*, **71**, 3722 (1967).
7. Sepa, D., A. Damjanovic, and J. O'M. Bockris: *Electrochim. Acta*, **12**, 746 (1967).
8. Bockris, J. O'M., A. Damjanovic, and R. Mannan: *J. Electroanal. Chem. and Interf. Electrochem.*, **18**, 349 (1968).
9. Mayell, J. S., and S. H. Langer: *Electrochim. Acta*, **9**, 1411 (1964).
10. Despic, A. R., and J. O'M. Bockris: *J. Chem. Phys.*, **32**, 389 (1960).
11. Bockris, J. O'M., R. Mannan, and A. Damjanovic: *J. Chem. Phys.*, **48**, 1898 (1968).
12. Bockris, J. O'M., M. A. V. Devanathan, and A. K. N. Reddy: *Proc. Roy. Soc., Ser.* A **279**, 327 (1964).
13. Damjanovic, A., M. A. Genshaw, and J. O'M. Bockris: *J. Phys. Chem.*, **70**, 3761 (1966).
14. Hoar, T. P.: *Proc. Roy. Soc., Ser.* A **142**, 628 (1933).
15. Wroblowa, H., M. L. B. Rao, A. Damjanovic, and J. O'M. Bockris: *J. Electroanal. Chem.*, **15**, 139 (1967).
16. Schuldiner, S., and R. M. Roe: *J. Electrochem. Soc.*, **110**, 1142 (1963).
17. Visscher, W., and M. A. V. Devanathan: *J. Electroanal. Chem.*, **8**, 127 (1964).
18. Devanathan, M. A. V.: Private communication, 1962.
19. Bockris, J. O'M., H. Wroblowa, E. Gileadi, and B. J. Piersma: *Trans. Faraday Soc.*, **61**, 2531 (1965).
20. Bockris, J. O'M., and L. F. Oldfield: *Trans. Faraday Soc.*, **51**, 249 (1955).
21. Gerischer, R., and H. Gerischer: *Z. Physik. Chem.*, **6**, 178 (1956).
22. Criddle, E. E.: *Electrochim. Acta*, **9**, 853 (1964).
23. Haber, F., and F. Fleischmann: *Z. Anorg. Allgem. Chem.*, **51**, 245 (1906).
24. Watanabe, N., and M. A. V. Devanathan: *J. Electrochem. Soc.*, **111**, 615 (1964).
25. Hoare, J. P., *J. Electrochem. Soc.*, **110**, 1019 (1963); "The Electrochemistry of Oxygen," Interscience Publishers, Inc., New York, 1968.

26. Vetter, K. J.: *Z. Anorg. Allgem. Chem.*, **260**, 242 (1949).
27. Bowden, F. P.: *Proc. Roy. Soc.*, **A125**, 446 (1929).
28. Butler, J. A. V., and A. Armstrong: *Proc. Roy. Soc.*, **A137**, 604 (1932).
29. Armstrong, A., F. R. Himsworth, and J. A. V. Butler: *Proc. Roy. Soc.*, **A143**, 89 (1934).
30. Butler, J. A. V., and G. Drewer: *Trans. Faraday Soc.*, **32**, 427 (1936).
31. Pearson, J. D., and J. A. V. Butler: *Trans. Faraday Soc.*, **34**, 1163 (1938).
32. Ershler, B. V., A. Deborin, and A. N. Frumkin: *Acta Physico Chim.*, *USSR*, **8**, 565 (1938).
33. Hickling, A.: *Trans. Faraday Soc.*, **41**, 33 (1945); **42**, 518 (1946).
34. Zalkind, Ts. I., and B. V. Ershler: *Zh. Fiz. Khim*, **25**, 565 (1951).
35. ElWakkad, S. E. S., and S. H. Emara: *J. Electrochem. Soc.*, **461**, (1952).
36. Becker, M., and M. Breiter: *Z. Elektrochem.*, **60**, 1080 (1956).
37. Vetter, K. J., and D. Berndt: *Z. Electrochem.*, **62**, 378 (1958).
38. Laitenen, H., and A. Enke: *J. Electrochem. Soc.*, **107**, 773 (1960).
39. Dahms, H., and J. O'M. Bockris: *J. Electrochem. Soc.*, **111**, 728 (1964).
40. Anson, F. C., and J. J. Lingane: *J. Am. Chem. Soc.*, **79**, 4901 (1957).
41. Reddy, A. K. N., M. A. V. Devanathan, and J. O'M. Bockris: *J. Electroanal. Chem.*, **6**, 61 (1963); *Proc. Roy. Soc.*, **A279**, 327 (1964).
42. Reddy, A. K. N., and J. O'M. Bockris: Proceeding of the Symposium on the Ellipsometer and Its Use, *Dept.* Comm. *Publ.* 229, 1964.
43. Reddy, A. K. N., M. A. Genshaw, and J. O'M. Bockris: *J. Electroanal. Chem.*, **8**, 406 (1964); *J. Chem. Phys.*, **48**, 671 (1968).
44. Visscher, W.: Doctoral dissertation, Technological University, Sudhoven, 1968; *Optik*, **26**, 402 (1968).
45. Ruetschi, P., and B. D. Cahan: *J. Electrochem. Soc.*, **104**, 406 (1957).
46. Rozenthal, K. I., and V. I. Vesolovskii: *Dokl. Akad. Nauk SSSR*, **111**, 637 (1956).
47. Bockris, J. O'M.: *J. Chem. Phys.*, **24**, 817 (1956).
48. Bowden, F. P.: *Proc. Roy. Soc.*, *Ser.* A **126**, 107 (1930).
49. Gorovich, M. A., R. I. Kaganovich, V. M. Vergelesov, and L. N. Goroshov: *Dokl. Akad. Nauk. SSSR*, **114**, 1049 (1957).
50. Beck, T. R., and R. W. Moulton: *J. Electrochem. Soc.*, **103**, 247 (1956).
51. Erdey Gruz, T., and I. Safarik: *Proc. 4th Conf. Electrochem.*, *Moscow*, 1956, Academy of Science, Moscow, 1959.
51a. Gileadi, E., J. O'M. Bockris, and S. D. Argade: *J. Phys. Chem.*, **70**, 2044 (1966).
52. Heyrovsky, J.: *J. Cas. cesk. lekain*, **7**, 242 (1927).
53. Berl, W. A.: *Trans., Electrochem. Soc.*, **83**, 253 (1943).
54. Davies, M. C., M. Clark, E. Yeager, and F. Hovorka: *J. Electrochem. Soc.*, **106**, 56 (1959).
55. Levich, V. G. (trans.): "Physicochemical Hydrodynamics," Prentice-Hall, Inc., Englewood Cliffs, N.J., 1962.
56. Muller, L., and L. N. Nekrasov: *Electrochim. Acta*, **9**, 1015 (1964).
57. Damjanovic, A., M. A. Genshaw, and J. O'M. Bockris: *J. Chem. Phys.*, **45**, 4057 (1966).
58. Damjanovic, A., M. A. Genshaw, and J. O'M. Bockris: *J. Electrochem. Soc.*, **114**, 466 (1967).
59. Damjanovic, A., M. A. Genshaw, and J. O'M. Bockris: *J. Electrochem. Soc.*, **114**, 1108 (1967).

60. Genshaw, M. A.: Doctoral dissertation, University of Pennsylvania, 1966; A. Damjanovic, M. A. Genshaw, and J. O'M. Bockris, *J. Electroanal. Chem. and Interf. Electrochem.*, **15**, 173 (1967); M. A. Genshaw, A. Damjanovic, and J. O'M. Bockris, *J. Phys. Chem.*, **71**, 3722 (1967).

61. Damjanovic, A., and V. Brusic: *Electrochim. Acta*, **12**, 1171 (1967).

62. Krasilshchikow, A. I., L. M. Volchkowa, and L. G. Antonowa: *J. Phys. Chem. (USSR)*, **27**, 512 (1953).

63. Vielstich, W.: *Z. Physik. Chem.* (N.F.), **15**, 409 (1958).

64. Yeager, E., and A. Kozawa: "Combustion and Propulsion, 6th AGARD Colloquium," Pergamon Press and Oxford University Press, New York, 1964.

65. Azzam, A. M., J. O'M. Bockris, B. E. Conway, and A. Rosenberg: *Trans. Faraday Soc.*, **46**, 918 (1950).

66. Krasilshchikow, A. I.: *J. Phys. Chem. (USSR)*, **26**, 216 (1952).

67. Bagotsky, V. S., and I. E. Jablokowa: *Zh. Fiz. Khim. (USSR)*, **27**, 1665 (1953).

68. Kolthoff, I. M., and J. Jordan: *J. Am. Chem. Soc.*, **74**, 4801 (1952).

69. Weiss, J.: *Trans. Faraday Soc.*, **31**, 1547 (1935).

70. Damjanovic, A., and J. O'M. Bockris: *Electrochim. Acta*, **11**, 376 (1966).

71. Ruetschi, P., and P. Delahay: *J. Chem. Phys.*, **23**, 556 (1955).

72. Subramanyan, P. K.: Private communication.

72a. Banks, E., and A. Wold: Chap. 1, in W. L. Jolly (ed.), "Preparative Inorganic Reactions," vol. 4, Interscience Publishers, Inc., New York, 1968.

73. Alabyshev, A. F., M. F. Lantratov, and A. G. Morochevski: "Reference Electrodes for Fused salts," English translation by A. Peiperl, The Sigma Press, Washington, D.C., 1965.

74. Jansz, G. J., and F. Saegusa: *Electrochim. Acta*, **7**, 393 (1962).

75. Adams, A. M., F. T. Bacon, and R. G. H. Watson: Chap. 4, in W. Mitchell (ed.), "Fuel Cells," Academic Press Inc., New York, 1963.

76. Bowen, R. J., and H. B. Urbach: *Nature*, **213**, 592 (1967).

77. Urbach, H. B., and R. J. Bowen: *Electrochim. Acta*, in press.

78. McDonald, J. J., and B. E. Conway: *Proc. Roy. Soc.*, Ser. A **269**, 419 (1962).

79. Krasilshchikow, A. O.: *Zh. Fiz. Khim.*, **37**, 531 (1963).

80. Brusic, V.: Private communication.

CHAPTER NINE

An Outline of Fuel-cell Research Techniques

1 INTRODUCTION

The techniques used in fuel-cell research are numerous, and it is not possible to deal with all the detailed aspects of this research in the present chapter. The most fundamental of the areas of research is the study of mechanisms of reactions occurring at each electrode in the cell, and such a study should be of help in reducing activation overpotential, which is the major cause for loss of cell potential at practical current densities. The rest of the chapter is devoted briefly (but is adequately referenced)† to the other aspects of fuel-cell research.

2 INVESTIGATIONS OF MECHANISMS OF ELECTRODE REACTIONS

2.1 Stages in Mechanism Investigations

The investigation of mechanisms of reactions in fuel cells involves determination of (1) the overall reaction, often obvious in fuel cells; (2) the rate-determining step; and (3) the reaction path, i.e., intermediate steps before and after the rate-determining step, in so far as such a determination is possible. Such a detailed investigation is desirable principally in giving catalytic research information that indicates the direction in which catalysts may be sought.

Reactants can only react if they are either within a few angstroms of the electrode surface or in contact with it by adsorption. Hence, the degree of adsorption of each reactant, particularly its dependence on the electrode potential and on concentration, becomes an important, although hitherto little investigated, aspect of mechanism determination, especially for organic fuels. To elucidate the reaction path and rate-determining steps, the methods

---

† A detailed account of the many techniques which are outlined here and a good basis for a tome concerning electronics in electrochemistry is given in the doctoral dissertation of B. D. Cahan,[81] University of Pennsylvania, 1968.

used may be classified into two types: (1) detection and identification of intermediates and (2) determination of electrode-kinetic parameters. Steady-state or non-steady-state measurements are involved in these methods.

Table 1 summarizes the principal stages in the determination of the

TABLE 1 Principal Stages in the Determination of the Mechanism of an Electrochemical Reaction

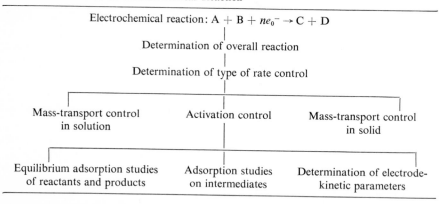

Electrochemical reaction: $A + B + ne_0^- \rightarrow C + D$

Determination of overall reaction

Determination of type of rate control

Mass-transport control in solution	Activation control	Mass-transport control in solid
Equilibrium adsorption studies of reactants and products	Adsorption studies on intermediates	Determination of electrode-kinetic parameters

mechanism of an electrochemical reaction. A schematic representation of the methodology of examination is shown in Table 2. Elucidation of the

TABLE 2 Methodology of Investigation of the Mechanism of an Electrochemical Reaction

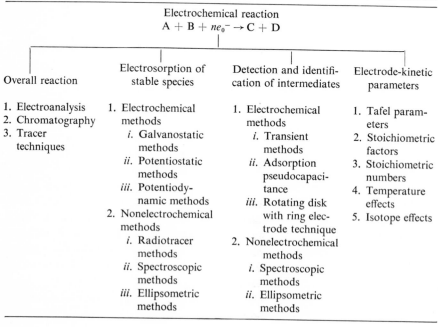

Electrochemical reaction
$A + B + ne_0^- \rightarrow C + D$

Overall reaction	Electrosorption of stable species	Detection and identification of intermediates	Electrode-kinetic parameters

1. Electroanalysis
2. Chromatography
3. Tracer techniques
	1. Electrochemical methods
	  i. Galvanostatic methods
	  ii. Potentiostatic methods
	  iii. Potentiodynamic methods
	2. Nonelectrochemical methods
	  i. Radiotracer methods
	  ii. Spectroscopic methods
	  iii. Ellipsometric methods
		1. Electrochemical methods
		  i. Transient methods
		  ii. Adsorption pseudocapacitance
		  iii. Rotating disk with ring electrode technique
		2. Nonelectrochemical methods
		  i. Spectroscopic methods
		  ii. Ellipsometric methods
			1. Tafel parameters
			2. Stoichiometric factors
			3. Stoichiometric numbers
			4. Temperature effects
			5. Isotope effects

rate-determining step becomes increasingly difficult if the number of intermediate steps in the overall reaction is high because the number of hypothetical rate-determining steps and pathways in the reaction can become very large.[1] This situation is alleviated to some extent by the fact that: (1) the rate-determining step is usually one of the first two or three steps in the reaction sequence[2] and (2) many purely hypothetical reaction paths may be excluded because they pass through states of reactions which are unlikely in energetic grounds.[3] Sometimes even when all the diagnostic criteria are available, the possible rate-determining step for multistep organic reactions can only be reduced from a large number to two or three.   There are some cases, however, where the rate-determining step is uniquely found.   Many inorganic fuel-cell reactions involve two to four steps.   Here, the evaluation of rate-determining steps and many aspects of mechanism determinations may be achieved with a high degree of probability.

2.2 Determination of Overall Reaction

This stage of mechanism determination is generally simple, except in cases where several products are simultaneously formed in either a consecutive or a parallel reaction path.   Gaseous products (for example, CO_2 formed during oxidation of organic compounds) may be removed from the electrolytic cell by passage of an inert gas and then passed through a gas chromatograph.[4]

Nongaseous inorganic products are determined by analysis of the electrolyte.   Electroanalytic[5] (polarographic[6]) methods are used with electroactive species.   Nongaseous organic products are extracted from the electrolyte and analyzed by conventional procedures[7] (e.g., mass spectrometry, gas chromatography, infrared or ultraviolet spectroscopy).

In cases where parallel reactions occur, it is necessary to check whether the faradaic efficiency varies with the potential of the test electrode.[8]   Thus, it is preferable to carry out a product analysis under potentiostatic conditions in these cases.

Product analysis also gives the number of electrons transferred in the overall reaction.

2.3 Determination of Equilibrium Adsorption of Reactants

2.3.1 Electrochemical Methods

2.3.1.1 Galvanostatic Methods.   Early workers used this method for the determination of coverages of intermediates, such as hydrogen[9-11] and oxygen,[12-14] on electrodes.   Recently, it has been used to determine coverages of organic species adsorbed on electrodes.[15-17]   For this purpose, the electrode is first maintained at the potential at which the coverage is required, for a time long enough for the adsorption equilibrium to be attained.   The electrode is then subjected to a high constant current pulse to oxidize the species adsorbed on the electrode, and the potential-time trace is recorded on an oscilloscope.

A typical charging curve to determine the extent of benzene adsorption on a platinum electrode is shown in Fig. 1. From the potential arrest observed on

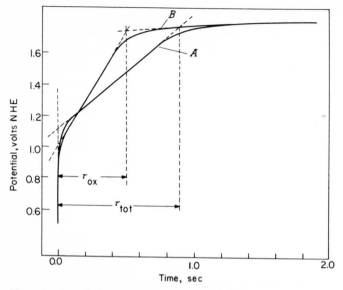

Figure 1 A typical galvanostatic charging curve (curve *A*) for the determination of adsorption of benzene on a platinum electrode from 1 *N* H_2SO_4 containing 10^{-5} M benzene at 25°C.[25] Curve *B* is the control transient with no benzene in solution.

the curve, which indicates the oxidation process, the amount of electricity required for this process is obtained. The fractional coverage is obtained by dividing this quantity of electricity by the quantity of electricity required to remove a monolayer of the adsorbed species from the electrode. One thus needs a knowledge of the number of electrons required for the removal of one molecule of the adsorbed species from the electrode.

A necessary criterion for the application of this method is that a clearly distinguishable potential arrest must be observed in the galvanostatic transient. Otherwise, problems in separating the amounts of electricity for the electro-oxidation of two competing reactions arise. Such problems have been overcome in the "double-charging galvanostatic method" which uses two galvanostatic transients.[18,19] One is begun at the potential at which the coverage of the test species does not adsorb on the electrode. An iteration procedure is used to determine the coverage of the test species. It depends upon a correction due to the partial current involved in the deposition of another species (e.g., oxide).

An alternative galvanostatic method, applicable in some cases, is an indirect one. Here, the amount of electricity required to cover completely the surface with hydrogen in the absence (Q_H^0) and in the presence (Q_H) of the adsorbed material is determined by using galvanostatic transients,[20–22] as previously described. Thus, the coverage of the adsorbed entity (Q_a) is given by

$$Q_a = \frac{Q_H{}^0 - Q_H}{Q_H{}^0} \tag{2.1}$$

The applicability of this method is based on several assumptions. The first is that hydrogen is adsorbed to the extent of a monolayer in the absence of the organic species. This may be true for some metals (e.g., platinum) but it is known not to be so in some cases, for example, Ni in alkaline solution.[19] The second is that the organic species remains adsorbed even at the negative potential required for the adsorption of hydrogen. Due to the potential dependence of adsorption of the organic species, one would expect some desorption to occur, even though the transient measurements are carried out in a short time. The third assumption is that hydrogen adsorption per site in the presence of the organic species is the same as that during its absence. This seems unlikely in view of the fact that adsorbed organic impurities have marked effects on the kinetics of hydrogen evolution.[23] The fourth is that during the cathodic transient all the current is consumed for the deposition of hydrogen and none for the reduction of the adsorbed organic species, which assumption seems unlikely on certain electrodes. Thus, the method is of value only if the validity of these assumptions is established in each system concerned.

2.3.1.2 Potentiostatic Methods. In this method, which has seldom been used previously,[24,25] the potential of the electrode is first maintained at the value at which the coverage of the test compound is required, and it is then instantaneously changed to another value at which the species is readily oxidized. The current-time plot during this potentiostatic transient may be readily recorded on an oscilloscope and photographed. The area under this curve gives the charge required to remove the adsorbed species from the electrode provided that no competitive reactions occur and that readsorption is negligible during this time interval. If competing reactions, e.g., oxide formation, occur, the problem may be met with by carrying out the potentiostatic transient in the absence and in the presence of the test material in solution.[25] Typical curves used to determine extent of adsorption of benzene on a platinum electrode are shown in Fig. 2. Thus, the extent of adsorption is given by

$$Q_a = \int_0^t (i_1 - i_2)\, dt \tag{2.2}$$

where i_1 and i_2 are the currents in the presence and in the absence, respectively, of the test compound in solution.

In the potentiostatic method, the major error arises from instrumental limitations because it is necessary for the rise time of potentiostat to be sufficiently small so that the potential may be constant for the whole course of the reaction. Because the potential is held constant during oxidation, there is less

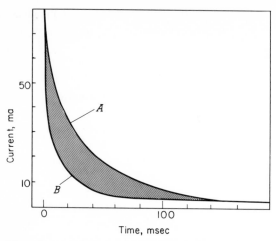

Figure 2 A typical potentiostatic charging curve (curve *A*) for the determination of adsorption of benzene on a platinum electrode from 1 N H_2SO_4 containing 10^{-5} M benzene at 25°C.[25]   Curve *B* is the control transient obtained with no benzene in solution.

likely to be an ambiguity concerning the reaction during the transient.   It may be assumed to be that occurring in the steady state at the same potential of oxidation.

Further, because the potential for the oxidation can be chosen over a range, it is often possible to oxidize organic compounds at a potential at which the substrate does not form an oxide, thus avoiding difficulties of the galvanostatic method.   Among the electrochemical methods, this method appears to involve the least number of assumptions.

2.3.1.3   Potentiodynamic Methods.   In the methods described in the two preceding subsections, either the current or the potential is maintained constant during the transient measurement.   In the potential sweep method, the potential is varied linearly with time and the current-time relation is observed on an oscilloscope.[25–30]   The *i-t* curves are recorded in the presence and in the absence of the adsorbable material in solution.   The difference in the areas under these curves is, with the applicability of the assumptions discussed below, a measure of the extent of adsorption of the test compound.   Typical curves obtained in a study of benzene adsorption[25] on Pt are shown in Fig. 3.   It is necessary to check the measurements over a range of sweep rates because at low sweep rates readsorption from solution may occur whereas at higher sweep rates the oxidation process may be incomplete or the capacitative charging current which is proportional to dV/dt becomes so large that it cannot be separated from the current for oxidation of the adsorbed layer.

The potentiodynamic method differs from the other transient methods in

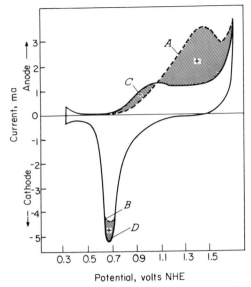

Figure 3 Typical current-time (or potential) curves (curve A is anodic, curve B is cathodic) obtained in a study of benzene adsorption on a platinum electrode from 1 N H_2SO_4 containing 10^{-5} M benzene at 25°C using the potential sweep method.[25] Curves C and D are the control anodic and cathodic transient with no benzene in solution.

that both current and potential are being changed at the same time. Its interpretation is thus more complex than with galvanostatic and potentiostatic procedures.[27] Thus, the potentiodynamic method gives correct results only if: (1) rate constants of all reactions concerned are relatively high so that in each part of the potential range the reaction goes to completion in the time determined by the sweep; (2) the adsorbed species is removed by electron transfer and not by desorption due to replacement by water molecules as a consequence of change of potential;[31,32] (3) the parallel reaction for formation of oxide on the surface takes place to the same extent in the presence and absence of organic by adsorbed organic compound. Most of these assumptions will not always be true. The degree to which they interfere with the results will depend upon the system and must be established for each system before the method can be used.

The galvanostatic method is also subject to some of the errors of the potentiodynamic method but seemingly to a lesser extent because, with respect to the electrostatic desorption mentioned above, in the potentiodynamic method the faradaic current does not usually rise for organic oxidation until the potential is in a more anodic region in which equilibrium desorption of organic occurs. Thus, any electrostatic desorption will account for some of the organic species adsorbed on the electrode. In the galvanostatic method, most of the layer will tend already to have been oxidized by the constant current before the potential reaches the point of desorption. Correspondingly, there are more difficulties in making a correction for the oxide in the potentiodynamic method than in the galvanostatic method.

A comparison of the results obtained by the three electrochemical transient methods and radioactive methods is made in Sec. 2.3.3.

2.3.2   Nonelectrochemical Methods

2.3.2.1   Radiotracer Methods. Two broad types of radiotracer techniques have been developed. In one, the change in radioactivity of the solution is obtained after equilibrium adsorption is allowed to occur on an electrode.[33,34] This method is limited to low concentrations in solution ($<10^{-6}$ mole l^{-1}), because if higher concentrations are present it is not possible to detect small changes in concentration.

In the second type, *in situ* isotope detection is made on the electrode. Two methods have been used. In the first, radiation from the adsorbed material is measured with a counter behind the electrode[35] (Fig. 4). This

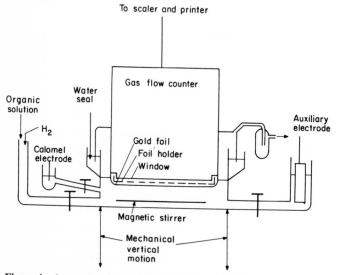

Figure 4   Apparatus in radiotracer "foil" method for the determination of adsorption of compounds from solution on electrodes.[35a]

requires that the electrode be made of an extremely thin foil covering the window of the counter or that the electrocatalyst material be deposited on a suitable inert foil. Background radiation from the solution must be kept low. Using this method, the adsorption of a number of organic compounds (e.g., benzene, naphthalene, ethylene, thiourea) on platinum and gold electrodes has been determined as a function of potential and concentration.[35a]

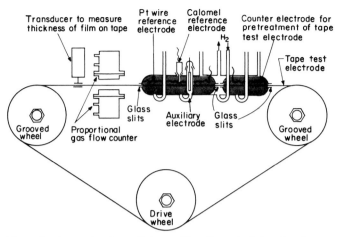

Figure 5 Apparatus in radiotracer "tape" method for the determination of adsorption of compounds from solution on electrodes.[36]

Many metals and alloys that cannot be prepared in thin enough layers and at the same time with sufficient mechanical strength can be used in the form of tapes that are drawn through the solution containing the radioactive adsorbate[36] (Fig. 5). The radiation is counted after a portion of the tape has been pulled out of the solution through a slit to a proportional counter in such a way that only a thin film adheres to the tape. This method can also be used to study the variation of adsorption with electrode potential or with concentration of adsorbate in solution.[36a]

2.3.2.2 Spectroscopic Methods. An ultraviolet spectroscopic method was developed in which the adsorption of a compound on an electrode is obtained from the change in ultraviolet absorption of the solution before and after adsorption on the electrode had occurred.[37] Large electrodes of nickel, copper, and silver in the form of gauzes were used. The adsorption of pyridine, quinoline, and acridine was studied.

Infrared absorption techniques have been used for studies of adsorption on metals from the gas phase.[38] A possible way of extending this method for electrosorption measurements is by using electrodes in the form of thin foils and making measurements through the electrodes.

2.3.2.3 Ellipsometric Methods. In the ellipsometric method[39] a beam of polarized light is passed through the solution and reflected from the electrode (Fig. 6). The state of polarization after reflection from the surface is measured. The change in the state of polarization gives information on the refractive index of film and on its thickness. The method has been used successfully for determining oxide films[39] on metals, and recently Genshaw and Chiu have achieved the measurement of surface concentration of ions at solid electrodes by ellipsometric means.[40]

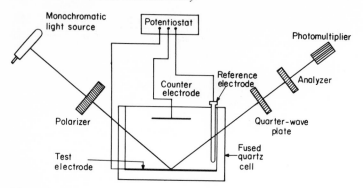

Figure 6 Ellipsometric method for the study of film formation on electrodes from solution.[39]

2.3.3 *A Comparison of the Transient Electrochemical and Radiotracer Methods for Surface-concentration Measurements*

A detailed comparative study of the potential- and concentration-dependence of the adsorption of benzene on platinum electrodes was made recently using the transient electrochemical and radiotracer techniques.[25]   Figure 7 shows the coverage-potential relations obtained using these methods at 50°C.   At potentials below 500 mv the agreement between these methods is quite good.   At potentials above this value, the three electrochemical methods yield similar results but they deviate from the results of the radiotracer methods.   A hypothesis that may be considered is that at potentials below 500 mv the adsorbed

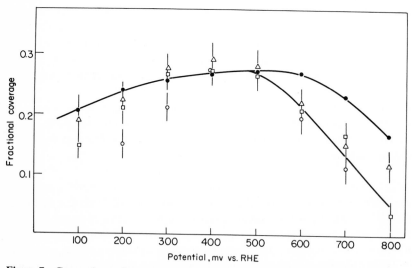

Figure 7 Comparison of coverage-potential relations for the adsorption of benzene on Pt from 1 N H_2SO_4 and 10^{-6} M C_6H_6 using the electrochemical ($\square$, galvanostatic; $\bigcirc$, potentiostatic; $\triangle$, potential sweep) and radiotracer ($\bullet$) methods.[25]

species is the molecule present in solution and that this is essentially in equilibrium with the solution; and that the net forward reaction rate in this potential range is negligible in comparison with the rates of the assumed equilibrium reactions between substrate and solution. Correspondingly, in the electrochemical methods, it is this species (at potentials negative to 500 mv) which is completely oxidized to carbon dioxide and water requiring 30 electrons for this process. At potentials above 500 mv, some adsorbed radical(s) in the reaction sequence attains concentration levels comparable to that of benzene. The radioactive method is unaffected because it counts all the carbon-containing radicals present (same intensity per atom, independent of radical). However, in the electrochemical methods, the partially oxidized radicals require a lesser number of electrons for their removal by further complete oxidation than that for the complete oxidation of benzene. Even though this hypothesis suggests that the radiotracer method is correct, such is not the case because the method assumes that the carbon adsorbed on the surface is all contained in the benzene and not in any of the radicals. As the number of electrons is still assumed to be 30, which is the number required for the complete oxidation of benzene to carbon dioxide, whereas for most of the radicals it should be a lesser value, a smaller result will be obtained than that which corresponds to the actual total amount of adsorbed material on the surface.

The adsorption isotherms obtained at a temperature of 50°C and at a potential of 500 mv (RHE) using the electrochemical transient and the radiotracer techniques are shown in Fig. 8. The agreement among the various methods is fairly satisfactory. At more anodic potentials, for the reasons stated above, adsorption isotherms obtained from the electrochemical methods, assuming that 30 electrons are required for the removal of the adsorbed species, deviate from the corresponding isotherms obtained from the radiotracer method. At higher temperatures, the equilibrium adsorption of benzene occurs at a faster rate than the oxidation reactions and the agreement between the radiotracer and electrochemical techniques occurs over a wider range of potential.

In comparing the two types of approaches, the radioactive approach probably needs simpler equipment. As long as the electrodes are not reprepared at each potential, it is quicker in recording a coverage-potential curve because the amount adsorbed is not swept off at each potential but the potential is altered to a new one. The significance of the result is completely unambiguous because this approach gives the number of tracer atoms present. It can be applied to adsorption measurements on any surface on which the reaction will occur, i.e., adsorption on metals other than on the noble ones can be examined. This is not the case with the electrochemical methods for nonnoble substrates dissolved during part of the sweep.

A weakness of the radioactive method is that a measurement is made of the total number of tracer atoms that is independent of the exact species in which they occur. Thus, to distinguish the coverage of an adsorbed benzene molecule from adsorbed radicals that increase in surface concentrations with potential,

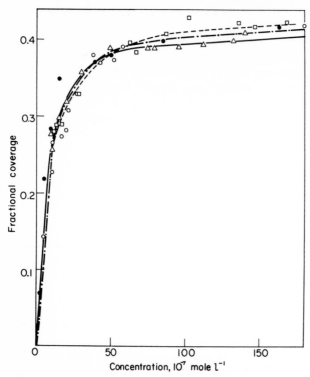

Figure 8 Isotherms for adsorption of benzene on platinum from 1 N H_2SO_4 containing C_6H_6 at 50°C using the electrochemical [galvanostatic ($\square$), potentiostatic ($\bigcirc$), and potentiodynamic ($\triangle$)] and radiotracer ($\bullet$) methods at a potential of 500 mv, RHE.[25]

it is necessary to use indirect arguments, as, for example, comparing entropy of adsorption with values expected for various sizes of adsorbate.[41] The radioactive method can perhaps be extended to using more than one tracer atom, e.g., tritium; and were it possible to measure ratio of T to C atoms, identification of the adsorbed species may be achieved. Difficulties of exchange of tritium with hydrogen of the solution might intervene. High surface areas have to be used to obtain sufficient signal.

The electrochemical methods, in conjunction with the radiotracer method, have considerable value because their development may lead to information on the nature of radicals on the surface.[42] Hypothetically, they might be used in the determination of several radicals, and were this possible it would be a considerable advantage in mechanism determinations of organic reactions and thus to electrocatalysis. On the other hand, all of the electrochemical methods involve a number of assumptions. Whether the error which these assumptions cover can be reduced to negligible proportions will have to be assayed with each new substrate because the errors depend on the rate constants on the substrates concerned. It may take longer to make a coverage-potential relation, because after each pulse, adsorption has to occur. It would probably be difficult to use electrochemical pulse methods for adsorption measurements other than on noble metals, for the dissolution reason noted above.

The situation at present is that each approach may have some advantage for a given purpose. The radioactive method should be developed for multi-channel analysis of different species (cf. importance of examining anion adsorption simultaneously with adsorption of organic molecules)[43] and the electrochemical transient methods for detection of radicals.[44,45]

2.4 Detection and Identification of Intermediates

2.4.1 Electrochemical Methods

2.4.1.1 Transient Methods. The methods described in the previous subsection, viz., galvanostatic, potentiostatic, and potential sweep methods, have also been used to detect and identify intermediates adsorbed on electrodes in electrochemical reactions, particularly for the hydrogen-[9-11] and oxygen-[12-14] electrode reactions on noble metals. More recently, intermediates in the oxidation of organic fuels have been under investigation.[16,44] Complications arise if several intermediates, which adsorb on the electrode, are formed in the reaction or if there is simultaneous reactant adsorption.

The following method has been proposed in order to gain information on radicals present on a surface at a desired potential.[42] The surface is first subjected to a cathodic galvanostatic transient and if assumptions of this method are applicable, the fraction of surface occupied by the organic species can thus be ascertained (Sec. 2.3.1.1). A similar surface is now subjected to an anodic pulse and the organic species is thereby oxidized. The charge for this process is hence known, and if it is assumed that one organic molecule occupies a single site on the electrode, information on the source of the anodic charge may be ascertained. Information of this kind is badly needed, although the many assumptions make it difficult to accept the method at the present time. The method has suggested that in using propane at low potential (below 0.3 volt) the adsorbate is probably C_3H_7Pt, whereas at higher potentials (above 0.3 volt) the adsorbate species is a hydrocarbon radical with a smaller H-to-C ratio or some oxygenated species.

In another type of study, the nature of the species adsorbed on the electrode is obtained from their cathodic desorption and subsequent use of gas chromatography in identifying the reduced gaseous products.[45] In this way, it was found that using ethylene as the fuel and with Pt electrodes, methane, ethane, propane, and butane were identified by gas chromatography. This indicates dissociative and associative adsorption of ethylene on the platinum surface.

2.4.1.2 Adsorption Pseudocapacitance. A knowledge of adsorption pseudocapacitance is useful in gaining information on coverages of intermediates in electrochemical reactions[46] (Chap. 2, Sec. 5). The most direct method of obtaining it is from the differential of a galvanostatic transient.

Thus

$$i = C \frac{dV}{dt} \tag{2.3}$$

where C represents the sum of the ionic double-layer capacity and the pseudo-capacity. Since pseudocapacities are generally large in comparison with the ionic double-layer capacities, C can be taken as the pseudocapacity when such a contribution is present. A second obvious method of obtaining the pseudo-capacity is by using the fast-potential sweep technique. Under these conditions, the measured current is predominantly pseudocapacitative. This method is more direct than the first one.

An ac bridge method may also be used to determine pseudocapacities. The electrode is maintained at a steady potential. An ac signal of low amplitude is then imposed on the electrode and the total capacity C_T of the electrode is measured as a function of frequency. C_T is given by

$$C_T = \frac{C_{ps}}{1 + R^2 \omega^2 C_{ps}} + C_{dl} \tag{2.4}$$

where C_{ps} is the pseudocapacitance, C_{dl} is the ionic double-layer capacity, ω is the angular frequency of the ac signal, and R is the reaction resistance. A difficulty of this method is that C_{ps} sometimes turns out to be frequency-dependent. Further theoretical development is necessary to separate C_T into its constituent capacitances. Attempts to determine adsorbed radicals by pseudocapacitative methods are exploratory. They depend on the fact that the radical concerned gives rise to a sufficient pseudocapacity, and this may not be generally so.

2.4.1.3   Use of Rotating-disk Electrode with Ring Electrode. In the case of intermediates that are stable in solution and readily desorb from the electrode (e.g., hydrogen peroxide, which is formed in certain instances during the electroreduction of oxygen), use may be made of the rotating-disk electrode with a ring electrode to detect and identify these intermediates.[47-49] The basic design of such an apparatus is shown in Fig. 9. The disk and ring electrode are mounted at the end of a small brass shaft. The rotating electrode mount is connected to a speed motor which enables one to vary the speed of rotation from 0 to 10,000 rpm. The electrochemical reaction under consideration occurs on the disk electrode. The desorbable intermediate diffuses to the ring electrode where it is oxidized. For a reaction of the type:

$$A \xrightarrow{n_A} B \xrightarrow{n_B} C \tag{2.5}$$

the relation between the disk i_d and ring i_r currents is given by

$$i_r = \frac{n_B}{n_A} \frac{N i_d}{1 + k\delta/D} \tag{2.6}$$

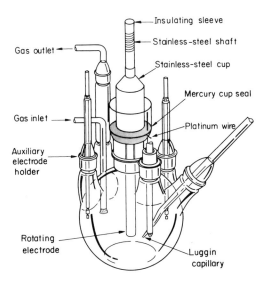

Gas outlet

Insulating sleeve

Stainless-steel shaft

Stainless-steel cup

Mercury cup seal

Gas inlet

Platinum wire

Auxiliary
electrode
holder

Rotating
electrode

Luggin
capillary

Figure 9 Basic design of a rotating-disk electrode apparatus for the detection of intermediates on electrodes.[49a]

N is a constant between 0 and 1, k is the rate constant for the oxidation of B to C at the disk, δ is the diffusion layer thickness, and D is the diffusion coefficient of B in the electrolyte.

This technique may be applied to the studies of overall reactions, where several final products form at the electrode depending on electrocatalysis or on the potential of the electrode, as, for example, in the case of ethylene oxidation on gold or on palladium, where the products range from aldehydes to carbon dioxide.[50]

2.4.2 Nonelectrochemical Methods

The present electrochemical methods are satisfactory only in detecting and identifying intermediates formed in simple reactions because the charge associated with the adsorption or desorption of more than one intermediate in a reaction cannot be easily separated. Nonelectrochemical methods may be of value in these cases. Until the present time, only a little effort has been expended in developing such techniques. The methods that appear promising are briefly discussed in the following sections.

(i) Ellipsometry

This technique was briefly described in Sec. 2.3.2. The development of ellipsometry for the detection and identification of stable organic compounds adsorbed on electrodes gives rise to the expectation that intermediate radicals may also be thus determined. Thus, if light sources of different wavelengths are used, a kind of spectroscopy may be developed to determine the nature of radicals present.[51]

(ii) Spectroscopic methods

Infrared adsorption spectroscopic techniques have been attempted.[52] Several problems were encountered, such as (1) interference due to absorption of radiation by the solvent and (2) the necessity of using multiple reflections when only monolayers or less are present.   It has been suggested that infrared procedures could be adopted using thin-film electrodes and the radiation be allowed to traverse through the electrode rather than through the solution.

Electron-spin resonance methods have been used to detect short-lived intermediates in solution.[53]   Attempts made to investigate intermediate radicals produced during oxidation of alcohols on electrodes have not been successful. It is necessary that the electrode material not interfere with the field in the resonant cavity of the instrument.   Further work must be done before the usefulness of the method can be assessed.

The method of internal reflectance spectroscopy is widely used to study interfacial phenomena.[54]   It has recently found application in attempts to identify species formed in electrochemical reactions at or near electrode surfaces.[55]   The principle of the method is as follows: The light entering the glass substrate coated with a doped-tin oxide layer is partially reflected with Fresnel coefficient r and phase angle γ_1 at film-glass interface (Fig. 10).   The transmitted

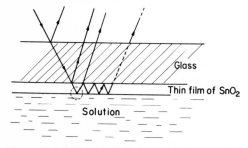

Figure 10   Principle of internal reflectance spectroscopy method for the determination of adsorption of species on electrodes.[55]

part travels through the film of thickness d, being attenuated by a factor α and undergoing a phase lag of δ.   This ray is further reflected with a Fresnel coefficient r_2 and a phase angle γ_2 at the film-solution interface and undergoes multiple reflections in the film.   These partially emergent electric vectors may interfere constructively or destructively with the first reflected ray.   The *measured reflectivity* represents the net addition of these vectors, yielding the information about the film-solution interface.

To obtain the spectrum of the species under study, the difference in the value of the reflectance absorbance with and without the generated species at the surface is plotted against wavelength. (Fig. 11). The reflection from thin films gives rise to maxima and minima in the reflectance absorbance, the distance between peaks being dependent upon the thickness of the film.

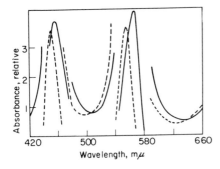

Figure 11   A typical plot of the reflectance spectra of SnO_2-glass absorbance in air (– – –) and in solution (—).[55]

The problems of the method are that (1) information is obtained on species adsorbed as well as in the solution layer within about 100 Å from the electrode, (2) the calculation of the penetration depth may be in error because of possible multiple reflections in the thin film, and (3) there is an intrinsic difficulty of refraction at three interfaces, which makes interpretations of the results rather complex.

2.5 Determination of Kinetic Parameters

2.5.1 Tafel Parameters

Under certain conditions (Chap. 2, Sec. 3.6.6), electrode reactions obey a linear logarithmic law [Chap. 2, Eq. (3.78)]—the so-called Tafel relation. The transfer coefficient α is an important criterion of a given rate-determining step, because as shown in Chap. 2, it often changes upon change of rate-determining step. The transfer coefficient α may be obtained by determining the slope of the relation of the overpotential to the log current density from steady-state measurements of the potential of the electrode as a function of current drawn from it, or vice versa.[56-58] Correspondingly, an extrapolation of the overpotential gives the exchange current density i_0 (Chap. 2, Sec. 3.6.6).

For fast electrode reactions, it becomes difficult to separate the contributions of activation and concentration overpotential. In these cases, it may be possible to obtain the exchange current density at very low overpotentials where the i-η relation is linear. Faradaic rectification[59] and ac impedance[60] methods may also be used to obtain the Tafel parameters.

These methods, for which a theoretical basis was given in Chap. 2, apply directly for reactions at planar electrodes and indirectly at porous electrodes that are mostly used in fuel cells. The determination of the mechanistically important parameters α and i_0 for porous electrodes is less easy than for planar electrodes because the current-potential relations for porous electrodes (Chap.

5, Secs. 5 to 8) are far more complicated than are those for planar electrodes. Thus, for the latter, the distinction between atomically available surface area and that measured superficially is largely two to three times, and even if this factor is not known accurately, the semilogarithmic relation between current density and overpotential is not significantly affected.† However, with porous electrodes, the active area is more difficult to determine and may be a very small fraction, perhaps 1 percent, of the surface area of pores. Diffusional and resistive factors influence the relation between current density and potential. At the present time, experimental methods for determining the active area of porous electrodes under a given set of conditions are not well developed.

Hence, most of the investigations of mechanisms of reactions important to fuel cells are carried out on planar surfaces. It is an assumption that the rate-determining step of the electrochemical interfacial reaction on planar electrodes is the same as that on porous electrodes, so long as the solution, catalyst, and temperature remain the same. Mass-transfer and ohmic limitations will always partly influence a reaction at porous electrodes. These influences are expressed mathematically in Chap. 5, Secs. 5 to 8.

The parameters α and i_0 are the Tafel parameters. The exchange current density i_0 has a greater significance in electrocatalytic research (Chap. 6, Secs. 1 and 4) than in mechanism determinations.[61] The dependence of exchange current density upon concentrations of reactants or products may be of mechanistic importance (see Chap. 2, Sec. 3.6.5).

2.5.2 Stoichiometric Factors

A knowledge of stoichiometric factors is of fundamental importance in a determination of the mechanism of an electrochemical reaction. The entry of stoichiometric factors into electrode-kinetic equations was indicated in Chap. 2, Sec. 3.6.5.

Essentially, one obtains the stoichiometric factor of some entity in the reaction analogous to the order of a reaction with respect to some entity in chemical kinetics‡ by determining the variation of current at a constant potential as a function of the concentration of a reactant, or product, while maintaining the concentrations of other reactants or products and temperature constant.

Such determinations have been described extensively by Vetter.[58] If the Tafel parameters and all the stoichiometric factors are known, a major part of the determination of the rds can generally be carried out (so long as general information concerning coverage—high or low—is available). It may be necessary, however, to determine the stoichiometric factors with respect to all reactants and products of the reaction—sometimes a lengthy task and one which

† This difficulty of obtaining mechanistic information *while using porous electrodes* is a general one in fuel-cell research. It is much simpler to use *planar* or *gauze-formed* electrodes for such studies.

‡ They are not called reaction orders because they are given by $(\partial \ln i / \partial \ln c_i)$ and not by $(\partial v / \partial c_i)$, where v is the velocity of reaction, as in chemical kinetics.

implies that the reaction can be examined in both directions. In practice, this is not always so. In the oxidation of ethylene, the anodic reaction is the formation of carbon dioxide, but upon the passage of a cathodic current in the presence of carbon dioxide and ethylene, ethane is produced. Correspondingly, in some systems, when the potential range is changed from that for the cathodic reaction to that for the anodic one, the surface of the electrode changes. This, of course, invalidates the kinetic parameters for the anodic path of a reaction in an analysis of its cathodic path on an original substrate. This is the case for platinum, which forms a phase oxide at about 0.95 volt (NHE).[51] Evolution of oxygen takes place at potentials positive to 1.23 volts in acid solution and therefore on an oxide-covered platinum. Reduction can be made to occur on the oxide, but under practical conditions, it occurs on platinum.

2.5.3 Stoichiometric Numbers

The stoichiometric number v expresses the number of times the rate-determining step takes place for one act of the overall reaction, and it is sometimes a useful diagnostic criterion. Methods for its determination are discussed in Chap. 2, Sec. 3.6.7.

2.5.4 Temperature Effects

A determination of the exchange current density of the reaction as a function of temperature sometimes yields useful qualitative information on mechanisms of reactions. It gives the heat of activation of the reaction, which information is useful for electrocatalytic purposes.[61,62] Temperature effects are also useful in obtaining information on the tunneling contributions to the rate of an electrode reaction and hence are of aid in electrocatalytic studies.

2.5.5 Isotope Effects

Determination of the ratio of reaction rates of two isotopic species is sometimes useful in mechanism determinations, particularly in cases where hydrogen-atom or ion-transfer reactions are involved. Isotope effects may be obtained by a determination of the ratio of exchange current densities in pure protonated and deuterated (or tritiated) solutions.[63] This method has yielded useful information on the mechanism of ethylene oxidation on platinum, gold, and palladium electrodes.[64] Another possible method is by determination of hydrogen/deuterium or hydrogen/tritium separation factors, which have been extensively determined and used in studies of electrolytic hydrogen-evolution reaction on several metals.[65]

2.5.6 Summarizing Remarks

By determination of (1) the steady-state electrode-kinetic parameters, (2) adsorption characteristics of stable species, e.g., reactants, products, and (3) information on intermediates, it is usually possible to determine the rate-determining step in an electrode reaction. Evaluation of details of the mechanism of the reaction *after* the rate-determining step is much more difficult and perhaps less necessary.   In complicated multistep reactions, it is sometimes necessary to be satisfied with a considerable reduction in the number of possibilities as to the rate-determining steps to two or even three rather than simply one.

3   APPARATUS, ELECTRICAL CIRCUITS, AND PURIFICATION TECHNIQUES FOR STUDIES OF MECHANISMS OF ELECTRODE REACTIONS

3.1   Electrochemical cells

A cell design that appears most suitable to electrode-kinetic studies[56] is shown in Fig. 12.   It consists basically of three compartments, one each for the test,

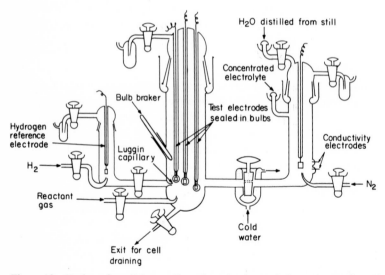

Figure 12   Design of a cell for studies of mechanisms of electrode reactions.[56a]

auxiliary, and reference electrodes.   Water-sealed stopcocks and/or fritted disks are used between the compartment to minimize transport of reactants, intermediates, or products from one electrode compartment to the other (tap grease is to be avoided).   To reduce the contribution of ohmic overpotential to the measured potential between the test and reference electrodes, a Luggin-Haber capillary leading from the reference electrode compartment practically touches the test electrode.   The cell is also provided with inlets for bubbling of reactant or inert gases.   The gases leave the cells via bubblers.   The use of water-sealed stopcocks and bubblers reduces the possibility of entry of contaminants into the cell from the atmosphere.   Cells have generally been constructed out of Pyrex glass. Recently, Teflon has been used increasingly instead of glass as a consequence of the pioneering work of Schuldiner.[65a] Teflon possesses the same inert properties as glass, though its surface must be purified by boiling in strong acid, and then in strong alkali.

The type of cell illustrated in Fig. 12 is convenient both for steady-state and transient measurements at room temperatures. For work at other temperatures, the cell may be placed in an air thermostat. Before use of the cell for electrode-kinetic studies, it is necessary to wash it thoroughly to eliminate traces of grease and other impurities. The commonly used cleaning agents are chromic acid, mixture of 1:1 concentrated nitric and sulfuric acid, or hot concentrated sodium hydroxide. Prolonged subsequent washing in conductivity water is desirable.

3.2 Electrical Circuits for Steady-state Measurements

3.2.1 Galvanostatic Circuits

Historically, this is the first type of circuit used for electrode-kinetic studies. In its simplest form, it consists of a circuit shown in Fig. 13. It is essential

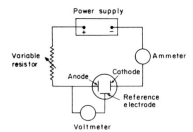

Figure 13 The original galvanostatic circuit used to obtain steady-state current-potential data for electrode reactions.

that the resistance in series with the cell be high in comparison with the resistance between the anodic and cathode compartments, at least by a factor of 100 times, so that any changes in the electrolyte resistance will not alter the current passing between the anode and cathode. This simple circuit is sufficient at low current outputs, say below 10 ma. If higher currents are required, it is necessary to use electronic devices that produce a constant current. A representative circuit[66,69] is given in Fig. 14. Such a circuit eliminates the requirement of a high resistance in series with the electrochemical cell. The current control is better with this type of circuit than with the older one.

The potential of the test electrode with respect to that of the reference electrode is measured using a high impedance (about 10^{14} ohms) electrometer. The ohmic potential drop between the test and reference electrodes may be measured by one of the methods described in Sec. 3.3.4.

3.2.2 Potentiostatic Circuits

The potentiostat is a device that controls the potential between the test and reference electrodes with passage of an appropriate current between the test

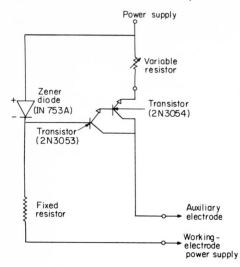

Figure 14 A modern transistorized gal-vanostatic circuit for steady-state current-potential measurements of electrode reactions.[69]

and counter electrodes.   Basically, a potentiostat is a high-gain differential amplifier, which measures a potential between the test and reference electrode, compares it to a set reference, and passes a current such that the difference between the two voltages approaches zero.   The basic unit of a potentiostat[67] is shown in Fig. 15.   The requirements of a potentiostat are determined by the

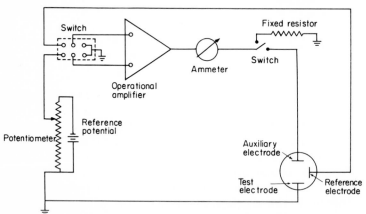

Figure 15   The basic unit of a simple potentiostatic circuit.[67]

output voltage and current, the rise time, the stability of the reference potential with respect to change of current output and load resistance, temperature, and line voltage.

3.2.3   Slow-potential Sweep Method

Since the steady state is established relatively fast in many electrode reactions, the current-voltage curve corresponding to the steady-state situation may be obtained using the slow-potential sweep method.[68]   Here, the potential of the electrode is varied linearly with time at a very slow rate over the desired potential range and the current is measured.   The selection of the rate for the potential scan depends on the time taken for the steady-state condition, of the reaction in question, to be established.   A simple synchronous motor driving a potentiometer, which produces a linearly varying potential, can be fed to the input of a potentiostat.

3.3   Electrical Circuits for Non-steady-state Measurements

3.3.1   Galvanostatic Transients

Galvanostatic steps can be obtained by the closing of a galvanostatic circuit (Fig. 14) with a fast switch or by producing repeated current pulses by means of a signal or pulse generator.   The requirement of such circuitry is that the rise time of the input pulse be short in comparison with the time variation of the phenomena under study.   Rise times of the order of a few microseconds can be achieved with standard equipment.

Most often, the transient should be started at some desired potential. Figure 16 shows a block diagram of a circuit that may be used in these cases.[69]

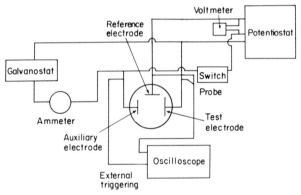

Figure 16   Coupling of a potentiostatic circuit with a galvanostatic one for galvanostatic transient measurements.[69]

Under these conditions, the current from the potentiostat is taken by the galvanostat when the switch is in the open position.

3.3.2   Potentiostatic Transients

This method has hardly been used.[24,25]   Most potentiostats are equipped with an external and internal potential source.   The potential can then be stepped from one value to another by adding the external to the internal source by means of a fast switch.   Alternatively, a pulse generator or signal generator may be used as an input to the potentiostat to vary the set potential periodically.

The rise time of the potentiostatic pulse is a critical feature of the potentiostat. While the rise time for the input potentiostat can be made very short (e.g., 1 μsec or less), the rise time for the output pulse (i.e., actual pulse applied between reference and working electrodes) is much longer. It depends on the design of the potentiostat as well as on the characteristics of the load, specifically its capacitative component. Electrochemical systems tend to have a high capacity (double-layer capacity is 20 μf cm^{-2}, whereas pseudocapacity is up to two orders of magnitude higher) and this usually limits the rise times of potentiostats. Although potentiostats that can deliver pulses with a rise time of $\frac{1}{2}$ μsec into a pure resistive load are available, the actual rise times for delivery into electrochemical systems may be much (e.g., 100 times) longer.

3.3.3 Fast-potential Sweep Methods

In recent years, the technique of triangular-potential sweep method has been used widely in research related to fuel-cell technology.[25,26] In this case, a function generator, which is commonly available, provides a triangular wave of variable amplitude and sweep rate. It is fed into the input of a potentiostat that controls the potential of the test electrode with respect to the reference electrode. An oscilloscope, operated as an (x/y) recorder, becomes necessary for recording the current-potential curves at fast sweep rates. Fast-potential sweeps (1 to 1,000 volts sec^{-1}) are most commonly used for determination of coverage of adsorbed species on electrodes. A block diagram of the circuit is shown in Fig. 17.

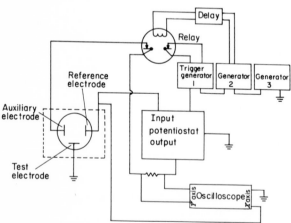

Figure 17 A block diagram of the circuit for the potentiodynamic method.[26]

3.3.4 Ohmic-potential-drop Measurements

Although electrochemical cells are constructed with the tip of the Luggin capillary from the reference electrode compartment practically touching the test electrode (Fig. 12), it is very often necessary to make measurements of ohmic drop between the tip of the Luggin capillary and the test electrode in order to separate it from activation and concentration overpotential. The basis of measurement of ohmic-potential drop is that it decays considerably faster (at least by 100 times) than activation and concentration overpotential upon interruption of the polarizing circuit.

Interrupter circuits in which the current is interrupted by means of a mechanical or electronic commutator are mostly used for measurements of ohmic potential between the anode and cathode in a fuel cell. The current and voltage changes upon making and breaking of a galvanostatic circuit are schematically represented in Fig. 18. Several types of interrupter circuits have

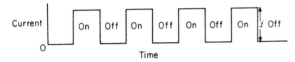

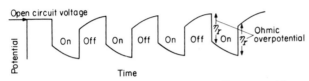

Figure 18 Current and voltage changes in a cell upon making and breaking of a galvanostatic circuit.[70a] The ohmic drop in the cell is shown.

been designed. The first included a thyratron for the interrupting circuit.[70] Recently, a circuit based on a half-wave, 60-cps-sine-wave pulse was developed.[71] This circuit was improved for greater stability, using transistors.[72] A simple interrupter circuit[73] for ohmic-drop measurements is shown in Fig. 19. A high resistance is inserted in parallel with the mercury relay to avoid turning off the

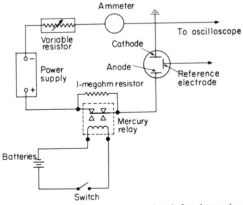

Figure 19 A simple interrupter circuit for determination of ohmic potential drop between test and reference electrodes.[73]

current completely, which may otherwise cause competing reactions to occur under open-circuit conditions.

3.4   Electrode Preparation and Examination Techniques

3.4.1   Types of Electrodes

The electrodes used for mechanism and fundamental studies are usually planar. Smooth electrodes may be in the form of wires, foils, or spheres of the electrocatalyst.   The advantage of using such electrodes is that the effective surface area upon which the reaction takes place is usually constant over a wide range of potential and is always clearly known, whereas, as has been seen in Chap. 5, the effective area of a porous electrode may be potential-dependent, particularly at higher overpotentials.   It has to be either calculated or measured at each overpotential.

Other advantages of using planar electrodes in a study of an electrode reaction are that it is often easy to avoid simultaneous mass-transfer control in steady-state measurements and it is possible to reduce ohmic effects.   With porous electrodes, it is practically always necessary to take mass-transfer and ohmic effects into account, and this introduces considerable complexities in the theory (Chap. 5, Secs. 5 to 8).

With very slow fuel-cell reactions, e.g., during the oxidation of hydrocarbons, it is difficult to utilize planar-smooth electrodes because the current on a reasonable area of them is below that necessary for easy measurement.   In these cases, only porous electrodes with their relatively large currents per geometric area are practical.   Sometimes, in these cases, one may use roughened gauzes, prepared by electrodeposition of the catalyst on an inert substrate, or a substrate of the same metal (e.g., platinized-platinum gauze).

3.4.2   Electrode Pretreatment

Many methods exist.   Typical of these are: (1) heating the material of the electrode preliminarily in some gases, for example, hydrogen;[74] (2) chemical polishing;[75] (3) electropolishing;[75] (4) preliminary cathodic reduction of hypothetical oxide films on the surface.[76]

Two methods have been used for investigations of the mechanisms of electrode reactions under ultrahigh purity conditions: (1) the electrode is sealed into a glass bulb in the presence of some gas, for example, argon or hydrogen (Fig. 20) and the bulb is broken and the electrode exposed to the solution only after the latter has been purified;[74] (2) the electrode can be introduced in a comparatively uncultivated state into the solution and it is then submitted to some potential variant regime whereby transient pulses are passed over it with the objective of reducing films and oxidizing impurities from the surface.[77,78]

Sealing of electrode material sometimes presents a problem because sealing

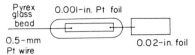

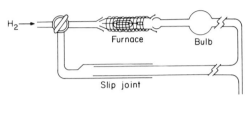

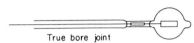

Figure 20 Techniques of preparing clean electrodes by sealing in glass bulbs in inert atmosphere.[56a]

with waxes, etc., may introduce significant impurities into the solution, which may set up undesirable reactions that could compete with the main reactions. Techniques of sealing directly into glass and highly purified Teflon have been discussed.[74,79]

3.4.3 *Examination of Surfaces*

Examination of surfaces of electrodes has importance in attempts to correlate their defect structures with rates of reaction occurring on them. In particular, the degree of change of electrode surface with time is worthy of examination, because one of the difficulties of some fuel-cell systems is a gradual increase in overpotential with time, and this may not be due to impurity buildup but to recrystallization processes of the catalyst.

The *in situ* examination of electrocatalysts is more difficult than that of chemical catalysts because of the presence of the solvent, which prevents, *inter alia*, the use of electron microscopic techniques, etc., due to the absorbing power of the solvent on the electron beam. For this reason, examination of electrode surfaces is made prior to or after the electrochemical measurement, using solid-state chemistry techniques, e.g., electron diffraction, low angle x-ray diffraction, etc. The disadvantage of removing the electrode from the solution and then examining it is that during the removal and drying, the potential control differs from that in solution and the surface condition may undergo change. It may be possible to freeze the electrode in its momentary situation by introducing oil or some other inert and nonconducting liquid instantaneously over the surface while the current is still passing, thus insulating the electrode surface from the liquid and cutting off the current.

Ellipsometric techniques have been developed recently,[39] particularly for examining electrode surfaces in solution *in situ*. These methods depend not on absorption of the light but on the change of the properties of polarized light, so that absorption in the solution is not of importance. The methods may certainly be used for the detection and knowledge of films on the surface.

3.5 Preparation and Purification of Solutions

3.5.1 *Aqueous Electrolytes*

Aqueous solutions, often used in fuel cells, are sulfuric acid, phosphoric acid, perchloric acid, hydrofluoric acid, sodium hydroxide, and potassium hydroxide. These electrolytes are usually used at high concentrations to reduce ohmic drops in solution.

One of the reasons for the delay in the development of electrode kinetics, and hence of electrochemical energy conversion, until the 1950s was the absence of realization of the sensitivity of rates of reactions at solid electrodes to trace impurities. Consequently, reproducibility in experimental measurements was rare.

The electrolytes used in electrochemical energy converters are usually purified—the question is to what degree. For reactions that are sufficiently fast, i.e., with an exchange current density of 10^{-4} amp cm^{-2} or higher, the degree of purification of electrolyte is that used in ordinary analytical chemistry. However, for electrode reactions that are slower ($<10^{-4}$ amp cm^{-2}), it may be necessary to use more stringent methods (Chap. 2, Sec. 12). At low current densities, the oxygen electrode reaction is remarkably sensitive to impurities present in solution.[80] Removal of impurities improves the performance considerably. When using porous electrodes, there is sometimes the problem of entry of impurities from the pores of the electrode into the solution, thus requiring more extensive purification techniques.

Successive recrystallization of certain of the electrolytes, particularly the alkali hydroxides, seems essential if reproducibility is to be obtained over a long period.[74]

For reactions with low exchange current densities, it is often necessary to purify the solutions more carefully for long (about 24 hr) times by anodic and/or cathodic preelectrolysis. Purely experimental aspects of this purification are described elsewhere.[56,74] A purification method, developed recently during studies on the finite-contact-angle model of porous electrodes, is quite successful[81] and it is briefly described as follows.

The purification system (Fig. 21) consists of a closed loop where the solution is circulated passing the electrodes (*A*) with an inert gas such as N_2 or argon rigorously purified by a gas pump. This inert gas also serves as a blanket to exclude air and purges volatile impurities from the solution as it passes through the preelectrolysis cell. The system may be used, as shown, as an external-solution preparation and purification system and reservoir, or the cell may be

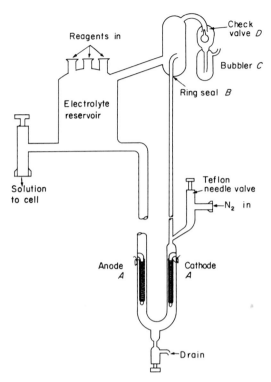

Figure 21 A new method for the purification of aqueous electrolytes.[81]

put in the place of the reservoir and the cell electrolyte circulated for an *in situ* preelectrolysis. (This latter procedure thus also cleans the cell walls.)

Only a few constructional restrictions have been found critical for optimum performance: (1) The electrodes are made from 10×10 cm sheets of very fine Pt screen. These screens are wound cylindrically around 14 cm lengths of 7-mm rod and tied in place with a few turns of fine Pt wire wound around the end of the cylinders. A piece of 10-mm-ID (13 mm OD) tubing is chosen to fit over this screen (not too loosely because the solution will easily flow between the tube and screen, and not too tightly because the solution flow will be impeded). A small 90° bend is made in the central rod, and the electrode is inserted in the tube with two ends (in case one breaks) of the wire drawn through small holes in the side of the tube. The rod is sealed internally to the tube wall and the bottom of the screen is pushed up to bulge the screen against the tube walls. (2) The optimum size tube for the pump is 4 to 5 mm ID, heavy wall and about 30 cm long. The tube ID should not be distorted at the ring seal (*B*). (3) the bubbler (*C*) should include a check valve (*D*) to prevent suck-back of air when the reservoir is emptied. (4) A 1.35-volt Hg cell connected directly between the two electrodes is a suitable polarizing source. (5) A presaturator should be used to saturate the gas with H_2O to prevent excessive evaporation from the cell and to wash out any dust particles from the gas at the same time.   (6) A very low flow rate (1 to 2 bubbles per second in the pump tube) is sufficient, and a good Teflon-and-glass needle valve should be used.

If the impurity concentration is sufficiently small so that the rate of its aggregation to the electrode is diffusion-controlled, the impurity concentration c_t after preelectrolysis for time t is related to the original concentration c_0 before preelectrolysis commences by the equation (Chap. 2, Sec. 12):

$$c_t = c_0 \exp\left(-\frac{DAt}{V\delta}\right) \tag{3.1}$$

where D is the diffusion coefficient of the impurity in the electrolyte, δ is the diffusion-layer thickness, A is the area of the electrode, and V is the volume of the electrolyte.   Substitution of typical values in Eq. (2.1) shows that during preelectrolytic purification, there is little change in the amount of impurity present initially, but that a marked reduction in concentration occurs towards the end of the process.   The necessary time for a reduction of the impurity level by four orders of magnitude is 1 to 10 hr, and in practice the upper end of this range is usually found to be necessary.   An increase in electrode area is clearly very helpful.   The most common sources of entry of impurities into solution are from (1) the holder of the electrode, particularly if porous carbon is used, (2) the binder material, and (3) the porous electrode substrate.

Although purification of electrolytes is a technique that has been described in the literature during the past 10 years for electrode-kinetic studies on solid electrodes and before this for those involving mercury, it still needs improvement.   Thus, for example, techniques involving a series of electrode surfaces held respectively at a series of the likely range of potentials of maximum adsorption of the impurities present provide developmental possibilities (Chap. 2, Sec. 12).

3.5.2   Molten Electrolytes

The most common electrolytes in electrochemical energy converters operating at high temperatures, to overcome the catalytic problems encountered in low-temperature systems, are molten alkali halides, potassium hydroxide, or mixed alkali carbonates (Chap. 10, Secs. 2.13 and 2.23).

In all these cases, extensive purification must be carried out, above all for the removal of water, which is particularly difficult for the first two types.   The purification consists of classical drying, the passage of various gases, for example, HCl, and/or preelectrolysis.

3.5.3   Solid Electrolytes

Solid mixed oxides, for example, yttria and zirconia (Chap. 10, Sec. 2.1.4), are usually available in a highly purified state and do not need further purification.

3.6 Purification of Gases

The degree of purification of reactant gases is determined in a manner analogous to that proposed for solution purification.   Thus, it must be experimented upon for each system and the generalities are that the lower the exchange current density, and the longer the time in which the reaction has to be carried out, the more stringent the purification will have to be.

Hydrogen may be purified by passage through silver-palladium tubes.[82] Gas purification trains of varying degrees of complexity have also been described for hydrogen[74,81,83] and for oxygen.[84]   Hydrocarbons are more difficult to purify, and often the purification methods lead to their decomposition, which may yield misleading results in the subsequent electrochemical measurements. For example, to examine the reactivity of hydrocarbons, a purification method which produces 0.1 percent of the hydrogen by decomposition may lead to observations of the electrooxidation characteristics of hydrogen rather than of the hydrocarbons, because the velocity of electrooxidation of hydrogen at anodes is several times greater than that of hydrocarbons.   Passage through concentrated sulfuric acid is helpful in removing unsaturated hydrocarbon impurities from saturated hydrocarbons.   Hydrogen may be removed from the hydrocarbon stream by a liquefaction of the hydrocarbon and by allowing the hydrogen to flow through.[85]   The reacting gases must be presaturated with electrolyte to avoid loss of electrolyte from the cell.

4 STUDIES USING POROUS ELECTRODES

4.1 Model Pore Studies

4.1.1 Single-pore or Single-slit Studies

It is difficult to study electrochemical reactions in a single pore because so little current is generated in it.   It is, therefore, better to study such reactions at a single *slit*, namely at an electrode-solution interface where the solution layer is narrow and maintained between two parallel, optically flat solid sections, one of which contains a thin evaporated film of catalyst and the other of which is optically transparent.   The width of the slit enables significant currents to be available.   Such an arrangement was made by Bockris, Nanis, and Cahan[86] and yielded results of particular interest.   The apparatus[86,87] is shown in Fig. 22. It is possible to vary the width of the slit and the height of liquid in the slit. Current-potential relations for the electrodissolution reaction of hydrogen and of oxygen on platinum catalysts in H_2SO_4 have been obtained as a function of these variables.

Of particular importance in the study of this model of porous electrodes is the meniscus shape above the visible "top" of the solution.[87]   Two optical techniques were used.   In one, interferometry with a Na-D light was used to

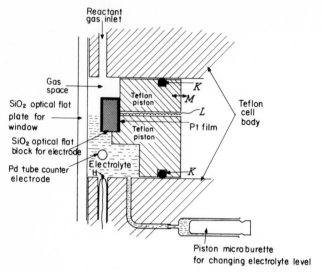

Figure 22 Apparatus for the study of an electrode reaction in a single slit.[87]   *H*, Pd-H reference electrode; *K*, vitron O-ring seal; *L*, contact to electrode; *M*, movement of block and piston for slot-width adjustment.

measure the thickness of the liquid in the meniscus and in any thin films that might be present.   The fringes were measured visually by microphotography. In the second method, the local curvature of the meniscus served to focus light from a point source into a fine line superimposed on the image of the meniscus in a microscope (Fig. 23).   From its geometry, the slope of the meniscus at

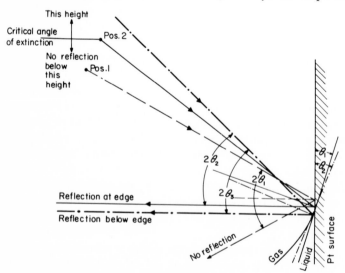

Figure 23 Principle of optical method for determination of shape of meniscus of electrolyte in a single slit.[87]

the locus of the line could be calculated down to and including the contact angle at the meniscus edge. These are useful in determining whether the meniscus has a finite contact angle or whether it continues into a thin film. In the work carried out using polished metal foils or sputtered metal films, it was found that when impurities were present, the meniscus shape was erratic and irregular. On clean surfaces, reproducible results, showing a *finite contact angle and no thin film above the meniscus*, were obtained but the shape was dependent on the potential of the electrode. Such measurements enabled a theoretical calculation of the current-potential and current-distribution relations as a function of the meniscus dimensions. The agreement between the experimental and theoretical current-potential relations for the hydrogen- and oxygen-dissolution reaction is excellent (Chap. 5, Sec. 7). This work showed that there could be considerable economic advantages in the localization of expensive catalyst materials in these cases.

Due to the high current densities in the small regions near the top of the meniscus, one should expect considerable heat generation in these areas. Evidence for this has been obtained from a microscopic examination of the electrode which revealed evaporation and formation of bubbles of water accompanied by the agitation of the meniscus, in this region at medium and high overpotentials.[86,87]

4.1.2 Thin-film Studies

Several studies have been conducted on wettable electrodes, in which cases there is a thin film of electrolyte above the intrinsic meniscus.[88–90a] A novel technique was used by Bennion[89] and Tobias, together with later work by Müller.[90] The electrode surface at which a meniscus and film formed was divided into two sections insulated from each other (Fig. 24), and the current

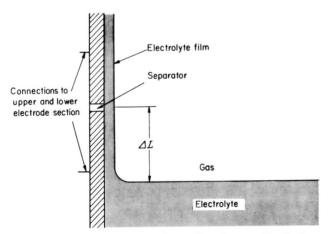

Figure 24 Sectioned electrodes for studies of current distribution according to a thin-film model of porous electrodes. ΔL is depth of liquid level below separator.[89]

generated in each half was measured as a function of the meniscus and film shape.   The meniscus and film shape was determined by interference techniques. It was shown that some of the current is generated in the upper (i.e., thin-film) region for low exchange current density reactions, for example, the oxygen-reduction reaction in alkaline solution on nickel and on silver.

4.2 Multipore Studies

4.2.1 Preparation of Porous Electrodes

There are two main kinds of porous electrodes: (1) those consisting entirely of the material identical to the catalyst, e.g., nickel, and (2) those consisting of a conducting substrate, e.g., carbon, on the surface of which is deposited some catalyst.   The latter type is the predominant one.

For electrodes consisting entirely of the catalyst material, a principal objective is to obtain a stable meniscus.   One way this can be done is by the use of "biporous" electrodes[91] (Fig. 25).   This consists of two layers, one

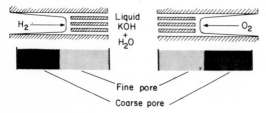

Figure 25   Representation of sections of "biporous" electrodes in a Bacon hydrogen-oxygen fuel cell.[91a]

consisting of fine pores and the other consisting of coarse pores.   The latter are toward the gas and the former are in contact with the solution.   The gas pressure is kept such that it can resist the capillary action of the solution to invade the second coarse pore layer, and it just keeps the solution in the finer capillaries.   The preparation of biporous electrodes[91] is carried out by compacting a mixture of metal powder, the average particle size being in the region of a few microns, and 10 to 20 percent by weight of some salt, for example, ammonium carbonate.   The mixture is sintered under appropriate conditions of pressure, temperature, and time.   Such an arrangement gives rise to a highly porous structure.   The structure thus obtained (one-half of the sandwich structure which makes up the biporous electrode) is then connected to another plaque that has been made in a similar way but with large particles.

Homoporous electrodes are those in which the particle size is the same and a uniform gas pressure maintains a stable meniscus in the single structure.   If the electrode is made of polyporous materials and does not have two layers, a given gas pressure will be less than that required to prevent the passage of solution through the smaller pores into the gas space, whereas for larger pores, the gas pressure will be sufficiently large so that the gas enters the solution side of the electrode, thus wasting fuel.

Techniques in which the porous electrode is not made entirely out of the catalyst are numerous.[92-94] A typical one has the catalyst dispersed in Teflon.[92] In this case, the catalyst particles must, of course, be in contact either with each other if the substrate is not conducting or with the substrate if it is conducting. The purpose of Teflon as a medium for holding catalyst particles is to provide a hydrophobic situation so that the tendency of the electrode to flood is reduced. A Teflon film may be formed by spraying a Teflon suspension diluted with water on an aluminum foil. The foil with the dried film is then pressed to the desired thickness. A mixture of the catalyst, for example, platinum black, and a Teflon suspension is then spread on another aluminum foil similar to the first. A metal screen is placed between the two films, one of Teflon and one of Teflon containing platinum, the aluminum sides facing outward. The two parts of the electrode are pressed together at a specific pressure. The aluminum is dissolved away by dipping the electrode in hot concentrated sodium hydroxide. When such electrodes are used in a fuel cell, the side with the film which is entirely of Teflon faces the gas compartment. The Teflon film controls the wetting characteristics of the electrode so that the solution and gaseous film come together at a suitable and stable position within the electrode.

Experimental work on the distribution of catalyst in a Teflon-containing electrode, and the fraction of this catalyst which is active, has been little attempted, but *theoretical calculations suggest that only a small fraction of the catalyst material is active* (Chap. 5, Secs. 5 to 7). The development of a technique in which the menisci of the solution are maintained stable at the positions of the effective area of the electrode may reduce catalyst costs per kilowatt in direct hydrocarbon-air fuel cells to a degree that makes them economically acceptable.

4.2.2 Physical Methods of Characterization of Porous Electrodes

4.2.2.1 Porosity. Porosity is defined as the ratio of the void to the total volume of the porous electrode. The most general method of obtaining the effective porosity[95] is by a determination of the total volume (i.e., the volume of the entire porous material) which is done by immersing the porous material in a liquid which does not enter the pores, e.g., mercury at ordinary pressures. At high pressures, mercury enters the pores. It is then transferred at low pressure to a container of known volume. The container is evacuated and some inert gas is introduced. The system is allowed to reach equilibrium. The new gas pressure is noted. An application of Boyle's law yields the volume of the open pores and, hence, from the experiments with mercury, the porosity.

4.2.2.2 Pore-size Distribution. The most common procedure of determining the distribution of pore sizes in the range of 10^{-6} to 10^{-2} cm is by using a mercury porosimeter.[96] In this method, the porous medium is placed in a cell and evacuated.   Mercury is then injected into the pores at various pressures and the volume of mercury taken up is obtained as a function of pressure.   If the radius of a pore is r, mercury will enter this pore when the pressure in the cell is equal to, or greater than, that expressed by the equation

$$P = \frac{2\gamma \cos \theta}{r} \tag{4.1}$$

where γ and θ are the surface tension and contact angle for the mercury-solid interface.   Thus, knowing γ and θ from independent measurements, one obtains the radius of the smallest pores, at and above which mercury enters the pores. One may now plot the volume fraction of mercury (volume fraction equals rate of measured volume of mercury entering the pores at a given pressure to total pore volume) versus the pore radius calculated according to Eq. (4.1).   A typical pore-size-distribution curve of $f(r)$ versus r is shown in Fig. 26.   The cumulative pore-size-distribution function $f(r)$ is defined as the fraction of the pore space having a radius greater than r.   It is expressed mathematically by

$$f(r) = \int_r^\infty W(r)\, dr \tag{4.2}$$

$W(r)$ is the differential pore-size-distribution function and it represents the probability of finding pores with radius between r and $r + dr$.   Typical plots of $W(r)$ and of $f(r)$ versus r are shown in Fig. 26.   The area under the curve

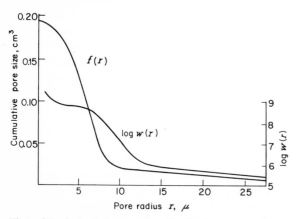

Figure 26 A typical pore-size distribution curve for a porous electrode.[96a]

between $r = r$ and $r = \infty$ is $f(r)$.   The mercury porosimeter cannot be used if amalgamation of the porous material occurs, but one can still use the method with other liquids that do not interact with the material concerned.

   Gas-adsorption measurements (Sec. 4.2.2.3) can also be used in an indirect manner to obtain pore-size-distribution curves.

4.2.2.3 Surface Area. The most common method of determining surface area is the Brunauer-Emmet-Teller (BET) method. The method is well known and described in physicochemical texts.[97] The method gives the entire area of porous electrode available for adsorption of gas molecules, and it is probable that only a relatively small fraction of the area registered by the BET method is available for adsorption of reactant molecules of the fuel-cell reaction. It is possible to distinguish between the total porous area available and the area of catalyst available by first utilizing inert gases and then gases which adsorb only on the catalyst. Of course, all such measurements have to be made as a function of treatment of the catalyst.

Electrochemical methods for determination of the surface area are described in the electrochemical literature.[98,99] Again, the main question remains, as with the BET method, as to how much of the area indicated by the electrochemical method is relevant to the active area in the fuel-cell reaction at the electrode during its steady-state functioning. Thus, as seen in the chapter on porous electrodes (Chap. 5, Secs. 5 to 8), the distribution of current within the pores of a wetted electrode in a fuel-cell reaction is probably such that only a small area is active. In a transient method for electrochemical determination of surface area, at time $t = 0$, a much larger area of the pore is active because the diffusional component of rate limitation of a fuel-cell reaction at steady state in a porous electrode has not yet built itself up.

A possible electrochemical method to overcome this difficulty might be to allow a steady state under constant current to be established in the porous electrode and then impose on it an extra-potential difference, say 0.1 volt, and record the transient change in current due to this impingement. The condenser charging current, which might be extracted from the electrode's behavior, could then refer to a capacitance that reflects only the surface area being used at that particular current density, i.e., the effective surface area for the current density concerned.

4.2.2.4 Permeability of Gases. In Chap. 5 on the kinetic of reactions at porous electrodes, it was indicated that in addition to the process at the electrode-electrolyte interface, or in solution, the flow of reactant gas from the gas compartment through the pores to the gas interface may be the source of rate limitations. The permeability constant K of a gas is a quantity to which reference can be made in discussing the matter of its flow through the electrolyte-free part of the porous electrode. It is obtained by measuring the flow rate of the gas through the porous media[95] as a function of the pressure gradient $\Delta P(\Delta P = P_1 - P_2)$ across it. The gas flow rate Q is expressed by[95]

$$Q = \frac{K\bar{P}\Delta P}{P_1 t} \tag{4.3}$$

where $\bar{P} = (P_1 + P_2)/2$ and t is the thickness of the porous medium.

4.2.2.5   Microstructure.   A possible method of determining the micro-structure of a porous material involves slicing the electrode successively with a very thin knife and making replicas of the revealed surface for electron micro-scopic examination.   One would thus obtain information concerning the distribution and shape of the deposited catalytic particles, pore shapes, inter-connections between the pores, and the relative dispersions of catalyst and water-proofing agents.   An electron micrograph of a typical porous material is shown[98] in Fig. 27.

Figure 27   An electron micrograph of silica replica of surface of a porous electrode.[98a]

4.2.2.6   Particle Size of the Catalyst.   The common methods of determin-ing particle sizes of catalysts impregnated in porous media[98] are by using x-ray diffraction and electron microscopy techniques.   These methods are sensitive enough to determine particle sizes as low as 50 Å.   Crystallite sizes depend on their methods of preparation.

4.3   Use of Electrical Analogs for Solutions of Current-distribution Problems in Porous Electrodes

The solution of current-distribution problems at porous electrodes is often complex (see Chap. 5).   Electric analogs have recently been used for some simple cases.[100] Several assumptions have been made, of which the most important one is that the reaction occurs under conditions close to equilibrium so that the current-potential relations are linear. At the present time, if this assumption is not made, the system becomes too complex for an electrical analog solution.

Using the model of a partly immersed electrode at which the hydrogen-dissolution reaction is occurring (Fig. 28), the electrical analog is shown in

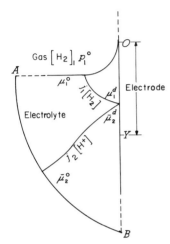

Figure 28 Model of hydrogen-dissolution reaction at a partly immersed electrode.[100]

Fig. 29. The areas 1 and 2 represent conductors of specific resistivities ρ_1 and ρ_2 and simulate diffusion of molecular hydrogen towards the electrode OY and the migration of hydrogen ions away from the electrode surface $O'Y'$, respectively. The equipotential metal strips OA and $B'A'$ represent respectively the

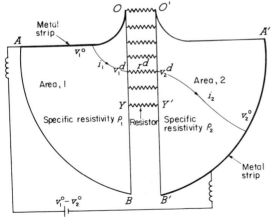

Figure 29 Electrical analog of the hydrogen-dissolution reaction at a partly immersed electrode[100] (see Fig. 28).

gas-electrolyte interface and an arbitrary line in the bulk of the electrolyte where the concentration of hydrogen ions is assumed constant. The reaction resistance R_r is shown by a number of equal resistances connected to the two areas of the analog along the boundaries OY and $O'Y'$, which correspond to the immersed portion of the electrolyte. Varying the magnitudes of ρ_1, ρ_2, and R_r, the current-distribution relations for the assumed model of partly immersed electrodes have been obtained. An extension of the method to the more realistic situation where activation overpotential is tafelian seems rather desirable.

5 STUDIES ON SINGLE CELLS

5.1 Necessity of Both Half- and Single-cell Studies

Most of the studies described so far have been concerned with the individual electrodes, two of which are required for a single cell. During the technological development of rechargeable batteries, this type of study was seldom made and studies were conducted only on single cells. Such an approach to fuel cells gives rise to confusion as to the seat of the key phenomena, i.e., the potential and thus energy loss observed with increase of current drawn from the cell. Although now, and probably in the future, half-cell studies are those which predominate, there must be a stage in the investigation when the overall fuel cell is the entity which must be examined. Thus, the total ohmic overpotential in a fuel cell depends not only on the resistance to ionic transport drop within the pores, particularly in the region of the menisci of electrolyte, but also on the resistance between the electrodes. In addition, the reactants or products of the reaction at one electrode may diffuse and come in contact with the other electrode, provoking disturbing reactions (see Chap. 10, Sec. 5). Deterioration processes at electrodes are associated with local potential differences between sections of the electrodes and depend on the distance apart of the electrodes, on the position of the separators, packing case, etc. Thus, after the half-cell studies have been carried out, it is necessary to construct an actual cell and examine its performance as a function of the new factors arising in construction, including positioning of electrodes, separators, packaging, flow rates, fuel supplies, effect of long-time polarization, and, particularly for high-temperature cells, effect of the corrosion.

5.2 Measurements on Single Cells

The actual measurements[101] consist first of the open-circuit potentials and thereafter of the cell-potential–current-density relations. These results must, of course, be compared with the corresponding ones obtained at the individual electrodes. Reasons have been mentioned above as to why the net result on a single cell will deviate from those calculated on the basis of individual half-cell-reaction studies. It is important to determine the differences so that they may be attacked rationally. The overall cell reaction will respond, in respect to its limiting current, to happenings at *one* of the electrodes that will be rate-controlling for the whole cell. From the tests on individual cells, one calculates the efficiency and power density as a function of current density (Chap. 4, Secs. 5 and 7).

5.3 Life Tests on Single Cells

When cells have been devised and shown worthy of development from determinations of open-circuit–cell-potential and cell-potential–current-density relations, the question of their ability to perform for relatively long times, e.g., above a year, becomes an important aspect.[101] The usual way in which storage batteries are tested involves allowing the cells to run constantly in charge and recharge cycles, with continuous recording of current-voltage curves. The disadvantage of this is obvious, because to find out whether the storage battery will perform for a certain number of years it is necessary to test it for that number of years. Correspondingly, tests on electrochemical energy converters must eventually be carried out for the period in which they are expected to perform. The aim of such testing is at first to find the breakdown point and then to make changes in design so that a breakdown point at a longer time occurs. With this approach to life-testing, the progress of research becomes very slow.

The subject of "accelerated testing" has received insufficient attention. With increase of operating temperature, velocities of all reactions occurring in the cell, including those tending to give rise to breakdown, will increase. If the time of breaking down at various temperatures varies linearly with the reciprocal of the absolute temperature, the reaction that influences the break-down is the same over the temperature range concerned. It is then valid to carry out (the much shorter) tests simply at higher temperatures and calculate the breakdown time for the temperature at which the cell is actually working. For example, if the reaction rate doubles for every 10° rise in temperature—the usually observed order of magnitude of variation in reaction rates—then a fuel cell working at room temperature can be tested at 100°C with something like one order of magnitude in reduction of the testing time, i.e., a few weeks instead of a year. Such an accelerated approach may be of great use in much of the materials stability work that is necessary with a developed or practical fuel cell. Finally, of course, when most of the testing and materials development work has been done, tests must be carried out over the actual time and for the conditions in which the cell is to be used. This is because of the possibility that at longer times new reactions may occur, because of, for example, new components entering the system, small amounts of materials produced by corrosion catalyzing other reactions, etc.

Accelerated testing is of particular importance in high-temperature fuel cells and rechargeable batteries, because if the difficulties of stabilities of materials used in such devices were to be overcome, they would offer power/weight and energy/weight ratios more than one order of magnitude greater than those of low-temperature devices.

Many possibilities of nondestructive testing of electrochemical devices await development.   Thus, early detection of the existence of some types of corrosion reactions could be made by measurements of changes of conductance or refractive index of the solution.   Indicator materials may be introduced into the solid materials in the cells, and the detection of these in the solution could be a sensitive measure of early stages of corrosion.   Similarly, the mechanical stability of the parts of a device (which may be affected by an incipient corrosion situation) can be followed *in situ* during the working of the cell by hardness testing, stress-strain measurements, and ultrasonic crack-detection methods. The electrode surfaces gradually change and this may be examined by optical reflectometric and, perhaps, by ellipsometric methods.

Testing of fuel-cell performances passes through several stages, for example, 10^1-to-10^4-hr stages, at each of which new problems of stability of materials must be examined.

6 MULTICELL STUDIES

If individual fuel cells are joined together into a stack to produce an electrochemical energy converter with an output of many volts, e.g., 100 volts, the first assumption is that the performance will be the sum of the performances of all the cells.   This is sometimes not true.   For example, reactant gas pressures may not be equal in all cells because of slight differences in porosities.   Alternatively, if some heat is developed during the reaction, there may be hot spots reached in one of the cells that may cause a break in this cell and thus lead to a breakdown of the entire battery.   In certain cases, the electrolytes of individual cells are electrically in contact.   For example, it may be desired to pump the electrolyte through the whole battery, and in such a case, the electrodes in each single cell react to some extent with electrodes in other cells, causing a diminution in the overall potential due to what is actually a partial "shorting" of the cells.

There are many detailed considerations in the setting up of fuel-cell batteries, but these border over into engineering aspects of fuel cells and are outside the scope of the present book.   They are discussed in an article by Wynveen,[101] where they are arranged under the headings: fuel storage; fuel regulations; product removal; electrical control; temperature control; etc. Thus, the basic electrodic theory of electrochemical energy conversion, which is the principal subject of attention in this book, must be developed to connect up with the operation of two electrodes confined to a fuel cell (Chap. 4).   Thereafter, the extension of the theory to many cells is relatively simple.   The various engineering aspects, particularly in the storage and regulation of fuels, the product removal, and the control of environmental conditions, are all factors vital to the success of the many practical devices, which rest on the basis of a knowledge of the interfacial charge-transfer reactions presented in this book.

REFERENCES

1. Despic, A. R.: *Bull. Acad. Serbe Sci. et Arts, Class Sciath et Natur., Bull. Sci. Natur.*, **12** (1969).
2. Piersma, B. J., and E. Gileadi: Chap. 2, in J. O'M. Bockris (ed.), "Modern Aspects of Electrochemistry," vol. 4, Plenum Publishing Corporation, New York, 1966.
3. Conway, B. E., and J. O'M. Bockris: *Electrochim. Acta*, **3**, 340 (1961).
4. Dal Nogare, S., and R. S. Juvet: "Gas Liquid Chromatography, Theory and Practice," Interscience Publishers, Inc., New York, 1962.
5. Lingane, J. J.: "Electroanalytical Chemistry," Interscience Publishers, Inc., New York, 1958.
6. Kolthoff, I. M., and J. J. Lingane: "Polarography," vols. 1 and 2, Interscience Publishers, Inc., New York, 1952.
7. Shriner, R. L., and R. C. Fuson: "The Systematic Identification of Organic Compounds," John Wiley & Sons, Inc., New York, 1948; N. D. Cheronis, J. B. Entrikin, and E. M. Hodnett, "Semimicro Qualitative Organic Analysis: The Systematic Identification of Organic Compounds," 3d ed., Interscience Publishers, Inc., John Wiley & Sons, Inc., New York, 1965; R. M. Silverstein and G. C. Bassler, "Spectrometric Identification of Organic Compounds," 2d ed., John Wiley & Sons, Inc., 1967.
8. Gileadi, E., and S. Srinivasan: *J. Electroanal. Chem.*, **7**, 452 (1964).
9. Bowden, F. P., and E. K. Rideal: *Proc. Roy. Soc., Ser.* A **120**, 59 (1928).
10. Butler, J. A. V., and G. Armstrong: *Proc. Roy. Soc., Ser.* A **137**, 604 (1934).
11. Slygin, A., and A. N. Frumkin: *Acta Physicochim (USSR)*, **3**, 791 (1935).
12. Laitenen, H. A., and C. G. Enke: *J. Electrochem. Soc.*, **107**, 773 (1960).
13. Schuldiner, S., and T. B. Warner: *J. Electrochem. Soc.*, **112**, 212 (1965).
14. Wroblowa, H., M. L. B. Rao, A. Damjanovic, and J. O'M. Bockris: *J. Electroanal. Chem.*, **15**, 139 (1967).
15. Pavela, T. O.: *Ann. Acad. Sci. Fennicae, Ser.* A *II, Chem.*, **59**, 1 (1954).
16. Niedrach, L. W.: *J. Electrochem. Soc.*, **111**, 1309 (1964).
17. Warner, T. B., and S. Schuldiner: *J. Electrochem. Soc.*, **111**, 992 (1964).
18. Devanathan, M. A. V., J. O'M. Bockris, and W. Mehl: *J. Electroanal. Chem.*, **1**, 143 (1959/60).
19. Devanathan, M. A. V., and M. Selvaratnam: *Trans. Faraday Soc.*, **56**, 1820 (1960).
20. Oikawa, M., and T. Mukabo: *J. Electrochem. Soc. Japan*, **20**, 568 (1958).
21. Franklin, T. C., and R. D. Sothern: *J. Phys. Chem.*, **58**, 951 (1954).
22. Schuldiner, S., and T. B. Warner: *Electrochim. Acta*, **11**, 307 (1964).
23. Conway, B. E., J. O'M. Bockris, and B. Lovrecek: *Compt. Rend. CITCE*, **VI**, 207 (1955).
24. Gerischer, H., and W. Mehl: *Z. Electrochem.*, **59**, 1049 (1954).
25. Gileadi, E., L. Duic, and J. O'M. Bockris: *Electrochim. Acta*, **13**, 1915 (1968).
26. Breiter, M. W., and S. Gilman: *J. Electrochem. Soc.*, **109**, 622 (1962).
27. Srinivasan, S., and E. Gileadi: *Electrochim. Acta*, **11**, 321 (1966).

28. Hale, J. M., and R. Green: *Electrochim. Acta*, **12**, 1409 (1967).

29. Conway, B. E., E. Gileadi, and H. Angerstein-Kozlowska: *J. Electrochem. Soc.*, **112**, 341 (1965).

30. Breiter, M. W.: *Electrochim. Acta*, **9**, 827 (1964).

31. Butler, J. A. V.: *Proc. Roy. Soc.*, *Ser.* A **122**, 399 (1929).

32. Bockris, J. O'M., M. A. V. Devanathan, and K. Müller: *Proc. Roy. Soc.*, Ser. A **274**, 55 (1963).

33. Balaschova, N. A.: *Zh. Fiz. Khim.*, **32**, 2266 (1958).

34. Kolotyrkin, Ya. M.: *Trans. Faraday Soc.*, **55**, 455 (1959).

35. Blomgren, E., and J. O'M. Bockris: *Nature*, **186**, 305 (1960).

35a. Wroblowa, H., and M. Green: *Electrochim. Acta*, **8**, 679 (1963); H. Dahms and M. Green, *J. Electrochem. Soc.*, **110**, 1075 (1963); E. Gileadi, B. T. Rubin, and J. O'M. Bockris, *J. Phys. Chem.*, **69**, 3335 (1965); and reference 41.

36. Green, M., D. A. J. Swinkels, and J. O'M. Bockris: *Rev. Sci. Inst.*, **33**, 18 (1962).

36a. Bockris, J. O'M., M. Green, and D. A. J. Swinkels, *J. Electrochem. Soc.*, **111**, 743 (1964); J. O'M. Bockris and D. A. J. Swinkels, *ibid.*, p. 736.

37. Conway, B. E., R. A. Barradas, and T. Zawidski: *J. Phys. Chem.*, **62**, 676 (1958).

38. Eischens, R. P., and W. A. Pliskin: *Advan. Catalysis*, **10**, 1 (1958).

39. Reddy, A. K. N., and J. O'M. Bockris: Proceedings of the Symposium on the Ellipsometer and Its Use, *Dept. Comm. Publ.* 229 (1964).

40. Genshaw, M. A., and Y. C. Chiu: *J. Phys. Chem.*, **72**, 4325 (1968).

41. Heiland, W., E. Gileadi, and J. O'M. Bockris: *J. Phys. Chem.*, **70**, 1207 (1966).

42. Brummer, S. B., J. I. Ford, and M. J. Turner: *J. Phys. Chem.*, **69**, 3424 (1965).

43. Bockris, J. O'M., E. Gileadi, and G. Stoner: *J. Phys. Chem.*, **73**, 427 (1969).

44. Gilman, S.: *J. Electrochem. Soc.*, **113**, 1036 (1966).

45. Niedrach, L. W., S. Gilman, and I. Weinstock: *J. Electrochem. Soc.*, **112**, 1161 (1965).

46. Gileadi, E., and B. E. Conway: Chap. 5, in J. O'M. Bockris and B. E. Conway (eds.), "Modern Aspects of Electrochemistry," vol. 3, Butterworth & Co. (Publishers), Ltd., London, 1964.

47. Müller, L., and L. Nekrassow: *Electrochim. Acta*, **9**, 1015 (1964).

48. Frumkin, A. N., E. I. Kruscheva, M. R. Tarasevich, and N. O. Shumilova: *Electrokhimiya*, **1**, 17 (1965).

49. Damjanovic, A., M. A. Genshaw, and J. O'M. Bockris: *J. Electrochem. Soc.*, **114**, 466 (1967).

49a. Greene, N. D.: "Experimental Electrode Kinetics," Rensselaer Polytechnic Institute, Troy, N.Y., 1965.

50. Dahms, H., and J. O'M. Bockris: *J. Electrochem. Soc.*, **111**, 728 (1964).

51. Reddy, A. K. N., M. A. Genshaw, and J. O'M. Bockris: *J. Electroanal. Chem.*, **8**, 407 (1964).

52. American Oil Company, Whiting Laboratories, Indiana: Quarterly reports 1–9, contract no. DA-11-022-ORD-4023.

53. Geske, D. H., and J. L. Ragle: *J. Am. Chem. Soc.*, **83**, 3532 (1961).

54. Wendlandt, W. W., and H. G. Hecht: "Reflectance Spectroscopy," Interscience Publishers, Inc., New York, 1966.

55. Hansen, W. W., T. Kuwana, and R. A. Osteryoung: *Anal. Chem.*, **38**, 1809 (1966).

56. Bockris, J. O'M.: Chap. 4, in J. O'M. Bockris and B. E. Conway (eds.), "Modern Aspects of Electrochemistry," vol. 1, Butterworth & Co. (Publishers), Ltd., London, 1954.

56a. Genshaw, M. A.: Doctoral dissertation, University of Pennsylvania, 1966.

57. Frumkin, A. N., V. S. Bagotskii, S. A. Iofa, and B. N. Kabanov: "Kinetics of Electrode Processes," Moscow University Publication, 1952.

58. Vetter, K. J.: "Electrochemische Kinetik," Springer-Verlag OHG, Berlin, 1961; "Electrochemical Kinetics, Theoretical and Experimental Aspects," Academic Press Inc., New York, 1967.

59. Doss, K. S. G., and H. P. Agarawal: *J. Sci. Ind. Res. (India)*, **9B**, 280 (1950).

60. Delahay, P.: Chap. 5, in P. Delahay and C. W. Tobias (eds.), "Advances in Electrochemistry and Electrochemical Engineering," vol. 1, Interscience Publishers, Inc., New York, 1961.

61. Srinivasan, S., H. Wroblowa, and J. O'M. Bockris: Chap. 6, in D. D. Cley, H. Pines, and P. B. Wiesz (eds.) "Advances in Catalysis and Related Subjects," vol. 17, Academic Press Inc., New York, 1967.

62. Bockris, J. O'M., R. J. Mannan, and A. Damjanovic: *J. Chem. Phys.*, **48**, 1898 (1968).

63. Bockris, J. O'M., and D. F. A. Koch: *J. Phys. Chem.*, **65**, 1941 (1961).

64. Kuhn, A. T., H. Wroblowa, and J. O'M. Bockris: *Trans. Faraday Soc.*, **63**, 1458 (1967).

65. Bockris, J. O'M., S. Srinivasan, and D. B. Matthews: *Discussions Faraday Soc.*, **39**, 239 (1965).

66. Gileadi, E.: Private communication, 1967.

67. Razumney, G. R.: Private communication, 1967.

68. Delahay, P.: "New Instrumental Methods in Electrochemistry," Interscience Publishers, Inc., New York, 1954.

69. Bockris, J. O'M., H. Wroblowa, E. Gileadi, and B. J. Piersma: *Trans. Faraday Soc.*, **61**, 2531 (1965).

70. Hickling, A.: *Trans. Faraday Soc.*, **38**, 27 (1942).

70a. Andrew, M. R., and F. Jones: Chap. 3, in K. R. Williams (ed.), "An Introduction to Fuel Cells," Elsevier Publishing Company, Amsterdam, 1966.

71. Kordesch, K. V., and A. Marko: *J. Electrochem. Soc.*, **107**, 480 (1960).

72. Pollnow, G. F., and R. M. Kay: *J. Electrochem. Soc.*, **109**, 648 (1962).

73. Devanathan, M. A. V.: Private communication, 1963.

74. Pentland, N., J. O'M. Bockris, and E. Sheldon: *J. Electrochem. Soc.*, **104**, 182 (1957).

75. Tegart, W. J. McG.: "The Electrolytic and Chemical Polishing of Metals," Pergamon Press, New York, 1959.

76. Srinivasan, S., and E. Gileadi: Chap. 2, in C. Berger (ed.), "Handbook of Fuel Cell Technology," Prentice-Hall, Inc., Englewood Cliffs, N.J., 1968.

77. Bockris, J. O'M., I. A. Ammar, and A. K. M. S. Huq: *J. Phys. Chem.*, **61**, 879 (1959).

78. Gilman, S.: *J. Phys. Chem.*, **66**, 2657 (1962).

79. Hoare, J. P.: *J. Electrochem. Soc.*, **112**, 602 (1965).

80. Damjanovic, A., A. Dey, and J. O'M. Bockris: *Electrochim. Acta*, **11**, 791 (1966).

81. Cahan, B. D.: Doctoral dissertation, University of Pennsylvania, Philadelphia, 1967.

82. Hunter, J. B.: *Am. Chem. Soc., Div. Petrol. Chem. Preprints*, **8**(4), B49–B60 (1963).

83. Srinivasan, S.: Doctoral dissertation, University of Pennsylvania, Philadelphia, 1963.

84. Bockris, J. O'M., and A. K. M. S. Huq: *Proc. Roy. Soc.*, Ser. A **237**, 277 (1956).

85. Piersma, B. J.: Doctoral dissertation, University of Pennsylvania, Philadelphia, 1965.

86. Bockris, J. O'M., L. Nanis, and B. D. Cahan: *J. Electroanal. Chem.*, **9,** 474 (1965).

87. Bockris, J. O'M., and B. D. Cahan: 153d Nat. Meeting Am. Chem. Soc., Div. Fuel Chem. preprint 11, 2301 (1967); *J. Chem. Phys.*, **50,** 1307 (1969).

88. Will, F. G.: *J. Electrochem. Soc.*, **110,** 145 (1963).

89. Bennion, D. N.: Doctoral dissertation, University of California, Berkeley, 1964; D. N. Bennion and C. W. Tobias, Extended Abstracts of the Battery Division, *Electrochemical Society*, **9,** 15 (1964).

90. Müller, R.: Optical Studies of Electrolytic Films on Metal Surfaces, paper presented at the Electrochemical Society Meeting, May, 1964.

90a. Lindholm, I., R. Eriksson, and O. von Krusentierna: Research on the Polarization in Porous Oxygen Cathodes, Fourth Quarterly Report for period Jan. 1–March 31, 1968, on contract no. NASW-1536, 1968.

91. Adams, A. M., F. T. Bacon, and R. G. H. Watson: Chap. 4, in W. Mitchell (ed.), "Fuel Cells," Academic Press Inc., New York, 1963.

91a. Cheney, E. O., P. J. Farris, and J. M. King: Open Cycle Fuel Cell System for Space Application, Publication of Pratt and Whitney, Division of United Aircraft Corporation, 1966.

92. Niedrach, L. W., and H. R. Alford: *J. Electrochem. Soc.*, **112,** 117 (1965).

93. Voorhies, J. D., J. S. Mayell, and H. P. Landi: in B. S. Baker (ed.), "Hydrocarbon Fuel Cell Technology," Academic Press Inc., New York, 1965, pp. 455–464.

94. Clark, M. B., W. G. Darland, and K. V. Kordesch: *J. Electrochem. Tech.*, **3,** 166 (1965).

95. Scheidegger, A. E.: "The Physics of Flow through Porous Media," The Macmillan Company, New York, 1960.

96. Ritter, H. L., and L. C. Drake: *Ind. Eng. Chem., Anal. Ed.*, **17,** 782 (1945); L. C. Drake, *Ind. Eng. Chem.*, **41,** 780 (1949).

96a. Iczkowski, R. P.: *J. Electrochem. Soc.*, **111,** 605 (1964).

97. Emmett, P. H.: Chap. 12, in R. Gomer and C. S. Smith (eds.), "Structures and Properties of Solid Surfaces," The University of Chicago Press, Chicago, 1953.

98. Haldeman, R. G., W. P. Colman, S. H. Langer, and W. A. Barber: *Advan. Chem. Ser.*, **47,** 116 (1965).

98a. Haldeman, R. G.: American Cyanamid Company, private communication, 1969.

99. Bonnemay, M., G. Bronoël, E. Levert, and A. A. Pilla: *J. Electroanal. Chem.*, **13,** 44 (1967).

100. Borucka, A., and J. N. Agar: *Electrochim. Acta*, **11,** 603 (1966).

101. Wynveen, R. G.: Chap. 10, in W. Mitchell (ed.), "Fuel Cells," Academic Press Inc., New York, 1963.

CHAPTER TEN

Types of Fuel Cells

1 THE CLASSIFICATION OF FUEL CELLS

Before describing the different types of fuel cells, it is necessary to have some method of classification of the various types of fuel cells, which either are in existence or are being invented. Several methods of classification of fuel cells have appeared in the literature. One of the difficulties in arriving at a systematic classification is that several operational variables exist. For example, fuel cells may be classified according to the temperature range in which they operate—low temperature (25 to 100°C), medium temperature (100 to 500°C), high temperature (500 to 1000°C), and very high temperature (above 1000°C). Another method would be according to the type of electrolyte, e.g., aqueous, nonaqueous, molten, or solid. One could also classify fuel cells according to the physical state of the fuel: gaseous-hydrogen, lower hydrocarbons, liquid; alcohols, hydrazine, higher hydrocarbons; solids; metals; etc.

In the present chapter,† a broad division is first made according to whether the fuel-cell system is a primary or secondary one. A primary fuel cell may be defined as one in which the reactants are passed through the cell only once, the products of the reaction being discarded. A secondary fuel cell is one in which the reactants are passed through the cell many times because they are regenerated from the products by thermal, electrical, photochemical, or radiochemical methods.

Primary fuel cells are further divided into various types depending on the kind of fuel and oxidant used. Oxygen is the most common oxidant, but air is generally substituted for oxygen. Under primary cells, the hydrogen-oxygen system is treated first. This is the most advanced system. The next most-researched fuel-cell system is the one using organic fuels (e.g., hydrocarbons, alcohols). The carbon-oxygen system is then dealt with. This was one of the earliest systems to be considered since Ostwald[1] realized the potentialities

† The most recent (April, 1969) performance figures for the various fuel cells which have been developed into batteries (low, medium, or high power) are briefly described in the following sections and are presented in Table 12.

of electrochemical energy conversion and pointed out in 1894 that coal could be used more efficiently in this manner than in conventional heat engines. A system of interest is carbon monoxide–air. Some work is being carried out with nitrogenous fuels (e.g., ammonia, hydrazine), which come next on the list of primary fuel cells. Metals may be used in a fuel cell although usually regeneratively. In these cases, air or the halogens may be used as the oxidant. Each type is further subdivided into low-, intermediate-, and high-temperature systems.

Regenerative systems are dealt with according to the methods discussed earlier.

An entirely different type of electrochemical energy converter is the biochemical fuel cell. Little effort is being expended in this direction at the present time, but systems of this type have distinct prospects. It is dealt with separately.

The performance data, quoted for most of the systems in the following sections, were obtained by private communication with representatives of the respective organizations during the period January to April, 1969.

2 PRIMARY SYSTEMS

2.1 Hydrogen-Oxygen (or Air) Fuel Cells

2.1.1 *Low-temperature Systems*

2.1.1.1 *The General Electric Ion-exchange-membrane (or Gemini) Fuel Cell*[2]

(i) *The basic design of a single cell and its mode of operation*

The basic design of the cell, which consists of a solid electrolyte ion-exchange membrane, electrocatalysts, current collectors, coolant tubes, water wicks, gas-feed tubes, and a structural frame, is represented in Figs. 1 and 2. The distinctive feature of this fuel cell is that it uses a solid electrolyte in the form of an ion-exchange membrane. The membrane is nonpermeable to the reactant gases, hydrogen and oxygen, which thus prevents them from coming into contact. The membrane, however, is permeable to hydrogen ions, which are the current carriers in the electrolyte.

The desired properties of an ideal ion-exchange-membrane electrolyte are (1) high ionic conductivity; (2) zero electronic conductivity; (3) low permeability of fuel and oxidant gases; (4) low degree of electroosmosis; (5) high resistance to dehydration; (6) high resistance to its oxidation or hydrolysis; and (7) mechanical stability. A considerable amount of research has been carried out in a search for the ideal membrane. Interpolymers of polyfluorocarbon and polystyrene sulfonic acids have been found to be quite satisfactory. In order that the electrolyte resistance be as low as possible, a thin sheet of this material, 0.076 cm in thickness, is used as the electrolyte. The use of even thinner electrolyte sheets is prevented by problems of gas permeability, mechanical

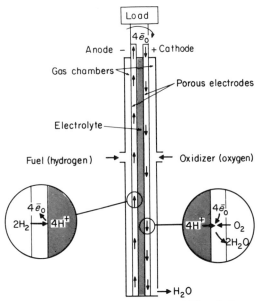

Figure 1 A single cell in the General Electric ion-exchange-membrane hydrogen-oxygen fuel cell.[2]

stability, etc. An advantageous feature of this electrolyte is that it retains only a limited quantity of water and rejects the excess water produced in the fuel cell.

The two electrodes, which consist of the electrocatalyst (finely divided Pt) and a plastic material for water-proofing the electrode (see Chap. 9, Sec. 5), are in the form of fine metallic wire screens. They are bonded on either side of the electrolyte layer. The wire screen material is titanium or platinum. Metallic current collectors are ribbed onto each electrode. The hydrogen compartment of the cell is enclosed; the hydrogen gas enters this compartment through a small inlet and circulates throughout the ribbed current collectors and

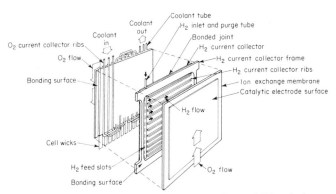

Figure 2 Assembly of a single cell in the General Electric ion-exchange-membrane hydrogen-oxygen fuel cell.[2a]

distributes itself evenly over the electrode. On the opposite side, oxygen or air enters its compartment. Coolant tubes run through the ribs of the current collectors. On the oxygen side, the current collectors also hold wicks which absorb water, the product of the fuel-cell reaction, and carry it over by capillary action. The water leaves the cell through an exit from the oxygen compartment. Oxygen is prevented from leaving its compartment by the inclusion of a differential-pressure water-separation system.

(ii) Reactions occurring at each electrode and overall reaction

The ion-exchange-membrane electrolyte is acidic, and the current carriers in solution are hydrogen ions. The hydrogen ions are produced by the reaction at the anode according to

$$H_2 \rightarrow 2H^+ + 2e_0^- \tag{2.1}$$

These ions are then transported to the cathode through the electrolyte and the electrons reach the cathode via the external circuit (Fig. 1). At the cathode, oxygen is reduced, producing water as represented by

$$O_2 + 4H^+ + 4e_0^- \rightarrow 2H_2O \tag{2.2}$$

Thus, the overall cell reaction is

$$2H_2 + O_2 \rightarrow 2H_2O \tag{2.3}$$

This cell operates at about 40 to 60°C. The thermodynamic reversible potential for reaction (2.3) is 1.23 volts at 25°C and is around 1.2 volts at 40°C.

(iii) Performance of a single cell

The current-density–terminal-cell-potential relation obtained in a single cell is shown in Fig. 3. There is a short initial region in which the potential changes rapidly with current density, which is followed by a long linear region where the change of potential with current is considerably slower. The slope of this line gives the resistance of the electrolyte per square centimeter of surface (Chap. 4, Sec. 3). Figure 3 shows that even though a thin enough electrolyte layer is used, it still has fairly high resistance (specific resistance is 20 to 30 ohm-cm). Since the overall efficiency of a fuel cell is linearly related to the terminal-cell potential, the same curve of Fig. 3 also represents the course of the variation of efficiency with current density (Chap. 4, Sec. 4). The power-density–current-density relation is also shown in Fig. 3. The maximum power density is not observed even at 100 ma cm^{-2}. A power density of about 100 mw cm^{-2} is obtained at a current density of about 125 ma cm^{-2}. Higher power densities may be obtained but efficiency would be lowered. At a current density of 125 ma cm^{-2}, the efficiency is over 50 percent.

(iv) Multicell design and performance

The ion-exchange-membrane cell forms the basic constituent of a 1-kw fuel-cell battery, developed for the Gemini program. Thirty-two single cells (each with an active electrode area of 348 cm^2) are connected in series to form a

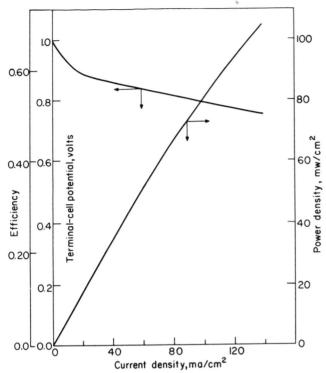

Figure 3 The terminal-cell potential[2] (or efficiency) and power-density–current-density relations for a General Electric ion-exchange-membrane hydrogen-oxygen fuel cell.

stack; three such stacks are connected in parallel and built into a tank to form the 1-kw fuel-cell battery. The layout of the fuel-cell battery is represented in Fig. 4. The tank containing the three stacks of cells is cylindrical, 2 ft long and 1 ft in diameter. An electrical monitoring control unit watches the performance of individual stacks.

Each stack is a self-contained 350-watt unit, and the battery may be used as a 350-, 700-, or 1,050-watt generator. Each cell operates at a current density of 50 to 100 ma cm^{-2} and a cell potential of 0.7 to 0.5 volt. The efficiency of the cell is 50 to 60 percent. The cell provides one pint of drinking water for 1 kwh of operation.

Such a battery has maintained the specified output for more than 1,000 hr of operation. This is equivalent to about three times that needed for the longest Gemini flight.

The power/weight and power/volume ratios of the unit are 15 watts lb^{-1} and 0.5 kw ft^{-3}, respectively. The corresponding projected figures are 35 watts lb^{-1} and 2 kw ft^{-3}.

One of the main features of this system is the water-removal mechanism that depends on capillary forces and differential oxygen pressure. It is independent

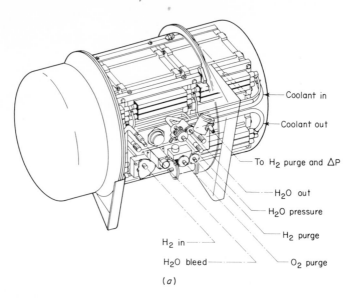

Coolant in

Coolant out

To H_2 purge and ΔP

H_2O out

H_2O pressure

H_2 purge

H_2 in

H_2O bleed

O_2 purge

(*a*)

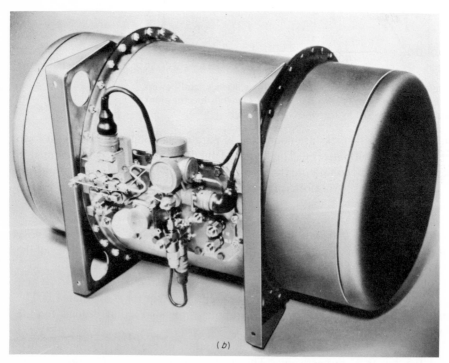

(*b*)

Figure 4 The General Electric ion-exchange-membrane hydrogen-oxygen fuel-cell battery. (*a*) Layout of a three-stack fuel cell; (*b*) photograph of Gemini 1-kw hydrogen-oxygen fuel-cell battery.[2a]

of gravity and is ideally suited for space applications. The fuel-cell battery is provided with control services such as shutoff valves, purge valves, and hydraulic and electrical connections.

(v) Advantages and disadvantages

The main advantage of the cell is the use of an ion-exchange-membrane electrolyte. This makes it possible to use thin electrolyte layers as well as to facilitate removal of product water from the cell. The use of wicks and oxygen-pressure differential for the water removal is advantageous for space applications and works satisfactorily independent of flight altitude or orbit of the space vehicle. Another advantage is that the cell works at a low temperature and pressure. The cell performance is unaffected by CO_2 impurity. Since strong electrolytes are not used, material problems are considerably reduced.

The main problem encountered with this cell is its fairly high internal resistance. As a consequence, there could tend to be local overheating, drying, and pinholing of the electrolyte. Local overheating is reduced by circulation of a liquid coolant. A considerable amount of effort has been expended to develop new ion-exchange-membrane electrolytes with increased life. Most of the difficulties, except polarization losses, have been largely overcome, and this system has been successfully used in the Gemini space flights.

A disadvantage from the point of view of large-scale commercial application is that platinum is used as the electrocatalyst. Research is being carried out with the aim of developing a cell that uses either smaller quantities of platinum or nonnoble metal catalysts.

2.1.1.2 Union Carbide Carbon-electrode Fuel Cell[3]

(i) The basic design of the single cell and its mode of operation

This fuel cell employs two thin carbon electrodes. A cut through a tin electrode showing the various sections is represented in Fig. 5. The metal

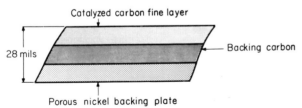

Figure 5 A cross section of a thin carbon electrode used in the Union Carbide hydrogen-oxygen fuel cell showing the various sections.[3]

backing plate is a Ni screen with carbonyl nickel sintered on top and around it. It is impregnated with Teflon to make it water-repellant. Adjacent to it is the carbon layer, also impregnated with Teflon. The catalyst layer consists of active carbon with a small quantity of Teflon binder; for better performance, small quantities of noble metals may be added. Such an electrode arrangement enables semiwetting in the fine layer and nonwetting in the nickel backing layer. This arrangement allows the flow of the reactant gases to the reaction sites in the fine layer (Fig. 5).

The electrolytes used vary in composition from 6 to 14 *N* KOH. A basic cell assembly is shown in Fig. 6. The hydrogen and oxygen gas streams are

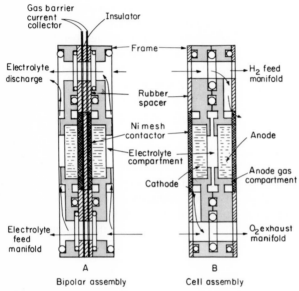

Figure 6 A basic cell assembly of the Union Carbide hydrogen-oxygen fuel cell.[3a]

recirculated through condensers to remove the product water carried over. This process helps in maintaining a uniform gas composition and constant flow rate through the cells in a fuel-cell battery. In order that the temperature in the cell be maintained constant, the electrolyte is also circulated through the cell and a heat exchanger. The cell usually operates at a temperature of about 60°C.

(ii) Reactions occurring at each electrode and overall reaction

In this cell, the reaction occurring at the anode is

$$H_2 + 2OH^- \rightarrow 2H_2O + 2e_0^- \tag{2.4}$$

and at the cathode is

$$O_2 + 2H_2O + 4e_0^- \rightarrow 4OH^- \tag{2.5}$$

The current carriers in solution are predominantly the OH^- ions which are formed at the oxygen electrode and are consumed at the anode. Since water is formed at the anode but is a reactant at the cathode, there is a dilution of the electrolyte near the anode and a concentration of it near the cathode. However, the circulation of the electrolyte through the cells helps in maintaining a constant electrolyte concentration.

The overall reaction in the cell is the same as in acid electrolytes and is represented by Eq. (2.3).

A problem commonly encountered is the formation of the peroxide ion (Chap. 8, Sec. 6) either as an intermediate in the four-electron transfer-oxygen reduction [Eq. (2.5)] or by the two-electron transfer-oxygen reduction:

$$O_2 + H_2O + 2e_0^- \rightarrow HO_2^- + OH^- \tag{2.6}$$

However, if the concentration of the HO_2^- ion is kept at a vanishingly low level by effective catalysts, the potential of the cathode is not affected. Additional catalysts are incorporated in the cathode to facilitate HO_2^- decomposition by either electrochemical

$$HO_2^- + H_2O + 2e_0^- \rightarrow 3OH^- \tag{2.7}$$

or by chemical

$$2HO_2^- \rightarrow 2OH^- + O_2 \tag{2.8}$$

means. The O_2 formed is then electrochemically reduced. It is necessary for oxygen to be completely reduced to hydroxyl ions; otherwise, there is a loss in faradaic efficiency (Chap. 3, Sec. 4).

(iii) Performance of single cell

Typical polarization curves obtained with air or oxygen as the oxidant at varying pressure are shown in Fig. 7 for these cells. The performance with oxygen becomes increasingly superior compared with that with air as the current density is increased. Up to about 150 ma cm^{-2} the performances are comparable. The polarization curves with air tend to show a limiting current density at about 300 to 350 ma cm^{-2}, whereas this is not the case with oxygen up to current densities of 500 ma cm^{-2}. The curves with oxygen show a long linear region. The slope of this line in the high current-density region is indicative of the internal resistance of the cell. The efficiency of the cell as a function of the current density is shown by the same lines.

The power-density–current-density relations (Fig. 7) show that with oxygen as the oxidant, the maximum power is not reached up to 500 ma cm^{-2}. With air as oxidant, the maximum power density is attained near the limiting current density (see Chap. 4, Sec. 6). The maximum power density attained in this cell is about three times better than that of the ion-exchange-membrane cell because the internal resistance of this cell is considerably smaller than that of the latter.

(iv) Multicell design and performance

The individual cells are assembled into a battery by potting between end plates using a suitable strength of plastic. The reactant gases and electrolyte enter the battery through holes in the end plates. A representation of

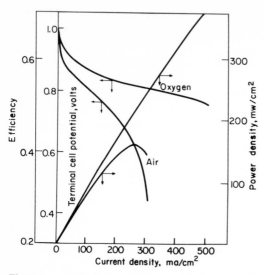

Figure 7   Terminal-cell potential, efficiency, and power-density–current-density relations for Union Carbide hydrogen-oxygen and hydrogen-air fuel cells.[3]

the fuel-cell system is shown in Fig. 8.   Batteries generating 1 kw at a current density of 200 ma cm^{-2} have been constructed. The power/weight and power/volume ratios are about 16 watts lb^{-1} and 1 kw ft^{-3}.   The projected figures are 50 watts lb^{-1} and 2 kw ft^{-3}.

The systems are shock-resistant and have been tested for over 5,000 hr.

(*v*)   *Advantages and disadvantages of the system*

These cells use very small quantities of noble metal catalysts (1 to 2 mg cm^{-2}).   For use with air as the oxidant, the cathode employs nonnoble metal catalysts.   The performance of the cell (efficiency, power density) is quite good up to about 500 ma cm^{-2} with oxygen and about 250 ma cm^{-2} with air.   The internal resistance of the cell is low because concentrated alkali solution is used as the electrolyte.

The high power density at which the cell operates and the relatively low operating temperature necessitate forced liquid cooling; this is accomplished by circulating the electrolyte through a heat exchange.   The use of alkaline electrolytes may cause problems if CO or CO_2 is present in the gas streams.

2.1.1.3   *The Justi DSK Electrode Fuel Cell*[4]

(*i*)   *Basic design of a single cell and its mode of operation*

This cell was invented by Justi and coworkers and has been developed by Varta A. G. in West Germany.   A highly active Raney nickel "double skeleton catalyst" serves as the anode.   Details of electrode preparation are given in

Figure 8 A Union Carbide 1-kw hydrogen-oxygen fuel-cell battery.[3b]

Chap. 9, Sec. 5. A similar electrode structure is used for the cathode, but the catalyst is silver. The electrolyte is 6 N KOH. The operating pressure of the reactant gases is 1 to 2 atm.

The electrodes are homoporous, and a stable meniscus of the electrolyte within the electrode is obtained by maintaining a differential gas pressure.

(ii) Performance of a single cell

The performance of a single cell at three different temperatures is shown in Fig. 9. The polarization at the hydrogen electrode is negligible over the entire current-density range at temperatures above 40°C. Thus, the variation in cell potential with current density exclusive of the *IR* drop in the cell is effectively the potential variation at the oxygen electrode. An open-circuit potential of 1.13 volts is obtained. The power-density–current-density variation is also shown in the same figure. The performance of this cell compares very favorably with other low-temperature hydrogen-oxygen fuel cells.

The consumption rates of hydrogen and oxygen have been obtained as a function of the current drawn from the cell at three different temperatures. The points obtained experimentally fall on the theoretical lines corresponding to a two-electron transfer for the hydrogen-dissolution reaction and a four-electron transfer for the oxygen-dissolution reaction (Fig. 10). The dotted line represents the theoretical one for a two-electron oxygen reduction to hydrogen peroxide.

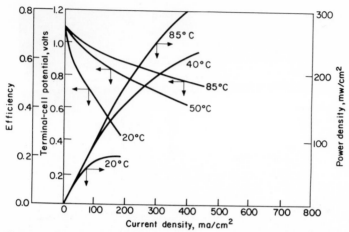

Figure 9 Terminal-cell potential and power-density–current-density relations for a hydrogen-oxygen Justi DSK electrode fuel cell at different temperatures.[4,4a]

Single cells have been tested for over 25,000 hr.   The weight of a single cell containing a 1-mm-thick electrolyte layer is 2.0 g cm^{-2}.   The maximum power density at a temperature of 67°C, the usual working temperature of the cell, is 0.154 watt cm^{-2} (current density of 250 ma cm^{-2} at a terminal-cell potential of

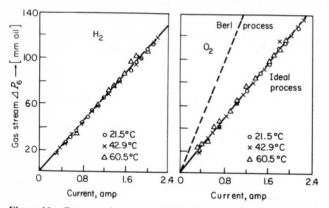

Figure 10 Consumption ratio of hydrogen and oxygen as a function of current drawn from the cell at different temperatures.[4]

0.615 volt, ohmic loss included).   Thus, the power/weight ratio of a single cell is 35 watts lb^{-1} exclusive of auxiliaries.   Each electrode is 2.5-mm thick.   Thus, the power/volume ratio is 7 kw ft^{-3} excluding the volume occupied by auxiliaries.

(iii) Multicell design and performance

In collaboration with Justi and coworkers, Varta A. A., Kelkheim, is in process of developing automatically operated multicell units.   For this purpose,

multilayer DSK electrodes of bilateral "Janus" type and postcard size
(2×187 cm^2) are fabricated in semiindustrial scale. A 500-watt unit that
consists of 70 cells is shown in Fig. 11. The unit has been tested for over
9,000 hours in uninterrupted service. The unit performs nearly as well on air
as on pure oxygen.

Figure 11 A 500-watt Varta fuel-cell battery.[4b]

(*iv*) *Advantages and disadvantages of the system*

The performance of this cell is quite good, particularly since it works at low
temperatures and pressures. A significant advantage is that it does not use
noble metal catalysts; but the cost of fabrication of the electrodes is relatively
high at present. The electrolyte concentration is also not too high (only
6 N KOH). Because of the use of an alkaline electrolyte, it is necessary that
the gas streams be free of CO_2. This system is said to be preferred in eastern
countries.

2.1.1.4 *The Allis-Chalmers Capillary-membrane Fuel Cell*[5]

(*i*) *Basic design of a single cell and its mode of operation*

The anode is a sintered nickel plaque impregnated with platinum, palladium, or, for much cheaper operation, nickle boride. The cathode is made of
high-surface-area silver. This cell uses an asbestos capillary membrane, with

pores of smaller size than those of the electrode, to retain the KOH electrolyte. This arrangement of electrolyte enables the utilization of electrodes of a single porosity and thus avoids the difficulty of constructing electrodes of a double porous structure.

The cell operates at 80°C and its mode of operation is schematically represented in Fig. 12. The asbestos capillary membrane is first completely

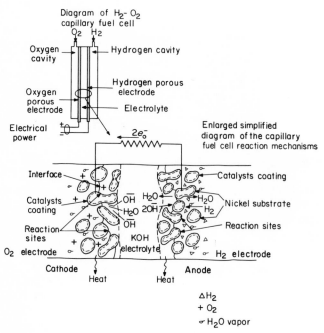

Figure 12   An Allis-Chalmers hydrogen-oxygen fuel cell and a schematic representation of its mode of operation.[5a]

soaked in the electrolyte and during assembly its compression causes some of the electrolyte to penetrate the pores of the electrodes to form the necessary electrolyte-electrode interface. The difference in capillary pressure of the asbestos and the electrode and the gas pressure permits a stable meniscus, as indicated in Fig. 12. The removal of water from the cell is by a novel method. An asbestos membrane, similar to the one used for the electrolyte, is placed next to the anode chamber on the side opposite to that of the electrolyte membrane. This asbestos membrane is soaked with KOH of a higher concentration that than in the electrolyte membrane. The arrangement is shown in Fig. 13. The higher concentration of KOH in this (water-transport) membrane rather than the cell aids the transport of water to it. Water travels through it to vent channels on the opposite side. The cavity adjacent to the support plaque on

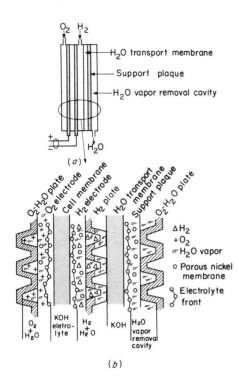

Figure 13 A representation of the water-removal mechanism in the Allis-Chalmers hydrogen-oxygen fuel cell. (*a*) Static vapor-pressure-control fuel cell; (*b*) static vapor-pressure-control concept (simplified and enlarged).[5a]

the farther side of the membrane contains only water vapor. By lowering this pressure, water vapor is withdrawn from the cell. The water vapor also carries away about a third of the heat generated in the cell. The components of a single-cell unit are illustrated in Fig. 14.

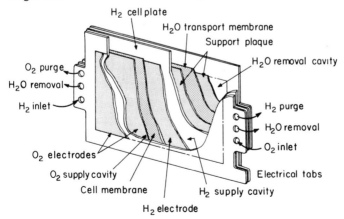

Figure 14 Components of a single cell in the Allis-Chalmers hydrogen-oxygen fuel cell.[5b]

(ii)   Reactions occurring at each electrode and the overall reaction

The reactions occurring at each electrode and the overall reaction are the same as in the previous cases.   The thermodynamic reversible potential of the cell is about 1.15 volts because the cell operates at about 80°C.

(iii)   Performance of a single cell

A typical polarization curve is shown in Fig. 15.   This curve shows that the cell efficiency is about 75 percent at a current density of 200 ma cm^{-2}.   The

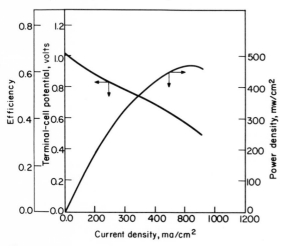

Figure 15   The terminal-cell potential (or efficiency)[5] and power-density–current-density relations for the Allis-Chalmers hydrogen-oxygen fuel cell.

power-density–current-density plot (Fig. 15) shows that the maximum power density is about 500 mw cm^{-2}.

The performance of the cell as a function of temperature is shown in Fig. 16. Increase of temperatures is quite favorable up to about 90°C.   Above this temperature, the improvement in performance is slower and further complications arise.

It is interesting to compare the performances of the cells using Pd and Ni_2B as the anode materials.   This is shown in Fig. 17.   The initial decrease of cell voltage with increase of current density is faster with the nickel boride catalyst, but thereafter the variations of cell potential with current density are similar in both cases.   For example, at a current density of 100 ma cm^{-2} the difference in cell potential is less than 0.1 volt.   However, there is one problem with the nickel boride catalyst—a slight decrease in performance with time (Fig. 18).   The decrease after the initial period of 200 hr has been ascribed to problems of cell control and not to a decrease in performance of the anode catalyst.

(iv)   Multicell design and performance

A 29-volt 2-kw power supply has been developed for use as an aerospace power supply (Apollo Applications Program).   The fuel-cell battery consists

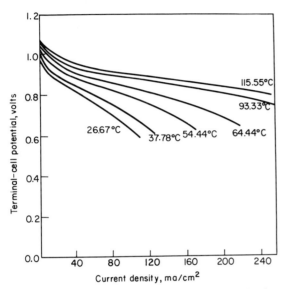

Figure 16 The terminal-cell potential–current-density relations at several temperatures for the Allis-Chalmers hydrogen-oxygen fuel cell.[5]

of 31 cell sections connected in series.   Each cell section consists of two cells, described earlier, in parallel.   The active electrode area in each cell is 372 cm[2].

The heat generated in the battery is transferred to the finned edges of the cell plates.   It is then conducted away by helium coolant gas, which is circulated by two fans through plastic distribution ducts across the plate fins and through

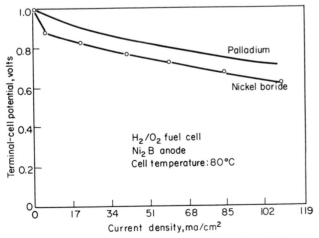

Figure 17 The terminal-cell potential–current-density relations for the Allis-Chalmers hydrogen-oxygen fuel cell using Pd and Ni_2B as the anode catalysts.[5c]

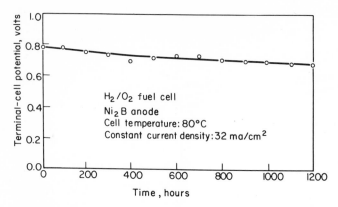

Figure 18 The terminal-cell potential–time plot for the Allis-Chalmers hydrogen-oxygen fuel cell using Ni_2B as the anode catalyst at a current density of 32 ma cm^{-2}.[5c]

the heat exchanger located above the module assembly. The main components of the power supply are schematically represented in Fig. 19. A photograph of the power supply with the canister removed is reproduced in Fig. 20.

The power-battery–voltage relation is shown in Fig. 21 as a function of time of operation. There is very little falloff in performance after 720 hr.

The power/weight and power/volume ratios presently achieved are 30 watts lb^{-1} and 3 kw ft^{-3} exclusive of auxiliaries. However, including the auxiliaries, the corresponding figures become 18 watts lb^{-1} and 1.1 kw ft^{-3}. The cell has been tested for nearly 1,000 hr.

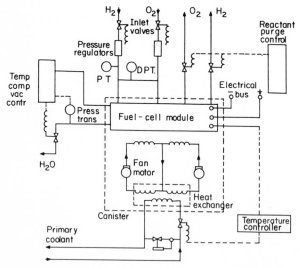

Figure 19 Main components of the Allis-Chalmers 2-kw hydrogen-oxygen fuel-cell battery.[5b]

Figure 20 Photograph of the Allis-Chalmers 2-kw hydrogen-oxygen fuel-cell battery.

(v) *Advantages and disadvantages of the system*

This fuel-cell performance is quite competitive with the other hydrogen-oxygen low-temperature systems.   The successful use of nickel boride or some nonnoble metal as the anode catalyst would help considerably in reducing the cost of the cell.   The water-removal system is quite novel.   The water-removal technique carries away 35 to 40 percent of the heat generated in the cell as latent

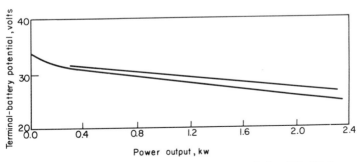

Figure 21 The power–battery-potential relation of the Allis-Chalmers 2-kw hydrogen-oxygen fuel-cell battery.[5d]

heat of vaporization of the product water, thus minimizing heat-dissipation problems.

However, if the power supply is to be used as a water supply as well, the water vapor rejected from the cell by the static vapor-pressure technique may be condensed outside the assembly but at a loss of some of the thermal advantages.

2.1.2   Intermediate-temperature Systems

2.1.2.1   The Bacon[6]–Pratt and Whitney[7] Fuel Cell

(i)   The basic design of a single cell and its mode of operation

This is one of the earliest fuel cells and was first successfully developed by Bacon,[6] the leading pioneer in fuel-cell research of the postwar period. Bacon started his work on hydrogen-oxygen fuel cells, which operate at intermediate temperatures, in the thirties. Electrodes of a double porous structure were used to obtain a stable meniscus of the electrolyte within the electrode (Fig. 22). A

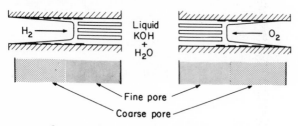

Cross section of sintered electrode 250X

Figure 22   Structure of porous electrode in the Bacon–Pratt and Whitney fuel cell.

dual porous nickel electrode for the anode and a dual porous lithiated nickel oxide electrode for the cathode were used. The electrolyte used was 30 percent KOH; and the cell operating temperature and pressure were 200°C and 50 atm, respectively. Pratt and Whitney Aircraft has recently modified the Bacon cell to work at atmospheric pressure but with KOH concentration of 80 to 85 percent (i.e., practically molten KOH). The cell temperature is also higher—250°C.

Two designs have been developed. The original, by Bacon, is a sandwich arrangement in which two circular disk electrodes are placed to face each other with a thin electrolyte layer between them and sealed around the edge with an insulating gasket. The electrodes are about 12.7 cm in diameter. Such a cell is represented in Fig. 23.

The second is a folded-can design. Two oxygen electrodes are arranged back-to-back in the center of a hollow circular nickel canister, the walls of which serve as two hydrogen electrodes. There are thus two cells that are arranged in parallel (Fig. 24). This arrangement has the advantage that no insulating seal along the edge is required except at the top of the can, which is not in contact with the electrolyte. The first is more advantageous for space applications.

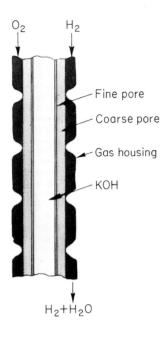

O$_2$ H$_2$

Fine pore

Coarse pore

Gas housing

KOH

H$_2$+H$_2$O

Figure 23   The sandwich design for a single cell in the Pratt and Whitney hydrogen-oxygen fuel cell.[7b]

The dual porous structure of the electrode facilitates the formation of stable reaction zones.   The reactant gas diffuses through the thin film and small pores to reach the electrocatalytic sites.   One of the main developments by Pratt and Whitney is the method of making electrodes with a fairly uniform pore structure. Photomicrographs of two nickel electrodes by the old and present techniques are shown in Fig. 25.

(ii)   Reactions at each electrode and the overall reaction

These are the same for alkaline electrolytes at low temperatures.

(iii)   Performance of a single cell

There has been considerable improvement in the performance of the Pratt and Whitney fuel cell over that first developed by Bacon.   Plots of the terminal cell potential versus power density of cell since 1959 are given in Fig. 26.   In 1959, the maximum power density area was 125 mw cm^{-2}.   Since 1962, no maximum in the curve is seen for double this value of the power density.

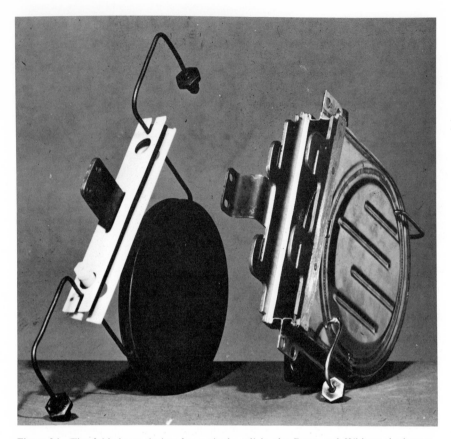

Figure 24   The folded-can design for a single cell in the Pratt and Whitney hydrogen-oxygen fuel cell.[7b]

The present terminal-cell-potential–current-density relation is shown in Fig. 27.   The relation is practically linear from 1.2 volts, indicating that problems of activation overpotential in the cell are largely overcome in the system at these operating temperatures.   The efficiency–current-density relations for this cell are better than the corresponding ones for the low-temperature systems. This is a distinct advantage of the cell, since it does not use any noble metal catalysts.   Further, on open circuit, the thermodynamic reversible potential is attained, which is not the case with low-temperature systems.

(iv)   Multicell design and performance

The Apollo cell system is as follows: Thirty-one single cells of the sandwich type described earlier are connected in series to form a stack.   This stack occupies the bottom two-thirds of the power plant.   The heat-removal, water-removal, reactant-control, monitor instrument sensors, and operational control

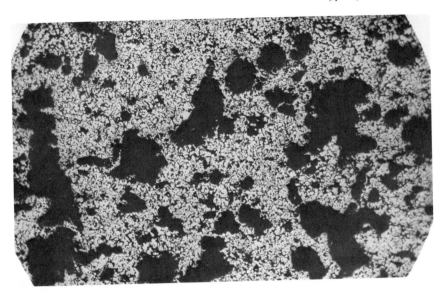

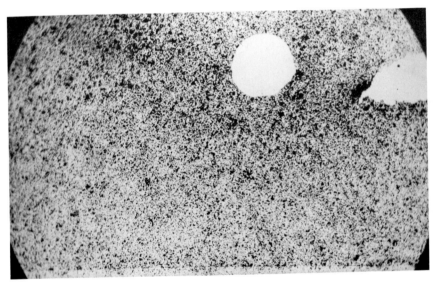

Figure 25 Photomicrographs of nickel electrodes prepared by old and new techniques for the Pratt and Whitney hydrogen-oxygen fuel cell.[7c]

components are situated in the upper one-third section of the system. A photograph of the power supply is shown in Fig. 28. Three of these power plants are connected in parallel to supply power for the Apollo L.E.M. project. The reactants are supplied to the cell at a pressure of nearly 2 atm. The hydrogen circulates through the cells at a rate in excess of what is consumed in the

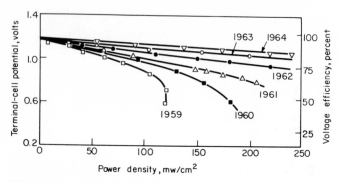

Figure 26   Terminal-cell potential–power-density relations since 1959 for the Pratt and Whitney hydrogen-oxygen fuel cell.[7]

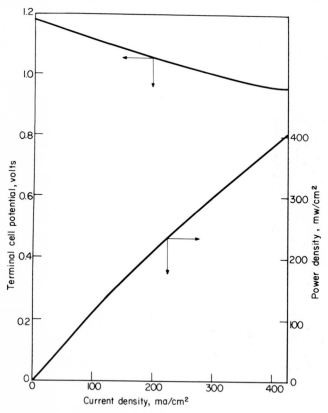

Figure 27   Relations of terminal-cell potential (or efficiency) to current density for the Pratt and Whitney hydrogen-oxygen fuel cell.[7]

Figure 28 Photograph of the Pratt and Whitney hydrogen-oxygen fuel-cell battery.[7] (*Pratt and Whitney Aircraft.*)

cells so as to carry away the water and heat generated in the cell. The fuel-cell power system is schematically represented in Fig. 29.

The power supply is designed to operate over a power range of from 560 to 1,400 watts for corresponding cell voltages of from 31 to 27 volts. It has a

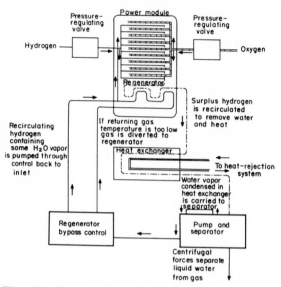

Figure 29 Components of the Pratt and Whitney 2-kw hydrogen-oxygen fuel-cell battery power system.[7d]

maximum power output of 2,300 watts at 20.5 volts. The water produced is quite pure and is being used for drinking purposes by the astronauts. The power/weight and power/volume ratios obtained at the present time are 10 watts lb^{-1} and 1 kw ft^{-3}.

Pratt and Whitney have also built smaller units of a similar type.

(v)   Advantages and disadvantages of the system

The efficiency of the Pratt and Whitney power supply is the highest achieved for medium- and low-temperature systems (Fig. 27). This cell does not use noble metal catalysts and its performance is still very good. Bacon's early ambition to develop a fuel-cell system not using noble metal catalysts has thus been realized.

The use of practically molten KOH electrolyte at intermediate temperatures causes corrosion problems and restricts the life of the cell. These problems are not too severe for space trips of about a month. Since heat rejection is proportional to the fourth power of the source-to-sink temperature, lighter and smaller radiators are required for fuel cells operating at 250°C rather than for the ones operating at room temperature.

2.1.3 High-temperature Systems

In most of the high-temperature fuel cells, molten carbonate mixtures are used as the electrolyte. The fuels are generally H_2 or mixtures of H_2 and CO formed in the steam reforming of hydrocarbons and other organic fuels. Thus, these fuel cells are better classified under "indirect organic compound-air fuel cells," and the details of this type of fuel cells are accordingly dealt with under this type.

2.1.4 Very-high-temperature Systems—The Westinghouse Solid-electrolyte Fuel Cell[8]

(*i*) *The basic design of a single cell and its mode of operation*

The distinctive feature of this fuel cell is that it uses a solid electrolyte,† $(ZrO_2)_{0.85}(CaO)_{0.15}$ [or $(ZrO_2)_{0.9}(Y_2O_3)_{0.1}$]. This electrolyte is an impervious ceramic and its ionic conductivity is quite high at temperatures above 1000°C. The specific resistivities of the two electrolytes as a function of temperature are given in Fig. 30. The current carriers in the electrolyte are oxide ions.

† A solid electrolyte fuel cell has also been developed at the General Electric Co.[9] The electrode is fabricated in somewhat of a different manner: natural gas decomposes in the anode compartment to carbon and hydrogen; the carbon deposits on the zirconia electrolyte to form the anode. Molten silver is the cathode. No details of performance are available.

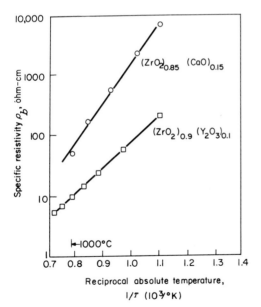

Figure 30 The specific resistivity of the solid electrolyte $[(ZrO_2)_{0.85}(CaO)_{0.15}]$ used in the Westinghouse hydrogen-oxygen fuel cell as a function of temperature.[8]

The single cell is fabricated by applying porous platinum electrode on both sides of a short cylindrical electrolyte segment, whose shape is such that these cells fit into one another by bell-and-spigot joints into a long tube to connect the cells in series.   A cross section for the basic bell and spigot unit is shown in Fig. 31.   The dimensions chosen to maximize the power/volume ratio of the

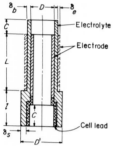

Figure 31   Cross section of bell-and-spigot unit in a Westinghouse solid electrolyte fuel cell.[8a]

single cell are given in Table 1.   The fuel gas (H_2) passes through the tube and the outer surface of the tube is exposed to air.

For single-cell studies, circular-disk electrolytes were used (area 10.5 cm² and thickness 0.051 cm).   A porous platinum catalyst was deposited on its two

TABLE 1   **Dimensions of Westinghouse Solid Electrolyte Fuel Cell to Maximize Power/Weight and Power/Volume Ratios[8a]**

Dimension	Symbol	Typical value, cm
Cell diameter	D	1.05
Length of electrode portion of cell	L	0.6
Length of seal (outside)	l	0.6
Length of seal (inside)	C	0.5
Electrolyte thickness in electroded portion of cell	δ_b	0.04
Electrolyte thickness in seal region	δ_s	0.10

sides.   The resistance of this cell is 0.4 ohm.   The operating temperature of the cell is 1010°C.   Such a cell is represented in Fig. 32.   The oxide ions formed at the cathode by the electroreduction of oxygen are transported through the electrolyte to the anode where it is oxidized.   The water formed at the anode is carried away from the exit in the anode gas chamber.

(*ii*)   *Reactions occurring at each electrode and the overall reaction*

According to Archer et al.[8] oxygen is reduced at the cathode according to the equation

$$O_2 + 4e_0^- \rightarrow 2O^{2-} \tag{2.9}$$

The oxide ions migrate through the electrolyte and reach the anode where they are reconverted to oxygen.   The oxygen then combines with the hydrogen, this

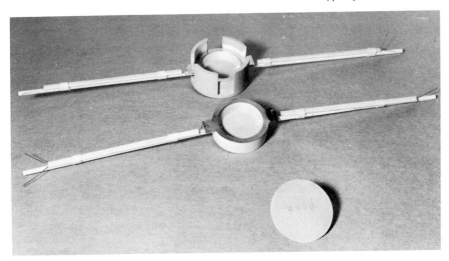

Figure 32 Cell design for experimental studies on Westinghouse solid electrolyte fuel cell.[8]

reaction being catalyzed by the platinum anode to form water:

$$2O_2^- \rightarrow O_2 + 4e_0^- \tag{2.10}$$

$$O_2 + 2H_2 \rightarrow 2H_2O \tag{2.3}$$

Although it has been suggested that oxygen evolution occurs first at the anode and is followed by an oxygen combination with H_2, it appears more likely that the anode reaction is the direct electrooxidation of H_2, according to

$$H_2 + 2M \rightarrow 2MH \tag{2.11}$$

$$2MH + O^{2-} \rightarrow 2M + H_2O + 2e_0^- \tag{2.12}$$

The hydrogen-dissolution reaction is quite fast on a Pt electrode at room temperature ($i_0 = 10^{-3}$ amp cm^{-2}) and one could expect it to be considerably faster (>1 amp cm^{-2}) at 1000°C. At this temperature, the oxygen electro-reduction of oxygen should also have a high exchange current density.

(iii) *Performance of the single cell*

Current-potential relations obtained for the single cell, with the disk-electrolyte arrangement, are shown in Fig. 33. The open-circuit voltage is 1.15 volts, which is within 15 percent of the thermodynamic reversible potential of the cell. The current-potential relation is practically linear over the measured range. The slope of this line (0.35 ohm) corresponds approximately to the resistance of the electrolyte layer (0.4 ohm), thus showing that polarization losses are essentially ohmic in character (Chap. 4, Sec. 3). This may be antici-pated at the very high operating temperatures, under which conditions acti-vation overpotential is reduced to zero. The same diagram also shows the efficiency of the cell as a function of the current drawn from the cell.

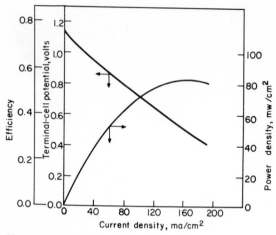

Figure 33 Terminal-cell potential (or efficiency) and power-density–current-density relations for a Westinghouse hydrogen-oxygen fuel cell using solid disk electrolyte.[8]

The power density is also shown as a function of current in Fig. 33. The maximum power density is 0.08 watt cm^{-2}, which occurs at a current density of 150 amp cm^{-2}.

The performances of the tubular cells are reported in the case of 3- or 20-cell batteries, which will be discussed in the next subsection.

(iv)   Multicell design and performance

Battery fabrication using the tubular cells is quite simple. It is similar to the connection of sewer pipes. Photographs of a 3- and 20-cell battery with the bell-and-spigot joints are shown in Fig. 34. The inner electrode of each segment is the anode, and the outer one is the cathode. The fuel gas flows throught the tube. It is necessary to have tight seals between cells to prevent the mixing of fuel and oxidant gases. Air or oxygen is used as the oxidant. The performance of a 3-cell battery using oxygen is shown in Fig. 35. The current-potential relations for a 20-cell battery for various flow rates of hydrogen are represented in Fig. 36. The physical characteristics of this battery are presented in Table 2 and the performance characteristics in Table 3. The latter table shows that the power/weight and power/volume ratios of this cell are about three times better than the corresponding figures for the best available low-temperature fuel cells.

(v)   Advantages and disadvantages of the system

The use of a solid electrolyte in this fuel cell permits very thin electrolyte layers (0.05 cm), which helps reduce the weight and volume of the cell. Further, in this physical state of the electrolyte, problems encountered normally with

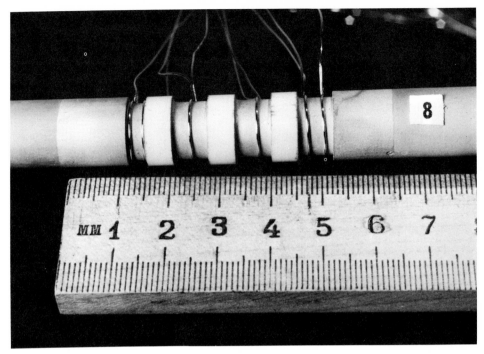

(a)

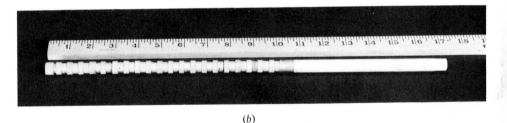

(b)

Figure 34 Westinghouse solid electrolyte fuel-cell batteries. (a) 3-cell battery[8]; (b) 20-cell battery.[8a]

aqueous electrolytes (such as leaks and loss of electrolyte by irreversible heating effects) are avoided. The electrocatalysts are easily coated in a porous state on both sides of the electrolyte. The performance figures on this cell at a fairly early state of development reflect the advantages of the use of the solid electrolyte.

One difficulty of the system is that it needs a very high operating temperature (1000°C) because at lower temperatures, the electrolyte conductivity decreases markedly. Even at 1000°C the specific resistivity of the electrolyte is

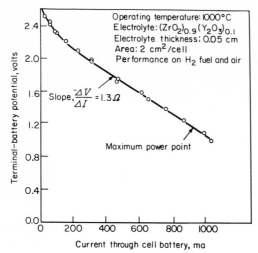

Figure 35 The performance of a Westinghouse 3-cell hydrogen-oxygen fuel-cell battery.[8]

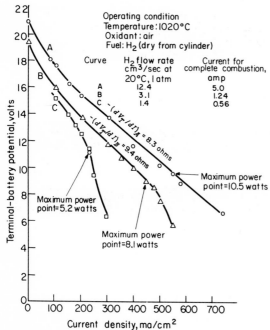

Figure 36 The terminal-battery potential–current-density plot for a Westinghouse 20-cell hydrogen-oxygen fuel-cell battery as a function of hydrogen-flow rate.[8a]

**TABLE 2   Physical Characteristics of Westinghouse[8a]
20-cell Hydrogen-oxygen Fuel Cell[8a]**

Characteristic	Symbol	Typical value
Electrolyte:		
$(ZrO_2)_{0.9}(Y_2O_3)_{0.1}$		
Resistivity	ρ_b	9.0 ohms cm^{-1}
		(at 1000°C)
Thickness	δ_b	0.04 cm
Electroded area	A_b	2.0 cm² per
		cell
Electrode:		
Porous platinum		
Resistivity	ρ_e	
	ρ_e/δ_e	0.4 ohm
Thickness	δ_e	
Battery:		
Cell weight (20 cells)		40 g
End tube and cap weight		70 g
Total weight		110 g
Cell volume		28 cm³
End tube and cap volume		28 cm³
Total volume		56 cm³

ten times that of aqueous electrolytes used in low-temperature fuel cells. This problem is somewhat overcome here by using thinner electrolyte layers. The cost of this electrolyte is also somewhat high (about a tenth of the cost of Pt required for the cell). Platinum is used as the catalyst. But the use of other metals in these cells is a probability. The presently estimated figure of the cost of the fuel cell is around $100 per kilowatt.

Although the temperature of operation is high, heat-transfer problems are eliminated. Product removal from the cell is also quite simple. The system is not affected by gravitational forces and is thus suited for space applications.

**TABLE 3   Performance Characteristics of Westinghouse
20-cell Hydrogen-oxygen Fuel Cell[8a]**

H_2 fuel-flow rate, cm³ sec^{-1} at 20°C, 1 atm	Maximum battery power, watts	Power/total battery weight, watts lb^{-1}	Power total battery volume, watts ft^{-3}	Fraction of fuel used at maximum power in a single pass
12.4	10.5	43.3	5,270	0.220
3.1	8.1	33.4	4,070	0.725
1.4	5.2	21.4	2,610	0.822

2.2 Organic Compounds–Oxygen (or Air) Fuel Cells

2.2.1 *Low-temperature Systems*

2.2.1.1 *The Esso Methanol Fuel Cell*[10]

(i) *Basic design of the single cell and its mode of operation*

Methanol is one of the most electroactive organic fuels at the present time in the low-temperature range—mainly because (1) it has a low carbon content; (2) it possesses a readily oxidizable group (hydroxyl); and (3) it has high solubility in aqueous electrolytes. Only formaldehyde is more active. However, because of its lower energy content, it has not been extensively investigated. Single methanol cells 0.6 cm thick have been designed.[10] Such a cell is schematically represented in Fig. 37. The electrolyte in the central

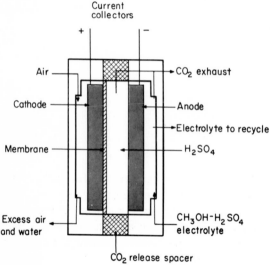

Figure 37 Representation of a single cell in the Esso methanol fuel cell.[10a]

compartment (H_2SO_4) is stationary. The electrolyte in the anode chamber on the right contains methanol and is circulated. A membrane is inserted adjacent to the cathode on the electrolyte side to minimize diffusion of methanol to the cathode. A photograph showing the process of assembly of a single cell is shown in Fig. 38. The electrodes shown here are American Cyanamid Company porous platinum electrodes.[11] Several other types of electrodes are being investigated.

The cathode functions as in hydrogen-oxygen cells. Since a liquid fuel soluble in the electrolyte is used, it is already dissolved in the electrolyte and thus concentration-polarization phenomena are greatly reduced. It is necessary to circulate the electrolyte containing the fuel through the anode chamber. The electrolyte concentration is 3.7 M and the cell operates at 60°C. One of

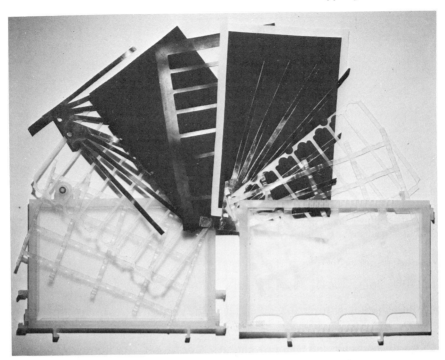

Figure 38 The process of assembly of a single Esso methanol fuel cell.[8a]

the problems in this cell is the diffusion of the dissolved methanol through the electrolyte in the central compartment to the cathode, at which point a direct chemical oxidation of the methanol occurs. In addition, cathodic polarization is increased by the presence of methanol near the electrode. The membrane adjacent to the cathode on the electrolyte side helps reduce the rate of this diffusion process. The diffusion rate is highest under open-circuit conditions. It varies directly with methanol concentration in the fuel chamber. In Fig. 39 the current equivalent for chemical oxidation of the methanol at the cathode is plotted as a function of methanol concentration in the fuel chamber both under open-circuit and load conditions. For methanol concentrations below 0.2 M, there is hardly any diffusion of methanol to the cathode. Pure oxygen, as well as air, has been used as the oxidant.

(ii)   Reactions occurring at each electrode and the overall reaction

The methanol reaches the anode by mass transfer through the electrolyte and is oxidized according to the equation

$$CH_3OH + H_2O \rightarrow CO_2 + 6H^+ + 6e_0^- \tag{2.13}$$

At the cathode, oxygen is reduced, as represented by Eq. (2.2). Thus, the

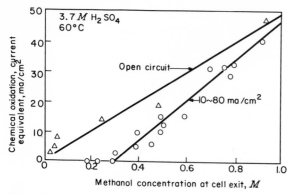

Figure 39 Current equivalent for chemical oxidation of methanol at cathode under open-circuit and load conditions in the Esso methanol-oxygen fuel cell.[10]

overall reaction occurring in the cell is

$$CH_3OH + \tfrac{3}{2}O_2 \rightarrow CO_2 + 2H_2O \tag{2.14}$$

The thermodynamic reversible potential of the cell at 25°C is 1.20 volts.

(iii) Performance of the single cell

An open-circuit voltage of around 0.9 volt is observed.   Most of the loss is associated with irreversible anodic reactions.   A contributing factor is the characteristic inefficiency of the oxygen electrode reaction.   Transport of methanol to the cathode under open-circuit conditions reduces the cathode performance.   If the reaction under consideration has an exchange current density not very different from that of the alternate reaction at an electrode, such departures from reversible potentials are observed (Chap. 2, Sec. 10).

The terminal-cell potential is plotted in Fig. 40 as a function of current density for methanol-oxygen and methanol-air fuel cells.   The performance with air is somewhat less satisfactory than that with oxygen.   The efficiency scale is also shown.   There is a fairly sharp decrease in cell potential with current density up to a current density of 40 ma cm^{-2}.   Thereafter, the E-i relation is practically linear with a small slope, indicating a low internal resistance of the cell.   The power-density–current-density relation is also shown in Fig. 40. The maximum in the P-i relation is not yet reached at 100 ma cm^{-2}.   The power density at 100 ma cm^{-2} is around 40 mw cm^{-2}.   This figure is about five to ten times lower than the maximum power outputs of hydrogen-oxygen fuel cells, but the investigation of the engineering aspects of the system is in a comparatively early stage.   Fuel costs per kilowatthour with methanol are of the same order as with hydrogen.   The temperature of the cell can be maintained without auxiliary heating.

(iv) Multicell design and performance

The multicell design of this fuel cell is at an experimental stage.   Single cells, containing electrodes of area 10×10 cm^2 and also 23×15 cm^2, have

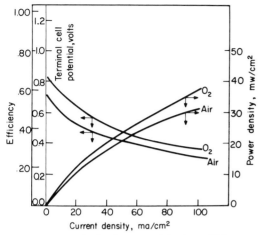

Figure 40 Terminal-cell potential (or efficiency) and power-density–current-density relations for the Esso methanol-oxygen fuel cell.[10]

been assembled into batteries, each containing 16 cells (larger units have also been built). The auxiliaries necessary for its operation are electrical monitoring and control equipment, an air blower, an electrolyte pump, a fuel pump, and heat-and-water-balance equipment.

The performances of these cells have not shown any significant change in a 3-month life test. The cell stack weighs 20 lb and is capable of generating 120 watts of useful power. Complete systems have been designed which weigh 24.5 lb including a 12-hr fuel supply.

(*v*)   *Advantages and disadvantages*

The use of methanol has several advantages. It is a liquid, quite soluble in the electrolyte, which thus reduces concentration polarization problems encountered with gaseous fuels. It is cheap and easy to handle and store. It is a very electroactive organic fuel.

An important main problem with the methanol fuel cell is the migration of the fuel to the cathode. The chemical oxidation of methanol at the cathode reduces the efficiency of methanol utilization in the cell. The presence of methanol near the cathode also affects its performance. The use of a membrane between anode and cathode reduces this diffusion process but increases the ohmic drop in the cell. Trade-offs of ohmic losses with electrode losses have yielded 0.2 volt improvement in cell performance. However, existing membranes degrade slowly, and the life of these systems suffers. Though methanol is the most electroactive organic fuel, its performance is still considerably less than that of hydrogen. For example, the open-circuit potential is only about 65 percent of the thermodynamic reversible cell potential. At a current density of 100 ma cm^{-2}, the voltage efficiency is about 35 percent. Platinum alloys are still the best catalyst. For example, Pt-Ru-Re alloy is 0.3 volt better than Pt alone at open circuit. Redox couples have also been examined (cf. next subsection). It is necessary to find cheaper catalysts for the methanol fuel cell if it is to be a large-scale power producer. The power/weight and power/volume ratios of the present-day methanol fuel cell are far too low to be considered for space applications (Chap. 7, Sec. 3).

An advantage of the use of an acid electrolyte is that removal of CO_2, a product of the reaction, is greatly simplified.

(vi) The use of redox couples in the methanol-oxygen fuel cell

One of the main problems with most fuel cells is the reduction of activation polarization at one or both of the electrodes. For example, in hydrogen-oxygen fuel cells, the activation polarization losses are mainly at the oxygen electrode; in organic compounds–oxygen fuel cells, considerable activation polarization exists at both electrodes. One way of using fuels and oxidants more efficiently would be as chemical agents for regeneration of reactants from products formed at the anode and cathode in a redox fuel cell.[12] The principles of a redox fuel cell have been outlined in Chap. 4. The advantage of using some redox systems is that their electrode reactions are relatively fast. Furthermore, the chemical regeneration steps are also sufficiently rapid. This indirect method should thus help increase the efficiency of utilization of the organic fuel and oxygen markedly.

The Mo^{5+}/Mo^{6+} and the HNO_3/NO couples have been examined by the Esso Research & Engineering Co.[10] The electrode reactions are

$$Mo^{5+} \rightarrow Mo^{6+} + e_0^- \tag{2.15}$$

and

$$4H^+ + NO_3^- + 3e_0^- \rightarrow 2H_2O + NO \tag{2.16}$$

The regeneration reactions are

$$CH_3OH + 6Mo^{6+} + H_2O \rightarrow CO_2 + 6H^+ + 6Mo^{5+} \tag{2.17}$$

and

$$4NO + 3O_2 + 2H_2O \rightarrow 4HNO_3 \tag{2.18}$$

The latter reaction has been studied well in the chemical synthesis of nitric acid.

There are no results available for a cell in which both redox couples have been used. Half-cell studies have, however, been made. The molybdenum redox couple has been examined by introduction of molybdates into solution. There is an improvement in performance with the redox couple at low current densities as compared with the direct oxidation of methanol. However, at higher polarizations, there is hardly any difference in performance for the oxidation of methanol in the absence and in the presence of the molybdate. It is necessary for the molybdate species to remain adsorbed for it to function effectively. At higher polarizations, the molybdate is irreversibly desorbed from the surface whereafter the direct electrooxidation of methanol occurs.

Studies on the HNO_3/NO couple showed that there is an improved performance over the direct electroreduction of oxygen. Noble metal catalysts were used. It was found that there is a small net loss in nitric acid. The loss is decreased when oxygen instead of air is used for its regeneration. A disadvantage of the system is that there is some migration of nitric acid to the anode chamber, where it chemically oxidizes the methanol. Migration of methanol from the anode to the cathode chamber may also occur. Possible remedies are to use some kind of membrane that is impermeable to either the methanol or nitric acid or to insert a scavenger electrode between the anode and the cathode. The kinetics of the latter process is treated in Chap. 4, Sec. 8.

This system serves as an example of a redox fuel cell. Such systems seem to merit much greater research effort than they have received.

2.2.1.2 The Allis-Chalmers Methanol Fuel Cell[13]

(i) Basic design of the single cell and its mode of operation

In the original cells, designed for methanol as a fuel, the oxidant was hydrogen peroxide. The present fuel cells work on air as the oxidant. Bipolar electrodes, with the solid anode and porous cathode attached to a sheet of nickel (Fig. 41), are used to facilitate series connections of the single cells. Air

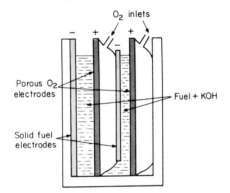

Figure 41 The Allis-Chalmers methanol-oxygen fuel cell (single cell).[13]

or oxygen enters into a thin pocket between the nickel sheet and the cathode. The electrolyte is a thin layer of 6 M KOH containing 6 M methanol. Because of carbonate formation in the electrolyte, it is circulated through the cell. It was found that methanol is only partly oxidized using Pt as a catalyst, and although oxidation is complete with Pd, the latter metal is a poor catalyst. However, with a Pt-Pd alloy complete oxidation to carbon dioxide occurs and its performance is also good.

Cobalt oxide (Co_3O_4) spinel (i.e., heavy-metal oxide) catalysts have been examined for the electroreduction of oxygen. Though the performance of this catalyst was found to be satisfactory, there was a tendency for these electrodes to flood and thereby reduce their efficiency of operation. At the present time, silver is being used as the cathode catalyst. The silver electrode is prepared by impregnating a porous nickel plaque with silver nitrate and heating it over a

Meeker burner flame.   The electrode is then waterproofed with Teflon.   This electrode does not corrode in alkaline media.

A single unit, which is a dual cell, is represented in Fig. 41.

(ii)   Performance of the single cell

The terminal-cell potential (IR free)–current-density relation is shown in Fig. 42 as a function of operating temperature.   The efficiency of the cell is

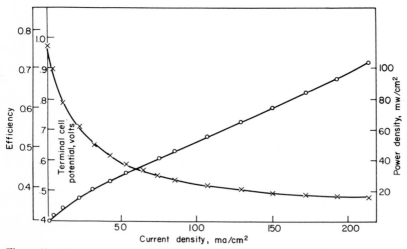

Figure 42   The terminal-cell potential (or efficiency) and power-density–current-density relations for the Allis-Chalmers methanol-oxygen fuel cell.[13]

also shown on the ordinate axis.   There is a marked decrease in the terminal-cell potential (or efficiency) at low current densities.   This is as expected, because both electrode reactions are somewhat irreversible (Chap. 4, Sec. 3).   Above 60 ma cm^{-2}, the change in cell potential with current density is considerably slower.   With an electrolyte layer of thickness 1 to 2 mm, the ohmic drop in the cell is about 30 to 50 mv at a current density of 30 ma cm^{-2}.

The power-density–current-density relation for the cell (IR free) is also shown in Fig. 42 for the cell at 60°C.   The maximum power density is not reached even at 200 ma cm^{-2}.   Inclusion of the IR drop in the cell makes the maximum in this curve appear at a current density of about 165 ma cm^{-2} as seen from the power–current-density relation for the battery (see next section).

(iii)   Multicell design and performance

Multicells using bipolar electrodes have been constructed.   Each unit consists of 40 cells.   The multicell is designed for proper electrolyte flow through the cells.   A photograph of a multicell is reproduced in Fig. 43.   The cell and auxiliaries necessary for operation of the multicell are schematically represented in Fig. 44.

The operating characteristics of a multicell are tabulated in Table 4.   The operating voltage and power output of the cell are plotted as a function of the

Figure 43   Allis-Chalmers methanol-oxygen fuel-cell battery.[13a]

current (or current density) in Fig. 45.   The cell is designed for operation at 0.375 volt per cell generating a power of 500 watts.   At this power level, the voltage efficiency of each cell is 0.31.

(*iv*)   *Advantages and disadvantages of the system*

The advantages of using methanol as a fuel have been outlined in the previous section.   The improved performance of this system over the one described in the last section may be associated with the greater degree of

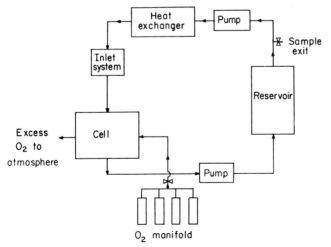

Figure 44   The cell and auxiliaries of Allis-Chalmers methanol-oxygen fuel cell.[13a]

TABLE 4 Operating Characteristics of Allis-Chalmers Methanol-Oxygen Fuel-cell Battery[13]

	Operating	*Range*	*Overload output*
Power output, watts	440	570	750
Total operating voltage, volts	16	14	10
Total operating current, amp	27.5	41	73
Operating voltage/cell, volts	0.4	0.35	0.25
Current density, ma cm^{-2}	57	85	151
Power volume ratio, kw ft^{-3}	0.365	0.46	0.605
Power weight ratio, watts lb^{-1}	2.94	3.80	5.00
Pressure, PSIG	0–5	0–5	0–5
Temperature, °C	50	50	50

reversibility of the oxygen electrode in alkaline medium.   The use of a flowing electrolyte system aids the diffusion process of the methanol to the electrode. It also serves the purpose of a coolant.   The idea of adding the fuel external to the cell is helpful.

One of the disadvantages of the cell is the formation of potassium carbonate.   If it were not for circulation of the electrolyte, large amounts of carbonate in the electrolyte could affect performance of the cell.   Because of carbonate formation, there is a loss of electrolyte which increases the cost of operation. Regeneration of the electrolyte by the action of lime on potassium carbonate has

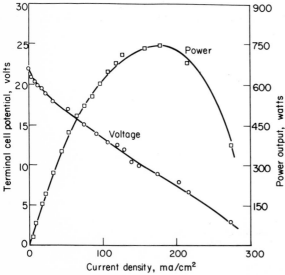

Figure 45 The terminal battery potential and power–current-density (or current) relations for Allis-Chalmers methanol-oxygen fuel-cell battery.[13]

been suggested. It would then be necessary to install lime kilns to convert the calcium carbonate to lime.

2.2.1.3 Hydrocarbon-Air Fuel Cells. The most desired fuel-cell system is one operating on hydrocarbons directly at temperatures below 100°C. The development of such systems has met with little success so far.

The best performances to date in hydrocarbon (saturated paraffinic)-air (or oxygen) fuel cells have been those by the Battelle Institute in Germany.[14] Using Raney platinum as the catalyst, current densities of the order of 100 ma cm^{-2} have been obtained at cell voltages of about 0.5 volt in propane-air fuel cells. Sulfuric acid (5 N) was used as the electrolyte and cell temperatures were varied from 25 to 80°C.

Hydrocarbon-air cells operating at 89°C using propane, cyclopropane, and propylene in 3 M H_2SO_4 have been examined.[15] Platinized-platinum electrodes with the Niedrach-Alford structure[16] were used. The current-potential relations observed in these cells are shown in Fig. 46. Cyclopropane

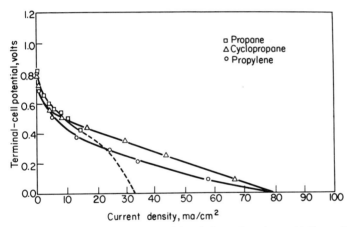

Figure 46 Current-density–potential relations for the oxidation of propane, cyclopropane, and propylene in 3 M H_2SO_4 at 81°C.[15]

was found to be the best. Oxidation to CO_2 was found to be nearly complete (over 90 percent) over the entire range except with propylene, where it is around 80 percent.

2.2.2 Intermediate-temperature Systems

2.2.2.1 Direct Hydrocarbon-Oxygen (or Air) Fuel Cells Using Phosphoric Acid Electrolyte

(i) Basic design of the cell and its operating conditions

Due to the necessity of increasing the reactivity of hydrocarbons, a number of investigations are in progress at temperatures in the range 100 to 200°C.[17]

The advantage of working in an acid electrolyte medium has been pointed out earlier. To work in this temperature range and at atmospheric pressure, higher concentrations of acid must be used. Concentrated sulfuric acid is a strong oxidizing agent under these conditions. For example, it chemically oxidizes propane to give CO_2, SO_2, and H_2S as products. The last two products can poison the anode. Because of this chemical reaction, this acid cannot be used much above 120°C.

A most important property required of an electrolyte is that it must be able to withstand temperatures above 100°C. Further, it must also possess good electrical conductivity. It must also support complete electrochemical oxidation of carbon-containing fuels. Another requirement is that it must not contain anions which adsorb strongly on the electrode and block reaction sites.

One of the electrolytes which seems to satisfy several of these criteria and in particular allows the system to work at moderate temperatures is concentrated phosphoric acid. The cross section of a single cell, used at the General Electric research laboratory[18] with concentrated phosphoric acid as the electrolyte and a gaseous hydrocarbon as the fuel, is shown in Fig. 47. The thickness of the electrolyte layer is 0.3 cm, and the electrodes are circular with an active area of 11.4 cm². Platinum-deposited electrodes of the Niedrach-Alford structure[16] are used. The concentration of phosphoric acid has been varied from 70 to about

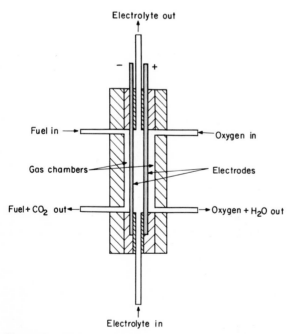

Figure 47   Cross section of a single cell in the General Electric gaseous hydrocarbon-oxygen fuel cell with phosphoric acid as electrolyte.[18]

110 percent (i.e., electrolyte contains anhydrous phosphorous pentoxide). Cell operating temperatures from 120 to 200°C have been used. In most work, 14.6 M H$_3$PO$_4$ (85 percent) has been used as the electrolyte at an operating temperature of 150°C.

A fuel cell using liquid hydrocarbons (e.g., decane) as the fuel and phosphoric acid as the electrolyte is being investigated by the Esso Research & Engineering Company.[19] An advantage of using a liquid hydrocarbon as the fuel is that it facilitates removal of gaseous products such as CO$_2$. Further, liquid hydrocarbons are available in large quantities and are easily transported. The cell design is shown in Fig. 48. A main feature of the cell is the inclusion of

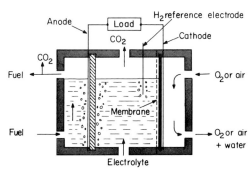

Figure 48 The Esso liquid hydrocarbon-air fuel cell.[19]

a porous Teflon barrier on the fuel side of the electrode. This barrier probably controls the rate of flow of the fuel to the electroactive sites. The Teflon dispersion in the electrodes is obtained by mixing the platinum catalyst with a Teflon emulsion (particle size 0.1 μ), controlling the rate of the Pt-Teflon gelation, and sintering the electrode at the optimum temperature.

(ii) Performance of a single cell

It is interesting to compare the performances of hydrogen-oxygen and hydrocarbon-oxygen fuel cells. In Fig. 49, terminal-cell potential–current-density relations for fuel cells using the straight-chain paraffinic hydrocarbons from propane to octane are represented by the lower band.[18] The performance decreases with increase in number of carbon atoms in the fuel. These data were obtained in cells using 95 percent phosphoric acid electrolyte at 150°C. The performances of H$_2$-O$_2$ fuel cells are independent of the acid concentration. This is not the case with propane-oxygen fuel cells[18] (Fig. 50).

In order that the performances of straight-chain saturated hydrocarbons may be compared, a plot is made of the current density at a terminal-cell potential of 0.3 volt versus the number of carbon atoms in the hydrocarbon for cells using phosphoric acid (85 percent) as the electrolyte at 150°C.[18] Hydrocarbons ranging from methane to octane were studied. Their comparative

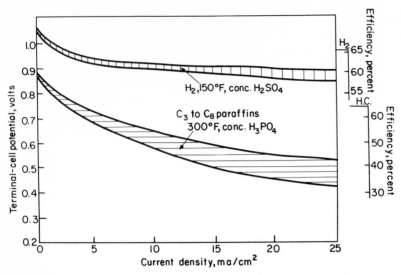

Figure 49 Terminal-cell potential–current-density relations for hydrocarbon-oxygen and hydrogen-oxygen fuel cells.[18]

performances in fuel cells are shown in Fig. 51, which indicates that the current density at a terminal-cell potential of 0.3 volt starts to increase at first, is a maximum at propane or butane, and then starts to decrease again. At the present time, it is difficult to explain this behavior. Methane is considered by organic chemists to be highly inert. It is probable that the decrease in reactivity beyond butane is associated with the decrease in solubility and also with the diffusion coefficient of the organic compound in the electrolyte. A study was

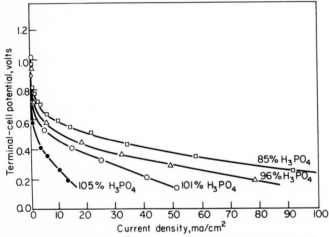

Figure 50 Terminal-cell potential–current-density relations[18] for propane-oxygen fuel cells in phosphoric acid as a function of its concentration at 150°C.

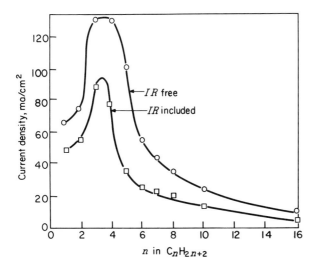

Figure 51 A comparison of the performances of straight-chain and cyclic hydrocarbons in hydrocarbon-air fuel cells in H_3PO_4 at a temperature of 150°C and a terminal-cell potential of 0.3 volt.[18]

also made to examine the effect of branching, the introduction of double bonds, and also aromaticity. The current densities at a terminal-cell potential of 0.3 volt for fuel cells using organic compounds, representative of these structures, are indicated by points on the same figure. It appears that the linear-saturated isomer of the hydrocarbon shows the best performance for fuel cells using H_3PO_4 as the electrolyte at 150°C (cf. at lower temperatures in sulfuric acid electrolyte, when ethylene has the best performance). Cyclic molecules are less reactive than branched compounds.

One fact must, however, be noted. The conversion to carbon dioxide is nearly 100 percent in the case of the straight-chain saturated hydrocarbons and at least over 80 percent (in several cases over 95 percent) for the other hydrocarbons.

Because of the high reactivity of propane (butane is nearly as good), this compound is being used in most work on hydrocarbon-air fuel cells. Of the liquid hydrocarbons, an effort has been made to develop the decane-air fuel cell.[19] (Decane is one of the main constituents of diesel oil.) The results with these systems will be examined further in this section.

The terminal-cell potential–current-density relations for propane-oxygen fuel cells in varying concentrations of phosphoric acid and temperatures are shown in Fig. 52.

A comparison of the rates of electrooxidation of propane on the noble metals shows that platinum is superior to the others by at least two orders of magnitude, even though the surface area per gram of catalyst is by no means as high as with some other noble metals (Table 5).[18]

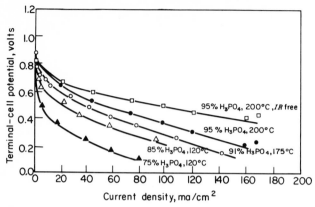

Figure 52 Terminal-cell potential–current-density relation for propane-oxygen fuel cells as a function of H_3PO_4 concentration and temperature when the vapor pressure of solution is 600 mm Hg.[18a]

The cell potential and power density for the propane oxygen fuel cell using 85 percent H_3PO_4 at 150°C are shown as a function of current density in Fig. 53.

A problem encountered with propane-oxygen fuel cells under open-circuit conditions is the formation of methane. Methane is formed by the cracking of the propane on the electrocatalyst (cf. the behavior of propane in gas-phase catalysis). Methane is less electroreactive than propane at temperatures of

TABLE 5   Current Density for Propane Oxidation at 0.5 Volt (RHE) for Some Noble Metal Catalysts along with Their Surface Areas[18]

Electrocatalyst	Surface area m^2 per gram of catalyst	Current density at anode potential of 0.5 volt (RHE)
Pt	20	125
Pd	28	0.7
Rh	0.6	0.05 ± 0.05
Ir	82	0.05 ± 0.05

100°C or less. Methane-oxygen fuel cells were recently shown to have a performance comparable with that of a propane-oxygen fuel cell at low current densities using 85 percent H_3PO_4 as the electrolyte at 150°C.[18] The formation of methane is suppressed under load, which is desired from the point of view of attaining a high performance. Under load, the adsorbed hydrogen atoms formed by the cracking reaction are removed by ionization quite easily and this process thus prevents methane formation.

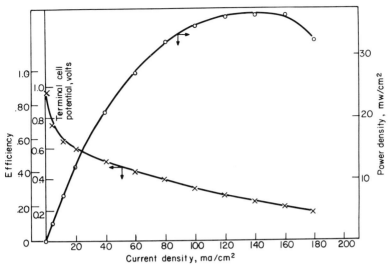

Figure 53 The terminal-cell potential (or efficiency) and power-density–current-density relations for a propane-oxygen fuel cell in 95 % H_3PO_4 at 200°C.[18a]

The performance of a decane-oxygen fuel cell[19] in 14.7 M H_3PO_4 at 150°C is shown in Fig. 54.[16] With the necessary steps taken to prepare Pt-Teflon electrodes in a state of high dispersion, the performance with liquid decane is

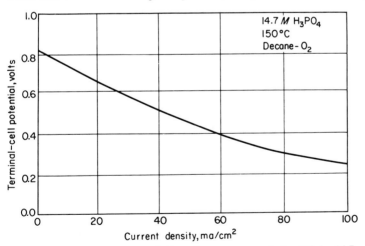

Figure 54 The performance of Esso decane-oxygen fuel cell[19] in 14.7 M H_3PO_4 at 150°C.

nearly as good as with vaporized decane. However, the performance with decane is inferior to that of a butane-oxygen fuel cell. (Figure 55 shows anode polarization versus current density for the two cases.)

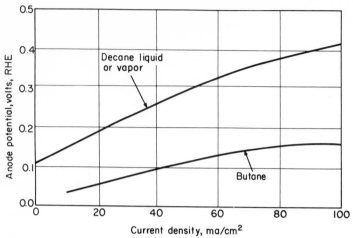

Figure 55 Anode-polarization–current-density relations for butane and decane oxidation.[19]

(*iii*) *Multicell design and performance*

The hydrocarbon-air fuel cells using phosphoric acid electrolytes may be developed into a fuel-cell battery.

A 5-cell decane-air fuel cell[19] is shown in Fig. 56.

(*iv*) *Advantages and disadvantages of the system*

The performances obtained with the saturated hydrocarbons in fuel cells using phosphoric acid as the electrolyte are quite encouraging, since these fuels were thought a few years ago to be electrochemically inert. The maximum attainable power level is less by only a factor of about 10 than that of the best available hydrogen-oxygen fuel cells. Considering the fact that the hydrocarbon fuel-cell research is only about 5 years old, one can be optimistic about the development of these systems.

Phosphoric acid is quite corrosive and materials problems are encountered in these systems. The only satisfactory catalyst is Pt, and it is necessary at the present time to use about 10–50 mg of Pt cm^{-2} of the electrode, which makes the system uneconomical. It seems likely that such situations can be improved on the basis of theoretical work which suggests that the current is generated in an extremely small part of the pore (Chap. 5, Secs. 5 to 8). An initial experimental attempt resulted in a reduction in the weight of catalyst by about 100 times for the electrooxidation of hydrogen or the electroreduction of oxygen.[20]

Future research in this area of fuel cells should concentrate on studies of the mechanism of hydrocarbon oxidation, i.e., gaining a knowledge of the various possible rate-determining steps in order to introduce increased reasoning into the search for improved and cheaper catalysts. Only a small range of electrocatalysts have been investigated. Researchers heretofore have depended on metals, and in the potential region of oxidation of hydrocarbons, most

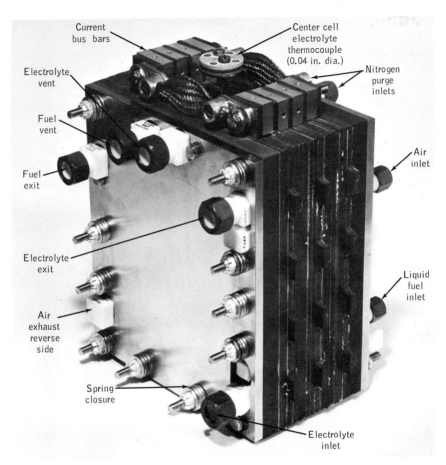

Current
bus bars

Center cell
electrolyte
thermocouple
(0.04 in. dia.)

Electrolyte
vent

Nitrogen
purge
inlets

Fuel
vent

Fuel
exit

Air
inlet

Electrolyte
exit

Liquid
fuel
inlet

Air
exhaust
reverse
side

Spring
closure

Electrolyte
inlet

Figure 56   The Esso decane-oxygen fuel-cell battery.[19]

metals, except the noble ones, dissolve. Nonmetallic oxides[21] and organic semiconductors represent important areas of investigation, but the most important lack is still the small knowledge of the rate-determining step in oxidation, and the lack, through absence of work, of basic knowledge of electrocatalysis.

2.2.2.2   Direct Hydrocarbon-Oxygen (or Air) Fuels Cells Using Fluoride Electrolytes

(i)   Basic design of a single cell and its operating conditions

It has been found that an aqueous solution of a mixture of the carbonate and bicarbonate of cesium is a suitable electrolyte for the oxidation of methanol and of ethylene.[22] The performance of this electrolyte with saturated hydrocarbons was not satisfactory. However, with the addition of HF to a fuel cell containing cesium carbonate as the electrolyte there was a marked increase in the rate of propane oxidation (potential 0.5 volt versus RHE) at the neutralization point[23] (pH = 7). The optimum water content for a CsF-HF electrolyte is about 12 to 15 mole % in the temperature range 90 to 150°C.[23a] RbF may be used instead of CsF, but the latter is more economical. The other alkali fluorides are not sufficiently soluble nor do they reduce the vapor pressure of HF markedly. Aqueous solutions of HF have also been used as electrolytes at lower temperatures.

Because of the corrosive nature of the fluoride electrolytes, the General Electric cell was made of Teflon. The monel and plates do not come in contact with the electrolyte. Circular electrodes (area 11 cm²) with the Niedrach-Alford structure[16] are used. The electrocatalyst is platinum or platinum on carbon[23b–d]. The electrolyte layer is 3 mm thick.

(ii)   Performance of a single cell

Using an electrolyte, CsF·HF·H₂O, with composition close to that of the optimum value, the terminal-cell-potential efficiency and power density are plotted as a function of current density in Fig. 57. The operating temperature

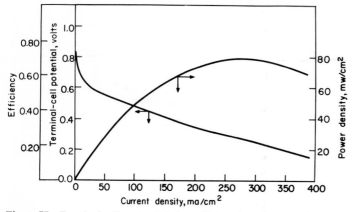

Figure 57 Terminal-cell potential (or efficiency) and power-density–current-density relations for a propane-oxygen fuel cell[22] in CsF·HF·H₂O at 150°C.

was 150°C. The electrode contained 50 mg Pt cm⁻². The maximum current density attainable is 400 ma cm⁻² at a terminal cell potential (IR free) of 0.2 volt. The propane anode shows a Tafel behavior between 40 and 250 ma cm⁻² with a transfer coefficient of one-half. Above 250 ma cm⁻², the anode performance could be improved by using a higher flow rate of the fuel, indicating a gas-phase mass-transport limitation. The performance in this electrolyte compares favorably with that in phosphoric acid at 150°C. Similar performances with propane were obtained using the HF-H₂O azeotrope at lower temperatures in the range 100 to 110°C and high-activity platinum on carbon electrocatalysts (near 10 mg Pt/cm^2) and platinum obtained from Adam's catalyst.[23b]

(*iii*) *Advantages and disadvantages of the system*

The work on this system was started only within the past few years, and the performances are as good or even better than the best available hydrocarbon-air fuel cells which operate at intermediate or low temperatures. Like H_3PO_4, HF is also corrosive, which causes a severe materials problem. The platinum content of the electrodes is now near 10 mg cm^{-2} and is somewhat high at the present time to allow a commercially economical cell. If, however, the attitude is taken that 90 percent of the platinum is recoverable, this fuel cell also shows some promise from the economic standpoint.

2.2.2.3 *Methanol-Oxygen Fuel Cells Using Carbonate Electrolyte*

(*i*) *Basic design of a single cell and its operating conditions*

Because of the problem of carbonate formation in alkaline electrolytes (which are preferable because of better performance of the oxygen electrode and also because they have less corrosive action than acids such as phosphoric or hydrofluoric), the use of aqueous carbonates themselves as electrolytes was envisaged. Molten carbonates are used at high temperatures. The carbonates and bicarbonates of lithium, sodium, and potassium are only sparingly or moderately soluble. The carbonates of rubidium and cesium are quite soluble; and with highly concentrated aqueous solutions of these carbonates as electrolytes, operating temperatures as high as 200°C may be used. The instability of the bicarbonate ion above 100°C minimizes the problem of CO_2 rejection. Cesium carbonate is being tested as an electrolyte at the General Electric Company.[22]

The cell, made for experimental studies, is made of Teflon. Electrodes are of the Niedrach-Alford structure.[16] The electrolyte (cesium carbonate) is recirculated. The fuel is injected into the anode gas chamber, and since operating temperatures of over 100°C are used, the methanol vaporizes immediately in this chamber. A schematic representation of the cell and auxiliary equipment used for this system is shown in Fig. 58.

(*ii*) *Performance of a single cell*

The terminal-cell-potential–current-density relations (IR free) for the cell at three different temperatures are shown in Fig. 59. These plots are obtained with methanol in the vapor form as fuel. Complete oxidation to carbon dioxide was observed. The power-density–current-density relations are also represented in Fig. 59. The anode potential, under open-circuit conditions, was within 80 mv of the reversible potential for the oxidation of methanol to carbon dioxide. (Thermodynamic reversible potential at 127°C is -0.03 volt.) The anodic and cathodic potentials, with respect to a reference electrode potential, when plotted as a function of current density, followed Tafel behavior except

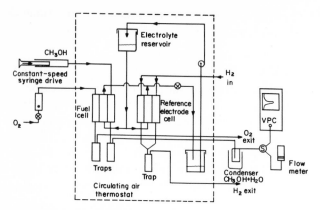

Figure 58 Cell and auxiliary equipment for methanol-oxygen fuel cell in cesium carbonate electrolyte.[22]

at high current densities where mass-transfer effects are introduced. No migration of methanol to the cathode was observed.

The limiting current density was shown to depend on the partial pressure of methanol. Below the limiting current density, the performance of the cell is practically independent of the partial pressure of methanol.

The cell has been tested for over 560 hr at a current density of 20 ma cm^{-2}. The trend was a slight improvement in performance with time. Other fuels, such as hydrocarbons and carbon monoxide, have been used. Only carbon monoxide gave a performance comparable with that of methanol.

(iii) *Advantages and disadvantages of the system*

The maximum power density attained is over 40 mw cm^{-2} at 126°C. This figure compares quite favorably with the power densities obtained for the hydrocarbon-air fuel cell in this temperature range. The performance of this

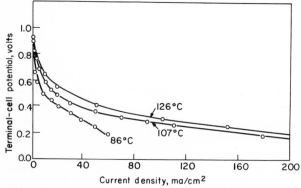

Figure 59 Terminal-cell potential and power-density–current-density relations at three different temperatures for a methanol-air fuel cell[22] in Cs_2CO_3 electrolyte.

fuel cell is about the same as that of low-temperature methanol-air fuel cells. It is encouraging to note that CO fares nearly as well as methanol.

2.2.2.4   Internal Reforming Organic Compounds–Air Fuel Cells

(i)   Basic design of a single cell and its mode of operation

The steam-reforming of organic fuels to produce hydrogen at appreciable rates requires temperatures of the order of 800°C over some mixed oxide catalysts. An internal-reformer fuel in which this reforming takes place at much lower temperatures (about 200°C) was recently devised by Leesona Moos Corporation[24] and by Pratt and Whitney Aircraft Division.[25] The basic design of the cell is shown in Fig. 60. The organic fuel vapor and steam, in stoichiometric proportions, are passed into the reformer-anode chamber, which contains the catalyst for the reforming reaction and the electrode, which serves

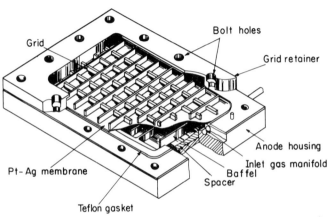

Figure 60   Basic cell design for internal reforming organic compound-air fuel cell.[25]

both as a separator of the hydrogen from the other products or unconverted reactants and as the anode for the hydrogen-dissolution reaction. The anode is a thin foil of Ag-Pd alloy (75 percent Pd). The electrolyte is 85 percent KOH, and a Bacon lithiated nickel oxide cathode is used for the air electrode. The important feature of this fuel cell is that even though the equilibrium concentration of hydrogen produced by the stream-reforming reaction at 200°C is low, the constant removal of hydrogen when the fuel cell is under load forces the reaction to take place. It is possible to obtain 100 percent conversion at 200°C. The main problem is whether the hydrogen production rate and its diffusion rate through the Ag-Pd foil are fast enough to sustain the required current densities from the cell. The fuels that have been used so far in this cell are methanol, methane, *n*-octane, and a commercial kerosene fuel—JP150.

(ii)   *Reactions occurring in the cell*

When methanol is used as the fuel, the reactions occurring in the cell are as follows:

Chemical:

$$CH_3OH \rightarrow CO + 2H_2 \tag{2.19}$$

$$CO + H_2O \rightarrow CO_2 + H_2 \tag{2.20}$$

Electrochemical:

$$H_2 + 2OH^- \rightarrow 2H_2O + 2e_0^- \tag{2.4}$$

$$O_2 + 2H_2O + 4e_0^- \rightarrow 4OH^- \tag{2.5}$$

An undesirable chemical reaction which occurs is the methanation of the carbon monoxide formed in reaction (2.19):

$$CO + 3H_2 \rightarrow CH_4 + H_2O \tag{2.21}$$

Fortunately, however, this reaction is inhibited by the fuel-cell reaction due to the removal of hydrogen. Reaction (2.21) is catalyzed by the same catalysts used for the steam-reforming reaction. Methanol performs better in the steam-reforming reaction than do hydrocarbons, particularly if it is used in a very pure condition. Further, the complete miscibility of methanol and water simplifies the design of the system.

With hydrocarbons, too, the steam-reforming reaction first produces carbon monoxide as, for example,

$$C_8H_{18} + 8H_2O \rightarrow 8CO + 17H_2 \tag{2.22}$$

which is followed by the oxidation of CO with steam to produce further quantities of hydrogen and then the fuel-cell reaction. Here, too, the methanation of CO may take place. The extent to which it occurs decreases with increasing current drain from the fuel cell.

Since the overall reaction is the oxidation of the organic compound, the thermodynamic reversible potential is the one corresponding to its operating temperature—around 1.1 volts for most fuels in the vicinity of 200°C.

(iii)   *Performance of a single cell*

Of all the fuels used, the performance with methanol was the best.[24] Terminal-cell potential and power-density-versus-current-density relations for this cell at 200°C are shown in Fig. 61. However, there is a marked decrease in the fuel-cell performance for a lowering of cell temperature by 10°C. This behavior is due to a considerable reduction in hydrogen production below 200°C and hence a lowering of its partial pressure in the anode chamber.

At a power density of 150 mw cm^{-2}, the overall efficiency of this cell is 64 percent. The current-density–voltage relation with methanol is considerably

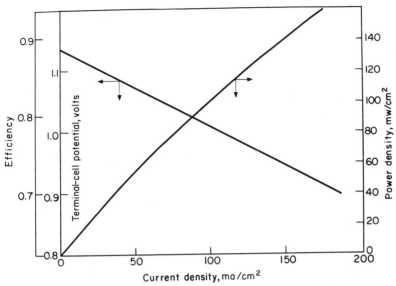

Figure 61 Terminal-cell potential (or efficiency) and power-density–current-density relations for an indirect internal reforming methanol-oxygen fuel cell.[24]

better than with gasoline. Further, the internal reformer fuel cell shows a marked increase in performance over the corresponding direct cells using hydrocarbons or methanol (Fig. 62).

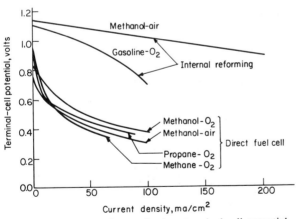

Figure 62 A comparison of the terminal-cell-potential–current-density relations for direct and indirect internal reforming fuel cells using organic fuels.[24]

(iv) Advantages and disadvantages of the system

The terminal-cell-potential–current-density relations of this system are a marked improvement over direct organic compounds–air fuel cells (Fig. 62).

The reforming operation uses cheap catalysts. Thus, the expensive Pt catalyst is replaced by Ni. The anode material is fairly expensive. However, reduction of its thickness by three to four times should help reduce its cost considerably as well as improve the performance of the cell.

The advantage of internal reformer fuel cells over the external reformer fuel cell is that considerably lower operating temperatures are possible in the former case without affecting the fuel-cell performance. However, the latter systems use cheaper catalysts. Furthermore, the integrated unit should have a lower volume. It has been estimated that the power/volume ratio for this cell is about 3 kw ft^{-3} and for the external-reformer fuel cell is about 0.5 kw ft^{-3}. Less accessory equipment is required for the integrated unit.

2.2.2.5   *External Reforming Fuel Cells Using Methanol*

(*i*)   *Main units of the system*

The system developed by Shell Research, Ltd., U.K., consists essentially of two units—the reformer and the fuel-cell battery.[26]   The steam-reforming is carried out at 375°C and at a pressure of nearly 20 atm.   A thin silver palladium tube is used to separate the hydrogen from the other constitutents of the gas mixture.   Methanol is also used to supply heat to the reforming unit.   During the process of diffusion of hydrogen through the Ag-Pd alloy, it undergoes some cooling.   The gas is further cooled to 30 to 65°C by fans and fed into the fuel battery.   The battery consists of two stacks, each of which contains 62 cells connected in series.   Air is the oxidant.

(*ii*)   *Basic design of a single cell and its mode of operation*

A single cell consists of thin microporous electrodes separated by an open mesh sheet of plastic to contain the electrolyte.   The electrodes are prepared by vapor depositing Ag or Au on a microporous plastic (thickness 0.76 mm).   The plastic is polyvinyl chloride (PVC) and has the trade name Porvic.   The electrode is then coated with a noble metal catalyst, generally Pt.   An advantage of this structure for the electrodes is that the porosity is quite uniform (pore size about 5 μ).   In addition, the electrodes are quite thin, strong, and flexible.   Catalyst loadings are relatively low (1 mg cm^{-2}).   Metal frames around the periphery of the electrode serve as connectors for the cells in series.   Each cell is 3 to 4 mm thick and 4 to 5 cells can be connected in series per inch.

(*iii*)   *Performance of a single cell*

The cells are operated between 25 and 60°C. The current-density–overpotential relation for the oxygen electrode shows only a small initial drop followed by a long linear region.   The cells perform equally well in acid and in alkaline media (Fig. 63).   Most of the work has been carried out in alkaline electrolyte.   Current densities of 100 to 150 ma cm^{-2} are obtained at cell voltages of 0.7 to 0.8 volt.

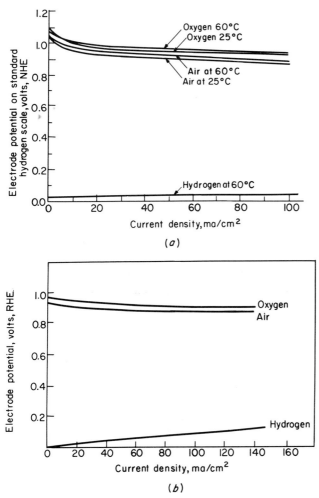

Figure 63   Anode and cathode polarization curves for fuel cell of Shell Research Ltd. in (*a*) acid solution and (*b*) alkaline solution.[36]

(*iv*)   *Multicell design and performance*

A 5-kw generator has been built.   The auxiliaries require 0.9 kw of power. Figure 64 shows the entire assembly, consisting of the reformer and the fuel-cell battery.   The unit is started with the aid of lead acid batteries.   Once it is on, the lead acid batteries may be recharged.   The system has been tested for over 500 hr.   The overall thermal efficiency of the unit is 25 to 30 percent.

(*v*)   *Advantages and disadvantages of the system*

The oxygen electrode performance is about the best for low-temperature fuel cells.   The electrodes are light (density of approximately 1 g cm^{-3}) and

Figure 64 The assembly of reformer and fuel cell developed by Shell Research Ltd.[36]

thin. The electrodes contain only small quantities of catalysts and this reduces the cost of the electrodes. The overall efficiency of the system is comparable with that of a diesel-engine generator.

The disadvantages of the system are mainly the high weight and volume of the system owing to the necessity of having a separate reformer unit. Further, the expensive Ag-Pd alloy and Pt are used for isolation of hydrogen from the reformer products and as the electrocatalyst for the hydrogen-dissolution reaction, respectively.

2.2.3   High-temperature Fuel Cells
2.2.3.1   The Fuel Cell of Broers et al.[27]

(i)   Basic design of a single cell and its mode of operation

The work of Broers et al.[27] stemmed from the early work of Baur et al.[28] and of Davytan[29] who were the first to use molten carbonate as electrolytes at high temperatures. The operation of fuel cells at high temperatures using molten carbonate electrolytes has two advantages, particularly with organic fuels. First, the problems of overpotential losses at the fuel and oxygen electrodes are considerably reduced at high temperatures. Second, the problem of CO_2 rejection, which exists in low-temperature alkaline electrolyte cells, is circumvented by using molten carbonate electrolytes.

The cells of the early workers,[28,29] who used hydrogen or carbon monoxide as the fuel, were complicated, and the performances were rather unsatisfactory. However, this work formed the basis of most of the present-day work on molten carbonate electrolyte fuel cells.

From 1964 onward, MgO as inert (powder) "carrier" has been substituted by alkali-aluminates $LiAlO_2$, $NaAlO_2$, and $KAlO_2$ as solid constituents. This resulted in much better performances, in particular at current densities of 50 to 200 mA/cm^2 and more. These currents can at present be drawn continuously for periods of over one year without any damage to the Ag or CuO cathodes or to the Ni anodes. Probably the improvement is due to the equilibrium

$$2 MAlO_2(s) + CO_2 = M_2CO_3(l) + Al_2O_3(s)$$

where M = Li, Na, and K. This causes the carbonate-aluminate system to act as a "CO_2 buffer" in the sense that it prevents excessive CO_2 pressure buildup at high anodic discharge rates [compare Eq. (2.23) below], which would otherwise disrupt the contact between the Ni anode and the electrolyte paste (as is the case with MgO).

Broers et al. have used two types of cells with this paste electrolyte. In one, the electrolyte is in a disk form and is pressed against the inner wall of an Al_2O_3 tube. The working electrodes on either side of the disk are held in position with the aid of concentric Al_2O_3 tubes of smaller diameter. The fuel and oxidant gases enter through the respective central tubes. The cell design is shown in Fig. 65. It is essential that the various parts of the cell be gas tight.

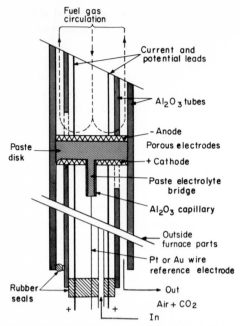

Figure 65   The disk-electrode fuel-cell design of Broers et al. using molten carbonate electrolyte.[27]

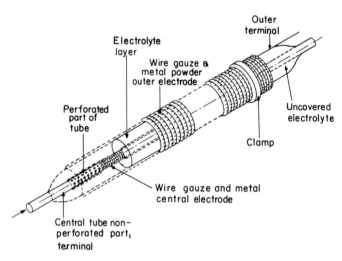

Figure 66   The tubular-electrode fuel-cell design of Broers et al.[27]

In the second design, the electrolyte is hand-molded around a central tubular porous electrode and then a wire gauze ribbon catalyst is wrapped around the smooth structure for the other electrode (Fig. 66). At the present time, the first cell design is mostly used since it is the more convenient one for obtaining data on these systems.

The electrocatalysts are nickel or iron powder for the anode and silver for the cathode. In the high-temperature cells a distinction should be made between the "primary" fuel, i.e., the fuel feed, and the actual fuel prevailing inside the anode space. Pure H_2 is *never* used as primary fuel because for carbonate cells this hardly makes sense. Primary test fuels are $H_2 + CO_2$, $CO + CO_2$, and hydrocarbon plus steam mixtures. In the anode space all these fuels come to equilibrium to form a C-H-O gas mixture. At 700°C or higher this is essentially $H_2 + CO + CO_2 + H_2O$, apart from a small amount of CH_4. It is mandatory that the C:O:H ratio be outside the carbon-deposition range (Fig. 65).

With hydrogen as fuel and air as oxidant, the reactions occurring at the anode and the cathode are

$$CO_3^{2-} + H_2 \rightarrow H_2O + CO_2 + 2e_0^- \tag{2.23}$$

$$\tfrac{1}{2}O_2 + CO_2 + 2e_0^- \rightarrow CO_3^{2-} \tag{2.24}$$

respectively. Owing to the loss of electrolyte at the anode in the form of CO_2, this gas is passed along with air through the porous cathode where the carbonate ion is reformed. Small three- to four-cell "modules" were tested in 1968 for about four months at 100 mA/cm^2 and at 0.6 volt per cell of 100 cm^2 electrode area, i.e., 18- to 24-watt-module output. The main problems (apart from finances) are carbonate "creep" in series connections and thermal expansion compatibility, i.e., essentially material problems.

(ii) Performance of a single cell

With a fuel stream consisting of 20 percent H_2, 10 percent CO, and 70 percent CO_2 obtained by steam-reforming and an air stream having the composition 85 percent air and 15 percent CO_2, the terminal-cell-potential–current-density relation for a cell operating at 700°C is shown in Fig. 67. The anode is an inconel sieve and the cathode is of silver. The current-density–potential relation is practically linear up to a current density of 200 ma cm^{-2}. The power-density–current-density relation corresponding is also shown in Fig. 67.

Nickel anodes and silver cathodes are being currently used. The electrolyte is an aluminate-carbonate paste. At the present time, single cells are able to sustain current densities of 100 ma cm^{-2} at 0.6 to 0.7 volt for continuous periods of more than 1 year.

(iii) Advantages and disadvantages of the system

The main advantage of this system is the use of nonnoble metals instead of noble metals, which are used in low-temperature systems. Its longevity and

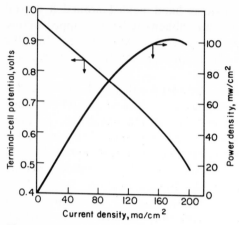

Figure 67 Terminal-cell potential (or efficiency) and power-density–current-density relations for the Broers cell.[27]

inherent stability surpass by far any result obtained with any low-temperature system, a surprising fact and a real challenge to "low temperature" electrochemists. The CO_2 rejection problems are eliminated. When organic compounds are used as fuels, they are first chemically converted to hydrogen and CO. It is not necessary, however, to separate H_2 by using the expensive Ag-Pd alloy. The paste form of the electrolyte creates no problems of gastightness, which are encountered with ceramic diaphragm electrolytes. On the other hand, in contrast to liquid electrolytes the paste is stiff enough for cell constructions. A disadvantage of the system is the use of high temperatures, which causes materials problems.

2.2.3.2   *The Cell of Chambers and Tantram.*[30]   In this cell, the electrolyte (a binary mixture of lithium and sodium carbonates or a mixture of sodium potassium and lithium carbonates) is contained in a magnesia matrix. The cell is considered to function as an oxygen and carbon dioxide concentration cell. Thus, identical electrodes are used for the anode and cathode—porous zinc oxide coated with a layer of silver. The fuels, which have been tested, are hydrogen, carbon monoxide, methanol, and kerosene. The oxidant stream is a moisture of air and carbon dioxide. The current-voltage curves, with H_2, CO, and kerosene as the fuels, are shown in Fig. 68. The performance with hydrogen is only slightly better than with the other fuels, probably because kerosene and methanol are initially cracked to hydrogen and carbon monoxide, both of which are quite active fuels at this temperature.

The view that this cell functions only because of a difference in concentrations of O_2 and CO_2 at the cathode and the anode is unlikely because the cell operates in overpotential regions where the O_2 reaction is highly irreversible.

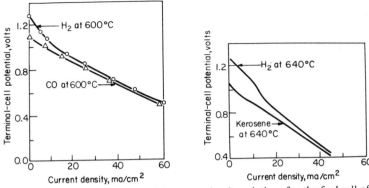

Figure 68 Terminal-cell-potential–current density relations for the fuel cell of Chambers and Tantram using H_2, CO, methanol, and kerosene as fuels.[30]

This work that was started at Sondes Place Research Institute is being carried out at Energy Conversion Limited, England, with the aim being to develop it into a large-scale power plant.

2.2.3.3 The Institute of Gas Technology Natural-gas Fuel Cell.[31]

(i) Cell design

As early as 1964 a 32-cell stack (Fig. 69) was constructed using the paste electrolyte configuration and nickel and silver electrodes. The system concept employed here is shown schematically in Fig. 70. Methane, natural gas, is reformed according to the reaction

$$CH_4 + 2H_2O \rightarrow CO_2 + 4H_2 \tag{2.25}$$

The products of this reaction enter the anode gas compartments. Since the fuel cell operates at a high temperature, it is possible to recover its waste heat for the purpose of sustaining the above endothermic reactions. Carbon dioxide, an anode product, and air are supplied to the cathode chamber.

More recent cells employ sintered nickel anodes in either powder or fibrous form. The cathodes are made of either nickel oxide or copper oxide, both of which show considerable economic advantages compared with silver. The electrolyte is a mixture of fused carbonates held in paste form by an inert metal oxide filler.

(ii) Performance characteristics

Laboratory versions of this type of cell have operated for periods in excess of 10,000 hr with only relatively small decay rates. A typical cell performance is shown in Fig. 71. Power density at the end of 10,000 hr was 55 watts/sq ft. Voltage efficiency of about 70 percent is achievable, and overall system efficiency in sizes greater than 5 kw might be as high as 50 percent.

Figure 69   The Institute of Gas Technology natural-gas fuel cell.[31a]

(iii)   Advantages and disadvantages of the system

The development of a fuel-cell battery using natural gas as a fuel has been demonstrated. Basic building components, electrodes, electrolyte, etc., are low cost and have good endurance characteristics. Material costs of $20/kw are foreseen.

Problem areas are associated with practical engineering configurations and nonactive material corrosion. If these problems can be overcome, the system may become useful for large-scale power generation, preferably in the form of on-site total-energy installations.

2.2.3.4   The Texas Instruments Slurried-electrolyte Fuel Cell.[32]   The main features of this cell are the use of a proprietary ceramic separator—10 to 30 mils in thickness—which holds the molten alkali metal carbonate electrolyte. The electrodes are corrugated wire screens alternately folded to form a continuously pleated pattern. Although physically it is one piece, the lateral

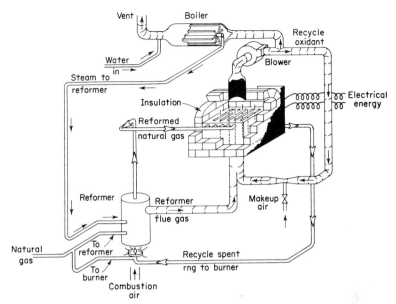

Figure 70 Auxiliaries for the Institute of Gas Technology natural-gas fuel cell.[31a]

symmetry of the electrode can be thought of and used as two electrodes connected in parallel. These electrodes are assembled in series-parallel arrangements to make subkilowatt modular units. Several of these units are assembled to make kilowatt systems.

The 1 kw system delivered to U. S. Army Mobility Equipment R & D Center, Fort Belvoir, Virginia, in conclusion of Texas Instruments work on fuel cells, had the performance shown in Fig. 72. The system was self-contained and operated on partially oxidized leaded gasoline at 700°C.

An important feature of this system is that no noble metals are used.

2.2.3.5 Miscellaneous Molten Carbonate Systems. There are several places where some work on molten carbonate fuel cells is being carried out— Battelle Memorial Institute,[33] Gaz de France,[34] and l'Electricité de France.[35] They are, with only minor variations, essentially the same as the ones described.

2.3 Carbon or Carbon Monoxide–Air Fuel Cells

2.3.1 *Use of Carbon*

The earliest attempt at using carbon in a fuel cell was made by Becquerel[36] (1855). By using a carbon rod as the fuel electrode, which was consumed directly, and platinum as the air electrode, a current was observed in the external circuit of a cell using molten potassium nitrate as the electrolyte. However, the faradaic efficiency was low because of the direct chemical oxidation of carbon by potassium nitrate.

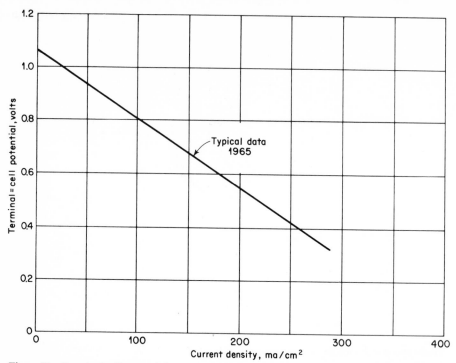

Figure 71 Terminal-cell-potential–current-density relation in a single-cell battery built by the Institute of Gas Technology.[31a]

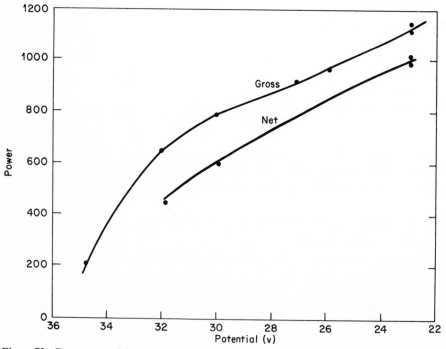

Figure 72 Power-potential performance for 8.4 to 8.8 hr of operation of the Texas Instruments 1-kw fuel-cell battery.[32a]

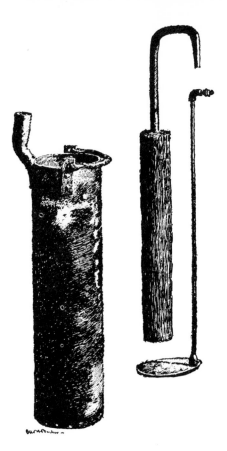

Figure 73 Basic components of the Jacques' carbon-air fuel cell.[37]

Figure 74 Photograph of 1.5-kw battery developed by Jacques.[37]

Perhaps the most remarkable achievements in research on energy conversion during the nineteenth century were those of Jacques.[36]   Using a molten sodium hydroxide electrolyte contained in an iron pot, which served as the air cathode, and a carbon rod as the consumable anode, current densities of over 100 ma cm^{-2} were obtained at stable cell potentials of 1 volt.   The components of the cell used by Jacques are shown in Fig. 73.   A 1.5-kw battery consisting of over 100 of these cells was constructed (Fig. 74) and it operated intermittently for over 6 months!   Cell temperatures of about 500°C were used.   The reactions occurring in the cell are as follows:

Anode:

$$C + 4OH^- \rightarrow CO_2 + 2H_2O + 4e_0^- \qquad (2.26)$$

Cathode:

$$O_2 + 2H_2O + 4e_0^- \rightarrow 4OH^-$$

A further chemical reaction

$$CO_2 + 2OH^- \rightarrow CO_3^{2-} + H_2O \qquad (2.27)$$

occurs at the anode.

Haber and Brunner[38] suggested that the electrochemical reaction at the anode is not the oxidation of carbon.   According to these workers, hydrogen was produced by the reaction of carbon with sodium hydroxide, and it is the hydrogen which is electrochemically oxidized at the carbon electrode.   Because of carbonate formation, there was a loss of the expensive electrolyte NaOH, and so this approach was abandoned.

An alternative approach was adopted by Baur and Preis[34] (1937), who used a solid oxide as the electrolyte with a coke anode.   The overall reaction is the production of carbon dioxide.   The electrolyte is zirconia stabilized with magnesia or yttria.   High operating temperatures (>1000°C) had to be used because the conductivity of the electrolyte is satisfactory only at these temperatures.   Unfortunately, at these temperatures, it is thermodynamically possible to carry out only a partial oxidation of carbon, which would hence reduce the fuel-cell efficiencies considerably.

The most common naturally occurring form of carbon is coal.   It is not electronically conducting.   Graphite is the only form of carbon that is electronically conducting, but it is found in considerably smaller quantities.   Moreover, it does not appear feasible at the present time to use carbon directly as a fuel.   Thus, the only practical way of using carbon as a fuel is by an indirect method.   The water-gas reaction produces hydrogen and carbon dioxide or can be controlled to produce hydrogen and carbon monoxide according to the reactions

$$C + 2H_2O \rightarrow CO_2 + 2H_2 \qquad (2.28)$$
$$C + H_2O \rightarrow CO + H_2 \qquad (2.29)$$

It is then possible to use hydrogen or a mixture of carbon monoxide and hydrogen in a fuel cell in which the direct electrochemical oxidation of these gases can be carried out.   The types of hydrogen-oxygen fuel cells have been treated in Sec. 2.1.   The use of carbon monoxide in fuel cells will be treated in the next section.

At the present time, Westinghouse[40] is concentrating on the development of coal-based fuel cells in its fuel-cell research program.   The coal is converted to a mixture of CO and H_2, and these gases enter their solid electrolyte fuel cell.

Since coal or coke cannot be used directly in a fuel cell, one may consider using it along with a suitable redox couple.   In addition, because of the fairly low reactivity of oxygen, another redox couple may be used for the cathodic reaction as well.   Posner[41] has used coke and coal as fuels, indirectly, with redox couples.   The reactions occurring with Sn^{2+}/Sn^{4+} and Br^-/Br_2 couples are

Anode reaction:

$$Sn^{2+} \rightarrow Sn^{4+} + 2e_0^- \tag{2.30}$$

Anode reactant regeneration:

$$2Sn^{4+} + C + 2H_2O \rightarrow 2Sn^{2+} + CO_2 + 4H^+ \tag{2.31}$$

Cathode reaction:

$$Br_2 + 2e_0^- \rightarrow 2Br^- \tag{2.32}$$

Cathode reactant regeneration:

$$4Br^- + 4H^+ + O_2 \rightarrow 2Br_2 + 2H_2O \tag{2.33}$$

This cell yielded a current density of 10 ma cm^{-2} at 0.62 volt.

This and several other potential redox systems have not been systematically investigated.

2.3.2   Use of Carbon Monoxide

The electrochemical activity of carbon monoxide is fairly low at temperatures below 100°C (Chap. 7, Sec. 7.2).   Very little work has been done in examining carbon monoxide–air fuel cells at intermediate temperatures.   Carbon monoxide has been used in a number of high-temperature fuel cells.[27,32,35,40]   In most high-temperature fuel cells using organic fuels, with water vapor accompanying the gas stream, it is most probable that the steam-reforming reaction occurs first and produces hydrogen and carbon monoxide.   Thereafter, the electrochemical oxidation of these species occurs according to the equations

$$H_2 + CO_3^{2-} \rightarrow H_2O + CO_2 + 2e_0^- \tag{2.23}$$
$$CO + CO_3^{2-} \rightarrow 2CO_2 + 2e_0^- \tag{2.34}$$

in a cell in which the electrolyte is a molten carbonate mixture (e.g., mixtures of carbonates of Li and Na or Li, Na, and K).

In Sec. 2.2.3.2, it was seen that the performance with carbon monoxide is comparable with that of hydrogen for a cell operating at 600°C.   Thus, activation overpotential problems are considerably minimized at high temperatures.   One of the reasons for the low reactivity of carbon monoxide at low temperatures may be because of its strong adsorption on the electrode.   This is probably the cause for the peculiar mixture of the current-density–overpotential relation obtained for its electrochemical oxidation (Chap. 7, Fig. 16). Higher temperatures facilitate the desorption of the adsorbed carbon monoxide. The comparable reactivities of hydrogen and carbon monoxide at high temperatures favor the use of organic fuels in fuel cells indirectly. It is thus possible to use cheaper catalysts for the anode in these cases rather than the expensive Ag-Pd alloy used in low-temperature systems, where it is necessary to separate the CO from H_2.

Figure 75 shows the terminal-cell-potential–current-density relations for

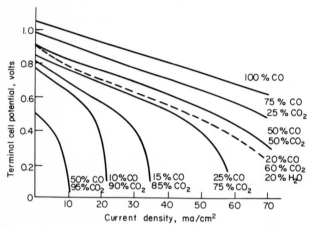

Figure 75 Terminal-cell-potential–current-density relations for carbon monoxide–air fuel cells as a function of percentage CO in the fuel stream.

carbon monoxide–air fuel cells as a function of the percentage of carbon monoxide in the fuel stream. If the percentage of CO is less than 25 percent, limiting current densities of less than 50 ma cm^{-2} are observed. However, injection of water vapor into the fuel stream improves the performance to some extent, probably as a result of the water-gas shift reaction.

As pointed out previously, carbon monoxide is being successfully used in solid electrolyte fuel cells.[40] These cells, which operate at temperatures of over 1000°C, cannot use organic fuels (e.g., hydrocarbons) directly because carbon deposition occurs. However, by mixing these fuels with water vapor and with passage over a reformer catalyst, a mixture of CO and H_2 is obtained. These gases may then be oxidized in the solid electrolyte fuel cell without any difficulty.

Open-circuit voltage determinations in solid electrolyte fuel cells using mixtures of H_2, CO, CO_2, and H_2O in varying proportions agree with thermodynamic predictions within 3 percent. Cells operating on CO-CO_2 fuel mixtures are not so good as H_2-O_2 fuel cells using solid electrolyte. However, by using a mixture of H_2, CO, CO_2, and H_2O, there is an improved performance, especially if some catalyst to promote the water-gas shift reaction is

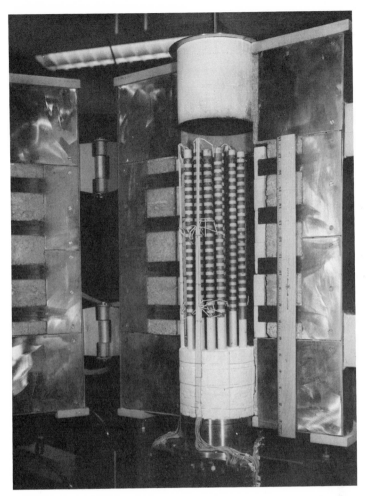

Figure 76 Westinghouse 100-watt solid-electrolyte fuel-cell battery operating on a mixture of H_2 and CO as fuels.[40b]

incorporated in the anode. At a current density of 450 ma cm^{-2}, the cell potential for a fuel cell using an H_2-CO mixture as the fuel is only 0.1 volt less than that using pure H_2.

A fuel-cell battery consisting of 400 cells—2 groups of 200 cells connected in series—has been constructed (Fig. 76). The open-circuit voltage is 200 volts. The maximum power is 102 watts at which the cell generates a current of 1.2 amp. At this power output, the voltage efficiency of the cells is nearly 60 percent. The current-potential relation for the fuel-cell battery is shown in Fig. 77. The linearity of this relation shows that the voltage losses are a result of the ohmic drop in the electrolyte.

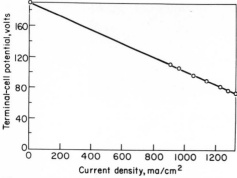

Figure 77   Terminal-voltage–current-density relation for Westinghouse 100-watt solid-electrolyte fuel-cell battery.[40b]

2.4   Nitrogenous Compounds–Oxygen (or Air) Fuel Cells

2.4.1   Ammonia-Air Fuel Cells

2.4.1.1   Criteria for Selection of Ammonia as a Fuel.   One of the main considerations for the selection of ammonia as a fuel is its low cost. The cost per kilowatthour ratios for some typical fuels are shown in Table 6,[42] assuming an overall efficiency of 50 percent for fuel cells. Thus, apart from the naturally occurring hydrocarbons, ammonia is relatively economical. A second advantage of ammonia over many fuels is its liquefaction. It has a

TABLE 6   Cost Per Kilowatthour for Several Fuels Assuming a 50 Percent Efficiency of Electrochemical Energy Converters Using These Fuels[42]

Fuel	Cost, cents kwh^{-1}
Natural gas (fuel grade)	0.2
Premium gasoline	0.8
Ammonia	3.6
Methanol	3.1
Hydrogen (cracked NH_3)	3.7
Hydrogen (high purity)	4.6
Zinc	45.0

relatively high density (42.1 lb ft^{-3}) at moderate pressures. Heavy pressure vessels are therefore not required (cf. difficulties in storage of hydrogen).

Ammonia can be used in two ways as a fuel in electrochemical energy conversion. It can be first converted to hydrogen and nitrogen, a reaction that is readily carried out on some promoted iron catalyst, and the hydrogen can, in turn, be used in one of the many types of hydrogen-oxygen fuel cells. Alternatively, it may be used directly as the anodic reactant in a fuel cell.

2.4.1.2 Types of Ammonia-Air Fuel Cells and Their Performance Characteristics. The Allis-Chalmers Mfg. Co.[43] has investigated a low-temperature direct ammonia-air fuel cell. The cell used in this work is shown in Fig. 78. The electrodes are of porous carbon, on which a platinum catalyst is deposited. The electrolyte is a strong KOH solution that is held in a porous diaphragm. The electrodes are pressed against this diaphragm.

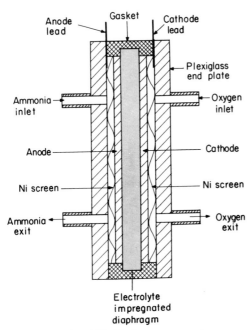

Figure 78 The Allis-Chalmers ammonia-oxygen fuel cell.[43]

The reactions occurring at the electrodes are

Anode:

$$NH_3 + 3OH^- \rightarrow \tfrac{1}{2}N_2 + 3H_2O + 3e_0^- \tag{2.35}$$

Cathode:

$$O_2 + 2H_2O + 4e_0^- \rightarrow 4OH^- \tag{2.36}$$

Thus, the overall cell reaction is

$$4NH_3 + 3O_2 \rightarrow 2N_2 + 6H_2O \tag{2.37}$$

The standard thermodynamic reversible potential for the cell at 25°C is 1.14 volts.

Coulombic efficiencies of 100 percent have been obtained. The observed open-circuit potentials are between 0.45 and 0.55 volt, which is slightly below half the theoretically expected value. By using a silver oxide catalyst for the oxygen electrode and the Pt catalyst for the ammonia electrode, an open-circuit voltage of 0.7 volt has been observed. Figure 79 shows the terminal-cell-potential–current-density relations for the cell at three temperatures.

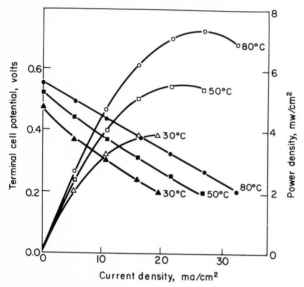

Figure 79 Terminal-cell potential (or efficiency)[43] and power-density–current-density relations for Allis-Chalmers ammonia-oxygen fuel cells at three temperatures.

Because of the fairly low electroactivity of ammonia at low temperatures, the Electrochimica Corporation is investigating an ammonia-oxygen fuel cell at intermediate temperatures[42] (180 to 300°C). The electrolyte used is fused potassium hydroxide contained in a magnesium oxide matrix. Nickel electrodes containing a platinized-platinum catalyst were employed. Teflon is used as a sealing material for the cell. Current-potential relations for the cell at temperature intervals of 30° between 180 and 300°C are shown in Fig. 80. There is a marked increase in cell performance with increase of temperature. At 300°C the open-circuit voltage is 1.0 volt. An ammonia-air fuel is being investigated at the General Electric Company.[43a] Teflon-bonded platinum black electrodes with a Niedrach-Alford structure are used. The electrolyte is 54 percent KOH. The platinum loading is 50 mg cm^{-2} and the cell resistance is 0.03 ohm. The open-circuit potential at 140°C is 0.8 volt, and at a current density of 500 ma cm^{-2}, the cell potential is 0.5 volt. The reaction at the anode tended towards a limiting current density of 1 amp cm^{-2}.

An indirect ammonia-air fuel cell is being studied by the Pratt and Whitney Company.[44] It is quite similar to their indirect hydrocarbon-air fuel cell. A

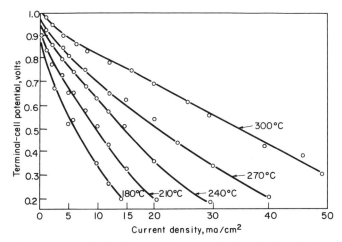

Figure 80   Terminal-cell-potential–current-density relations for the
Electrochimica Corporation ammonia-oxygen fuel cell[42] at temperature intervals of 30° from 180 to 300°C.

silver-palladium alloy is used to separate hydrogen from N_2 and also as the
anode catalyst.

2.4.1.3   Advantages and Disadvantages of Ammonia-Air Fuel Cells.   The
advantages of using ammonia are its low cost and ease of storage.   One of the
problems with ammonia is its toxic nature.   However, its presence in even
small quantities can be detected by its pungent odor.   The observed performance levels of the ammonia-air fuel cell at low temperatures are not too
satisfactory.   At intermediate temperatures, its performance is considerably
better but much below that of a corresponding hydrogen-oxygen fuel cell.
From the point of view of increasing the efficiency of its utilization, an indirect
approach appears most feasible at the present time.

2.4.2   Hydrazine-Oxygen (or Air) Fuel Cells

2.4.2.1   Criteria for Selection of Hydrazine as a Fuel.   The exchange
current densities for the electrooxidation of hydrazine on platinum, palladium,
and even nickel boride catalysts are high (over 10^{-3} amp cm^{-2}). It is a liquid at
ordinary temperatures (MP is 1.5°C and BP is 113.5°C) and is readily soluble
in aqueous solutions.   It is commercially available in various concentrations
but is quite expensive at the present time.   However, hydrazine is presently
made in small quantities.   Were it manufactured in larger quantities, its price
could be lowered considerably.   Unlike gaseous fuels such as hydrogen, it is
easy to store as an aqueous solution.   It thus appears to be suitable for space
applications as well as for submarine power sources.   The advantages of
hydrazine over hydrogen as a fuel in fuel cells for space missions of varying

TABLE 7 Comparison of Performance Characteristics of Hydrogen-Oxygen and Hydrazine-Oxygen Fuel Cells[48]

Basis: 300-watt Fuel Cell; 5-, 14-, and 30-day Continuous Operation; 60 percent Overall Efficiency; Cryogenic Hydrogen and Oxygen Storage

| Type of fuel cell | Days† | Anodic fuel | | | Oxygen | | | | Fuel + O₂ + tankage | |
		Fuel weight, lb	Tankage weight, lb	Total volume, ft³	Oxygen weight, lb	Tankage weight, lb	Total volume, ft³	Total weight, lb	Total volume, ft³
Electrochimica Hydrazine-Oxygen Fuel cell	5	25.2	2.52	0.37	25.2	6.8	1.14	59.7	1.51
	14	70	7.0	1.02	70	11.8	1.86	158.8	2.88
	30	150.5	15.05	2.2	150.5	21.9	3.05	337.8	5.25
Hydrogen-Oxygen Fuel cell	5	4.4	39.6	1.78	25.2	6.8	1.14	86.4	2.93
	14	11.0	54.0	4.7	70	11.8	1.86	176.8	6.56
	30	26.4	84.0	11.15	150.5	21.9	3.05	345.2	14.20

† Mission duration.

duration are presented in Table 7. Owing to the present high cost of hydrazine,† it cannot be considered for terrestrial commercial applications.

2.4.2.2 Types of Hydrazine-Air Fuel Cells and Their Performance Characteristics. Hydrazine-oxygen fuel cells have been investigated by the Chloride Electric Storage Company, Ltd.,[45] Shell Research, Ltd.,[46] Allis-Chalmers Mfg. Co.,[47] Electrochimica Corporation,[48] and Monsanto Company.[49]

In the Chloride Electric Storage Company hydrazine-oxygen fuel cell,[45] the hydrazine electrode consists of two thin porous metal plates separated by a space for the supply of fuel. The plates are cemented to a frame of epoxy resin. The oxygen or air electrode is constructed in a similar way using porous carbon plates. Two hollow posts are welded to each electrode. These provide the electrical connection and are also used to introduce the fuel or oxidant.

The hydrazine fuel cell contains five oxygen and four hydrazine electrodes (14×11 cm) in a polystyrene container and uses an electrolyte of 7 M KOH. The fuel is stored as concentrated hydrazine hydrate and is led into the stream of electrolyte circulating through the fuel electrodes giving a fuel concentration of about 0.5 M.

Cells will give usable outputs at temperatures as low as $-30°C$ and at $+40°C$ will deliver 100 amp at about 0.55 volt. They are capable of outputs of 800 to 1,000 watts/ft^3 and have a power density of 8 to 10 watts/lb.

The Shell Company, Ltd., demonstrated a hydrazine-oxygen fuel that delivers 20 amp at 18 volts using an alkaline electrolyte.

The Allis-Chalmers Mfg. Co. developed a 3-kw hydrazine-air fuel cell that was used to power a golf cart. At this power level, the efficiency of the battery is 40 percent. The electrodes are porous nickel sheets with Pd as catalyst for the hydrazine electrode and silver for the oxygen electrode. The electrolyte is a 25 percent KOH solution containing 3 percent hydrazine and is recirculated from a reservoir. The terminal-cell potential (or efficiency) and power-density–current-density relations for a single cell are given in Fig. 81. The E-i relation is practically linear from the open-circuit potential. The maximum power density is about 250 Mw cm^{-2}. The reaction occurring at the anode is

$$N_2H_4 + 4OH^- \rightarrow N_2 + 4H_2O + 4e_0^- \tag{2.38}$$

The overall reaction in the cell is

$$N_2H_4 + O_2 \rightarrow N_2 + 2H_2O \tag{2.39}$$

The thermodynamic reversible potential for the cell is 1.56 volts. The open-circuit voltage of 1.16 volts is considerably less than this theoretical value. It is

---

† The cost would be reduced manyfold if there were large-scale chemical production. Correspondingly, the electrochemical production by the reduction of H_2O is possible.[44a] If the latter substance could be economically obtained by sparking air, a radical revision in the price of N_2H_4 would seem likely.

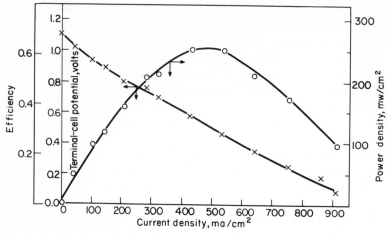

Figure 81   Terminal-cell potential (or efficiency) and power-density–current-density relations for hydrazine-oxygen fuel cell of Allis-Chalmers.[47]

probable that the anode reaction occurs as a result of the initial chemical production of hydrogen followed by the electrochemical dissolution of hydrogen. It has been found that the electrooxidation of hydrazine proceeds faster in basic medium than in acids.   Nickel boride has also been used as an anode catalyst and its behavior was shown to be comparable with that of the palladium catalyst.[47a]

Allis-Chalmers have also constructed a 7-kw battery to power an industrial fork-lift truck and a 1-kw battery for submarine propulsion.

The Electrochimica Corporation has developed a 300-watt unit for aerospace application.   The efficiencies obtained in this system are higher because the cells operate at a lower current density.   This system's working temperature is between 20 and 35°C.   The total weight of a 300-watt system, *including tankage* for hydrazine and oxygen for a 5-day mission, is 120 lb, yielding an energy density of 300 whr lb^{-1}.   This compares to only about 240 whr lb^{-1} for an equivalent hydrogen-oxygen system, which involves hydrogen tankage of greater weight.   The energy density yield of a hydrazine-oxygen system is thus three times greater than that of low-rate silver-zinc batteries.   The fuel cell can operate on a mixture of hydrazine and unsymmetrical dimethyl hydrazine.

A portable hydrazine-air fuel-cell battery for terrestrial applications was developed by Monsanto Corporation.   It weights 12 lb and has a power output of 60 watts.   It can operate on 1 pint of fuel for 12 hr.

2.5   Metal-Oxygen (Other Oxidant) Fuel Cells

2.5.1   *Sodium Amalgam–Oxygen (or Air) Fuel Cells*

The successful development of a metal-air fuel cell depends to a large extent on the ease with which the metal fuel can be led into the fuel cell.   With a liquid metal, this problem is simplified.   Yeager developed a sodium amalgam–oxygen fuel cell using sodium hydroxide as the electrolyte.[50]   Based on the preliminary work of Yeager, the M. W. Kellogg Co. initially built a 6-kw unit.[51] The amalgam is prepared by dissolving sodium in mercury.   The concentration of sodium in the amalgam is 0.5 percent.   The amalgam is fed into the cell (Fig. 82) via capillary tubes directed at the top of a steel plate from where it flows

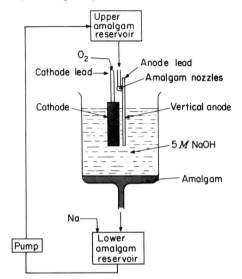

Figure 82   The sodium amalgam–oxygen fuel cell.[50]

down the plate.   The amalgam wets the steel plate completely.   The anodic reaction is

$$NaHg_x + OH^- \rightarrow NaOH + e_0^- + xHg \qquad (2.40)$$

A catalyzed porous carbon electrode is the cathode at which the oxygen-reduction reaction occurs.   The back of the steel plate is coated with a plastic film to isolate it from the solution.   The spent amalgam, which leaves the cell, enters a lower amalgam reservoir where sodium is added to it to bring it up to the weight concentration; it is then transferred to the upper reservoir by means of a pump.

The terminal-cell-potential–current-density relation for a sodium amalgam–oxygen cell is shown in Fig. 83.   Overpotential losses are negligible at the amalgam electrode.   The cell performance is stable.   The self-discharge rate is small, but if lithium amalgam is used instead, the self-discharge rate is higher. The M. W. Kellogg Company built a second pilot plant based on metallic electrodes designed for a maximum power output of 15 kw.   It was operated at a power level in excess of 8 kw.   It contained five batteries of 37 tubular cells.

The advantages of this system are the high open-circuit potential, low operating temperature, and easy fuel storage (air can be used instead of oxygen

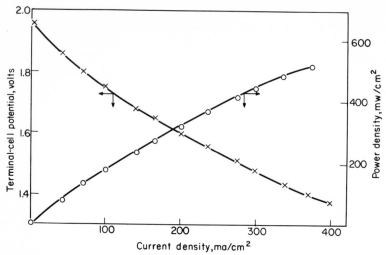

Figure 83   Terminal-cell potential–current-density relations for the sodium amalgam–oxygen fuel cell.[50]

and thus the problem of storage of oxidant may be eliminated). The disadvantages are the cost of the sodium, circulation of the electrolyte, and the high weight of the system because of the use of mercury.

   A possible way of improving this cell would be to combine it with a nuclear liquid-metal fuel cell[52] (a concentration cell), where the sodium amalgam is formed as a result of the overall reaction occurring in the fuel cell.

2.5.2   *Zinc-Oxygen (or Air) Fuel Cell*

Most of the zinc-air batteries must be considered essentially as energy *storage* devices because the fuel (zinc) is contained within the battery and regenerated electrically. The air electrode, however, is similar to that used in fuel cells. The use of the highly active oxygen electrodes, developed in fuel-cell work, has shown improvements in these cells, which have been in existence for many years in less efficient forms.

   A zinc-air fuel cell in which both the reactants are fed in continuously has been studied by ESB Incorporated.[53] The zinc is in either powdered or solid form. The reaction products are also continuously or intermittently removed from the cell. A schematic representation of the cell is shown in Fig. 84. Open-circuit voltages are approximately 1.4 volts. A power density of 200 Mw cm^{-2} is attained at a current density of 200 ma cm^{-2}. There are problems of feeding the fuel into the cell. The fuel costs are high. Current investigations are under way to reduce the oxidized zinc electrolytically both within and without the cell. If Zn could be regenerated from ZnO, for example, by reduction of ZnO by C according to

$$2ZnO + C \rightarrow 2Zn + CO_2 \qquad (2.41)$$

this cell would be more economical.

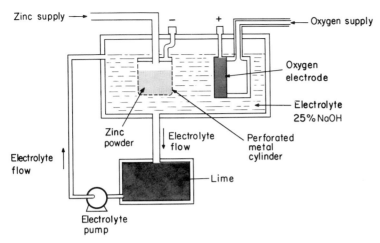

Figure 84 A zinc-air fuel cell.[53]

2.5.3 *Aluminum-Oxygen (or Air) Fuel Cells*

An electrochemical energy converter which has been little investigated but shows great promise is the aluminum-oxygen (or air) fuel cell. Aluminum is obtainable in a very pure condition and at low cost. In addition, the metal is quite electropositive. Using an alkaline electrolyte, two types of reactions are possible in an aluminum-air fuel cell:

$$4Al + 3O_2 + 6H_2O \rightarrow 4Al(OH)_3 \tag{2.42}$$

or

$$4Al + 3O_2 + 4OH^- \rightarrow 4AlO_2^- + 2H_2O \tag{2.43}$$

In the first case, the anode reaction is

$$Al + 3OH^- \rightarrow Al(OH)_3 + 3e_0^- \tag{2.44}$$

and in the second, it is

$$Al + 4OH^- \rightarrow AlO_2^- + 2H_2O + 3e_0^- \tag{2.45}$$

Reaction (2.44) occurs when the alkali concentration is below 3 M and reaction (2.45) occurs at higher concentrations. In some early work,[54,55] the aluminum-air cell was designed as a primary battery. Nickel cathodes were used. Since recent times, the Zaromb Research Corporation[55a] has been in the process of developing an aluminum-air fuel cell as a *chemically regenerative system*. An experimental 70-watt aluminum-air battery has been built. It consists of consumable Al anodes and Pt or Ag catalyzed cathodes. The electrolyte, a 3 to 4 M KOH solution, which is circulated past a precipitate collector and which retains the reaction product [Al(OH)$_3$], formed in the electrolyte, is pumped out of the cell and fresh electrolyte is introduced. The average power output from the cell is 60 to 70 watts, at which single cells perform at a current density of 40 ma cm^{-2} and 1.2 to 1.3 volts. Under these conditions, the energy density with respect to aluminum corresponds to 1,600 whr/lb. The battery has been tested for over a two-year period.

A detailed design analysis has been made for a 30 kw aluminum-air fuel cell. It is estimated that its power/weight ratio and power/volume ratio will be of the order of 30 watts/lb and 1 kw/ft^3 respectively.

The advantages of an aluminum-air fuel cell are (1) low cost of aluminum (25 to 30 cents/lb), (2) the system is rapidly chemically regenerative and cost of regeneration is low (10 to 15 cents/lb of Al), (3) no problems of polluting the air with noxious gas, (4) compactness of metal, and (5) low temperature of operation, hence fewer materials problems, higher reliability, and long life. At the present time, the high cost of the air cathodes (50 to 100 dollars per square foot if purchased in small quantities, 20 to 30 dollars per square foot if made on a pilot-plant scale) mainly determines the cost of this fuel cell. If cathode costs can indeed be reduced to 5 to 10 dollars per square foot on a mass scale, or estimated by several sources, this fuel cell should be one of the serious contenders as a power source for motor vehicle propulsion.

Another metal notably neglected is magnesium. This is also a relatively cheap metal and is available in plenty. (It is worth investigating magnesium-oxygen systems in a like manner.) Primary Mg-air batteries have been developed for military applications by the General Electric Co. However, the cost of Mg anodes is considerably higher than that of Al for a comparable energy output, which is why G. E. does not propose the use of Mg-air batteries for electric vehicle propulsion.

2.5.4   Moving-tape Fuel Cells

In the conventional fuel cell, there is a continuous introduction of fuel and oxidant and a withdrawal of products from the cell while the cell is in operation. Recently, the Monsanto Research Corporation[56] devised a moving-tape cell in which not only the fuel and oxidant but also the electrodes, separator, catalyst, and electrolyte, either in the form of a tape or deposited on it, are fed continuously into a set of current collectors. The electrochemical reaction occurs in the section of the tape that is between the current collectors. A schematic representation of the moving-tape cell is shown in Fig. 85. The electrolyte is in the form of capsules that are broken only in the region where it may enter the cell.

The advantages of the moving-tape concept are: (1) There is a reduction of activation and concentration polarization since the reactants are fed in continuously and the products are simultaneously removed. In addition, the electrode surface is also continuously renewed. (2) High-energy couples may be used at high current densities, and this may be contrasted with conventional battery systems where, because of mass-transport limitations, only low-current-density operations are possible. (3) The constituents of the system are

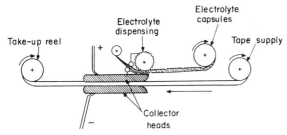

Figure 85   The Monsanto moving-tape cell.[56]

maintained in a pure condition and separately until they are used when the corresponding section of the tape passes through the current collector.

The silver oxide Ag_2O_2/Zn couple was first tested in this system and proved to be quite satisfactory.   The magnesium-potassium periodate couples functioned efficiently in the moving-tape cell.   The latter system has severe mass-transport limitations when it is used in a conventional battery system.   With the tape concept, such limitations are removed by mechanically feeding the reactants to the active sites.   Organic N halogen compounds (trichloro-triaminetrione and hexachloromalamine), which have even higher energy densities than potassium per iodate, have been coupled with magnesium in a dry-tape fuel cell.   Organic nitro compounds (picric acid, dinitro benzene) have also been used as oxidants.   Work on a lithium tape anode has also commenced.

The magnesium-potassium periodate system has yielded current densities of 70 ma cm^{-2} at terminal-cell potentials of 1.95 to 2.0 volts, which correspond to a power density of approximately 140 Mw cm^{-2}.   At the present time, it appears that this system is promising.   It should be possible to build light-weight cells containing a thin electrolyte layer.

3   REGENERATIVE SYSTEMS

3.1   Thermally Regenerative Fuel Cells

3.1.1   *Nuclear Liquid-metal Fuel Cells*

The Allison Division, General Motors Corporation, have developed a thermally regenerative fuel cell in which potassium and mercury react in the fuel cell and produce electric power and potassium amalgam.[52]   The amalgam is transferred to a boiler, where it is decomposed into its constituents which are fed back into the fuel cell.   The electrolyte is a molten salt mixture of the hydroxide, bromide, and iodide of potassium.   In this cell, the reactants and the electrolyte separated themselves because of a difference in their densities.   A schematic representation of the system is shown in Fig. 86.

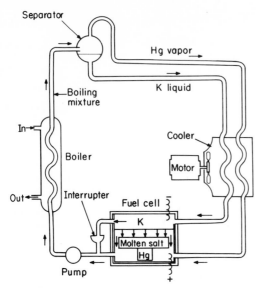

Figure 86   The regenerative nuclear liquid-metal fuel cell.[52]

At the anode, the reaction is

$$K \rightarrow K^+ + e_0^-$$ (3.1)

and at the cathode, it is

$$K^+ + e_0^- + xHg \rightarrow KHg_x$$ (3.2)

This may essentially be regarded as a concentration cell. A temperature of 630°C was used for the regeneration process. The current-potential relation in the cell is linear over a considerable range of current densities, which indicates that the losses in the cell are essentially ohmic in character. At a cell voltage of 0.4 volt, the current density in the cell is 100 ma cm^{-2}.

As was pointed out in Chap. 3, a thermally regenerative fuel cell has a maximum efficiency given by the Carnot theorem

$$\epsilon_m = \frac{T_1 - T_2}{T_1}$$ (3.3)

where T_1 is the regeneration temperature and T_2 is the cell temperature. Since mercury is a reactant, the weight of the system is fairly high. An advantage of this system is that it presents no problems of activation overpotential. It could be a convenient way of using nuclear power in space applications. The fuel-cell efficiency is over 70 percent at practical current densities.

3.1.2   Metal-Hydrogen Fuel Cells

Lithium hydride may be decomposed into lithium and hydrogen by heating it to about 900°C. Thus, with a fuel cell in which the reactions

$$Li \rightarrow Li^+ + e_0^- \tag{3.4}$$

and

$$\frac{1}{2}H_2 + e_0^- \rightarrow H^- \tag{3.5}$$

occur, a thermal regenerator may be coupled and the combined system could thus function as a secondary fuel cell. Calcium hydride may also be decomposed by heat, and if it could be formed in a fuel cell, it could be used likewise.

A lithium-hydrogen cell has been investigated in which the electrolyte is a lithium chloride–fluoride eutectic.[57] The cell operates at 600°C. Thin sheets of Fe or Nb, which are permeable to hydrogen, are used as the hydrogen electrode. The open-circuit potential of the cell is 0.45 volt. A current density of 1,400 ma cm^{-2} was obtained at a cell voltage of 0.32 volt. From 0 to 1,400 ma cm^{-2}, the overall efficiency of the cell varied from 16 to 10 percent.

3.2   Electrically Regenerative Fuel Cells†

3.2.1   *Lithium-Chlorine Fuel Cells*

Lithium is the most electropositive metal and fluorine is the most electronegative element. Thus, a cell in which the reactions

$$Li \rightarrow Li^+ + e_0^- \tag{3.4}$$

and

$$\frac{1}{2}F_2 + e_0^- \rightarrow F^- \tag{3.6}$$

occur at the electrodes has the highest possible thermodynamic reversible potential. Since fluorine gas is quite corrosive, its use is difficult.

The next best couple is the lithium-chlorine combination, a system that is being investigated at the Allison Division of General Motors Corporation.[58] Conventional fuels such as hydrogen and hydrocarbons have high theoretical values of energy/weight-of-fuel ratio, but their power output per unit area or per unit weight is not sufficiently high. The main limitations are because of activation overpotential losses at either one or both the electrodes in the cell. The dissolution of lithium as expressed by Eq. (3.4) and of chlorine according to

$$\frac{1}{2}Cl_2 + e_0^- \rightarrow Cl^- \tag{3.7}$$

are quite fast reactions. In addition, the advantage of a high thermodynamic reversible potential for the cell, 3.5 volts at 650°C, should make it an attractive system for energy conversion and storage.

The fuel cell consists of a molten lithium electrode, molten lithium chloride electrolyte, and a porous carbon or graphite electrode. The melting point of

---

† This can also be considered as an electrochemical electricity storer or fuel-cell battery.

lithium chloride is 613°C. In the work carried out at the Allison Division of General Motors, an operating temperature of 650°C is used. A single cell is schematically represented in Fig. 87. The overall reaction occurring in the cell is

$$2Li + Cl_2 \rightarrow 2LiCl \tag{3.8}$$

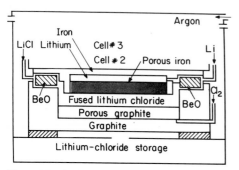

Figure 87   A lithium-chlorine regenerative fuel cell.[58]

Since the reaction product is the same as the electrolyte, there are no problems of change in electrolyte composition and concentration-overpotential problems are greatly reduced. Storage of reactants is quite simple. For example, chlorine may be stored as a liquid at a temperature of 30°C under 10-atm pressure. Lithium is stored as a solid.

The open-circuit voltage E of the system has been measured as a function of temperature t from the melting point of LiCl to about 850°C at 1-atm pressure and it may be expressed by the equation

$$E = 3.4906 - 0.64 \times 10^{-4}(t - 608) \quad \text{volts} \tag{3.9}$$

Plots of the open-circuit voltage and the calculated thermodynamic reversible potential as a function of temperature are shown in Fig. 88. The agreement is quite satisfactory.

The kinetics of the reactions at the electrodes were dealt with in Chap. 4. The only form of polarization loss in the cell is owing to the ohmic resistance of the electrolyte. The specific conductivity of LiCl at 650°C is 5.9 ohm^{-1} cm^{-1}. Laboratory power cells in which electrodes are spaced 6.5 mm apart show maximum power densities of the order of 6 watts cm^{-2}. The wide electrode spacing was necessary because of practical laboratory considerations. With closer electrode spacing, power densities of 10 to 20 watts cm^{-2} can be attained. This is about twenty to forty times better than that of the best hydrocarbon-oxygen fuel cell.

Because of the high cost of the reactants, this cell is used as a regenerative system, and becomes, in fact, a kind of secondary battery. The method of regeneration of the reactants is similar to the one used in industry for the

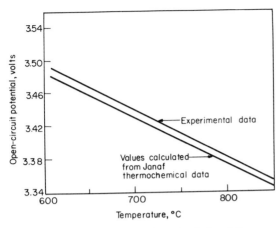

Figure 88 Plots of open circuit and calculated thermo-dynamic reversible cell potential for Li-Cl₂ fuel cell as a function of temperature.[58]

extraction of lithium. The discharging cell itself may be used for the recharging operation. An applied potential of 3.5 to 4 volts is necessary for the recharging operation.

In many ways the lithium-chlorine fuel-cell battery represents the nearest approach hitherto made in practice to the realization of the possibilities offered by an electrochemical power source. To begin with, its thermodynamic potential is near the maximum possible, because the two elements concerned are from extreme ends of the electrochemical series. The electrode reactions have very fast rate constants,[58,58a] and hence there is a negligible activation over-potential; the great problem of electrocatalysis has thus been elided. The fact that there is no solute, or that the solvent and solute are one, is an unusual and very attractive characteristic.

Moreover, the promised advances have been realized in practice. Looked at in terms of a fuel cell, an engineered multistack cell gives about 250 watts lb⁻¹, some five times greater than its nearest rival. The power per unit volume is 10 kw/ft³. The performance available from such cells for driving a car would correspond well to present-day cars driven by internal-combustion engines, and have marked advantages over these at low speeds.

There are three main real difficulties with such cells:

(*i*) A psychological difficulty associated with the presence of liquid chlorine and a high-temperature liquid. Protection for collision is assured in the weight figures given. The difficulty may be somewhat similar to that probably shown by the public at the beginning of the century in leaving horse-drawn vehicles to join the ranks of those utilizing evil-smelling explosive gasoline.

(*ii*) A start-up difficulty in the application to automotive traction. A number of untried solutions appear possible.

(*iii*) Material-stability problems. The cell has run continuously for less than 1,000 hr due to materials breakdown. The containment of lithium and chlorine is not a problem. But maintaining a satisfactory situation with the solvent LiCl (in which dissolved Li is present) is difficult. The existing problems, however, are not ones which alone should hold up, for more than a very few years, the development of this cell into a viable unit to drive electric cars. Questions of the disruption of existing situations and the availability as yet of the necessary electric power† are those that become determining.

3.2.2 Hydrogen-Bromine Fuel Cells

The reactions of hydrogen and of the halogens at electrodes have high exchange current densities. Thus, hydrogen and a halogen should form a suitable couple for a regenerative fuel cell. An additional advantage of this system is that it could be operated in aqueous solution at low temperatures.

One disadvantage of these aqueous electrolyte cells over molten-salt-formation cells (for example, Li-Cl$_2$ cells) is that concentration-overpotential phenomena arise at high current densities in the former case. In both the hydrogen-bromine and lithium-chlorine fuel cells, expensive reactants are used, and the only economical way of using them is as regenerative fuel cells. The hydrogen-bromine fuel cell was investigated by Ionics, Incorporated.[59] and the Douglas Aircraft Company, Inc.[60] A cutaway section of a single cell used for such studies is shown in Fig. 89. A thin sulfuric acid membrane separates the anode and cathode. The electrodes contain noble metal catalysts. In the regenerative system, bromine is kept in a closed compartment. Although

---

† Were all cars driven by rechargeable batteries, there would have to be about double the electricity-generating capacity. To obtain the desirable diminution in CO$_2$ pollution, this extra electricity must, of course, be from atomic sources.

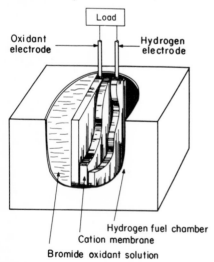

Figure 89 A cutaway section of a H$_2$-Br$_2$ fuel cell.[59a]

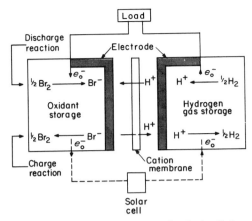

Figure 90   The H$_2$-Br$_2$ regenerative fuel cell for
the charging-discharging processes.[59b]

because of its considerably higher equivalent weight bromine used as the oxidant
appears to have a disadvantage as compared with oxygen, this is to some extent
offset by the fact that being a liquid, it can be conveniently handled.   It can be
stored in light plastic containers.   A schematic representation of a cell for the
discharge-recharge cycles is shown in Fig. 90.   In Fig. 91, the terminal-cell-
potential–current-density   relations   are   shown   for   hydrogen-oxygen   and
hydrogen-bromine fuel cells.[60]   Both show linear dependencies of the terminal-
cell potential on current density.   The higher slope in the case of the hydrogen-
bromine fuel cell is because of the higher internal resistance of the cell.   In both
cells, ion-exchange membranes were used as the electrolyte layer.   However,
because of the problem of migration of bromide ions through the membrane, the

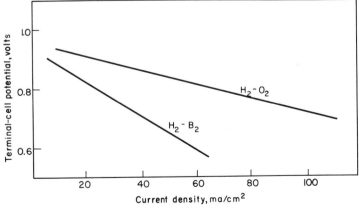

Figure 91   Terminal-cell-potential–current-density relation for H$_2$-O$_2$ and
H$_2$-Br$_2$ fuel cells using ion-exchange-membrane electrolytes.[60]

ion-exchange membrane in this cell has a finer structure.   Thus, the main problem with the cell is the internal resistance of the electrolyte layer.

At Ionics, Incorporated,[59] a current density of 80 ma cm^{-2} has been obtained at a terminal-cell potential of 1.05 volts.   This system shows promise of being developed into an efficient regenerative fuel cell, but seems to have been left in a relatively early stage of investigation.

3.3   Photochemically Regenerative Fuel Cells

3.3.1   *Inorganic Systems*

In this method, the products of the fuel-cell reaction are transformed into its reactants by light.   Because of the ample availability of solar energy, this method should be valuable, provided that there are suitable substances which can undergo photochemical dissociation.

Only a few inorganic systems have been investigated to date.   The nitric oxide–chlorine fuel cell,[61] in which the overall reaction is

$$2NO + Cl_2 \rightarrow 2NOCl \tag{3.10}$$

has a standard reversible-cell potential of 0.21 volt.   The reactants may be regenerated from NOCl in the liquid phase by light.   Under these conditions, the quantum yield (see Chap. 3, Sec. 6.3) is low because the back reaction is also rapid.   In the gas phase, regeneration is easier, although there is some problem of separating the NO and Cl_2.

Open-circuit potentials agree well with the reversible-cell potentials.   The currents obtainable are low, probably as a result of the low value of the reversible potential.

Another inorganic system that has been suggested is the hydrogen-iodine fuel cell.[62]   No results of cell performance are available.

3.3.2   *Organic Systems*

The principles of an organic photochemically regenerative fuel cell using an organic dye were outlined in Chap. 3, Sec. 6.3.   Such a system has been researched by the Electrochimica Corporation.[63]   A schematic representation of this system is shown in Fig. 13 of Chap. 3.   The system proflavine/ascorbic acid coupled with stannic chloride/stannous fluoride showed the best performance of the many couples that were investigated.   An open-circuit potential of 0.17 volt was observed.   The maximum power obtained was 20 μw cm^{-2}.   The poor performances are attributed mainly to low quantum efficiency, despite the good electrochemical efficiency obtained.

A general difficulty of photochemically regenerative systems is the low quantum yield for the regeneration process, which lowers the overall efficiency of the system.   A closely connected problem is the low solubility of these organic compounds.   However, these efficiencies are not much less than those obtained with solar cells.   These systems should be more economical than solar cells. Further investigation is necessary before an assessment can be made on these systems.

3.4 Radiochemically Regenerative Fuel Cells

3.4.1 *Principle of the Method*

In a radiochemically regenerative fuel cell, the products of the fuel-cell reaction are converted into its reactants by radiolysis. The net reaction is thus a conversion of nuclear energy to electrical energy *via* chemical energy. The essential difference between the electrochemical method and any of the other known methods of conversion of nuclear energy to electrical energy is that in the former case, the intermediary of chemical energy is involved, whereas in the latter cases, this is not the case. In most of the direct methods of conversion of nuclear to electrical energy, the ions generated by the nuclear radiation are directly involved. The principles of the direct methods and of the electrochemical ones are shown in Table 8[64] on pages 608–609. The table also shows a comparison of the relative performances of these energy conversion systems.

The efficiency of a radiochemically regenerative fuel cell is the product of two efficiencies: the efficiency of conversion of nuclear energy into chemical energy (ϵ_n) of the reactants of the fuel cell and the fuel-cell efficiency (ϵ_e). ϵ_n is obtained from the radiation yield g, which is defined as the number of molecules decomposed per 100 ev of radiation energy consumed.

3.4.2 *Hydrogen-Oxygen Fuel Cells*

The most extensively investigated radiochemically regenerative fuel cells are of this type.[65–67] Water, the product of the fuel-cell reaction, undergoes decomposition under the influence of γ radiation according to

$$H_2O^* \rightarrow H + OH \tag{3.11}$$

These radicals may dimerize to give molecular hydrogen and hydrogen peroxide. A possible detrimental reaction is the recombination of hydrogen and hydroxyl to produce water. The radiation yield depends on the specific ionization density of the radiation source and on the pH of the aqueous solution. g values for some types of radiation are given for the radiolysis of water[64] from oxygenated 0.8 N H_2SO_4 in Table 9. Hydrogen peroxide, formed by the dimerization of hydroxyl radicals, can be decomposed into oxygen and water by the action of some catalyst. The main reason for the low efficiency of this system is the low radiation yield for the decomposition of water. This is the result of a rapid recombination rate of hydrogen and hydroxyl radicals.

Rosenblum and English[65] were the first to investigate this type of fuel cell (Fig. 92). α rays emitted from ^{210}Po radiolyzed water. The efficiency of this system was less than 1 percent.

The stage of passing hydrogen peroxide through a catalyst was eliminated by Justi and coworkers,[66] who worked in strong alkaline solutions. The overall efficiency was again only about 1 percent.

TABLE 8 Comparison of Methods of Converting Nuclear to Electrical Energy[64]

Converter	Radiation	Method	Efficiency, percent ϵ_{act}	Efficiency, percent ϵ_{op}	Single-cell voltage, volts	Application	Damage by radiation
A. Physical							
1. Direct charging (vacuum dielectric)	α or β, uniform $\beta-$	Uniform radiation as charge carrier	15–20 >1	2–3	365,000	Good between −50 to +50°C	Vacuum needs pumping; dielectric damaged
2. Contact potential	α or $\beta-$	Gas ionized by rays between two methods	1–1.5	2–3	0.5–2	As flashlight battery	Corrosive gases produced O_2 at electrode by rays
3. Semiconductor junction battery	Soft, uniform $\beta-$	Radiation creates free electrons and defects	0.1–2	5–10	<0.25	Combination with transistors	Semiconductor damaged
4. Scintillation	Soft, uniform $\beta+$	Radiation produces light, photocell converts it	0.1–2		<0.25	Good at space temperatures	Semiconductor damaged
5. Neutron converter	Slow neutrons → α or $\beta-$	Neutron bombardment creates shortlived α or $\beta-$ emitters, then utilized as in No. 1	<0.7	1.5–2	See No. 1	Measures neutron flow	Undesired splitting; see No. 1
B. Electrochemical							
1. Radiolytically regenerated H_2/O_2 fuel cell	All particles that ionize water, also mixtures	Electrochemically combining separated O_2 and H_2 which are radiolysis products of water	<1	2.1	0.95	Large-scale utilization of radioactive garbage	None

No. / Cell	Radiation	Process			Efficiency	Remarks	Disadvantage
2. "Knallgas" fuel cell	All particles that ionize water, also mixtures	As above, with a $2H_2$-O_2 stoichiometric mixture not separated		2.1; ? for fission product (?)	0.95	As above	None
3. H/OH fuel cell	UV, X, γ, or β^-	Electrochemical burning of (mostly) radicals from water radiolysis	1.3		0.7–0.9	Analog of photo-cell; of only scientific interest	Decrease of selectivity
4. H_2/Fe^{3+} fuel cell	Type A: UV, X, α, or β^-	Electrochemical	1.7–2	5.5–6	0.77	Galvanic nuclear battery transportation	Separation damaged
	Type B: UV, X, γ, α, β^-; also mixtures	Using secondary radiolytic (Fe^{3+}, H_2) products; catching radicals, too	3			Can be combined with nuclear reactors	None
5. O_2/O_3 battery	Type A: UV, X, α, or β^-	Electrochemical reaction of ozone produced by radiolysis	?	20–25	0.84	Between 15 to 200°C; universal	Unknown
	Type B: UV, X, γ, or β; also mixtures		12–15			Very small units possible	None
6. Electrochemical homogeneous reactor	All rays that ionize water, also mixtures from homogeneous reactor or fission products	Combination of 3 with No. 1 or 2		5.5–6	0.95	To be combined with homogeneous reactor	Decrease of selective catalysis; atom-splitting at electrode

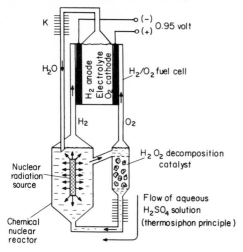

Figure 92   A radiochemically regenerative fuel cell of Rosenblum and English.[64]

This system was investigated very thoroughly at the Puerto Rico Nuclear Research Center.[67]   Methods were sought to prevent the recombination of hydrogen and hydroxyl radicals but with little success.

Attempts have been made to use the radicals formed by radiolysis of water.[68]   In these cases, either the fuel-cell electrodes are placed directly in the radiolyzed solution or some electrochemically active ions are used to trap the radicals (for example, Ce^4 and Fe^{3+} for trapping H radicals).

3.4.3   Other Types of Fuel Cells

Another system that has been examined at the Union Carbide Corporation is the hydrogen–ferric sulfate fuel cell.[69]   The reactions in the fuel cell are

$$H_2 \rightarrow 2H^+ + 2e_0^-$$ (3.12)

$$Fe^{3+} + e_0^- \rightarrow Fe^{2+}$$ (3.13)

TABLE 9   Radiation Yields for Radiolysis of Water for
Some Emitters from Oxygen-free 0.8 N H_2SO_4 Solution[64]

Type of radiation	$g(H)$	$g(OH)$	$g(H_2)$	$g(H_2O_2)$	$g(H_2O)$
$^{60}Co\text{-}\gamma$	3.65	2.95	0.45	0.80	4.55
$^{18}MeV\text{-}D^+$	2.39	1.75	0.71	1.03	3.81
$^8MeV\text{-}D^+$	1.71	1.45	1.05	1.17	3.80
$^{32}MeV\text{-}He^{2+}$	1.28	1.06	1.14	1.25	3.56
$^{18}B(\eta,\alpha)^7Li$	0.23	0.41	1.66	1.57	3.55

The overall reaction is

$$H_2 + 2Fe^{3+} \rightarrow 2H^+ + 2Fe^{2+} \tag{3.14}$$

The regeneration reaction is the reverse of (3.13). The regeneration is effected by irradiation of an oxygen-free ferrous sulfate solution with the high-energy γ emitter Co. This process has been extensively investigated in radiation dosimetry. The fuel-cell reactions are quite rapid. The regeneration process takes place with an efficiency of about 15 percent under conditions of low concentrations of hydrogen and ferric ion in solution. The efficiency of regeneration is lowered with increase in these concentrations.

In the studies at the Union Carbide Corporation, regeneration was carried out in a separate chamber to prevent losses in the fuel cell caused by concentration polarization and also to exclude the possibilities of radiation damage to the electrodes. In the fuel cell, a microporous polyvinyl chloride separator was used to prevent transport of ferric ion to the anode. The electrolyte was 0.25 to 0.5 M $FeSO_4$, 0.025 to 0.05 M $Fe_2(SO_4)_3$, 1 M H_2SO_4. Current densities of 10 ma cm^{-2} at terminal-cell potentials of 0.5 volt were obtained.

A system that shows a high overall efficiency is the oxygen-ozone battery.[70] The fuel-cell reactions are

Anode:

$$H_2O \rightarrow 2H^+ + \tfrac{1}{2}O_2 + 2e_0^- \tag{3.15}$$

Cathode:

$$O_3 + 2H^+ + 2e_0^- \rightarrow H_2O + O_2 \tag{3.16}$$

The overall reaction in the cell is thus

$$O_3 \rightarrow \tfrac{3}{2}O_2 \tag{3.17}$$

and has a standard reversible potential of 0.84 volt. The regeneration reaction is the conversion of oxygen to ozone by the action of α, β, or γ radiation. The conversion efficiency is high in this case (radiation yield is 12 to 15, corresponding to an efficiency of 20 to 25 percent).

The hydrogen-halogen systems are being currently examined at the Puerto Rico Nuclear Research Center.[67] The advantages of these systems is that high yields are possible and both half-cell reactions in the fuel cell are fast.

3.4.4 Comparison of the Electrochemical with the Other Methods of Conversion of Nuclear to Electrical Energy

The electrochemical approach of conversion of nuclear energy may prove to be simpler than the methods presently adopted. The advantage of radiochemically regenerative fuel cells over nuclear reactors is that no critical mass or hot reactors are necessary. Further, the Carnot limitation for the efficiency does not arise in the former case but does so in the latter. Thus, if radiochemical regeneration of reactants from the fuel-cell products takes place with 100 percent efficiency, the overall efficiency is then determined by the fuel-cell efficiency. This excellent prospect is to some extent diminished by the fact that an efficiency of considerably less than 100 percent is obtained in the regeneration process at the present time. One of the main reasons for a loss of efficiency is because of the recombination of the products of the regeneration chamber. The introduction of an electric or magnetic field in the regeneration chamber may prevent the recombination, since this process probably occurs when the regeneration particles are in an ionized state. It might be possible to radiolize steam in contact with palladium and thereby obtain a high degree of separation of H from OH.

In Table 8, the direct methods of conversion of nuclear energy to electrical energy are compared with the electrochemical ones. The efficiencies are of the same order in all cases except that in the case of the oxygen-ozone battery, the electrochemical path yields a far greater efficiency than other paths.

4 BIOCHEMICAL FUEL CELLS

4.1 Biological Systems as Fuel Cells

Del Duca and Fuscoe[71] developed the concept of biological systems as fuel cells.† Cells consume organic materials—food—and oxygen. At the same time, it has been shown that a potential difference exists between one part of a cell and another and that a corresponding ionic current flows through the surrounding biological fluid under the influence of this potential difference. It is therefore reasonable to regard a biological cell as an electrochemical energy converter—one end oxidizes food, the other reduces oxygen, ions pass through the solution, and presumably there is electron transport in the cell.

A more speculative aspect of this matter concerns the mechanism of electron transport. It is suggested that this occurs by a series of consecutive redox processes involving enzymes, in particular, the Fe-containing enzymes known as cytochromes. The transport of electrons from one center to another in biological materials may probably be rationalized in terms of electron tunneling. For example, if glucose is the food, it may lose H_2 at first, which may ionize to provide H^+ ions and electrons. These are then able to interchange with one redox system after another until they have transported themselves across the cell to a part at which O_2 undergoes reduction (see Fig. 93).

Such a model is at present very rudimentary but serves to explain the outstanding fact that cells exhibit potential differences. Further, such a model could lead to the beginning of an electrochemical theory of the mechanism of the effect of drugs. Depending upon the dipolar and adsorptive properties of drugs,[71b]

---

† Bockris and Srinivasan[71a] noted that the efficiency of energy conversion in the body is too large to be explained in terms of a heat engine; it is clearly not photovoltaic. No other principle of the conversion of chemical to mechanical work exists except the electrochemical, the functioning of which is, then, consistent with the high energy efficiency.

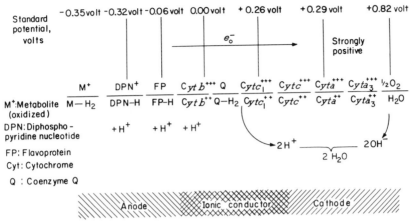

Figure 93 Analogy of biological oxidation of a metabolite to a conventional electrochemical oxidation reaction.[71]

they will cause an increase or decrease of current across either anode or cathode of certain types of biological cells and thus effect their actions.

The model suggests its research, for there should be, if it is correct, a series of cytochromic enzymes spatially placed in a cell to accomplish the electron transport, and they should be identifiable and in a certain order (cf. Fig. 93) with respect to their redox potentials.

The individual cell consists of two protein layers between which is a layer of lipids.   It is possible to regard the two protein layers somewhat as electrodes, in the way roughly illustrated in Fig. 94.

This pan-electrochemical theory of biological activity suggests other possibilities, particularly perhaps for understanding the mechanisms of the functioning of the brain, which might be described as an "electrochemical computer."   Correspondingly, for a long time there has been a partial electrochemical theory of the electric currents that pass through nerves.[72]   A primary concept here has been that of the Donnan membrane equilibrium, according to which the semipermeability of membranes gives rise to a difference of ionic concentrations on both sides of a membrane and hence a type of concentration cell.   Thus, an electrical stimulus in the brain causes—albeit the mechanism thereof is unclear—the membrane of an adjacent nerve segment to change its permeability with respect to sodium ions and these ions flow inward while potassium ions flow outward.   This change of concentration causes the potential difference, which caused it, to fall to zero (it is supposed that the sole cause of the potential difference is the concentration difference).   A repetition of this process takes place in each cell segment, and the consequent "hopping along" of the original stimulating potential difference is equivalent to the (relatively slow) transport of current along nerves.

Del Duca and Fuscoe[71] point out that such a mechanism is not only incomplete with respect to a model for the dependence of permeability upon

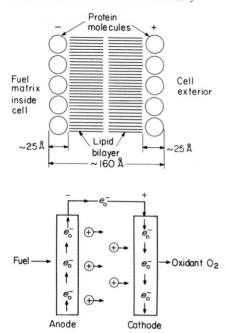

Figure 94 Resemblance of gross structure of membrane around biological cell (magnification $180,000\times$) to an electrochemical cell.[71]

potential, but it also says nothing which relates the energy of the metabolic reactions to the changes of ionic concentrations and potential differences that exist across cell membranes. An alternative view is that the energy-producing function is not separated from the production of potential. It may then be regarded as the fuel-cell equivalent of the thermodynamic energy of the metabolic reactions of a cell. The ionic transport observed would then not be a primary happening in a cell but something which occurs only as a secondary result of the anodic and cathodic reactions of the electrochemical cells.

Such a revolutionary and electrochemical viewpoint in biology appears to be supported by the work of Mandel,[72a] who observed that the relation of current density across a membrane to the change of applied potential obeys the Tafel equation; and, in particular, that the transfer coefficient is ½. The occurrence of this latter coefficient is difficult to rationalize except in terms of a rate-determining interfacial electron charge transfer. One may ask whether this is the fundamental step which controls many biochemical reactions involving a flow of electricity.

4.2 The Possibility of Tapping Biologically Produced Electrical Energy: Primary or Direct Biochemical Fuel Cells

Given the above concept—that some, possibly all, biological reactions must be understood in terms of electrodic reactions—there may be a possibility of extracting electricity directly from a living system.   It *is* practical to think of making a biochemical macromodel of a biological cell.   The protein walls of the cell are replaced by metal electrodes, the biological fluid which surrounds the cell by, for example, sulfuric acid, and the liquid by a metallic conductor; but the electrode reactions are meant to be analogous, or similar, to those occurring at biological cells in the body.   Moreover, enzymes are added because they are present in the biological reactions, although their function is not clearly understood (intermediate redox catalysts between the metallic electrode and the complex—hence perhaps slow—biochemical redox systems in solution?).

A *primary* or direct biochemical fuel cell (DBFC) consists, therefore, of one half-cell in which there is a metal electrode, biochemical redox couple in solution, and an enzyme to help it function; whereas the other half-cell is, for example, an oxygen electrode.

A list of possible couples with their corresponding enzymes is given in Table 10, the standard reversible redox potentials being quoted for a pH of 7.

TABLE 10   Open-circuit Potentials of Some Biochemical Half-cell Reactions at a pH of 7[71]

Fuel-electrode couple	Enzyme	Open-circuit potential at pH of 7, volts
Acetate-acetaldehyde	Xanthine oxidase	−0.58
Lactic acid/xanthine	Xanthine oxidase	−0.39
Gluconolactone/glucose	Glucose oxidase	−0.36
Cystine/cysteine	None	−0.33
Acetaldehyde/ethanol	Alcohol dehydrogenase	−0.20
Pyruvate/lactate	Lactic dehydrogenase	−0.18
Oxaloacetate/malate	Malic dehydrogenase	−0.16
Fumarate/succinate	Succinic dehydrogenase	+0.02
Dehydroascorbate/ascorbate	Ascorbic oxidase	+0.06
Ferricytochrome c/ferrocytochrome c		+0.27
Oxidized cyt. oxidase/cytochrome oxidase		+0.29
$O_2 + 4H^+ + 4e^- = 2H_2O$		+0.82

As an example, Bean[73] of Ford Aeroneutronic has studied the electrochemical oxidation of aromatic pyruvic acids.   At Pt electrodes, using indole-3-pyruvic acid, a current of 350 μa cm^{-2} at a cell potential of 0.2 volt has been observed.   The enzymes used were isolated from the host organism.

Relatively low power densities (in the region of 10 Mw cm^{-2}) and energy densities (in the region of 10 kwh ft^{-3}) are obtained from such cells, probably because of the poor electrode kinetics of the reactions concerned.   However, they may have certain uses. For example, they could operate as a low-power-density source in an isolated region, e.g., in the sea operating with fuel from algae, for years without attention. Alternatively, they may be used inside the body, as permanent implants, to power various microelectronic devices, which usually need a maximum power in the milliwatt range.

In order that one may get a picture of the process that occurs during electrochemical metabolism, one can consider the oxidation of glucose[74] according to

$$\text{Glucose} \xrightarrow{\text{DPN}} \text{Gluconolactone } (C_6H_{10}O_6) + 2H \tag{4.1}$$

$$\text{DPN} + 2H \longrightarrow \text{DPNH}_2 \xrightarrow{\text{MED}} \text{MED} \cdot H_2 + \text{DPN}$$

$$\text{DPN} + 2H^+ + 2e_0^- \qquad\qquad \text{MED} \cdot + 2H^+ + 2e_0 \tag{4.2}$$

other enzymes

$$\text{CO}_2 + \text{H}_2\text{O}$$

The system glucose–glucose oxidase was coupled with an oxygen cathode in a DBFC.[75] No current was observed under anaerobic conditions in the anode chamber. On addition of methylene blue, the potential of the anode was altered and current was produced in the external circuit. It was concluded that the methylene blue acted as an alternate hydrogen acceptor and the reduced dye was anodically oxidized.

Methane was anodically oxidized in the presence of the aerobic methane oxidizing bacterium pseudomonas methanica. The currents obtainable were extremely small.[76]

The Magna American Corporation[77] investigated a urea-air cell. An open-circuit potential of 0.8 volt and a short-circuit current density of only 3.6 ma cm^{-2} were obtained.

A convenient way in which a direct biochemical fuel cell could work is if the reduced form of an enzyme can be oxidized electrochemically at the electrode and the oxidized form could react with some species in solution (e.g., glucose). Several enzyme systems that were tested showed negligible activity.[78] Some that showed electrochemical activity are the flavo enzymes[79] (glucose oxidase, D amino oxidase). The presence of oxygen sometimes makes it possible for the enzymes to take part in an electrochemical reaction.

From the above results, it appears that the development of a direct biochemical fuel cell is a long way off. However, more work is needed before one can make a final conclusion on these systems.

4.3 Secondary or Indirect Biochemical Fuel Cells

The slowness of electrode reactions (and hence the low energy density) in primary biochemical fuel cells demands an alternative, and the one which began to be investigated from about 1962 was the indirect biochemical cell (IBFC).

The enzyme was still present and it acted† on the complex biochemical material in solution and broke it down to a product, for example, H_2, which underwent more rapid electrode reactions.   Some typical systems are shown in Table 11.

TABLE 11   Indirect Generation of Chemical Fuels from Biochemical Fuels and Their Energy/Weight Ratio[71]

Natural fuel	Natural source	Catalyst	Gaseous fuel	lb kwh⁻¹
Urea	Urine	Urease (crystalline enzyme)	NH_3	0.83
Amino acids	Protein digests	Amino acid oxidase (enzyme)	NH_3	1.2–3
Formic acid		Formic dehydrogenase (enzyme)	H_2	1.8
Propionic acid	Fats, oils	Methanobacterium propionicum (live bacteria)	CH_4	1.0

A 64-cell urea-air battery was constructed by TRW, Inc.[80]   It delivered 0.7 amp at a cell voltage of 28 volts.   The cell [in fact, an NH_3-air cell (see Sec. 2.4.1)] operates at 25°C and uses 3 M KCl in a citrate buffer at pH 6.

Hydrogen may be produced from formic acid using the bacteria *Escherichia coli*.   A systematic study of the rate of hydrogen evolution from formic acid using *E*-coli was made varying the enzyme and substrate concentration.[81]   There was a decrease in the rate of production of hydrogen with time, which was shown to be owing to the decrease in enzyme activity.   The electrooxidation of formic acid in the presence of large quantities of bacteria in solution gives rise to the same current-potential behavior observed for electrooxidation when hydrogen is bubbled through the solution without the bacteria in solution (Fig. 95).

The oxidation of glucose in the presence of yeast[74] is shown in Fig. 96. The first curve is obtained with yeast cells directly in contact with the electrode, whereas the second curve shows the current-potential behavior with the yeast cells separated from the electrode with a parchment paper.   Higher polarization is observed when the yeast cells are in contact with the electrode, probably due to poisoning of the electrode by adsorption of the yeast.

At the present time, the indirect method appears more promising.   The indirect method for biofuels may be compared with the indirect method for conventional organic fuels.   The efficiency of these systems, however, is fairly low at the present time.

---

† An enzyme is of course a catalyst suspended in solution.   It may be speculated that it, too, acts in a fuel-cell mode in bringing about reactions; i.e., on the enzyme surface there are sides at which electrons enter, supplied by the fuel, and others at which they exit to oxygen. Enzymes show a significant conductivity.   They might be regarded as electrodic biocatalysts.

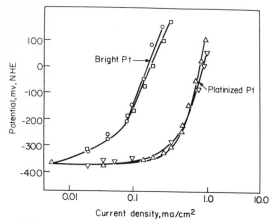

Figure 95 A comparison of the current-density–potential relation for the oxidation of formic acid on bright and platinized Pt electrodes; $\triangle$, $\bigcirc$ with the bacteria present; $\bigtriangledown$, $\square$ with hydrogen bubbled through the solution.[81]

4.4 Probable Applications of Biochemical Fuel Cells

It is of interest to note that about 24 percent of the countries of the world, containing about 37 percent of the world's population, have a yearly electrical energy consumption of 20 kwh per capita. At a 50 percent conversion rate, human urinary wastes could supply 18 kwh per capita per year. The bacteria *Bacillus pasteurii* (bacteria are used only on account of the enzymes† they

† One may speculate that there is a direct relation between the catalytic action of enzymes in biochemical fuel cells and of fertilizers in biological growth. The latter depends presumably upon electrochemical reactions, and these are then increased in velocity by the presence of certain enzymes which the fertilizer provides.

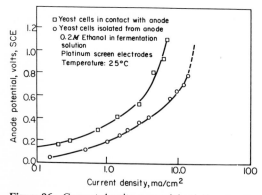

Figure 96 Current-density–potential relation for the oxidation of glucose in the presence of yeast. (*a*) Yeast cells directly in contact with the electrode; (*b*) yeast cells isolated from the electrode.[74]

contain) has been used by the Magna American Corporation in this connection.[77]

Indirect biochemical fuel cells would seem to have an important role in underdeveloped countries, e.g., as power sources in remote locations.

Some exciting possibilities of a far-reaching understanding of biological mechanisms in terms of electrochemical concepts exist in this area: (1) biochemical reactions may occur in electrochemical converters to give electrical energy; (2) the mechanism of the action of drugs may receive light; (3) sewage disposal on earth as well as in space missions might be carried out by using driven cells to oxidize waste matters to CO_2 perhaps locally. The beginning of bioelectrochemistry was many years ago. In 1786, Galvani[82] discovered electricity in frogs' muscles. In 1912, Potter[83] observed that the electric current and potential differences were associated with the oxidation of glucose in the presence of bacteria. Cohen,[84] in 1931, found that disintegration of organic compounds by micro-organisms yielded electrical energy. However, the entire area of electrochemistry of biological and biochemical reactions is still at a beginning stage in fundamental research in terms of modern concepts.

5 SUMMARIZING REMARKS ON THE PRESENT STATUS OF FUEL CELLS

5.1 General Criteria for Determining Present Status

A worker who has not been in the area of electrochemical energy conversion long sometimes asks the question: "Which is the best fuel cell at present?" Such a question reveals that the questioner possesses a less than complete grasp of the field of electrochemical energy conversion.

Because of the concentration of public discussion about the use of fuel cells as a power source for vehicular transportation, there has thus been some misunderstanding of how one must evaluate fuel cells. Fuel cells must not be judged solely in contrast with internal-combustion engines. The comparison between internal-combustion engines and fuel cells cannot be made directly. An internal-combustion engine is an energy converter which produces mechanical power. It should be compared with an electrochemical engine, namely, a combination between an electrochemical power source and an electric motor. However, the electrochemical energy converter is a much wider concept than the internal-combustion engine. It can supply electrical energy and power at all ranges of situations in which power is needed, from power sources which need milliwatts to those which need megawatts. Its range of potential usefulness is enormously greater than that of the internal-combustion engine. Correspondingly, however, the circumstances surrounding its use—for example, whether the weight needed for one unit of power is important or not—varies greatly with the situation concerned.

There is, thus, no question about which is the "best" fuel cell at a given time. It all depends on what is important with respect to its use—whether high power density is necessary, whether high efficiency is necessary, whether volume is important, whether the cost of fuel is a primary consideration, etc.

What has emerged from the first ten years of extensive work on electrochemical energy conversion? There are three main fuel cells—apart from those larger and more detailed classifications that have been given in this chapter: (1) the hydrogen-oxygen (air) fuel cell; (2) the hydrocarbon-oxygen (air) fuel cell; (3) the reformer fuel cell. Before making some brief comments on these systems, it is worthwhile examining Table 12 (on pages 622 to 623) which gives an up-to-date (April, 1969) picture of fuel cells which have been built into multicell units and concerning which reports have been published.

5.2 Hydrogen-Oxygen (Air) Fuel Cells

The maximum power density reached with this fuel cell is about 100 Mw cm^{-2} at temperatures below 100°C and increases to about 500 Mw cm^{-2} at temperatures in the region of 200°C. The power/weight ratio of this type of fuel cell is of the order of 30 watts lb^{-1}.

Several more indirect considerations govern the use of this cell in actual situations. In particular is the difficulty of storing hydrogen in such a way that weight is kept down sufficiently and the danger arising from explosion which must be eliminated. Thus, at the present time, the use of a hydrogen-air fuel cell is limited to one in which the power/weight ratio needed is less than 30 watts lb^{-1} and in which violent collision is not a practical possibility (i.e., it is not used for vehicles).

However, hydrogen-air fuel cells offer great possibilities. It seems probable that there will be improved ways found to store hydrogen, probably in solid form or in lower weight alloys, or plastics. More importantly, the price of hydrogen has fallen greatly in recent years. Cheap electricity in large quantities (from atomic sources) should decrease the price still further.

It is possible that the "pan-hydrogen theory of energy distribution" will come into use, namely, that hydrogen will be produced by electrolysis in large quantities at atomic power stations and will be distributed by pipelines to consumers, whereupon it will be reconverted to electricity by means of fuel cells at the source where the power is required (heat being produced by direct burning of H_2).

Research in hydrogen-oxygen electrochemical converters is at an advanced state as far as the anode is concerned. The major topics of research concern the cathode, of which much is still to be done, and also the methods of storage of hydrogen.

At the present time, most hydrogen-oxygen generators work with alkaline solutions because it is then possible to use nonnoble metals as cathode materials.

It is sometimes preferable to use acid solutions for various reasons (e.g., carbonate formation when using air instead of pure oxygen). Doped tungsten bronzes are possible materials for cathodes.[21]

5.3   Hydrocarbon-Oxygen (Air) Fuel Cells

Maximum power densities are in the region of 0.1 watt cm^{-2} at temperatures in the region of 150°C. The power/weight ratio of such cells is less than 10 watts lb^{-1}.

The best catalysts at present are platinum, or alloys of platinum, though not sufficiently effective. Power densities of at least five times higher than the ones presently achieved are needed to make the cells practical. It is possible, however, that the situation could be radically changed if electrodes corresponding to a more rational design of porous electrodes, discussed in Chap. 5, were made. These would lead to higher limiting currents, and it can be shown that with electrodes of low i_0 the power density per geometric square centimeter is roughly proportional to the limiting current.

The objection to the present hydrocarbon cells is the cost per kilowatt, which is high because of the large amount of platinum needed. This may contain a misconception, as has been suggested in Chap. 5, because the platinum is largely wasted in its present random distribution throughout the catalyst: Since most of the current is generated in a small region of the electrode for practical power outputs, pumping the electrolyte through the electrode should greatly increase the power density. Either of these two solutions—pumping or the use of electrodes with localization of catalysts—would be expected to reduce the catalyst needed by about 10^2 times (a change which would also solve the difficulty of lack of platinum availability; Chap. 6, Sec. 1).

It is possible, however, that other catalysts can be used in hydrocarbon cells. These will not be other metals, because nearly all of them dissolve in the potential regions corresponding to that in which the hydrocarbon cell works. The organic semiconductor electrode pioneered by Mehl and Hale[85] gives promise for use of these organic substances in redox reactions, and speculatively, for the oxidation of hydrocarbons as well.

In summary, the main goal of developing hydrocarbon fuel cells is to produce low-cost power. It is an area that has become open for research because of recent advances in the construction of electrodes and the fact that the field of electrocatalysis is very underdeveloped.

There is the alternative of reforming hydrocarbons for production of fuel for hydrogen-oxygen electrochemical converters. It is an interim path until sufficient progress is made in electrocatalysis research to enable the direct cells to be used.

5.4   Reformer Fuel Cells

The maximum power density of cells of this type is up to about 400 Mw cm^{-2} and the power/weight ratios are of the order of 30 watts lb^{-1}. There is, of course, the disadvantage of the high operating temperature in these cells, but the carbonate electrolytes used are relatively inert.

TABLE 12 The Status of Fuel-cell Batteries (April, 1969)

					Single-cell
System	*Company or institution*	*Design power output, kw*	*Anode catalyst*	*Cathode catalyst*	*Electrolyte*
Hydrogen-oxygen	General Electric	1	Pt	Pt	H_2SO_4
Hydrogen-oxygen	Union Carbide	1	C/Pt	C	KOH
Hydrogen-oxygen	Justi-Varta	1.0	Ni	Ag	KOH
Hydrogen-oxygen (liquid cooling)	Allis-Chalmers	5	Pt	Ag	KOH
Hydrogen-oxygen	Bacon–Pratt and Whitney			Lithated	
Hydrogen-oxygen	Westinghouse		Ni	nickel oxide	KOH
Hydrogen-oxygen	Chloride Electric Storage	1	Nonnoble metal	Nonnoble metal	KOH
Hydrogen-air (radiation cooled)	Allis-Chalmers	0.2	Pt	Ag	KOH
Hydrogen-air (gas cooled)	Allis-Chalmers	2	Pt	Ag	KOH
Methanol-oxygen	Esso	0.12	Pt	Pt	H_2SO_4
Methanol-oxygen	Allis-Chalmers	0.5	Pt-Pd	Ag	KOH
Decane-air	Esso Research	0.005	Pt	Pt	H_3PO_4
Methanol-air (indirect)	Shell Research	5	Pt	Pt	KOH
Natural gas-air (indirect)	Broers TNO	0.02	Ni	Ag or CuO	Fused carbonates and alkali aluminate
Natural gas-air (indirect)	Institute of Gas Technology		Ni	NiO or CuO	Fused carbonates and metal oxide
Gasoline-air (indirect)	Texas Instruments	1	Ni	Ag	Fused Na + Li carbonates
Carbon-air	Jacques	1.5	C	Fc	Fused NaOH
Coal-oxygen (indirect)	Westinghouse	0.1			Zirconia + yttria (solid)
Hydrazine-air	Allis-Chalmers	0.3	NiB	Pt	KOH
Hydrazine-air	Chloride Electric Storage	1	Ni	Nonnoble metal	KOH
Hydrazine-oxygen	Electrochimica Corp.	0.1–0.5	Pt		KOH
Hydrazine-air	Monsanto Research	0.6			
Hydrazine-air	Shell Research	2.5	Ni	Pd	KOH
Hydrazine-oxygen (or air)	Union Carbide	0.6	Pd	C	KOH
Hydrazine-oxygen	Union Carbide		Pd	C	KOH
Sodium amalgam-air	Kellogg	15		C	NaOH
Zinc-air	Electric Storage Battery				
Aluminum-air	Zaromb Research	0.07		Ag (or Pt)	KOH
Moving tape	Monsanto Research		Mg	C	$MgBr_2$
Potassium-mercury (thermally regenerative)	General Motors	5			KOH, KBr, KI
Lithium-chlorine (electrically regenerative)	General Motors	1–100		C	LiCl

Operating temperature, °C	Center voltage efficiency, %	Power density, mw/cm²	Power/weight, watts/lb	Power/volume, kw/ft³	Life tests, hr	Cost, $/kw Present	Projected	Applications, other comments
40–60	50–60	100	15	0.7	1,000			Electric power for space vehicles
65	65	50–150	24–72	1–3	5,000			Military and space
40–60	65	40	10.7		12,000			Stationary and mobile power sources
90	77	94	33.5	2.22	2,200			Advanced space vehicles
250	75	400	10	1.0	2,000			Electric power for space vehicles
0–70	50	60	10	0.7	1,000			
90	78		10	0.42	1,500			Aerospace
90	74	150	20	1.2	3,500			Aerospace
60	33	40	6		700		1,000	
60	31	25	5	0.6				
150	30	35			5,000			
60	50	100	25	1.0	1,000	1,000		Military
720	60	100	10 (estd.)	0.6 (estd.)	2,000		600	Large-scale power production (7 skw)
700	70	55		1	10,000			On-site power generation
700	70	30–70	15–35	0.6–1.2	200–500	5,000	1,000	
500	83	100			4,000			
1,000	58	154						
140–170	55	53	25	1.3	500			Power/wt. and power/volume ratios include 12 hr fuel supply
−30 to +70	45	70	16	1.2	500			
30–45	60–70	70–120	10–20	0.7	800–1,000			Communication and relay station, portable power (60–250 watts)
60	40–50	120	60	7	1,000	1,000		Military
65	55	75	12	1	500			Military
65	50	40–100						Military
25	66	150						Electrically powered vehicles, chemically rechangeable
25–40	35	50–80	25–40	1.0	1,000	1,000	100	Electrically powered vehicles, chemically rechangeable
25	84	34	60	5.2				
300	60	250	25	10				Electric power for space vehicles
650	80	40,000	100–200	5–10	2,000			Vehicle and military missile and torpedo power plants

Very wide ranges of fuels could be used for these cells—for example, coal—because of the necessity of producing only H_2, CO, and CO_2. Rubbish, grass, wood—all could be used as fuels to give rise to sufficient CO and CO_2 to power such cells.

This cell appears to have a very considerable future as a universal low-cost electricity producer used for conversion of the large reserves of natural gas recently discovered in Europe.

5.5 Other Types of Fuel Cells

There are a number of other fuel cells that use unusual fuels, such as hydrazine, the viability of which depends entirely upon the cost of production of the fuel at some future time.

Although electrochemical energy storers are not the subject of this book, some of the newer ones have been mentioned because they have often evolved from a fuel-cell program. They are likely to take the place, during the next few decades, in a number of situations in which at present pollutive internal-combustion sources operate, for example, the powering of vehicular transportation. One of these is the lithium-chlorine cell. The power density of this cell is of the order of 10 watts cm^{-2} (*sic*) and the power per unit weight is projected to about 4 lb kw^{-1}. These are outstanding figures and are better than those of any cell in operation at present. The material problems are significant owing to the corrosive nature of lithium dissolved in lithium chloride and of chlorine on cell materials.

The sodium-sulfur cell gained notoriety in 1966 in connection with the Ford Motor Company's development of electrochemical vehicular transportation.[86] The principal point of this cell is that it separates sodium from sulfur by a membrane of β alumina. This membrane, remarkably, allows atomic sodium to dissolve in it in an ionized state and to be transported through the membrane with sufficiently small resistance to make a practical cell.

The concept of an alkali metal in contact with a membrane on the other side of which is an aqueous alkaline solution contained in a cylinder of porous metal through which permeates air is one which is of great promise.[87] Here, of course, the main problem is the membrane research.

The situation at the time of completion of the writing of this book is that the developments that have taken place in the past few years in electrochemical energy conversion are now beginning to be accompanied by developments for vehicular transportation on the electrochemical energy storage side. The electrochemical energy converters were stimulated by NASA's need for the storage of a large *amount* of energy per unit weight and it was for this reason that an electrochemical method of energy *conversion* was chosen. In the vehicular transportation problem the aim is different: it is to obtain the maximum power per unit weight with the storage of only a few—say about 100 to 300—kilowatt hours of energy.

The essential concern here is to reduce the evolution of noxious fumes into the atmosphere and, secondarily,† the prevention of the injection into it of the noxious fumes as with internal-combustion engines.

Although these two needs—low weight sources of energy and sources of power that do not pollute the atmosphere—are of immense importance, it would be a misunderstanding to think that the development of electrochemical power sources depended upon their rapid practical fulfillment. The place in which electrochemical energy conversion is advantageous is entirely clear: up to about 100 kw and up to about four weeks. In situations with these needs, fuel cells will be developed and used independently of the complex situation relating to pollution, which, in its short-term effects on the development of electrochemically powered transportation, depends upon the strength of the effective wish of the community in comparison with the strength of the oil companies and manufacturers of motor vehicles (whose considerable resources will, according to the normal law of competitiveness, be used to delay the end of the present era of internal-combustion engines and its replacement by the atomic-electrochemical engine). Few aspects of the future are more certain than the increase in the direct use of electricity which will come increasingly from atomic energy. But there are intrinsic limits (in the region of tens of tons) to the minimum *possible* (not feasible) weight of atomic reactors. In mobile situations in which the carrying of a 10- to 100-ton energy source is not practicable, electrochemical power sources are the only devices hitherto suggested in which the electrical energy that will become available from atomic fission, and even fusion, can be stored and yet be made available immediately on demand.

6 SUMMARY OF THE PROBABLE APPLICATIONS OF FUEL CELLS

The applications of fuel cells in practice depend not only upon their electro-chemistry and engineering, but upon the relative economics of the operation of the cells in competition with other sources of power and political influences used against developing them. In this respect, an excellent review, entitled "Fuel Cell Economics and Commercial Applications," has been published by Verstraete et al.[88] This source has been extensively used in the following summary.

One statement must be made initially. All estimates of situations involve assumptions. The estimates made by the authors quoted depend upon assumptions concerning the cost of hydrogen and methanol. However, 1968 costs were utilized; and if hydrogen or methanol were used as fuels on a very large scale, the price of these fuels would most likely become significantly lowered so that a number of the predictions given below would become more favorable, and further possibilities could be considered (see point *xii* below).

---

† Secondarily, because pollution by partly burned hydrocarbons from internal-combustion engines can be partly removed by chemical means; or external combustion (steam engines) can greatly reduce it.

The future prospects may be summarized as follows:

(*i*) *Space power:* The very high cost of raising every pound of material in space ($5,000/lb) lays a great stress upon lightness of the power source carried. For a given amount of energy needed in a certain time, of the order of ten to some hundreds of hours, the fuel cell produces by far the lightest way of carrying a given amount of electrical energy; thus fuel-cell power for space and on the moon provides a clear advantage over other sources of on-board power. It is not known to what extent this will prove true for postlunar flights of more than a few weeks, where photovoltaic cells may become lighter.

(*ii*) *Portable generating sets* seem to be a favorable field for fuel cells. Here, already, fuel cells appear to be competitive, as compared with conventional sources. Low-temperature fuel cells have a favorable position for operating times of 3,000 to 4,000 hr per year, using methanol as a fuel.

(*iii*) *Power sources for isolated centers:* The transportation costs of fuel to isolated centers act in favor of the low-temperature hydrogen cells and stress the advantage of fuel cells compared with conventional sources.

(*iv*) *Forklift and small handling trucks* (vehicles involving frequent stopping and idling) appear to form a suitable application in the 10-kw range.

(*v*) *Automobile traction* offers prospects for vehicles, the characteristics of which are those of delivery and perhaps sufficiently large trucks. Methanol cells, or possible hydrogen, if its cost is somewhat lower than at present, would be suitable.

(*vi*) *Railway traction* presents favorable situations. The most favorable is offered by shunting engines. High-temperature cells could be used in this field.

(*vii*) *Naval propulsion* apears to be favorable. This applies particularly to submarine propulsion and also to surface vessels. Since atomic power for ships is uneconomical except for very large ones, high-temperature fuel cells offer advantages, in respect to cost, over steam turbines, particularly if natural gas and coal could be used.

(*viii*) *Marine deep-submergence vessels* offer a unique situation for fuel cells at the present time.

(*ix*) *Low-temperature liquid electrolyte cells*, using reformed hydrogen, and high-temperature cells, consuming natural gas, would provide cheaper power to *basic power plants, electrometallurgical plants, peak-power units*, and *isolated centers* (*mining camps, farms*).

(*x*) *Prosthetic* (*biological*) *applications:* Fuel-cell powered heart pacers would have considerable advantages over pacers powered by batteries, which at present must be recharged every few years. Prosthetic situations appear to offer a wide area for fuel-cell applications. Of the two possibilities being intensively researched for the development of an artificial heart, one involves an internally transplanted fuel cell driving an electric pump.

(*xi*) *Recreational applications:* There are a number of applications involving nonessential activities. The provision of local power at camp sites, or portably for campers, and for such applications as scuba diving, appears to be a fertile area for fuel cells. In the luxury recreation class, yachts, the so-called land yachts, and travel trailers could be self-contained for longer periods of time by using fuel cells.

(*xii*) *Conventional cars:* One of the most important potential uses of fuel cells would be made from possible to probable by a significant diminution in the price of hydrogen†: namely, fuel cells for conventional cars. Here condensed (perhaps solid?) hydrogen-air fuel cells would become attractive and of great sociological importance because of the complete elimination of noise and pollution.

This summary is one which results from economic considerations of applications available on the basis of *present* technology. It does not take into account what may be expected on the basis of further fundamental research, above all in the field of electrocatalysis; nor the effects of violent price reductions, as appears a possibility for a few fuels, notably hydrazine. Further, no consideration has been given to the possibilities arising from radiochemically regenerative fuel cells, or from biochemical fuel cells, both of which appear to be very underresearched.

Our considerations in this chapter have been factual, technological, and economically oriented. Such a down-to-earth summary of the situation at the end of the first decade of modern fuel-cell research is, we think, desirable. However, the future use of fuel cells is not adequately indicated thus. The first decade of development has suffered a rush of funding to areas in which the main lack is in fundamental understanding of the processes at electrodes, and in the education of scientists in electrochemical areas. Again the tangible factors (comparison of watts/lb, kw/ft³, $/kw, etc.) whereby research programs are continued or discontinued should by no means be the only ones which should decide the time of replacement of the old indirect energy conversion devices by the new electrically oriented ones: high watts per pound may be desirable but how to use it if one cannot see through the smog and dirt its fuels engender; or the noise vibration its production makes. Lastly, the clearly apparent changeover to the use of energy only in the form of electricity involves a vast technological revolution; and it is to be expected that the owners of the present means of production of energy (and they are among the most powerful interests in the Western world) will not encourage a revolution which would cause them so much disruption. Such factors must be weighed in estimating the rate at which electrochemical energy conversion and storage will become the central aspect of the evolution of a clean and livable urban environment.

REFERENCES

1. Ostwald, W.: *Z. Elektrochem.*, **1**, 122 (1894).

2. Cohen, R.: *Proc. Ann. Power Sources Conf.*, **20**, 21 (1966); H. J. R. Maget, Chap. 4, in C. Berger (ed.), "Handbook of Fuel Cell Technology," Prentice-Hall, Inc., Englewood Cliffs, N.J., 1968.

† Between 1965 and 1969, the cost of hydrogen fell from 89 to 35 cents/lb.

2a. Schanz, J. L., and E. K. Bullock: Paper presented at American Rocket Society, September 25–28, 1962, Santa Monica, Calif.

3. Clark, M. B., W. G. Darland, and K. V. Kordesch: *Proc. Ann. Power Sources Conf.*, **18**, 11 (1964); K. V. Kordesch, Chap. 3, in C. Berger (ed.), "Handbook of Fuel Cell Technology," Prentice-Hall, Inc., Englewood Cliffs, N.J., 1968.

3a. Litz, L. M., and K. V. Kordesch: *Adv. Chem. Ser.*, **47**, 166 (1965).

3b. Kordesch, K. V.: Private communication, Union Carbide Corporation. 1968.

4. Justi, E., and A. Winsel: "Kalte Verbrennung," Franz Steiner Verlag, Wiesbaden, Germany 1962; E. W. Justi and A. W. Winsel: *Allgemeine and praktische Chemie*, **18**, 131 (1967); E. W. Justi and A. W. Kalberlah, *Energy Conversion*, **8**, 47 (1968).

4a. Justi, E.: Private communication, 1969.

4b. Varta A. A., Kelkheim: Private communication (via E. Justi), 1968.

5. Jasinski, R. J., and T. Kirkland: Fuel Cells—A State of the Art Report, *Mech. Eng.*, **51** (March, 1964); J. L. Platner, IECEC 1968 Record, 52.

5a. Platner, J. L., and P. D. Hess: Allis-Chalmers Research Publication, September, 1963.

5b. Platner, J. L., D. Chere, and P. Hess: *Proc. Ann. Power Sources Conf.*, **19**, 32 (1965).

5c. Jasinski, R.: *Adv. Chem. Ser.*, **47**, 95 (1965).

5d. Allis-Chalmers Corporation: Private communication (via D. B. Smith), 1969.

6. Adams, A. M., F. T. Bacon, and R. G. H. Watson: Chap. 4, in W. Mitchell (ed.), "Fuel Cells," Academic Press Inc., New York, 1963.

7. Morrill, C. C.: *Proc. Ann. Power Sources Conf.*, **19**, 38 (1965).

7a. Cheney, E. O., Jr., P. J. Farris, and J. M. King, Jr.: Pratt and Whitney Aircraft Publication as Open Cycle Fuel Cell Systems for Space Applications, 1965.

7b. Gregory, D. P.: Hydrogen-Oxygen Fuel Cells of the Bacon type: A Lecture to UCLA on Electrochemical Energy Conversion, August, 1963. A Pratt and Whitney Aircraft Publication.

7c. Pratt and Whitney Aircraft, Division of United Aircraft Corporation (via J. T. Foley), 1968.

7d. Power Cells in Ground Application, Pratt and Whitney Aircraft publication, Division of United Aircraft Corporation, 1967.

8. Archer, D. H., J. J. Alles, W. A. English, L. Elikan, E. F. Sverdrup, and R. L. Zahradnik: *Advan. Chem. Ser.*, **47**, 332 (1965).

8a. Archer, D. H., R. L. Zahradnik, E. F. Sverdrup, W. A. English, L. Elikan, and J. J. Alles: *Proc. Ann. Power Sources Conf.*, **18**, 36 (1964).

9. Carter, R. E., W. E. Rocco, H. S. Spacil, and W. E. Tragert: General Electric Research Laboratory, press release, Dec. 26, 1962.

10. Heath, C. E.: *Proc. Ann. Power Sources Conf.*, **18**, 33 (1964); C. E. Heath, E. H. Okrent, M. Beltzer, and G. Ciprios, pp. 307–312 in Symposium on Power Sources for Electric Vehicles, Columbia University, 1967.

10a. Tarmy, B. L., and A. Ciprios: p. 272 in Engineering Developments in Energy Conversion, American Society of Mechanical Engineers, New York, 1965.

11. Haldeman, R. G., W. P. Colman, S. H. Langer, and W. A. Barber: *Advan. Chem. Ser.*, **47**, 106 (1965).

12. Austin, L. G., R. D. Chamberlain, and A. R. Schleicher: Final Report on Redox Fuel Cells: The fuel regenerator, *Dept. Comm. Rept.* AD 289, 559 (1962).

13. Murray, J. N., and P. G. Grimes: Fuel Cells, *Am. Inst. Chem. Eng. (Progr. Tech. Manual)*, 57 (1963).

13a. Allis-Chalmers Corporation: Private communication (via D. B. Smith), 1968.

14. Binder, H., A. Köhling, H. Krupp, K. Richter, and G. Sandstede: *J. Electrochem. Soc.*, **112**, 355 (1965).

15. Grubb, W. T., and L. W. Niedrach: *Proc. Ann. Power Sources Conf.*, **17**, 69 (1963).

16. Niedrach, L. W., and H. R. Alford: *J. Electrochem. Soc.*, **112**, 117 (1965).

17. Baker, B. S. (ed.): "Hydrocarbon Fuel Cell Technology," pt. V, Academic Press Inc., New York, 1965.

18. Grubb, W. T., and L. W. Niedrach: *J. Electrochem. Soc.*, **110**, 1086 (1963).

18a. Grubb, W. T., and C. J. Michalske: *J. Electrochem. Soc.*, **111**, 1015 (1964).

19. W. R. Epperly, *Proc. Ann. Power Sources Conf.*, **19**, 46 (1965); see also second paper of reference 10.

20. Bockris, J. O'M., and B. D. Cahan: 153d Nat. Meeting Am. Chem. Soc., Div. Fuel Chem., preprints, 11, 2301 (1967); *J. Chem. Phys.*, **50**, 1307 (1969).

21. Sepa, D., A. Damjanovic, and J. O'M. Bockris: *Electrochim. Acta*, **12**, 746 (1967); *J. Res. Inst. Cat.*, **16**, 1 (1968).

22. Cairns, E. J., and D. C. Bartosik: *J. Electrochem. Soc.*, **111**, 1205 (1965).

23. Cairns, E. J.: *J. Electrochem. Soc.*, **113**, 1200 (1966).

23a. Cairns, E. J.: p. 465, in B. S. Baker (ed.), "Hydrocarbon Fuel Cell Technology," Academic Press Inc., New York, 1965.

23b. Cairns, E. J., and E. J. McInerney: *J. Electrochem. Soc.*, **114**, 980 (1967).

23c. Cairns, E. J., and J. Paynter: *J. Electrochem. Soc.*, **115**, 1218 (1968).

23d. Liebhafsky, H. A., and E. J. Cairns: "Fuel Cells and Fuel Cell Batteries," John Wiley & Sons, Inc., New York, 1968.

24. Vertes, M. A., and A. J. Hartner: *Journées Intern. D'Etude Piles Combustible, Brussels* (June, 1965).

25. Gregory, D. P., and H. Heilbronner: in B. S. Baker (ed.), "Hydrocarbon Fuel Cell Technology," p. 509, Academic Press Inc., New York, 1965.

26. Pearson, J. W.: Chap. 11, in K. R. Williams (ed.), "An Introduction to Fuel Cells," Elsevier Publishing Company, Amsterdam, 1966; K. R. Williams, p. 525, in D. H. Collins (ed.), "Power Sources 1968," Pergamon Press, New York, 1969.

27. Broers, G. H. J., and M. Schenke: in B. S. Baker (ed.), "Hydrocarbon Fuel Cell Technology," p. 225, Academic Press Inc., New York, 1965; Intern. Symp. Brennstoffelemente at Dresden; Abh. Sach. Akad. Wiss. Leipzig, Bd. **49**, 398, Akad Verlag, Berlin, 1968.

28. Baur, E., W. D. Treadwell, and G. Trumpler: *Z. Elektrochem.*, **27**, 199 (1921).

29. Davytan, O. K.: *Bull. Acad. Sci. USSR Classe Sci. Tech.*, **107**, 125 (1946).

30. Chambers, H. H., and O. D. S. Tantram: Chap. 7, in G. J. Young (ed.), "Fuel Cells," vol. 1, Reinhold Publishing Corporation, New York, 1965.

31. Baker, B. S., L. G. Marianowski, J. Zimmer, and G. Price: in B. S. Baker (ed.), "Hydrocarbon Fuel Cell Technology," 293, Academic Press Inc., New York, 1965; D. Y. C. Ng and D. K. Fleming, 154th Nat. Meeting, Am. Chem. Soc., Div. Fuel Chem., preprints **11**, 281 (1967).

31a. Baker, B. S.: Private communication, 1969.

32. Trachtenberg, I.: in B. S. Baker (ed.), "Hydrocarbon Fuel Cell Technology," p. 251, Academic Press Inc., New York, 1965.

32a. Texas Instruments, Inc.: Private communication (via M. S. Bawa), 1969.

33. Hardy, R. W., W. E. Chase, and J. McCallum: in B. S. Baker (ed.), "Hydrogen Fuel Cell Technology," p. 213, Academic Press Inc., New York, 1965; J. K. Truit et al.: 15 kw Hydrocarbon Fuel Cell Electric Power Plant Modifications, Technical Report, November, 1968, Texas Instruments, Inc., Dallas, Texas, 75222.

34. Salvadori, A.: in B. S. Baker (ed.), "Hydrocarbon Fuel Cell Technology," p. 267, Academic Press Inc., New York, 1965.

35. Millet, J., and R. Buvet: in B. S. Baker (ed.), "Hydrocarbon Fuel Cell Technology," p. 285, Academic Press Inc., New York, 1965.

36. Williams, K. R.: Chap. 1, in K. R. Williams (ed.), "An Introduction to Fuel Cells," Elsevier Publishing Company, Amsterdam, 1966.

37. Jacques, W. W.: *Harper's Magazine*, **94**, 144 (December, 1896–May, 1897).

38. Haber, F., and R. Brunner: *Z. Elektrochem.*, **10**, 697 (1904); **12**, 78 (1906).

39. Baur, E., and H. Preis: *Z. Elektrochem.*, **43**, 727 (1937).

40. Zahradnik, R. L., L. Elikan, and D. H. Archer: *Advan. Chem. Ser.*, **47**, 343 (1965).

40a. Archer D. H. and R. L. Zahradnik: *Chem. Eng. Progr. Symp. Series*, **63**, 55 (1967).

40b. Archer, D. H., L. Elikan, and R. L. Zahradnik: pp. 51–75, in B. S. Baker (ed.), "Hydrocarbon Fuel Cell Technology," Academic Press Inc., New York, 1965.

41. Posner, A. M.: *Fuel*, **34**, 330 (1950).

42. Eisenberg, M.: *Proc. Ann. Power Sources Conf.*, **18**, 20 (1964).

43. Wynveen, R. O.: Chap. 12, in G. J. Young (ed.), "Fuel Cells," vol. 2, Reinhold Publishing Corporation, New York, 1963.

43a. Cairns, E. J., E. L. Simons, and A. D. Tevbaugh: *Nature*, **217**, 780 (1968).

44. Power Cells in Ground Application, publication of Pratt and Whitney Aircraft, Division of United Aircraft Corporation, 1966.

45. Gillibrand, M. I., and G. R. Lomax: in D. H. Collins (ed.), "Proceedings 3d International Symposium on Batteries, Bournemouth, 1962," p. 221, Pergamon Press, New York, 1963.

46. Andrew, M. R., and R. W. Glazebrook: Chap. 6, in K. R. Williams (ed.), "An Introduction to Fuel Cells," Elsevier Publishing Company, Amsterdam, 1966.

47. Tomter, S. S., and A. P. Antony: Fuel Cells, *Am. Inst. Chem. Eng. (Prog. Tech. Manual)*, 22 (1963).

47a. Jasinski, R.: Paper presented at 123d Meeting of Electrochemical Society, Pittsburgh, Pa., Apr. 15, 1963.

48. Eisenberg, M.: *Proc. Ann. Power Sources Conf.*, **17**, 97 (1963).

49. Terry, P., J. Gallagher, R. Salathe, and J. O. Smith: *Proc. Ann. Power Sources Conf.*, **20**, 39 (1966).

50. Yeager, E.: Chap. 7, in W. Mitchell (ed.), "Fuel Cells," Academic Press Inc., New York, 1963.

51. Dextermiller, K., Jr., Bränsleceller, 41, *Ingeniorsvetenskapsakademien*, Iva Meddelande N. R. 134, Stockholm, Sweden (1963).

52. Agruss, B.: *Proc. Ann. Power Sources Conf.*, **17**, 100 (1963).

53. Adams, D. K. et al.: "Fuel Cells—Power for the Future," Harvard Business School, Harvard University, Cambridge, Mass., 1960.

54. Foust, R. A., Jr.: *J. Electrochem. Soc.*, **109**, 198c (1962).

55. Zaromb, S., and R. A. Foust: *J. Electrochem. Soc.*, **109**, 1191 (1962).

55a. Zaromb, S.: pp. 255–267, in H. B. Linford, H. P. Gregor, and B. J. Steigerwald, "Symposium on Power Systems for Electric Vehicles" (Columbia University, New York, April, 1967), Public Health Service Publication No. 999-AP-37.

56. Gruber, B. A.: *Proc. Ann. Power Sources Conf.*, **18**, 94 (1964).

57. Taylor, J. E., N. Fatica, and G. H. Rohrback: Fuel Cells, *Am. Inst. Chem. Engr.*, (*Prog. Tech. Manual*), 13 (1963).

58. Swinkels, D. A. J.: *J. Electrochem. Soc.*, **113**, 6 (1966).

58a. Swinkels, D. A. J., and R. N. Seefurth: *J. Electrochem. Soc.*, **115**, 995 (1968).

59. Glass, W., and G. H. Boyle: *Advan. Chem. Ser.*, **47**, 203 (1965).

59a. Juda, W., C. E. Tirrell, and R. M. Lurie: Fuel Cells with Ion Exchange Membranes, Paper presented at ARS Space Power Systems Conference, Santa Marica, Calif., September, 1960.

60. Berger, C.: *Advan. Chem. Ser.*, **47**, 188 (1965).

61. McKee, W. E., E. Findl, J. D. Margerum, and W. B. Lee: *Proc. Ann. Power Sources Conf.*, **14**, 68 (1960).

62. Lurie, R. M., and C. Berger: Extd, Abs. 71, 120th Meeting Electrochem. Soc., Detroit Battery Division, October, 1961.

63. Eisenberg, M., and H. P. Silverman: *Electrochim. Acta*, **5**, 1 (1961).

64. Vielstich, W.: "Brenstoffelemente," Chap. 7, Verlag Chemie, GmbH, Weinheim, Germany, 1965.

65. Rosenblum, L., and R. E. English: Advanced Energy Sources and Conversion Techniques, *Office Tech. Serv., Dept. Comm. Rept.* PB 151461, 243 (ASTIA No. AD209301).

66. Grüneberg, G., W. Wicke, and E. Justi; Franz. Patent 1321373.

67. Gomberg, A., and R. A. Lee: Private communication, 1966.

68. Vielstich, W., "Brenstoffelemente," Verlag Chemie, GmbH, Weinheim, Germany, 1965.

69. Yeager, J. F., R. J. Bennett, and D. R. Allenson: *Proc. Ann. Power Sources Conf.*, **16**, 39 (1962).

70. Erkens, J. W., and M. C. Reder: Paper presented at National Meeting of American Institute of Chemical Engineers, March, 1963.

71. Del Duca, M. G., and J. M. Fuscoe: *Intern. Sci. Technol.*, **39**, 56 (1965).

71a. Bockris, J. O'M., and S. Srinivasan: *Nature*, **215**, 197 (1967).

71b. Srinivasan, S., R. K. Aaron, T. Lucas, and P. N. Sawyer: *Surg.*, **64**, 827 (1968); S. Srinivasan and P. N. Sawyer, *Fed. Proceedings*, **27**, 322 (1968).

72. Cole, K. S.: Chap. 7, in T. Shedlovsky (ed.), "Electrochemistry in Biology and Medicine," John Wiley & Sons, Inc., New York, 1955.

72a. Mandel, P.: Doctoral dissertation, University of Pennsylvania, 1969; private communication, 1969.

73. Bean, R. C., Y. H. Inami, P. R. Basford, M. H. Boyer, W. C. Shepherd, E. R. Walwick, and R. E. Kay: Study of Fundamental Principles of Bioelectrochemistry, final report on contract NASW-655 to NASA from Ford Aeroneutronic Division (Report U2670), June 30, 1964.

74. Shaw, M.: *Proc. Ann. Power Sources Conf.*, **17**, 53 (1963).

75. Davis, J. B., and H. S. Yarbrough: *Science*, **137**, 615 (1962).

76. Van Hees, W.: *J. Electrochem. Soc.*, **112**, 262 (1965).

77. Brake, J., W. Momyer, J. Cavallo, and H. Silverman: *Proc. Ann. Power Sources Conf.*, **17**, 56 (1963).

78. Yahiro, A. T., S. M. Lee, D. D. Lawson, and M. J. Allen: *Proc. Biochem. Fuel Cell Session, Santa Monica PIC–BAT* 20915, **5**, 1 (1962).

79. Yahiro, O. T., S. M. Lee, and D. O. Kimble: *Biochim. Biophys. Acta*, **88**, 375 (1964).

80. Del Duca, M. G., J. M. Fuscoe, and R. W. Zurilla: *Develop. Ind. Microbiol.*, **4,** 81 (1963).

81. Blasco, R. J., and E. Gileadi: *Advan. Energy Conv.*, **4,** 179 (1964).

82. Bern Dibner, Galvani-Volta, Burndy Library, Norwalk, Conn., 1952.

83. Potter, M. C.: *Proc. Roy. Soc. Ser.*, B **84,** 260 (1912).

84. Cohen, B.: *J. Bacteriol.*, **21,** 18 (1931).

85. Mehl, W., J. M. Hale, and F. Lohman: *J. Electrochem. Soc.*, **113,** 1166 (1966).

86. Kummer, J. T., and N. Weber: *Soc. Automotive Eng.*, *Automotive Eng. Congr.*, *Detroit, Preprint* 670, 179 (January, 1967).

87. Bockris, J. O'M.: Private communication, 1969.

88. Verstraete, J., D. Lefevre, R. Lefort, and J. Henry: Chap. 5, in E. Berger (ed.), "Handbook of Fuel Cell Technology," Prentice-Hall, Inc., Englewood Cliffs, N.J., 1968.

The Necessity of Finding Nonnoble Metal Catalysts

The exchange current densities for the oxidation of a number of hydrocarbons in acid solution on platinum at 80°C is around 10^{-9} amp cm^{-2}. The corresponding value for hydrogen on Ni is 10^{-3} amp cm^{-2}. In the case of hydrogen-oxygen fuel cells, nickel is extensively used as a catalyst. Nickel is a comparatively cheap catalyst and reasonably high power densities and power/weight ratios can be obtained using this metal. However, in the case of hydrocarbons, it is not possible to attain reasonable power densities at present unless a noble metal, particularly platinum, is used. In practically all fuel-cell systems, the oxidant is oxygen, either in the pure form or as air. The exchange current density for the oxygen-reduction reaction on the widely used electrocatalyst platinum is about 10^{-10} amp cm^{-2} at room temperature. On silver, which is also used for the oxygen electrode in alkaline solutions, it is about 10^{-9} amp cm^{-2}.

The requirement of platinum or other noble metals in hydrocarbon-oxygen energy converters is inhibitive to the future of these systems in electrochemical power generation. This is not only because of the cost of Pt but also because of the limited world supply. It is interesting to make a calculation of the quantity of platinum that would be required if 10 percent of the cars, manufactured annually in the United States, were powered by hydrocarbon-oxygen fuel cells using platinum electrodes.

Let (1) the total power required per car be P kw; (2) the number of cars which run on fuel cells be N; (3) the maximum power which can be obtained from a single cell be p watts cm^{-2}, which corresponds to a current density of i amp cm^{-2} at E volts; (4) the mass of platinum required per electrode be m grams cm^{-2}; (5) and the total quantity of Pt available be Q lb.

It is desired to find the total quantity of Pt required, and what fraction of annual supply would be required.

The total power required $= NP$ kw $\qquad = 10^3\, NP$ watts

$$\text{The area of Pt required} = \frac{2 \times 10^3 NP}{p}$$

$$= \frac{2 \times 10^3 NP}{iE} \qquad \text{cm}^2$$

$$\text{which corresponds to a mass} = \frac{2 \times 10^3 NPm}{iE} \quad g$$

$$= \left(\frac{2 \times 10^3 NPm}{453.6iE}\right) 16 \quad oz$$

$$\text{The fraction of the annual supply consumed} = \frac{2 \times 10^3 NPm}{453.6iEQ}$$

If N is 5×10^5 (i.e., some one-tenth of cars manufactured annually), P is 50 kw, $m = 10^{-3}$ g cm^{-2}, $E = 0.5$ volt, and $i = 5 \times 10^{-2}$ amp cm^{-2}, the amount of Pt required is 6×10^7 oz. The world supply is about 1 million oz per annum. It is thus insufficient to supply the electrocatalyst for hydrocarbon-air fuel cells even for one-tenth of the cars manufactured annually. Even if it were possible to increase the world supply of platinum by, for instance, increasing the depth of mining, the cost of the metal would be increased still further. If it were possible to reduce the mass of platinum required for each electrode (m) to 0.1 mg cm^{-2}, the amount of platinum required annually for the electrodes would still exceed the annual world supply. If the performance of hydrocarbon-air fuel cells were to improve to a level of 500 ma cm^{-2} at a cell potential of 0.5 volt, the annual world production of platinum might just meet the demands of the fuel cells for one-tenth of the cars manufactured annually.

The replacement of the insufficiently available noble metals by other electrocatalysts is a difficult task, not so much because of poor prospects in obtaining reasonable catalytic properties but because the region of potential for the oxidation of hydrocarbons is +0.3 to 0.9 volt on the reversible hydrogen scale. In this highly anodic region, many nonnoble metals dissolve. This situation is certainly alleviated in alkaline solutions but the difficulties here of CO_2 rejection cause further problems. Thus, in alkaline solution, CO_2 forms a solid carbonate and the efficiency of the system is further reduced. Thus, it is necessary to work in acid medium, where it now seems unlikely that a successful electrocatalyst will be developed using nonnoble *metals*. The tables of corrosion potential versus pH prepared by Pourbaix[1] are of great value in considering the applicability of possible nonnoble metals as catalysts.

In ordinary chemical reactions, metals and alloys are less frequently used as catalysts. More often semiconducting oxides or sulfides of transition metals are used. Such semiconducting catalysts, e.g., lithiated nickel oxide, nickel boride, silver oxide, have been used in a few cases in hydrogen-oxygen fuel cells. Much of the future of electrocatalysis for anodic reactions appears to be in this direction.

Passivated metal oxides, with doping agents to increase the conductivity, or organic semiconducting films on the surface of nonnoble metals, e.g., chelates, are little investigated. It is necessary to investigate these, as well as other potential catalysts, in a systematic manner. Further, semiconductor electrode kinetics is a less-developed field than metal electrode kinetics and this aspect has also to be examined.

The development of insulator electrodes, which in very thin layers conduct sufficiently, is not to be rejected particularly because theoretical considerations reveal particularly high catalytic rates on such substrates.[2]

REFERENCES

1. Pourbaix, M.: "Atlas D'Equilibres Electrochimiques," Gauthier-Villars, Paris, 1963; English Translation: M. Pourbaix, "Atlas of Electrochemical Equilibria in Aqueous Solution," Pergamon Press, New York, 1966.

2. Mehl, W., J. M. Hale, and F. Lohmann: *J. Electrochem. Soc.*, **113**, 75C, Abstract No. 159 (1966); W. Mehl and J. M. Hale, Chap. 5, in P. Delahay and C. W. Tobias (eds.), "Advances in Electrochemistry and Electrochemical Engineering," vol. 6, Interscience Publishers, Inc., New York, 1967; J. M. Hale, *J. Electrochem. Soc.*, **115**, 208 (1968).

An Important Parameter in Adsorption: the Potential of Zero Charge

If the surface tension of mercury in contact with a solution is plotted against potential, it passes through a maximum. The metal-solution interfacial tension in the absence of excess charge on the surface of a metal has a characteristic value. Both excess or decess electronic charge which is upon the surface of the metal will tend to lower the net surface tension because the force due to an electric charge on a conductor can be shown to be $2\pi\sigma^2\epsilon$, where σ is the charge density and ϵ is the dielectric constant. This force should be subtracted from the nonelectrically influenced surface tension to give the net surface tension, and it will always reduce the net surface tension, independently of the sign of the charge. Hence, the potential at which the surface tension versus potential curve reaches a maximum is also the potential at which the surface has zero net charge. It is the potential at which the surface of the metal in solution changes over from bearing an excess charge of one sign to that of the other.

The *potential of zero charge* is a very important concept in electrochemistry which may have much more use in the future than it has had in the past.[1] The potential of zero charge—sometimes abbreviated PZC—can be the basis of a scale of potentials which would be more rational than the scale at present used, namely, the scale in which the hydrogen electrode is regarded as the arbitrary zero. The latter scale involves complications because it includes a metal-metal potential difference at the junction of the electrode being examined and the metal of the reference electrode. Utilizing the potential of zero charge of a metal as a base to which its other potentials could be referred would be more fundamental. The reason why this is not done at the present time is that the potential of zero charge of a metal is not a well-known quantity in the experimental sense.

The importance of the potential of zero charge to the present discussions is that it is central to concepts of adsorption. If one recalls the theory of the variation of the adsorption of organic molecules with potential (see Chap. 7, Sec. 6.3.4), it will be seen that the changeover of the orientation of the water molecules should take place, if the model is viewed in its most simple way, at the potential of zero charge. Hence, as a first approximation, *the maximum in the plot of the adsorption of organic molecules as a function of potential should be at the potential of zero charge for the metal concerned.* This approximate statement has good applicability in respect to the adsorption of simple organic compounds from aqueous solutions. The "simple" in this case means organic compounds which do not have any electrically active groups inside the double layer—for example, a series of alcohols, in which the OH group is oriented towards the solution, the aliphatic head of the molecule being in contact with the electrode.

In this approximation, the adsorption of the organic molecules will clearly and simply follow, in an inverse sense, the strength of adsorption of the water molecule to the surface, and the adsorption-potential curve will be symmetrical with respect to the potential of zero charge (as it would be were the electrical attraction of the water molecule to the surface the same in either orientation).

There are many deviations from the rough approximation that the adsorption of organic molecules maximizes in the vicinity of the potential of zero charge. They arise for two reasons. Firstly, the organic molecule itself often has electrical components of charge, for example a strong dipole, which comes within the field of the double layer. Then, the adsorption becomes much more complicated, although the shape of it is still essentially parabolic. The model in which both water molecules and organic molecules interact electrically with the surface has been more recently calculated.[2]

Another reason for a lack of applicability of the rule is that the organic molecule may dissociate upon adsorption and not be largely controlled by the electrical interactions of the water molecules with the surface. In this case the curve of the degree of coverage of the organic molecule versus potential will not be parabolic.

In spite of these causes for deviation from the simple rule stated above, the first thing which must be done in deciding whether a fuel will adsorb upon an electrode is to ascertain how far the working potential of the electrode for the reaction concerned is from the potential of zero charge. Up to about 0.3 volt from the potential of zero charge, the adsorption is likely to be high. At greater potential differences, it is important to examine the matter and see if one of the deviations outlined above has caused the molecule to adsorb out of the region which would be indicated by the simple theory.

Having thus expounded the importance of the potential of zero charge to the first approximation appraisal as to whether the molecule will adsorb—and thus undergo an electrocatalytic reaction—it is important to note that a lack of the present situation in electrochemistry is in data on the potential of zero charge. Many of the older determinations were not satisfactory. Newer methods[3,4] include the measurements of friction with potential,[5] a measurement of capacitance as a function of potential,[1,6] and a change of capacitance current with surface area as a function of potential.[7,8]

Recent values of the potentials of zero charge on some metals (versus NHE) are presented in Table 1.

TABLE 1 Potentials of Zero Charge on Some Metals (versus NHE)[3]†

Metal	Potential of zero charge
Silver	−0.05
Copper	−0.04
Zinc	−0.63
Cadmium	−0.90
Mercury	−0.21
Lead	−0.6
Platinum	−0.50
Gallium	−0.60
Thallium	−0.80

† Values of the potential of zero charge are approximate and do not have a validity of more than about +0.05 volt. They are dependent upon the presence of anions, and change significantly with specific adsorption. If one needs to know the potential of zero charge on a certain metal, due to the linear relation between potential of zero charge and work functions, one can utilize an extrapolation procedure as shown in Fig. 1.

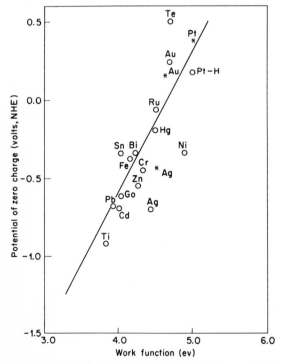

Figure 1 Potential of zero charge plotted against the work function; * indicates PZC values obtained in the electrochemistry laboratory, University of Pennsylvania.[3]

REFERENCES

1. Antropov, N.: "The Potential of Zero Charge and Its Application to Studies in Electrode Kinetics," LDNTP, Leningrad, 1965.
2. Bockris, J. O'M., E. Gileadi, and K. Müller: *Electrochim. Acta*, **12**, 1301 (1967).
3. Argade, S. D., and E. Gileadi: Chap. 5, in E. Gileadi (ed.), "Electrosorption," Plenum Press, New York, 1968.
4. Bockris, J. O'M., and S. D. Argade: *Electrochim. Acta*, in press.
5. Bockris, J. O'M., and S. D. Argade: *J. Chem. Phys.*, 1969.
6. Gileadi, E., S. D. Argade, and J. O'M. Bockris: *J. Phys. Chem.*, **70**, 2044 (1966).
7. Jakuszewski, J., and H. Kozlowski: *Rocknici Chem.*, **36**, 1873 (1962).
8. Perkins, D., T. Andersen, and H. Eyring: *J. Phys. Chem.*, **69**, 3329 (1965).

Indexes

Name Index

Subject Index